MODERN WOOD TECHNOLOGY

MODERN

DONALD F. HACKETT, Ed.D.

CHAIRMAN, INDUSTRIAL TECHNOLOGY DIVISION
GEORGIA SOUTHERN COLLEGE, STATESBORO, GEORGIA

PATRICK E. SPIELMAN

DEPARTMENT HEAD, GIBRALTAR AREA SCHOOLS
FISH CREEK, WISCONSIN

WOOD TECHNOLOGY

THE BRUCE PUBLISHING COMPANY / MILWAUKEE

Preface

This is a book about wood and some of the many ways in which its shape and nature are altered through manufacturing. It has been written for students of industrial arts in secondary schools and colleges.

As you study the following pages you will learn how the manufacturing industries in general, and the woodworking industries in particular, plan, prepare for, and produce a product. You will also learn something about the historical, cultural, economic, and technological developments that have given us the world's highest standard of living. Furthermore, you will learn how to identify and solve technical problems that involve the use of tools and materials.

Part I introduces you to several aspects of the wood manufacturing industries and to the material itself. Here you will learn about the research and development efforts of scientists, engineers, and technicians in providing new knowledge about and new uses for wood. You will also learn of the many people who are assembled within a company to plan, organize, and implement the production of a manufactured product. The furniture industry is used to illustrate this orchestration of men, materials, and machines for the production of our material welfare.

Part II deals with the tools, machines, and processes by which wood is given useful form. You will learn how primitive man produced the first tools and how these developed into the present day tools with which wood is sawed, planed, shaped, joined, assembled, and finished in the furniture manufacturing and construction industries. You will also have an opportunity to apply and experiment with these processes in your school shop.

Part III takes you into several industries where wood is the principal raw material used. Here you will learn of the technology by which man produces a variety of products.

During the course of this study, you will recognize that the manufacturing and construction industries require a great number of men and women with a technical background as well as certain specialized skills. These industries need managers, superintendents, foremen, engineers, accountants, draftsmen, secretaries, machine operators, skilled craftsmen, technicians, scientists, sales personnel, truck drivers, clerks, designers, and the like. Schools and colleges need many teachers of technical subjects. Some of these positions demand a person with a professional college degree; some require specialized training in vocational-technical schools; practically all of them require at least a high school education. So, as you move through this book, try to identify an occupation that seems to fit your needs, interests, and abilities. Ask your instructor and the school counselor to help you learn more about yourself, your occupational choice, and the opportunities and requirements associated with this choice.

DONALD F. HACKETT

PATRICK E. SPIELMAN

v

Acknowledgments

The authors thank the following manufacturers and associations who so willingly supplied illustrational materials for this text on the pages indicated.*

Adjustable Clamp Co., 347(l), 468, 469(tr)(mr)(ml)(b)
American Cyanamid Co., 683(mr)(br)
American Forest Products Industries, 5, 18, 21, 22, 31(t), 601, 603(tr)(br), 604 (K.S.Brown)(br), 606(mr)(bl), 607, 627(bl), 628, 629, 630(b), 654(mr), 682, 720, 722(t), 723(t), 726, 728(b), 729(b), 730, 731
American Plywood Assoc., (Douglas Fir Plywood Assoc.), 182(ml), 242(t), 344(tl), 637(b), 712(ml), 713(bl), 715, 716
American Woodworking Machinery Corp., 119
Amerock Corp., 473 (Fig. 26–84 b), 474 (Fig. 26–85 b, c, d; 26–86), 475(tl)(bl), 476(br)
Auto Nailer Co., 455(tr)

Behr-Manning, 487, 488, 489(l), 490(tl)(tr), 491(b), 497(t), 502(ml), 566(tr)(mr), 571(t), 572(tl)(tr), 582(r), 583, 585(tr)(br), 586(b), 587(tr)(mr), 589(m), 590(bl)(br), 592(t)
Bell Machine Co., 335(t), 359(t)
Beloit Corp., 605
Binks Mfg. Co., 521(b)
Black Bros. Co., Inc., 467, 470(tl)(mr), 471(t), 674(bl)(tr)(br), 700(tl)
Black and Decker Mfg. Co., 124(t), 135, 152, 153(tr)(b), 155, 277(tl)(ml), 301(b), 302(t), 303(t), 304(br), 327, 328(b), 341(t), 492(m), 506(tl), 581(t)
Black Diamond Saw & Machine Works, 128
Bostitch Inc., 454(r)
Brett-Guard Co., 184(t)
Brown-Saltman Furniture, 489(r), 538(b)
E. L. Bruce Co., 536(t), 538(b), 618(b), 619, 622(bl), 656(t)(mr)

---

* Key to abbreviations: t-top, m-middle, b-bottom, r-right, c-center, l-left.

Buck Bros. Inc., 231, 268
Buckeye Tools Corp., 275(bl)
Buss Machine Works, Inc., 231(l)

Carthage Machine Co., 721
Cincinnati Tool Co., 470(tr)
Clarke Floor Machine Div., Studebaker Corp., 492(b), 493(t), 503(b)
Comet Industries, 145(b)
Crane Creek Gun Stock Co., 294

John Deere, 608(t)
Delta Power Tools Division, Rockwell Mfg. Co., 107(t), 108(b), 110, 118, 124(b), 129, 141(b), 164, 171(b), 179(tl), 180(ml)(tr), 220, 221(t), 223(b), 225(b), 228(r), 230(b), 248, 251, 256(t), 257(t), 282(b), 283(tl), 285(bl), 286(l), 315, 317(tr)(br), 318(b), 319(b), 326(b), 330(l), 331, 346(t), 351(b), 376(b), 383(b), 384, 407(t), 409(t), 412(br), 493(b), 495(tr), 496(t), 510(br), 578, 579(t), 580(b), 588(t)(b), 589(t), 595(t), 596(tr)
Dependable Machine Co., 282(t), 580(t)(m)
DeVilbiss Co., 520, 523, 524, 525(t), 526, 529, 536(b), 555, 556, 557, 560(tl), 561(l), 562, 563
DeWalt Inc., 94, 117, 189, 190, 191, 192, 193, 194, 195, 196, 255(t), 352(tr), 404(t), 408(b), 587(b), 588(m), 597(b)
Diehl Machines Inc., 113, 115
Disston Division, H. K. Porter Co., Inc., 95, 96(tr), 98(b), 99(t), 142(t)(bl), 148, 150, 169, 170(m), 171(tr), 172(tr), 174, 595
Do-All Co., 125(tl), 162
Dowl-it Co., 424(tr)
Dremel Mfg. Co., 101(t), 274
Drexel Furniture Co., 43, 44, 45, 46, 50, 57, 58, 59, 60, 61
Dry Clime Lamp Co., 535, 537(b)
E. I. Dupont de Nemours & Co., 502(mr), 515, 516, 517, 542, 533(t), 567(bl)(br), 568(tl)
Duraflake Co., 123
Duro Metal Products Co., 494(l)

Eagle Mfg. Co., 551
Ekstrom, Carlson, & Co., 114, 121(b), 278(t), 292(t)

J. A. Fay & Egan Co., 236
Fine Hardwoods Assoc., 635, 636, 649
Foley Mfg. Co., 581(t), 584, 585(l)
Furniture Design & Manufacturing, 163(t), 278(br), 455(tl), 471(m), 494(m), 537(m), 559(b), (R. A. Helmers, ed.)

General Motors Corp., 42, 671
General Scientific Equipment Co., 111
Georgia-Pacific Corp., 633, 652(r), 670
Gizco, 386(b), 387
Goodspeed Machine Co., 381, 392, 393, 394
Grand Rapids Furniture Mfg. Assoc., 495(b)
Greenlee Bros. & Co., 93, 266(b), 267(ml)(mr), 270(tc), 286(b), 333(t), 335(b), 336, 340, 355, 358(b), 359(m), 369(t), 370, 590(t), 593

Harmony Co., 289(t)
Hardwood Plywood Institute, 644
Harnischfeger Homes, Inc., 47
Edward Hines Lumber Co., 678
Hitchcock's Woodworking Buyers' Directory, 1964 ed., 458, 459, 460, 461
Homecraft Div., Rockwell Mfg. Co., 285(tr)
Homelite Div., Textron Inc., 104

Insulation Board Institute, 677
International Harvester, 604(bl), 606(t)

Kingsbury Homes, 698(t)(m), 699(t)
George Koch Sons, Inc., 530, 532, 533, 534

Machine Design, 672(tl)(mr), 683(tr)
Magna American Corp., 164(bl), 177(l)(tr), 178(r), 508(t)
Marcoloy, Inc., 227(b)
Robt. A. Martin, Co., 498(b)
Masonite Corp., 683(tl)
Master Power Corp., 103, 328(t), 491(m)
Mattison Machine Works, 382(t)
McCulloch Corp., 105
Mereen-Johnson Machine Co., 116, 122
Fred Milke Photographers, 622(tr)
Millers Falls Tool Company, 76(bl), 156(b), 267(t), 269(m), 325(b), 326(t), 339, 452(l), 453(br), 481(tr)
Milwaukee Electric Tool Corp., 455(b), 506(b)
Minnesota Mining & Mfg. Co., 494(tr), 495(tl), 496(b), 497(b), 498(t), 500(t), 571(b)
Minnesota Woodworkers Supply Co., 241(t)
Mobile Homes Brokers, 702, 703

J. M. Nash Co., Inc., 332, 500(b)
National Forest Product Assoc., 705, 706, 707, 708, 714(tr)
National Homes Corp., 698(b), 699(m), 700 (tr)(ml)(bl)(br), 701
National Particle Board Assoc., 689
Newman Machine Co., 221(bl), 229
Nicholson File Co., 270(ml)(bl), 271(b), 272(t), 296(b)
Northfield Foundry & Machine Co., 119, 255 (m)

Old Sturbridge Village, 90(l), 203(bl), 204(br), 322(t)(r)
Oliver Machinery Co., 109, 121(tr), 176, 208 (b), 233, 234, 285(br), 292(b), 293, 385, 390
Onsrud Machine Works, Inc., 280, 288, 289(b), 290, 291, 471, 652(l), 673(b), 688

Peterson Builders, 672(br)
Porter Cable Div., Rockwell Mfg. Co., 101(b), 103(t), 216(b), 218(b), 231(r), 244(t), 275(t), 304(bl), 490(b), 492(t)
C. O. Porter Machinery Co., 278(bl)
Powermatic Inc., 357, 368

Ransburg Electro-Coating Corp., 528
Reynolds Aluminum, 437, 449
Rockwell Mfg. Co., 277(b), 330(b)
Rodgers Machinery Mfg. Co., 121(tl), 123(b), 301
B. M. Root Co., 333(b), 334

Saranac Machine Co., 456(r)
Schreiber System (USA) Ltd., 67(t), 288, 672 (t), 673(t)
Sears, Roebuck & Co., 151, 306(t), 420
Shelburne Museum, 89(m)(b), 202(br), 203(br), 204(tr), 264(t)(m), 324(mr)
Sherwin-Williams Co., 552, 553(br), 554(tr), 566(tl), 568(tr), 569(t), 570, 572(tl)
Simonds Saw & Steel Co., 142(br), 143, 145(t), 184(b), 271(m)
Skil Corp., 153(tl), 154, 216(t), 217(t), 218(t), 244, 245(t), 504
H. B. Smith Machine Co., 91, 207(b), 208(t), 211, 265, 329, 354, 367, 486(tl)
South Bend Lathe Co., Reprinted by arrangement with South Bend Lathe, Inc., from *To Run a Drill Press,* © 1951 by South Bend Lathe, all rights reserved. 348, 350(br), 362 (tl), 596(b)
Southern Screw Co., 442(t)
Stanley Works:

Stanley Tool Division, 71(b), 72(t)(m), 73(b), 74, 75(t)(b), 76(t), 77(tl)(bl), 97(b), 211, 213, 214, 215, 241(b), 266(t), 267(bl), 270(tr), 272(b), 273, 295(l), 323, 324(l), 337, 341(m), 416(t), 424(ml)(bl), 451(r), 452(r), 453(t)(mr), 481(tl)(bl), 506(tr), 592 (b)

Stanley Power Tool Division, 102, 162, 264 (b), 275(r), 276(tl)(mr), 302(bl)(br), 303 (br), 306(b), 307(t)(r), 308(l)(b), 361, 579 (b), 586(tl)

Stanley Hardware Division, 447(tr), 450, 473 (Fig. 26–84 c, d, e, f), 474 (Fig. 26–85 a), 475(tr), 476(m)(bl)(tr), 597 (tr)

Star Mobile Homes, 703

L. S. Starrett Co., 73(t), 74, 452

Stow Mfg. Co., 352(b)

Swift Homes, Inc., 120

Tannewitz Works, 112, 126, 127

Technical Assn. of Pulp & Paper Industries, 722(b), 724, 728(t)

Texas Forest Service, 627(t)

Timber Engineering Co., 713(br), 714(tl)

Toolkraft Corp., 314, 317(tl)(bl)

Triangle Mfg. Co., 476(tl)

Tri-State Machinery Co., 615

Union Tool Corp., 252

United Shoe Machinery Corp., 456(l)

U.S.D.A., Handbook, 709, 710, 711

U. S. Dept. of Commerce, 684

U. S. Forest Service Photo, 630(t)(m)

U. S. Forest Service, Forest Products Laboratory Photo, 14, 15, 16, 17, 19, 20, 29, 30, 39, 40, 147, 226, 439(t), 466, 484(b), 618(t), 639, 640, 641, 646(b), 651(br), 674(tl), 685, 710, 711(t), 714(bl)(br)

U. S. Plywood Corp., 41, 79(b), 120, 150, 156(t), 472(b), 499, 637(m), 642, 643(tr)(mr), 647(b), 650, 651(t), 653(r), 654(ml)(bl), 655 (ml)(tr), 656(ml), 664, 687, 689

J. D. Wallace Division, Union Tool Corp., 252

West Coast Lumberman's Assoc., 612, 620(t), 712(tr), 713(tr)

Westinghouse, 107(b)

Weyerhaeuser Co., 4, 602, 603(tl), 604(tl), 608(b), 609, 617, 622(tl), 637(t), 638(tl), 643, 651(bl), 652(l)

Baxter D. Whitney & Sons, Inc., 92(b), 206, 227(t), 228(l), 230(t), 232(t), 287(t), 356, 358(t)

Wilke Bros. Foundation, 87, 88, 92, 203, 577(t)

Wilson Imperial Co., 553(bl), 565, 567(t)

Wisconsin Knife Works, Inc., 146, 227(m), 235(tr), 237, 283(tr), 284(t)(m), 313, 369(b), 373, 396(t), 397, 426, 581(b)

Wood & Wood Products, 107

X-Acto Precision Tools, Inc., 269(t)

Special thanks and appreciation are due the staff of the Forest Products Laboratory, Madison, Wisconsin: Donald G. Coleman, Harold L. Mitchell, R. F. Blomquist, George H. Englerth, and Edward M. Davis. The authors called upon them freely and frequently for authoritative data and consultation.

The authors also had the privilege of associating with many other specialists in fields related to wood technology. We gratefully value the contributions they have made to this writing. Special thanks and gratitude go to: Miss June McSwain, Director, Educational Division, Forest Products Industries, Inc., and Darrell Ward, editor of *Woodworking Digest* and *Woodworking Educator's Journal;* and also Dennis Brennan, formerly managing editor of *Woodworking Digest.*

Thanks to our typists: Mrs. Patrick Spielman, who donated long hours typing correspondence and many drafts of the manuscript; and Mrs. Bill Simmons, Industrial Arts and Technology Division, Georgia Southern College.

The authors express their sincere appreciation to their families for their encouragement, understanding, and sacrifices during the time this text was being prepared; Mary Ann (Hynes) Hackett, and children Ann, Michael, Mary, and David; Patricia (Rogers) Spielman, and children Robert and Sherri.

D. F. H.

P. E. S.

Contents

Part I WOOD AND INDUSTRY

Chapter 1 The Development of the Wood Using Industries

Wood has always served man in one form or another. In most inhabited areas of the world, wood has been one of nature's most plentiful and easily obtainable resources (Fig. 1–1).

When primitive man learned that a fallen tree branch or a rock held in his hand made an effective tool or weapon, he was on his way to becoming a toolmaker and tool-user. Anthropologists tell us that by the end of the old stone age (about 8000 B.C.) all the basic tools had been invented. These were stone tools that enabled man to pound, chop, saw, bore, scrape, and cut. With these he was able to provide himself with the necessary food, clothing, and shelter. They served man's needs for almost 99 percent of his time on earth. As primitive man slowly developed his unique ability to invent, make, and use tools to aid him in solving the problems associated with survival, he was preparing the foundation for civilization.

Primitive man spent most of his time in roaming the earth to gather sufficient food merely to survive — and few survived longer than thirty to forty years. But, by 6000 B.C. he had learned that he could domesticate some of the animals he hunted. He also learned that the seeds

he had collected would grow if placed in the soil. In this way, man discovered agriculture and brought the need for a nomadic existence to an end. He began to concentrate his efforts on *producing* food rather than on *searching* for food. He invented the stick plow, the sickle, and other tools to help him farm better. In a short time he learned to produce food and fiber in such quantities that they exceeded his needs.

When assured of a sufficient supply of food, man settled in one spot. Villages developed and with them the need for government and other kinds of services. Men who were not needed to produce food were freed to develop other skills.

Some men were entrusted with the responsibility of supervising the stores of surplus foods; of distributing them to the needy or trading them for other goods. Some of these men recognized the need for a record-keeping system and in time developed a series of symbols to serve this purpose. By 3500 B.C. these symbols had been developed into a written language and recorded history began.

About the time that man learned to write he also discovered metals. Some curious individual probably found a nugget of copper or a meteorite. When he

Fig. 1—1. America's forests helped to build this nation.

hammered it he found that it could be formed into various shapes. Soon men (today called metallurgists) were extracting metals from ores and producing metal tools and weapons far superior to any previously known. Thus man moved from the stone age to the copper age, then to the iron age, and about the middle of the nineteenth century, to the steel age. (Anthropologists identify the industrial cultures of man by the principal tool-making material.)

Throughout most of man's time on earth, he has been primarily occupied in *producing goods* — at first food, then clothing and shelter, and later a host of other items. Today over 40,000 different manufactured products are available in

the United States. In 1870 about 200 manufactured items were all that could be purchased. This change came about through man's ability to make and use the tools with which the natural resources of the earth could be converted into useful products. For most of the working population, skill in *using* tools was of primary importance.

During the decade of the 1950's the United States changed from a goods producing to a service producing nation. This is to say that more people were employed in providing services than in producing goods. Technological changes now permit us to produce a surplus of goods with fewer people required to perform menial tasks. Machines have taken the drudgery out of work. This has freed more people to perform services, some associated with keeping the manufactured goods in operation. The premium today is being placed upon one's cognitive (mental-perceptive) abilities as they relate to solving the problems of our industrial-technological culture.

This book has been written to aid you in understanding how industry and technology have changed and how they function today. The wood-using industries have been selected to present this story because they are more or less typical of the manufacturing industries in general. As you study the following pages, you should begin to understand how American industry functions, how men and machines are employed in various ways to produce products made from wood,

and how you might find your place in this part of the working world.

The Wood Industries In America

When the earliest settlers arrived on this continent, they cut trees to make space for their homes and their farms. As early as 1603 a shipment of sassafras bark was sent to England. Sea captains from Great Britain took shiploads of white pine logs back from what is now Maine in 1605. Thus lumbering became one of the first businesses in this country.

Captain John Smith established the first colony of the Virginia Company at Jamestown in 1607. The headquarters of the Virginia Company were in Lon-

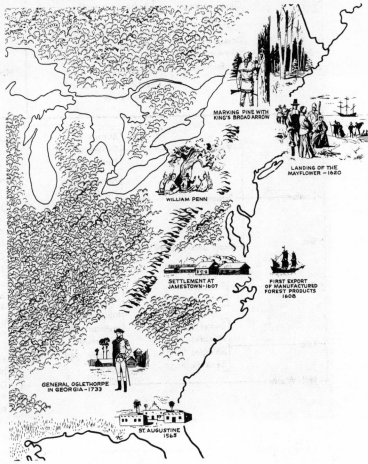

Fig. 1–2. Exports of American forest products date from early colonial times.

MARKING PINE WITH KING'S BROAD ARROW

LANDING OF THE MAYFLOWER – 1620

WILLIAM PENN

SETTLEMENT AT JAMESTOWN – 1607

FIRST EXPORT OF MANUFACTURED FOREST PRODUCTS 1608

GENERAL OGLETHORPE IN GEORGIA – 1733

ST. AUGUSTINE 1565

TABLE 1-1
WHAT WE GET FROM TREES

In Addition to
Poles Piles Posts

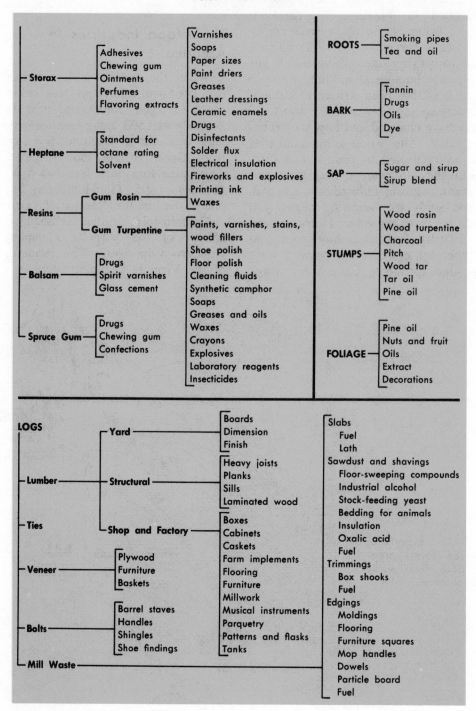

Storax
- Adhesives
- Chewing gum
- Ointments
- Perfumes
- Flavoring extracts

Heptane
- Standard for octane rating
- Solvent

Resins
- Gum Rosin
- Gum Turpentine

Balsam
- Drugs
- Spirit varnishes
- Glass cement

Spruce Gum
- Drugs
- Chewing gum
- Confections

- Varnishes
- Soaps
- Paper sizes
- Paint driers
- Greases
- Leather dressings
- Ceramic enamels
- Drugs
- Disinfectants
- Solder flux
- Electrical insulation
- Fireworks and explosives
- Printing ink
- Waxes
- Paints, varnishes, stains, wood fillers
- Shoe polish
- Floor polish
- Cleaning fluids
- Synthetic camphor
- Soaps
- Greases and oils
- Waxes
- Crayons
- Explosives
- Laboratory reagents
- Insecticides

ROOTS
- Smoking pipes
- Tea and oil

BARK
- Tannin
- Drugs
- Oils
- Dye

SAP
- Sugar and sirup
- Sirup blend

STUMPS
- Wood rosin
- Wood turpentine
- Charcoal
- Pitch
- Wood tar
- Tar oil
- Pine oil

FOLIAGE
- Pine oil
- Nuts and fruit
- Oils
- Extract
- Decorations

LOGS

Lumber
- Yard
  - Boards
  - Dimension
  - Finish
- Structural
  - Heavy joists
  - Planks
  - Sills
  - Laminated wood
- Shop and Factory

Ties

Veneer
- Plywood
- Furniture
- Baskets

Bolts
- Barrel staves
- Handles
- Shingles
- Shoe findings

Mill Waste

- Boxes
- Cabinets
- Caskets
- Farm implements
- Flooring
- Furniture
- Millwork
- Musical instruments
- Parquetry
- Patterns and flasks
- Tanks

- Slabs
  - Fuel
  - Lath
- Sawdust and shavings
  - Floor-sweeping compounds
  - Industrial alcohol
  - Stock-feeding yeast
  - Bedding for animals
  - Insulation
  - Oxalic acid
  - Fuel
- Trimmings
  - Box shooks
  - Fuel
- Edgings
  - Moldings
  - Flooring
  - Furniture squares
  - Mop handles
  - Dowels
  - Particle board
  - Fuel

don. Captain Smith's instructions were to find gold and silver. If he could not make the colonization venture profitable for the London bankers who financed the project, the colony would be abandoned.

Gold and silver did not exist near Jamestown. However, great forests were prevalent. From these forests, tar, pitch, and turpentine were collected. Trees were sawed into boards and wood was burned to make potash for use in soap and glass making.

Thus the first products manufactured in America were forest products and in 1608 they were shipped to England (Fig. 2-2). By 1620, the year the pilgrims landed, the Jamestown colony had proved its worth as a business venture.

The earliest saw mills utilized the ax,

saw, wedge, and sledge — all hand-powered. Later, when workers came from Europe, they brought saws powered by water wheels. These power saws had been in use from the middle of the fourteenth century. Sometimes men or animals provided the power. The first commercial water-powered mills of any size probably operated in Maine and New Hampshire as early as 1630. The first steam saw mill was set up in New Orleans in 1811. It was promptly destroyed by a mob of angry workers who viewed it as the end of their jobs.

Until the development of the power saw, wood was worked with hand tools. A form of lathe powered by a hand-operated bow was developed in Egypt about 740 B.C. One hand and one foot

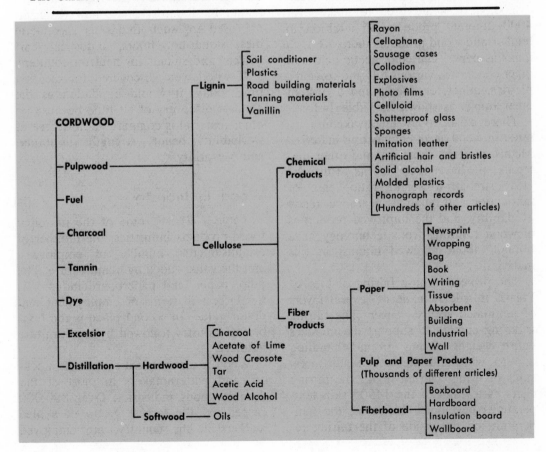

were used to control the tools. The table-model circular saw was invented by Samuel Miller about 1777. A few years later it was powered by one of James Watt's improved steam engines. Between 1791 and 1793, Samuel Bentham of London invented machines for planing, sawing, and boring wood. They were crude devices, made of heavy timbers with only the cutters and bearings made of metal. However, they made it possible for unskilled workers to perform certain operations as effectively as skilled wood craftsmen. Woodworking machines were not made entirely of metal until about 1860.

Wood Products Today

Today, trees are used to make over 4000 different products. In addition to lumber and wood products there are such items as paper, charcoal, acetic acid and other chemicals, various oils and solvents, plastics, adhesives, foods, and a host of other things as shown in Table 1–1.

There exists today an awakening interest in wood as an engineering material. Metals, plastics, ceramics, and other materials all have their merits. But, the great strength-to-weight ratio, ease of fabrication and repair, appearance, ready availability, and the improved properties of wood resulting from technology have brought about renewed interest in this material.

The protective nose fairing of the A3 Polaris missile is made of several layers of laminated spruce veneer. The fairing is strong enough to support the missile's entire weight during ground handling and to withstand the underwater pressures of firing. During flight, the fairing chars as a result of the 1450° skin temperatures developed. However, the temperature on the inside of the fairing re-

mains at 95° F. The charring does not jeopardize the structure because it happens after the critical air loading condition has been satisfied.

The Marcos 1800 Grand touring car made in England, uses a wooden frame and a body of one-eighth inch marine plywood. The frame and body weigh only 200 lb. A resin glue and only a few nails and screws hold it together. Powered by a four-cylinder, 108-hp Ford engine this car won European races in 1961 and 1962.

Reconstructed wood is a term applied to wood that has been reinforced with impregnants or layers of other materials, or that has had its fibers reoriented. Research has produced a host of denser, harder, and more wear- and water-resistant hardboards. These new materials are used for such things as sheetmetal dies, aquarium floors, industrial cart wheels, and shields for neutron counters.

If wood were discovered for the first time today, it would be hailed as the greatest discovery of all time because no other material is comparable in degree of workability, beauty, strength, durability, and versatility.

Wood in Industry

Table 1–2 lists some of the principal forest-products industries, the number of establishments, number of employees, and the value added by manufacture. The pulp, paper, and paperboard industry is the largest in terms of employment and dollar value. In second place is the lumbering industry followed by the furniture industry.

Wood is also worked by model, mock-up, and patternmakers in most of the durable goods industries. Over 800,000 carpenters, the largest group of skilled workers in the country, are employed

TABLE 1–2
THE PRINCIPAL WOOD USING INDUSTRIES — 1964

Industry	Number of Establishments	Number of Employees (Thousands)	Value Added by Manufacture (Millions)
All Manufacturing	298,182	16,766	$179,290
Wood Products Manufacturing	. . .	1,011	8,551
* Boats, Recreational	1,800	24	264
Containers, Wood	983	36	203
Furniture, Wood			
Case Goods	2,800	136	900
Upholstered	1,700	67	478
Office	. . .	6	48
Gum and Wood Chemicals	. . .	6	100
Hardboard	18	4	88
Homes, Mobile	300	29	222
Prefabricated	374	14	179
Lumber	33,000	265	1,553
Millwork	. . .	59	424
Particleboard	57	2	26
Plywood, Hardwood	164	30	183
Softwood	150	40	299
Pulp, paper and paperboard	849	282	3,500
Wood Preserving	385	11	84

* 60% are made of wood, 20% plastic, 20% metal.

to erect structures made of wood. Such things as railroad ties, telephone and power poles, concrete forms, and one third of all railroad freight cars are made of wood. Of all the raw materials available to man, wood is one of the few materials that is replenishable. Present day conservation and forest management practices assure us of a continuing supply of this valuable material.

Products made from trees are manufactured by companies of all sizes. For example, almost one third of the furniture companies in the United States are owned and managed by one individual who employs not more than four workers. The value of their shipments in 1958 was 2.1 percent of the industry total. Today, only 4 percent of the more than 2800 case goods (wooden furniture) manufacturers employ 250 or more workers, but the value of their shipments is over one third of the industry total. Over 70 percent of these case goods are manufactured in the South. There is a trend today toward merging and consolidating the smaller and medium-sized producers. The reasons are many: mass purchasing, longer production runs, reduced transportation costs to retailers, national advertising and distribution, tax benefits, a more efficient sales force, coordinated style groups for each room in the house, and the necessary financial strength and marketing scope to afford highly trained professional executives.

The largest companies employ workers in hundreds of different occupations. The line and staff organization chart, Table 1–3, is typical of large industries in general. In addition to administrative personnel, there are designers, scientists, engineers, salesmen, skilled craftsmen, machine operators, and many other specialized, semiskilled, and unskilled workers.

TABLE 1-3
SAMPLE ORGANIZATION CHART OF A
LARGE MANUFACTURING COMPANY

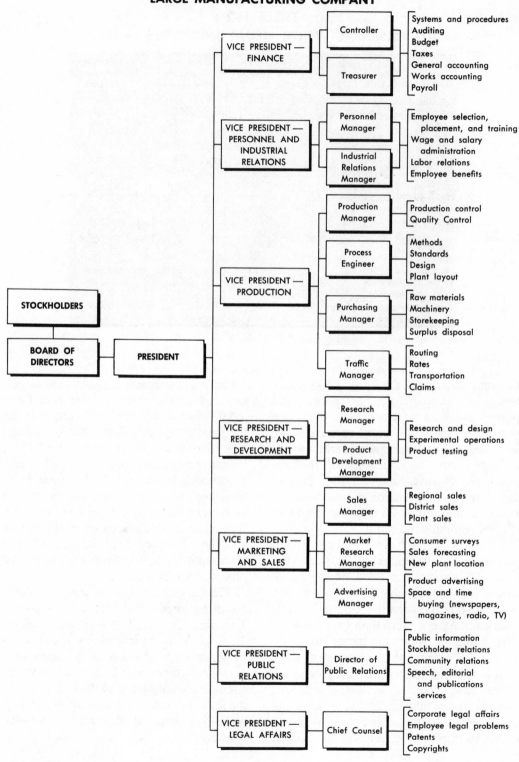

Most large companies have a number of stockholders. They are the people who invest their money in the company so that it can operate. They expect to receive a share of the company profits in return for the use of their money. Stockholders elect the board of directors. The directors are the policy-making group for a company. The company president carries out the policies adopted by the directors.

Your Introduction to Industry

Industrial arts classes are probably the first real introduction to industry that you have had. To gain a better understanding of industry, your class may wish to organize somewhat as shown in Table 1–3. If your class is small, it may be necessary to modify this organization somewhat. An organization that includes the production and the research and development functions is effective. Some students may hold two or more positions within this organization.

The purpose of organizing in this manner is to give you an opportunity to study and become better acquainted with the many different responsibilities found in modern industry. As the course progresses, you may wish to conduct a market survey to determine a product that your class could mass produce. The manufacture of this product will involve the class in research and development, designing, planning, purchasing, tooling, producing, advertising, and marketing the product. To finance this venture you may wish to sell "stock." Any profits would, of course, be distributed among the stockholders.

In addition to your teachers, you will find that industrial, engineering, and technical groups are valuable sources of help and information. You may also wish to join one of the national organizations that encourage this type of student activity.

DISCUSSION QUESTIONS

1. In what way is wood a replenishable material?
2. Throughout history, man has reacted against technological change because of a fear of unemployment and its consequences. What, in reality, have been the effects of these changes?
3. What are the responsibilities of the people in the various positions in a large industry?
4. Name some occupations existing in a furniture manufacturing plant. A pulp and paper mill. A lumber mill.
5. Which occupations interest you most? What are the requirements for admission to these occupations?

Chapter 2 The Material—Wood

If we were to ask "Why is a tree?" a botanist might provide an answer. He would explain the biological heredity of a plant as a function of genes, chromosomes, and cells. He would explain that the environmental conditions necessary for the formation of trees existed at least 300 million years ago, when the first conifers or evergreens developed. Broadleaved (deciduous) trees first appeared about 160 million years ago.

If we were to ask "What is a tree?" we could be assured of a more detailed answer. Even here, there are shades of difference in opinion. One definition states that a tree is a woody plant with one main, self-supporting stem at least 20 ft. tall at maturity, and crowned by leafy boughs. With this definition, palms, bamboo, and rattan may correctly be called trees. However, the wood they produce has little usefulness as wood.

The cells or fibers that constitute wood exist in these and many other plants. From a practical standpoint, a tree may be defined as a plant that produces wood of sufficient size and solidity to be usable. In any event, it must contain cells made of cellulose and its compounds which stiffen the plant and conduct sap.

When we raise the question "What is wood?" we must look to the biologist,

chemist, physicist, engineer, technician, and craftsman for our answer, and to each wood is something different. Because trees were readily available to early man, he learned to use wood long before he began to understand it.

The growing knowledge of wood and its characteristics has already had many practical applications. The manufacturers of pulp, paper, and synthetic fibers have been helped by knowing more about the smallest units of wood. Knowledge of the chemical nature of wood has aided in the development of the semichemical pulping process and the production of plastics. Knowledge of wood-fiber structure and chemistry has led to modern methods of stabilizing wood and producing new products.

Classification of Trees

Botanists classify the plant kingdom into several groups. All so-called seed-bearing plants are classed as spermatophytes. Except for tree ferns, all of our wood comes from plants in this class. Spermatophytes may be subdivided into:

A. Gymnosperms — largely the scale and needlelike leaved plants.

B. Angiosperms — largely the board-leaved plants. Angiosperms may be subdivided according to the manner in which the seed is built into:

1. Monocotyledons (single-seed leaves) — bamboos, grasses, palms.

2. Dicotyledons (two-seed leaves) — most angiosperms producing useful wood.

The classification into *A* and *B* above is based on the method of seed-bearing. The ovules (immature seeds) of the gymnosperms are exposed in leaf clusters or in pine cones, and are fertilized by windborne pollen. Trees in this group are commonly called softwoods, conifers, evergreens, or needle-bearing trees.

The angiosperms have a fruit which encloses the ovules. They are fertilized through the pistil (seed-bearing organ) of the flower, usually by insect-borne pollen. However, the stigmas (pollen-receiving part of a flower) of birches, poplars, oaks, and other nut trees receive only wind-borne pollen. Trees in this group are commonly called hardwoods, deciduous (leaf shedding), or broadleaf trees.

Each designation leaves much to be desired. The yellow pine and yew are harder than the so-called "hardwoods" such as basswood, balsa, and cottonwood. Several "hardwoods" such as the magnolia and holly are evergreen and broad-leaved while the "softwoods" larch, tamarack, and bald cypress are deciduous. In spite of this inexactness, "hardwood" and "softwood" are most commonly used to designate the two classes of trees that produce useful wood.

Wood Composition

Woody material is found in many plants, but its most useful form is in the limbs and trunks of trees. Carbon dioxide from the air, and water and minerals from the soil are manufactured by the leaves into starches, sugars, and cellulose that feed and build the tree. The energy in sunlight is harnessed by the green chlorophyll in the leaves to make this change. The process is known as photosynthesis.

The chemical action within the leaves produces a tree that is about 40 to 55 percent alpha-cellulose, something like cotton, and 15 to 25 percent hemicellulose. Another 15 to 30 percent is a cementing material known as lignin, and 2 to 15 percent is inorganic, ash-forming minerals and extractives. Together, they make up the wood structure. The chemical analysis of wood reveals its elemental composition to be approximately 49 percent carbon, 6 percent hydrogen, 44 percent oxygen, and 1 percent nitrogen and mineral ash.

Alpha-cellulose and hemicellulose make up what is known as holocellulose or the "whole carbohydrate" fraction of wood. Alpha-cellulose is the principal material in paper, explosives, synthetic fibers such as rayon, cellophane, and other plastics. Hemicellulose is still not well understood, but it has found use as an ingredient in cattle food, nylon, paper, and some solvents. The pure cellulose molecule is composed of carbon, hydrogen, and oxygen, and may be expressed in a general chemical formula as $(C_6H_{10}O_5)_x$. The subscript x signifies that a single molecule is made up of an indefinite number of these groups. Cellulose is insoluble in water and ordinary solvents. Strong acids will completely dissolve it.

Lignin exists within the cell walls as an amorphous uncrystallized constituent. For years lignin was wasted. Today it is used in plastics, man-made fibers, road binders, linoleum cements, electroplating, and storage batteries. While chemists know where lignin is, there is some disagreement on what it is. In the process of separating it from wood, its chemical identity is changed seriously.

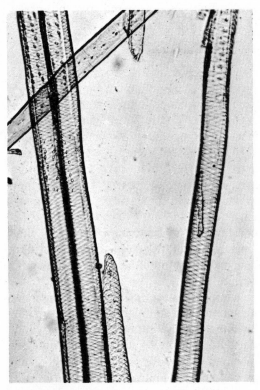

Fig. 2–1. Douglas-fir fibers (tracheids) enlarged many times. Part of the strength of the individual fiber lies in the helical winding of the fibrils.

The **extractives,** while not a part of the wood structure, contribute such properties as color, odor, resistance to decay, and taste. Coloring matter, fats, gums, oils, resins, starch, tannins, and waxes are included. Neutral solvents, such as water, acetone, alcohol, benzene, and ether will remove them from wood.

The **ash** that remains when lignin and cellulose are burned, is composed of minerals. These comprise the essential nutrients (food) of the tree.

Wood Structure

Wood cells are the minute units of wood structure that include fibers, ves-sels, and other elements. Fibers in soft-woods are technically called tracheids. The strength of wood is the result of millions of these tiny cells bound tightly together with an intercellular substance (middle lamella) composed chiefly of pectic (jellylike) compounds and possibly some lignin. Each fiber is needle shaped; about $\frac{1}{25}$ in. long in hardwoods and $\frac{1}{8}$ to $\frac{1}{3}$ in. long in softwoods. Tracheids average about 0.0019 in. in thickness. They are lined up in one direction with the ends of one fiber overlapping a portion of the next fiber.

Each fiber is a pipelike structure of layers, windings, and pierced openings as shown in Figure 2–1. The way in which the tree was nourished influenced the size and arrangement of the parts. As the parts were changed, so was the strength of the fiber and the wood. The outer layer of a fiber is a springlike winding one layer deep. When unwound, the layer below looks like the hundreds of fine wires in an electrical conductor. These are called fibrils. They may make an angle of 5 to 30 deg. with the axis of the fiber (Fig. 2–2). The smaller the angle, the stronger the fiber. The particular angle is determined by the conditions under which the tree grew. There are several layers of these fibrils. They add up to a wall thickness of 0.000011 in. in some hardwoods and to as much as 0.0004 in. in some softwoods.

Fibrils have been chemically reduced to a series of smaller shorter spindles called fusiform bodies. When chemically softened, these units resolve themselves into small chunks of cellulose which are at the limits of visibility under a high-powered optical microscope. Anything smaller would have to be examined with the aid of x rays or an electron microscope.

The internal surface area of a wood

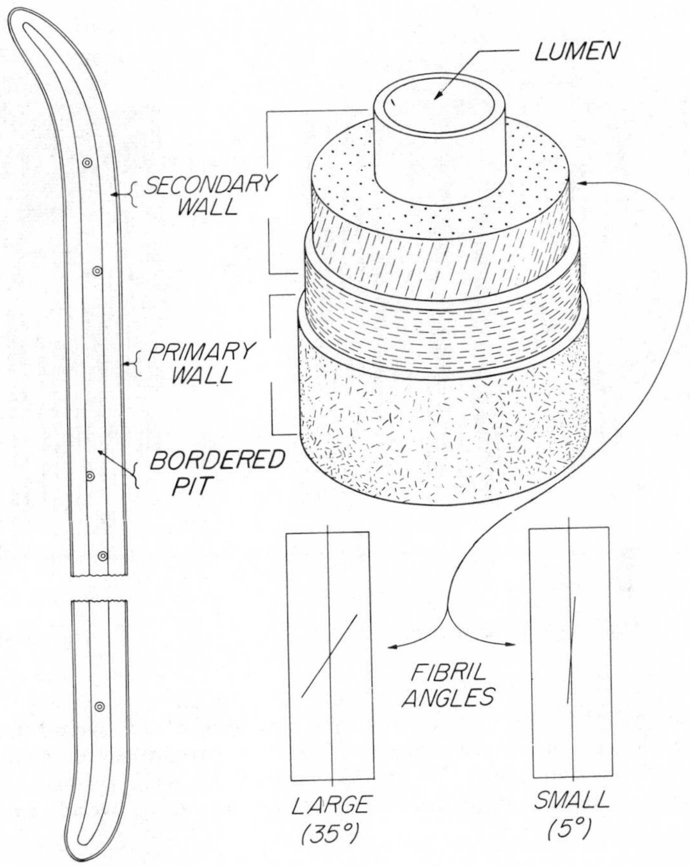

Fig. 2–2. The wall of the wood fiber is far from simple. A large fibril angle is associated with wood that is inferior in strength.

fiber staggers the imagination. The innumerable small parts, many of them separated by crevices, and the pores in focus under a high-powered microscope add up to a surface area of as much as 10 sq. ft. A cubic inch of wood with its infolded and intertwined surfaces totals approximately ½ acre in surface area.

Diagrams of the cell structure of hardwood and softwood are shown in Figures 2–3 and 2–4. They show the various cell openings within the wood structure. The largest openings in hardwood are the specialized vessels, or pores *P,* for conducting sap. These lie between the fibers *F* and can be seen with the naked eye in some species. They are relatively long cells with open ends set one above the other. In some species of hardwoods these cells are separated by a grating *SC* as shown in the diagram. Pits *K* in the fibers and vessels afford a means for the transfer of sap. Sap is transferred through the tracheids *TR* in softwoods. The various cell units are held together with a cementing layer of intercellular substance called the middle lamella *ML.* When dissolved by certain chemicals, the wood fibers may be separated as is done in making paper from wood. The smallest openings seen in the diagrams are the fiber cavities called lumens.

Within the tracheid walls there are numerous bordered pits *BP.* Each pit has

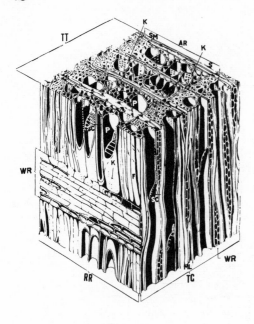

Fig. 2–3. Hardwood.   **Fig. 2–4.** Softwood.

The distinguishing features of the cell structure of hardwood and softwood. Each cube measures ½ inch on a side. Plane TT is a horizontal cross section of the tree; plane RR is cut radially and plane TG is cut tangentially with reference to the annual rings. AR represents an annual ring; S is the more porous spring wood, SM is summer wood.

a membrane covering as shown in Figure 2–5. They serve as tiny valves. When fluids swell the cell wall, the tiniest of all the openings, capillary channels, form in the pit membrane to permit sap to flow from the roots to the uppermost branches of the tree. They cannot be seen with a microscope. Simple pits *SP* permit the passage of sap between the rays and tracheids in the softwoods.

The horizontally oriented cells in both hard- and softwoods conduct the food material radially across the grain and are called wood rays *WR*. They are most conspicuous in oaks and sycamores, especially when quartersawed. Medullary rays extend from the pith to the inner bark. Softwoods contain fusiform (spindle-

shaped) wood rays *FWR* and horizontal *HRD* and vertical resin ducts *VRD*. Ducts are openings between the wood cells. Horizontal resin ducts occur in the wood rays and in some instances connect with the vertical ducts. Ray tracheids *RT* are horizontally oriented cells that form around the rays.

The difference in cell structure of the hardwoods and softwoods is a distinguishing feature. Hardwoods are called "porous" and softwoods "nonporous." The comparatively large open-end cells or pores in hardwoods make them "porous." They are found in practically all angiosperms. Since the gymnosperms elevate sap through the tracheids, they have no pores or open-ended cells for this purpose.

Tree Growth

Trees grow by forming cells or fibers of wood around the trunk, limbs, and roots, and at the ends of shoots and branches (Fig. 2–6). For this reason branches of trees will remain at the same height above the ground as they grow. All growth takes place in the microscopically thin, greenish cambium layer which lies beneath the inner bark.

Xylem, the woody portion of a tree, is formed on one side of the cambium while phloem, the primary bark tissue, is formed on the other. The phloem is soft and moist and carries the tree food from the leaves to all parts of the tree. The outer corky layer is composed of dry, dead cells and is known as the outer bark. This provides protection to the growing portion of the tree. The term "bast" is sometimes used as the equivalent of bark or inner bark. Most correctly it applies only to the lignified fibers found in many barks and other fibrous materials.

During the spring of the year growth is most rapid and the cells formed then are more porous than those formed during the slow summer growing period. The summer growth fibers are shorter, thicker, heavier, and stronger. Because of this difference in growth rate, a year's addition of wood can easily be observed in some species of trees such as the Douglas fir and longleaf pine. The spring and summer wood make up an annual ring as shown in Figure 2–7. Some trees, such as the maples and gums do not show these changes in growth rate. Consequently, the annual rings are difficult to

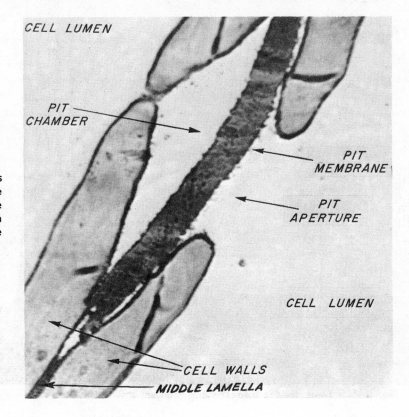

Fig. 2–5. Bordered pits act like valves in the fiber wall to permit the flow of fluids through the sapwood during the life of the tree.

CELL LUMEN

PIT CHAMBER

PIT MEMBRANE

PIT APERTURE

CELL LUMEN

CELL WALLS
MIDDLE LAMELLA

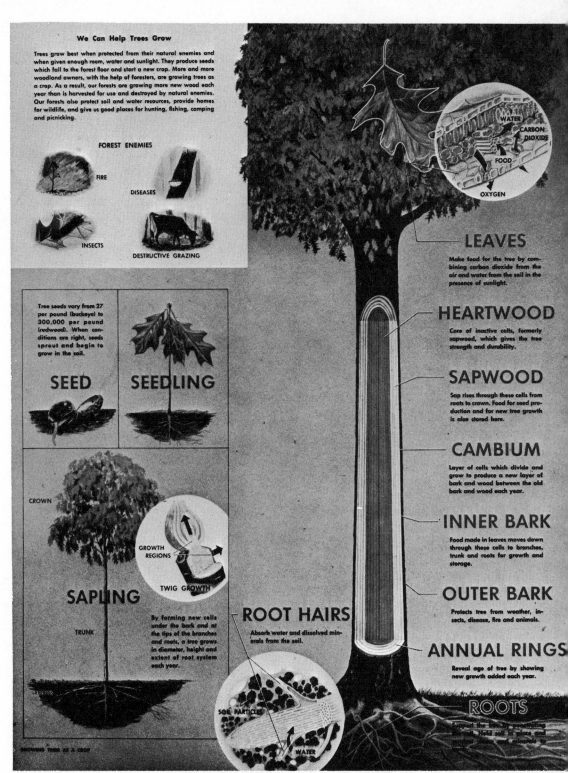

We Can Help Trees Grow

Trees grow best when protected from their natural enemies and when given enough room, water and sunlight. They produce seeds which fall to the forest floor and start a new crop. More and more woodland owners, with the help of foresters, are growing trees as a crop. As a result, our forests are growing more new wood each year than is harvested for use and destroyed by natural enemies. Our forests also protect soil and water resources, provide homes for wildlife, and give us good places for hunting, fishing, camping and picnicking.

FOREST ENEMIES

FIRE

DISEASES

INSECTS

DESTRUCTIVE GRAZING

Tree seeds vary from 27 per pound (buckeye) to 300,000 per pound (redwood). When conditions are right, seeds sprout and begin to grow in the soil.

SEED

SEEDLING

CROWN

GROWTH REGIONS

TWIG GROWTH

SAPLING

TRUNK

By forming new cells under the bark and at the tips of the branches and roots, a tree grows in diameter, height and extent of root system each year.

ROOT HAIRS

Absorb water and dissolved minerals from the soil.

SOIL PARTICLES

WATER

WATER
CARBON DIOXIDE
FOOD
OXYGEN

LEAVES

Make food for the tree by combining carbon dioxide from the air and water from the soil in the presence of sunlight.

HEARTWOOD

Core of inactive cells, formerly sapwood, which gives the tree strength and durability.

SAPWOOD

Sap rises through these cells from roots to crown. Food for seed production and for new tree growth is also stored here.

CAMBIUM

Layer of cells which divide and grow to produce a new layer of bark and wood between the old bark and wood each year.

INNER BARK

Food made in leaves moves down through these cells to branches, trunk and roots for growth and storage.

OUTER BARK

Protects tree from weather, insects, disease, fire and animals.

ANNUAL RINGS

Reveal age of tree by showing new growth added each year.

ROOTS

Support the tree by anchoring it in the ground. Hold soil in place and absorb water and minerals.

Fig. 2–6. Trees are the largest living things.

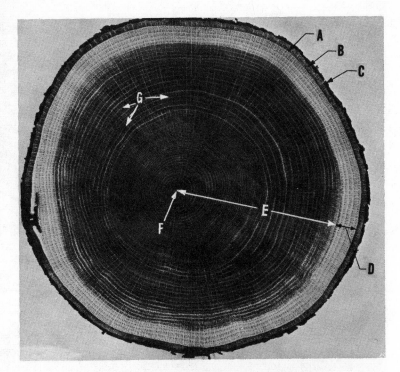

Fig. 2–7. A cross section of a tree trunk. A, Cambium layer where growth takes place. B, Inner Bark. C, Outer Bark. D, Sapwood. E, Heartwood. F, Pith. G, Woodrays. The age of the tree may be determined by counting its annual rings.

identify. Trees in tropical regions may also have poorly defined rings because of more-or-less continuous growth throughout the year.

Sapwood is the outer light-colored wood of a tree trunk. It stores excess food and conducts the water from the roots to the leaves. The species of trees that grow most rapidly have the widest layers of sapwood. In maple, hickory, ash, and some species of pine, the sapwood may be 3 to 6 in. or more in thickness, especially in second-growth trees. In the chestnut and black locust, the sapwood contains very few growth rings and may not exceed a thickness of ½ in. Sapwood deteriorates rapidly when exposed to weather unless it is chemically treated. Sapwood takes preservative treatment better than heartwood. It has fewer defects such as knots, shakes, and pitch, and less odor and taste.

Heartwood is the central core of the tree trunk. When the cells of a tree have served their purposes of conducting water and storing food, they become inactive. Changes take place in the cells and they become heartwood. In most species the heartwood is darker in color as a result of the deposits of various materials in the cavities. In some species, such as most spruces, true firs, basswood, cottonwood, and tupelo gum, the heartwood is not dark colored.

Because of the infiltrations and deposits in the cells of heartwood, lumber cut from it is usually more durable than from sapwood in exposed conditions. Ashes, hickories, and certain oaks make the change to heartwood after the pores become plugged with frothlike cell ingrowths known as tyloses. The heartwood of white oak is suitable for tight cooperage (barrels) when its pores are thus tightly plugged.

The mechanical properties of sapwood

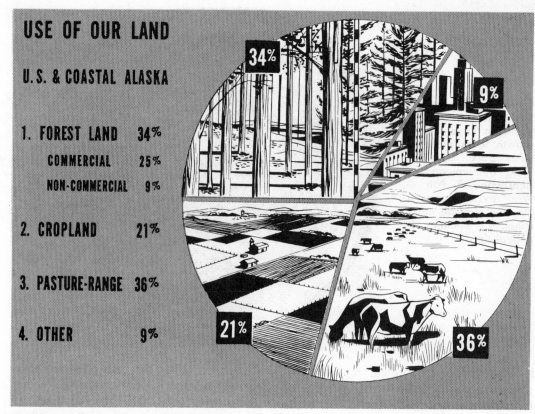

USE OF OUR LAND

U.S. & COASTAL ALASKA

1. **FOREST LAND** 34%
   COMMERCIAL 25%
   NON-COMMERCIAL 9%

2. **CROPLAND** 21%

3. **PASTURE-RANGE** 36%

4. **OTHER** 9%

Fig. 2–8. Percentage distribution of land usage.

and heartwood do not differ significantly in most species. The heartwood of oak, pine, Douglas fir, hickory, and ash is not intrinsically stronger than the sapwood. Growth conditions at the time the wood is formed affect these properties more than does the change from sapwood to heartwood. Infiltrated materials increase the weight, strength, and crush resistance considerably in some species such as redwood, western red cedar, and black locust. Dry wood cells may be empty or partly filled with gums, resins, or tyloses.

The Species of Trees

It is estimated that there are approximately 150,000 species of hardwoods in the world. At least 1182 species of trees exist in the United States. England has only 29 different species, France 34, Germany 60, and all of Europe, less Russia, has only 85.

Forests cover approximately 29 percent of the world's land area. South America and Africa have 44 percent of the world's forests; Europe has 4 percent; Asia, 14 percent; Russia, 19 percent; and North America, 17 percent. Only 30 percent of the world's forest area is in use.

The United States has about 8 percent of the world's forests, covering 775 million acres, an area greater than all the states east of the Mississippi River. But only 75 percent of this land area produces wood for commercial purposes. The remainder is noncommercial. Some serve as national parks and recreation areas, but much is of low value or in inaccessible timber areas. Figure 2–8 shows how our land is used, and Figure 2–9 shows the distribution of ownership of the commercial forests.

Different species of trees grow in the different climates and soils of the United States. With the exception of very high altitudes, grasslands, and arid regions, trees grow in all parts of the country. They are found in rather definite groupings of species. Because of these natural groupings, it is possible to identify 10 forest regions in the United States as shown in Figure 2–10.

Only 100 species of trees have much commercial value for their wood and other products. About 35 species produce most of our lumber and pulp. Of the 100 commercially useful species, approximately 40 are softwoods. They provide most of our building materials and pulp. Of the 60 species of hardwoods, oak is the most important commercially. It finds extensive use in construction and in furniture, showcase, and cabinet making.

The **species** of trees in greatest use today are listed in Table 2–1. Both the common and botanical names are given

OWNERSHIP OF FOREST LAND

INDUSTRIAL 13%   FARMERS AND OTHER SMALL OWNERS 60%   GOVERNMENT 27%

Fig. 2–9. The United States has 535 million acres of commercial forest land. More than half of it — 60 percent — is in private ownerships of less than 5,000 acres. A quarter of the commercial forest land is owned by the government. Wood-using industries own only 13 percent of the nation's forest lands. Privately owned forests produce about 90 percent of the nation's wood harvest.

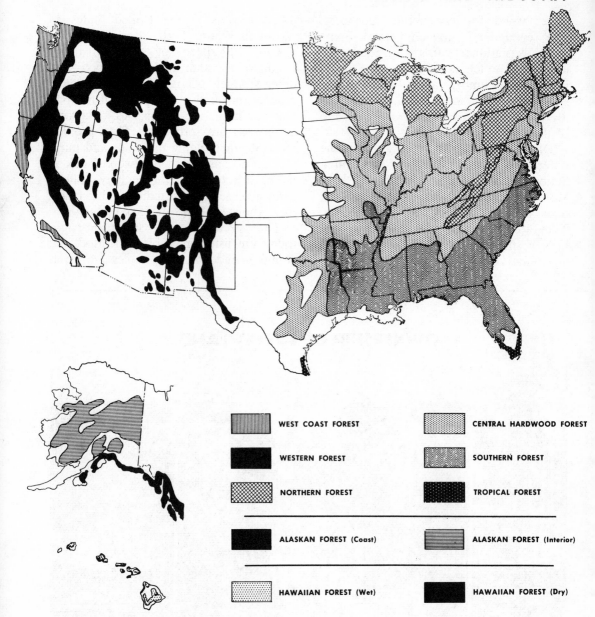

Fig. 2–10. Forest regions of the United States.

to eliminate confusion resulting from the many common names applied to certain species.

The **forest region** in which each species grows is identified in Table 2–1. While several species grow in many forest regions, they are considered to be of greatest commercial importance in those indicated. The forest regions are shown in Figure 2–10.

Properties of Wood

Specific gravity is the ratio found by dividing the weight of a substance by the weight of an equal volume of pure water at its greatest density. The specific gravity of pure water is 1.0. Any substance with a specific gravity of more than 1.0 will sink in water; if less than 1.0 it will float. Next to actual tests of wood strength, the specific gravity is the best indication of its strength properties.

The true specific gravity of wood is based on its oven-dry weight and volume. However, the specific gravity may also be based upon the volume of the wood in the green air-dry condition. Since the volume of wood is different in each case, it is important to state which condition existed when the test was made. The specific gravity values in Table 2–1 are based on the oven-dry weight of the wood and its green volume.

Density is the mass (quantity of matter) of a body per unit volume (cubic centimeter, cubic inch). Density of wood is the mass of wood substance in a given volume. In its dry state, the density of wood is numerically equal to its specific gravity. The density, or specific gravity, of the actual wood substance itself is about 1.54. This value is practically the same for all species of wood. Because wood is porous, it contains air which reduces the weight of a given volume and permits it to float on water.

Weight of wood is expressed as the pounds of wood substance and water present in a cubic foot (Fig. 2–11). The weight of resins, gums, and infiltrated materials is not considered as a separate quantity. The weights expressed in Table 2–1 are the weights in pounds of 1 cu. ft. of wood at 12 percent moisture content. One species weighs more than another because it contains a greater amount of wood substance in thicker cell walls with correspondingly smaller cavities. The weight of a cubic foot of any wood at the current moisture content may be determined from the specific gravity, based on oven-dry weight and volume at test, as follows:

Weight per cubic foot =

$$\frac{\text{S.G.} \times 62.4 \times (100 + \text{M.C.})}{100}$$

S.G. — Specific Gravity
62.4 — Weight in pounds of 1 cu. ft. of water
M.C. — Moisture Content at Test

Grain and **texture** are terms commonly used in connection with wood. They have no definite meaning. "Grain" may refer to the spacing or pattern of the annual rings, to the direction of the fibers, or to the porous nature of the wood. Woods may be placed into three groups according to their porous nature. Ring porous woods, such as oak and ash, have large, distinct cells. Semi-ring porous woods, such as hickory and elm, have cells that are fairly distinct. Diffuse porous woods, such as birch, poplar, and cherry, lack a distinctive cell pattern. In Table 2–1, the term *grain* identifies the hardwoods that are sufficiently porous or open-grained to require a paste wood filler to produce a smooth finish. Cherry

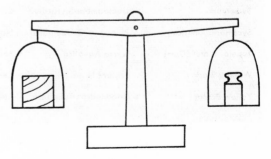

Fig. 2–11. Determining "weight" of wood.

TABLE 2–1   COMMON COMMERCIAL WOODS COMPARATIVE

Hardwoods (Angiosperms)	Botanical Name	Forest Region of Growth	Specific Gravity	Weight Per Cu. Ft. at 12% M.C.	Grain	Hardness	Workability With Handtools
				Pounds		Pounds	
Ash, White	Fraxinus Americana	Northern, Central	.55	42	O	1240	Hard
Aspen, Quaking	Populus Tremuloides	Northern	.35	27	C	350	Easy
Basswood, American	Tilia Americana	Northern, Central	.32	26	C	310	Easy
Beech, American	Fagus Grandifolia	Northern, Central	.56	45	C	1130	Hard
Birch, Yellow	Betula Alleghaniensis	Northern, Central	.55	43	C	1010	Hard
Cherry, Black	Prunus Serotina	Central	.47	35	C	850	Hard
Cottonwood, Eastern	Populus Deltoides	Central, Southern	.37	23	C	430	Fair
Elm, American	Ulmus Americana	North, Cen. South	.46	35	O	770	Hard
Elm, Rock	Ulmus Thomasii	Northern, Central	.57	44	O	1320	Hard
Hickory, Shagbark	Carya Ovata	Central, Southern	.64	50	O	1820	Hard
Magnolia	Magnolia Grandiflora	Southern	.46	35	C	1020	Fair
Mahogany, Honduras	Swietenia	Central American	.55	32	O	930	Fair
"Mahogany," Philippine (Red Lauan)	Shorea Negrosensis	Philippine Islands	.40	36	O	670	Easy
Maple, Sugar (Rock)	Acer Sacchorum	Central, Southern	.56	44	C	1450	High
Oak, Red	Quercus Rubra	North, Cen., Southern	.56	44	O	1290	High
Oak, White	Quercus Alba	North, Cen., Southern	.60	48	O	1360	High
Sweetgum	Liquidambar Styraciflua	Central, Southern	.46	35	C	710	Fair
Sycamore, American	Plantanus Occidentalis	North, Cen., Southern	.46	34	C	750	Fair
Tupelo, Water (Gum)	Nyssa Aquatica	Southern	.46	35	C	880	Fair
Walnut, Black	Juglons Nigra	Central	.51	38	O	1010	Fair
Yellow Poplar	Liriodendron Tulipifera	Central, Southern	.40	28	C	540	Easy

PHYSICAL PROPERTIES AT 12% MOISTURE CONTENT

Tendency to Warp	Tendency to Shrink & Swell	Volumetric Shrinkage When Dried to 0% M.C.	Decay Resistance of Heartwood	Compressive Strength Endwise	Stiffness	Shock Resistance	Bending Strength	Principal Uses
		%		P.s.i.	1000 P.s.i.	Inches	P.s.i.	
Med.	Med.	13.4	L	7410	1770	43	8900	Tool handles, cooperage, boxes, furniture, sporting goods, veneer
Med.	Med.	11.5	L	4250	1180	21	5600	Boxes, core stock, excelsior, matches, pulp
Med.	High	15.8	L	4730	1460	16	5900	Venetian blinds, cheap furniture, millwork, excelsior, cooperage
High	High	16.3	L	7300	1720	41	8700	Food containers, furniture, handles, woodenware, veneer, pulp
Med.	Med.	16.7	L	8170	2010	55	10100	Furniture, boxes, baskets, woodenware, spools, flooring, veneer.
Low	Med.	11.5	L	7110	1490	29	9000	Furniture, electrotype plate blocks, carvings, patterns, woodenware
High	Med.	14.1	L	4910	1370	20	5700	Baskets, boxes, crates, pulp
Med.	High	14.6	L	5520	1340	39	7600	Hoops, staves, furniture, flooring, sporting goods, containers
High	Med.	14.1	L	7050	1540	56	8000	Framework timbers, bent wood parts
Med.	High	17.9	L	8000	2160	67	10700	Tool handles, vehicle parts, ladder rungs, athletic goods, furniture
Low	Med.	12.3	L	5460	1400	29	6800	Boxes, furniture, venetian blinds, sashes, doors, veneer
Low	Low	8.0	H	7560	1720	25	9500	Fine furniture, cabinets, veneer, boats
Low	Med.	11.7	M	6740	1620	33	7900	Furniture, veneer, cabinets, display cases, boat planks
Med.	Med.	14.9	L	7830	1830	39	9500	Furniture, flooring, handles, woodenware, spools, veneer
Med.	Med.	13.5	L	6760	1820	43	8500	Flooring, furniture, millwork, caskets, woodenware, R.R. cars, boats
Med.	Med.	15.8	M	7440	1780	37	8200	Barrels, furniture, flooring, millwork, all purpose wood
High	High	15.0	M	6320	1640	32	6600	Interior finish, millwork, veneer, furniture, cooperage, pulp
High	Med.	14.2	L	5380	1820	26	6400	Interior trim, veneer, furniture, flooring, handles, butcher blocks
High	Med.	12.5	L	5920	1260	23	7200	Furniture, boxes, baskets, pulp, cooperage, R.R. ties
Low	Med.	12.8	Hi.	7580	1680	34	10500	Fine furniture, veneers, cabinets, gunstocks
Med.	Med.	12.3	L	5540	1580	24	6200	Trim, moldings, sashes, doors, furniture, pulp, excelsior, siding

TABLE 2–1 (cont.)

Hardwoods (Angiosperms)	Botanical Name	Forest Region of Growth	Specific Gravity	Weight Per Cu. Ft. at 12% M.C.	Grain	Hardness	Workability With Handtools
				Pounds		Pounds	
Cedar, Western Red	Thuja Plicata	Alaskan, Western	.31	23	C	450	Easy
Cypress, Bald	Taxodium Distichum	Southern	.42	32	C	610	Fair
Fir, Douglas	Pseudotsuga Menziesii	Western, West Coast	.45	33	C	710	Fair
Fir, White, (True)	Abies Concolor	Western, West Coast	.35	27	C	480	Fair
Hemlock, Western	Tsuga Heterophylla	Western, West Coast	.38	29	C	580	Fair
Pine, Loblolly	Pinus Taeda	Southern	.50	38	C	660	Hard
Pine, Longleaf	Pinus Palustris	Southern	.55	41	C	840	Hard
Pine, Eastern White	Pinus Strobus	Northern, Central	.34	25	C	380	Easy
Pine, Shortleaf	Pinus Echinata	Southern	.49	38	C	690	Hard
Pine, Sugar	Pinus Lambertina	West Coast	.35	25	C	430	Easy
Pine, Western White	Pinus Monticola	Western	.36	27	C	400	Easy
Pine, Ponderosa	Pinus Ponderosa	Western	.38	28	C	480	Easy
Redwood	Sequoia Sempervirens	West Coast (Calif.)	.39	28	C	630	Fair
Spruce, Englemann	Picea Engelmannii	Western	.34	23	C	380	Easy
Spruce, Sitka	Picea Sitchensis	Alaskan, West Coast	.37	28	C	530	Fair

is diffuse porous, a close-grained wood, but a better finish results if a thin pastewood filler is applied.

Hardness is a measure of the ability of a wood to resist indentation (Fig. 2–12). It represents the ability of a wood to resist abrasion, scratching, or denting. Hardness is primarily dependent on the density or amount of wood substance present in a given volume. Toughness, size, and arrangement of fibers are also factors. The wearing qualities of any given wood may be altered by the manner in which it is cut. Wood cut so that edge grain is exposed (quarter or rift sawed) wears better than wood in which the slash grain is exposed (plain sawed). See Figure 2–13.

Hardness values are expressed as the pounds of pressure required to embed a .444 in. diameter steel ball ½ its diameter in the wood. The values in Table

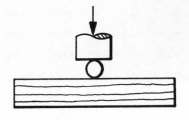

Fig. 2–12. Hardness.

Tendency to Warp	Tendency to Shrink & Swell	Volumetric Shrinkage When Dried to 0% M.C.	Decay Resistance of Heartwood	Compressive Strength Endwise	Stiffness	Shock Resistance	Bending Strength	Principal Uses
		%		P.s.i.	P.s.i.	1000 Inches	P.s.i.	
Low	Low	6.8	Hi.	5020	1120	17	5300	Shingles, siding, novelties, poles, posts
Low	Low	10.5	Hi.	6360	1440	24	7200	Tanks, vats, gutters, siding, shingles, trim, poles, posts
Med.	Med.	11.1	M	7430	1950	31	7800	Plywood, framing, millwork, piling, flooring, ships, furniture
Med.	Med.	9.8	L	5350	1380	17	6500	Framing, veneer, pulp, millwork, boxes, interior trim
Med.	Med.	11.9	L	6210	1200	26	6800	Framing, sheathing, millwork, pulp
Med.	Med.	12.3	L	7080	1800	30	7800	Framing, sheathing, millwork, interior finish, pulp
Med.	Med.	12.2	M	8440	1990	34	9300	Construction, timbers, posts, piling, pulp
Med.	Low	8.2	M	4800	1240	18	5700	Patterns, millwork, matches, carving, veneers, construction, pulp
Med.	Med.	12.3	L	7070	1760	33	7700	Construction, flooring, millwork, boxes, cooperage, pulp
Low	Low	7.9	L	4770	1200	18	5700	Cabinets, carving, patterns, fancy woodwork, trim
Low	Med.	11.8	L	5620	1510	23	6200	Construction, boxes, matches, patterns, millwork, trim
Low	Med.	9.6	L	5270	1260	17	6300	Millwork, panels, veneer, furniture, patterns, general building
Low	Low	7.0	Hi.	6150	1340	19	6900	Construction, millwork, tanks, vats, posts, caskets, outdoor furniture
Low	Med.	10.4	L	4770	1280	18	5500	Construction, mine timbers, R.R. ties, poles, pulp
Low	Med.	11.5	L	5610	1570	25	6700	Trailer frames, ladder rails, millwork, piano sound boards, crates, pulp

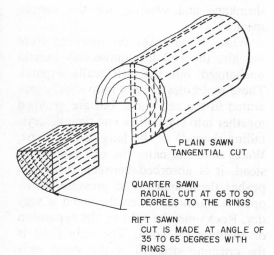

PLAIN SAWN
TANGENTIAL CUT

QUARTER SAWN
RADIAL CUT AT 65 TO 90
DEGREES TO THE RINGS

RIFT SAWN
CUT IS MADE AT ANGLE OF
35 TO 65 DEGREES WITH
RINGS

Fig. 2–13. Methods of sawing wood.

2–1 are the averages of radial and tangential side grain surfaces.

Workability with hand tools is a relative thing, but some woods are easier to shape, cut, and fasten together than others. For some types of work this is an important factor. Sharp tools help in working any wood.

Some woods are hard to work because the wood fibers curl or spiral in various directions. This makes it difficult to produce smooth surfaces. Others split easily and give difficulty. In general any wood weighing about 38 lb. or more per cubic foot is hard to work because of its density. This character is relatively unimportant when using machine tools, however. Table 2–1 indicates the relative workability of the various species.

Warping is the general term used to describe any variation from a true surface. Wood may bow, crook, cup, or twist as shown in Figure 2–14. Warping is generally caused by changes in the moisture content of wood which makes it shrink or swell unevenly. Warping is the cause of much waste. To prevent it, wood should be maintained at a uniform moisture content. The tendency for the various species to warp is shown in Table 2–1.

Warping usually results when compression wood is present. This is an abnormal type of wood that is characteristic of most softwood species. It is denser and harder,

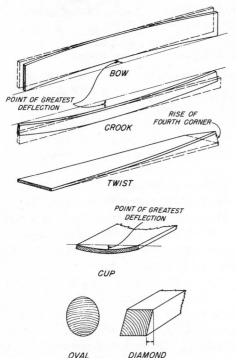

Fig. 2–14. The common kinds of warpage found in wood. Wood warps because it shrinks or swells unequally due to moisture changes. Compression and tension wood also cause warpage.

but weaker than normal wood. Compression wood has larger shrinkage along the grain. This sets up internal stresses in the wood. When it is planed or sawed the material warps.

Many hardwood species have an abnormal type of wood known as tension wood. Its effects are similar to those of compression wood in softwoods. In addition to warping, when sawed, this wood will usually show projecting, fuzzy fibers. Planed surfaces will have torn or raised grain.

Shrinking and swelling is an inherent property of wood and must be recognized when designing objects made of wood. It is beyond ordinary mechanical control. Any piece of wood is constantly seeking a moisture balance with the atmosphere. Since the atmospheric humidity is constantly changing, the moisture content of the wood is changing and correspondingly the dimensions of the wood. See Figure 2–18. When the humidity is controlled, wood may attain a balance with the atmosphere and is said to be at equilibrium moisture content. It is expressed as a percentage of the oven-dry weight of wood. Table 2–1 gives the relative shrinkage and swelling for the various species.

When wood takes on moisture from the air, the cellulose molecules remain unchanged but the cell walls expand. These molecules are not individually separated in the cell walls, but are grouped together into crystallites (no definite crystalline shaped) of the long "chain" type. Water does not enter the crystallites. Instead, it is absorbed between them and pushes them apart. The pressure developed is enormous when the wood is very dry. Rocks may be split by the expansion or swelling of wood. The only limit is the crushing strength of the wood cells themselves. When the cells reach their

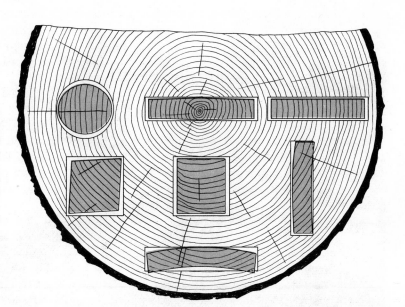

Fig. 2–15. When wood cut from various sections of a green log dries, it shrinks differently as shown here. A circular piece of wood will have an oval shape; a square piece will have a diamond shape in some cases. This is explained by the fact that tangential shrinkage is greater than radial shrinkage.

water saturation point, no further expansion takes place.

Wood shrinks most in a plane tangent to the annual rings. Radial shrinkage when compared to tangential, is in a ratio of about 1 to 2, but may range from a ratio of 1 to 1.1 up to 1 to 3.7. Longitudinal or lengthwise shrinkage is, as a rule, very slight. It ranges from 0.1 to 0.3 percent of the green wood dimension. This may be explained by the linear structure of the cellulose molecule. The total swelling of wood is numerically equal to the total shrinkage. Figure 2–15 illustrates how this varying shrinkage rate affects several typical wood shapes when they dry.

Green wood from the various species of trees contains from 30 to 300 percent of water based on its oven-dry weight. For this reason, some logs sink in water while others will float. Part of this water is free water in the various cell cavities within the wood. The remainder is absorbed by the walls of the fibers and cells because they are hygroscopic (readily absorb moisture). When only the free

water is removed, the wood fibers are at their saturation point. This is approximately 30 percent moisture content for all species.

As the moisture is removed below this 30-percent fiber saturation point, shrinkage occurs in the cell walls. For each 1 percent loss in moisture, the shrinkage is about $\frac{1}{30}$ of the total possible for that species. Shrinking and swelling are expressed as percentages of the green dimensions of the wood.

With some exceptions, hardwoods and the heavier species shrink more than softwoods and the lighter species. Heavier pieces of the same species generally shrink more than lighter pieces.

The application of various coatings may retard the absorption of moisture. If the seal can be made absolutely vapor tight, no change in the moisture content takes place. However, even tiny openings in the coating permit the eventual absorption — or evaporation — of moisture with its corresponding changes in the dimensions of the wood.

Chemical stabilization of wood is prac-

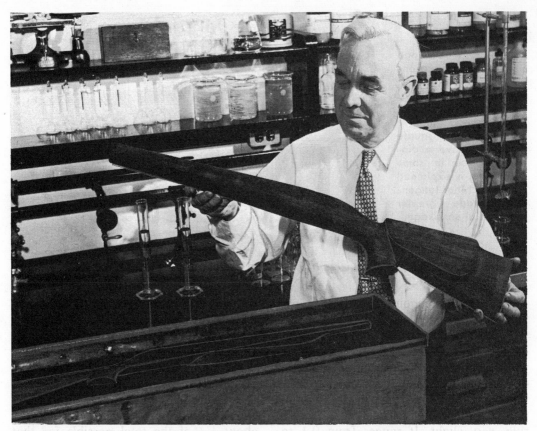

Fig. 2–16. These gun stocks were shaped on a wood carving machine while green. They were then treated with polyethylene glycol-1000 and kiln dried. This chemical stabilization of wood prevents it from shrinking and swelling.

ticable by soaking it in a 50-percent water solution of polyethylene glycol-1000 for ten to twenty days at 150 deg. F. This material curbs shrinkage, swelling, and warping by "bulking" the lattice-like structure of the individual fiber walls of wood. The wood should be shaped and treated while in its green condition and then kiln dried. Dry wood cannot be effectively stabilized. The treated wood shrinks very little when dried to 6-percent moisture content and swells very little when exposed to moisture. Physical and mechanical properties are not altered significantly. Polyurethane

resin-base varnishes are best for finishing since the glycol treatment produces a waxy surface. Figure 2–16 shows some gun stocks that were shaped and gylcol-treated while green.

Figure 2–17 illustrates the effects of chemical treatment on the amount of shrinkage in two 11-in. diameter western red cedar poles. The larger pole was peeled and sprayed with a saturated urea solution for 30 seconds. Both were then dried under the same conditions to 23-percent moisture content. Diametral shrinkage was approximately 10 percent greater in the untreated pole.

Fig. 2–17. These cedar poles were the same diameter before one was treated with a saturated urea solution. After kiln drying, the untreated pole had shrunk considerably more than the other.

Volumetric shrinkage (Fig. 2–18) is generally greater for hardwoods than softwoods, true mahogany being an exception. The values in Table 2–1 are based on the change in volume when green wood is oven-dried to 0-percent moisture content. This is determined by calculating the volume of a 1 in. long block of wood cut at least one foot from the end of a green board. The block is then placed in an oven heated to 214 to 221 deg. F. and kept there until it reaches constant weight. This takes 12 to 48 hours. The volume is again calculated and the volumetric shrinkage determined by the following formula:

Percent Volumetric shrinkage =

$$\frac{\text{Vol. green} - \text{vol. oven-dry}}{\text{Volume green}} \times 100$$

The *moisture content of wood* may also be determined by this procedure. Weigh the block on a balance sensitive to 0.05 gm. Then heat it until a constant weight is attained. Record this dry weight. The moisture content of the block may be found with the following formula:

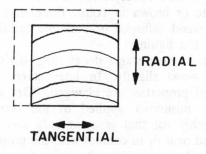

Fig. 2–18. Shrinkage of wood.

Percent moisture content =
$$\frac{W - WOD}{WOD} \times 100$$
W — Weight When Cut
WOD — Weight Oven Dry

Decay, molds, and **stains** in wood are caused by fungi. Fungi are minute plants. They live on organic material such as wood when temperatures are mild and moisture content exceeds 20 percent, but remains below a soaking wet condition. Wood that is continuously wet or dry does not decay. Decay-producing fungi seriously reduce the strength of wood. The relative decay resistance of the several species is indicated in Table 2–1.

Molds and stains are usually confined to sapwood. Molds are usually surface growths and may easily be removed. They cause little staining. Stains penetrate the sapwood. They are of various colors, but the "blue" stain is most common. Molds and stains are not decay, but both increase the likelihood of decay developing. Strength is only slightly impaired. Stains may impair the appearance of wood. Various chemical preservatives will prevent their formation.

Fungi may attack either heartwood or sapwood producing the condition known as decay, rot, or dote. These fungi produce surface growths that are usually fluffy, fan-shaped, or root-like structures, white or brown in color. Fungi live on the wood cellulose or both the cellulose and the lignin.

In its early stages decay fungi discolor the wood slightly. In later stages the wood properties are changed. "Dry rot" is a misnomer applied to the brown, crumbly rot that is commonly seen on wood near or in contact with the ground. This decay begins only under favorable moisture conditions. The wood subse-

quently becomes dry. Some fungi are capable of carrying water through conducting strands to otherwise dry wood. All woods will decay if exposed to dampness and mild temperatures over a long enough period of time.

Strength of Wood

The strength values of woods, including hardness, given in Table 2–1 are representative of those obtained from tests on small, clear pieces of wood at 12 percent moisture content. Knots, cross-grain, checks, splits, tension, and compression wood were eliminated. Specimens were 2 by 2 in. or smaller in cross section and of lengths appropriate to the test. All data are based on tests made by the Forest Products Laboratories using the standard testing procedures of the American Society for Testing Materials.

Compressive strength (Fig. 2–19) is a measure of the force parallel to the grain that a specimen will support. It is an

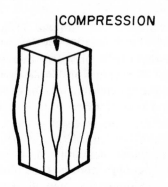

Fig. 2–19.   Compressive strength.

evaluation of the strength of posts or short blocks that might be used to support loads.

The specimens tested had lengths of less than eleven times the least cross-sectional dimension. The load was slowly applied until the wood fibers began to

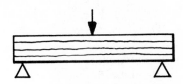

Fig. 2–20.   Stiffness.

Fig. 2–21.   Shock resistance.

crush. The Table lists the pounds per square inch sustained by each species.

Stiffness (Fig. 2–20) is a measure of the rigidity or resistance of a member to deflection when placed under a load. It is expressed by a factor known as the modulus of elasticity. It is the ratio of stress (load) per unit area to corresponding strain (deformation) per unit length, the strain being within the elastic limit. Steel has a high modulus of elasticity because it deflects but little under a given load. Rubber has a low value. Wood is elastic within relatively narrow limits. The values given in the table are the moduli of elasticity for the various species.

Up to its elastic limit, the deflection or bending of a member is directly proportional to the applied load. As an example, a stick that bends ⅛ in. under a load of 5 lb. will bend ¼ in. under a load of 10 lb. However, beyond a certain load, the bending will increase faster than the value of the load. The stick will not return to its original shape after being stressed beyond its elastic limit.

Stiffness is important in the design of beams, joists, rafters, rails, and stretchers. Deflection or bending in these members must usually be held within a small fraction of the length of the span.

In a column or post, endwise compressive strength is the controlling element until the length exceeds about eleven times the least cross-sectional dimension. As the length of the column increases, stiffness becomes more of a factor and compressive strength less. Beyond a cer-

tain length, stiffness is the controlling feature.

Shock resistance (Fig. 2–21) is a rating of the capacity of a material to withstand suddenly applied loads. This character of wood is sometimes called toughness. Woods that rank high in this respect resist cross-breaking and are able to bend considerably before breaking. Woods high in shock resistance are capable of withstanding repeated shocks, blows, and jolts. As a group, gymnosperms do not have the shock resisting abilities of the angiosperms. Shock resistance of moist wood is usually greater than that of dry wood.

The resistance of wood to shock is usually determined by supporting a piece of uniform size at both ends and dropping a heavy weight on its center. After each drop, the height of the weight is increased until the piece fails. Table 2–1 reports the height in inches that a 50-lb. weight fell to break the test pieces of each species.

Bending strength (Fig. 2–22) is a measure of the energy absorbed by a beam supported at both ends and stressed to its proportional limit. The proportional

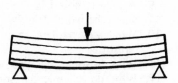

Fig. 2–22.   Bending strength.

limit is that point at which the deflection is no longer directly proportional to the stress or load applied. It indicates the ability of wood to absorb shock or carry loads without permanent damage. Floor joists are an example of structural members that are chosen for their bending strength. The Table indicates the pounds per square inch applied in the tests.

Appreciating Wood

It is not necessary to be an expert to build things with wood. Once you get started, however, it is probable that you will become one because there is a certain satisfaction that one gets from analyzing a problem, planning, creating, and performing the work.

As we have seen, wood comes from trees, the biggest living things. From man's earliest beginnings wood has been identified with his material and esthetic progress. Thus, wood's appeal to man is natural.

Wood is easy and pleasant to work. It can be shaped with the simplest pocket knife or the most complicated automatic machines. It is widely available. It can be bought hard, soft, thick, thin, long, short, rough, smooth, flexible, stiff, heavy, or light. Pound for pound it is stronger than steel. This factor when combined with its light weight, durability, and adaptability makes it our leading building material.

No two pieces of wood are identical in grain pattern or figure. Within species the color, texture, and natural markings differ. This individuality is unique with wood. To help you gain a greater understanding and appreciation of wood, you should study samples of the various species available in your community and those in greatest use commercially. You should be able to identify these species and their principal characteristics. The Forest Products Laboratory in Madison, Wisconsin, provides a wood identification service. The Laboratory has a wood collection of over 20,000 specimens.

DISCUSSION QUESTIONS

1. If the building block of trees is cellulose, what directs it to form an oak, apple, or walnut tree?
2. Water may be siphoned a maximum height of about 32 ft. How does a tree 300 ft. tall get water from the soil to its uppermost leaves in order to make food?
3. What are some common uses for wood cellulose? Lignin?
4. How are wood fibers made into paper?
5. Why are some hardwoods (angiosperms) porous?
6. Why are the annual rings in some species of trees difficult to distinguish?
7. Why does sapwood take preservatives better than heartwood?
8. What protection should be provided lumber that will be used for construction?
9. A hole is bored in the face of a wet plank. Will the hole get larger or smaller when the wood dries?
10. What will happen to a mitered joint if the wood takes on moisture? Loses moisture?
11. Why do some logs sink while others float on water?
12. Why do chemically stabilized woods have a high degree of dimensional stability?

13. Why does wood shrink less in its lengthwise (parallel to grain) dimension? What happens to the wood fibers when the moisture content falls below 30 percent?
14. What are the important strength characteristics of wood? For what use is each important?

SUGGESTED STUDENT ACTIVITIES

1. Prepare a display of various species of wood, leaves, and seeds.
2. Study several species of wood under a microscope.
3. Make a sketch of: a wood fiber; the cell structure of wood; a cross-section of a tree trunk. Label the parts.
4. Ascertain: the specific gravity of a wood sample; its density; weight.
5. Design and construct a device to measure the hardness of wood.
6. Prepare a treatment for wood to prevent warping.
7. Ascertain the volumetric shrinkage of a piece of green wood.
8. Ascertain the moisture content of a piece of kiln dried lumber.
9. Compare the strength values of sapwood and heartwood from the same wood species.
10. Design and construct a device to measure the strength values of wood.
11. Ascertain the strength values of several species of wood common to your region.
12. Prepare a report on the responsibilities, opportunities, requirements, and working conditions of a person in an occupation of interest to you.

Chapter 3 Product Development

In the United States, the average person has many conveniences which in most other countries would belong only to the most wealthy families. It is just in very recent years that the industrialized nations of Western Europe have begun to have the mass distribution of the "luxuries" most Americans accept as commonplace. The newly developing nations of Africa, the Middle East, the Far East, and most of South America are barely able to keep their people fed without even thinking of such things as automobiles, refrigerators, and bathtubs. Even though there are many Americans whose conditions are poor, our nation has produced the highest material standard of living in the world. How, then, has America been so successful?

As a matter of fact, many of the inventions that led to the development of American industries had their origins in Europe and Asia. Steelmaking, the automobile, synthetic drugs, printing, and hundreds of other inventions were developed in foreign countries. So, visitors may not be too impressed with our technology and craftsmanship because these exist in their own countries. But they are most impressed with the extent to which most Americans **own** the products of all this technology.

Americans Become Manufacturers

For many of us living today it is difficult to visualize life in this country as ever having been different. And yet it can be said without exaggeration that technology has literally transformed the United States within a relatively few years. This transformation has been so sweeping that it would be well to ask how and why it came about.

The progress made in the United States since Colonial days is widely attributed to "Yankee ingenuity." It is common belief that to be born in this country is to be born a mechanical genius of some sort, but this idea can only result from thinking backward. It is true that many boys in the United States are handy with tools, are able to analyze and correct all sorts of mechanical troubles, and are often apt students of mathematics, chemistry, electronics, mechanics, and physics. History shows, however, that this has not always been the case and even today it is not necessarily true of all parts of this country.

After the American Revolution and as soon as independence was achieved, many of the mechanics, carpenters, blacksmiths, and other skilled persons moved westward to settle the wild country and become farmers. The result was a shortage of skilled craftsmen in the young eastern states. It was because of this shortage that Eli Whitney left Georgia in the 1790's and returned to his home in Connecticut to manufacture his cotton gins. Even there he found similar conditions. After several futile attempts to produce gins in quantity, he finally had to abandon his idea. Handcrafting a product was simply too slow to meet the market demands.

Whitney's experience with the cotton gin and the growing demand for goods in this country led him to realize that a substitute was needed for the skilled craftsman. By 1798, Whitney's vision of this substitute had matured enough to enable him to enter into a contract with the government to produce 10,000 muskets in two years. His "vision" was of a manufacturing process in which *identical parts* would be produced by the use of machines, jigs, fixtures, templates, automatic stops, and the like. Thus, Whitney introduced the important concept of *in-terchangeability* into the production of goods. Employing this concept, it was only necessary to devise machines to perform a certain few operations over and over. Workers with little or no skill could be hired to operate the machines. In this way guns, axes, clocks, sewing machines, reapers, and eventually automobiles and most other products were produced in such quantity that practically everyone could afford to buy them. The old adage, "necessity is the mother of invention" can be seen as applying in Whitney's case.

Americans Become Consumers

The early settlers of this country were a hardy, freedom loving, independent group. They admitted that others might be richer, smarter, or stronger, but insisted that each person had rights which he possessed as fully as any other person. With this point of view, anything that one person possessed, the next person believed he too could rightfully possess — if he could find a way to pay for it. To make it easier for his customers to

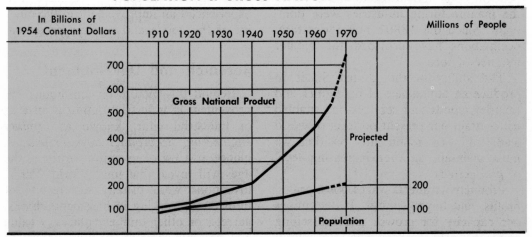

Fig. 3–1. The Gross National Product is expected to exceed $700 billion by 1970.

TABLE 3–1
IMPORTANT PATENTED AMERICAN INVENTIONS

Invention	Inventor	Date Patented
Cotton Gin	Eli Whitney	Mar. 14, 1794
Steamboat (Commercial)	Robert Fulton	Feb. 11, 1809
Reaper	Cyrus H. McCormick	May 21, 1834
Telegraph	Samuel F. B. Morse	May 20, 1840
Vulcanization of Rubber	Charles Goodyear	May 15, 1844
Sewing Machine	Elias Howe, Jr.	Sept. 10, 1846
Typewriter	C. L. Sholes	June 23, 1868
Air Brake	George Westinghouse, Jr.	April 13, 1869
Telephone	Alexander Graham Bell	Mar. 7, 1876
Phonograph	Thomas A. Edison	Jan. 27, 1880
Induction Motor	Nikola Tesla	May 1, 1888
Production of Aluminum	Charles M. Hall	April 2, 1889
Linotype	Ottmar Mergenthaler	Sept. 16, 1890
Motion Picture Projector	Thomas A. Edison	Mar. 14, 1893
Airplane	Orville and Wilbur Wright	May 22, 1906
Three-Electrode Vacuum Tube	Lee De Forest	Jan. 15, 1907
Thermosetting Plastics (Bakelite)	Leo H. Baekeland	Dec. 7, 1909
Oil Cracking	William M. Burton	Jan. 7, 1913

When the Patent Office celebrated in 1940 the 150th anniversary of the founding of the American patent system, seventy-five scientists, industrialists, and statesmen were asked to select what they thought were the greatest American inventions patented by the United States Patent Office.

From: NAM, Patents and Your Tomorrow

buy reapers, Cyrus McCormick introduced the "buy now, pay later" plan in 1844. In this setting, a mass market for the output of the early industries was assured. The economy of the country gradually shifted from one entirely dependent upon agriculture to one in which the manufacturing industries were dominant. Since the 1880's non-agricultural occupations have provided the greater number of jobs.

The ability of the United States to produce an abundance of necessities and luxuries, goods and services has enabled us to attain our present position of world leadership. To retain this position we must maintain an ever increasing level of *productivity*.

Productivity affects wages, jobs, prices, profits, and buying power. It determines our capacity for growth and for selling goods in world markets. The total output of final goods and services, in terms of

their market value is called the *Gross National Product*. In terms of 1954 dollars it increased from $205.8 billion in 1940 to $487.4 billion in 1963. It is expected to reach $700 billion by 1970. See Figure 3–1. Paralleling this tremendous increase in output we have also experienced an improvement in the quality of the goods and services produced.

Research and Development

Behind this picture of continuous improvement in industrial output is an area of industrial effort known as *product engineering* or *product development*. A glance at a list of inventions through the ages will reveal that until World War II inventions were usually the results of individuals working in basements, barns, garrets, or other unlikely places. (Table 3–1 presents some of the most important inventions.) Since the war we find that

Fig. 3–2. This electronic machine measures the properties of wood and automatically records the result for use in engineering investigations.

Fig. 3–3. The complex chemistry of wood cellulose, lignin, and extractives is studied by chemical engineers and theoretical chemists in an attempt to exploit our forest's store of chemicals.

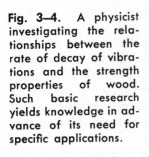

Fig. 3–4. A physicist investigating the relationships between the rate of decay of vibrations and the strength properties of wood. Such basic research yields knowledge in advance of its need for specific applications.

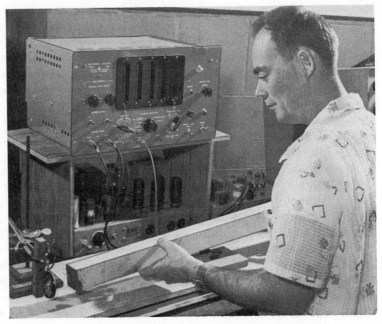

Fig. 3–5. Research must carry ideas from the laboratory to the pilot plant stage to prove that scientific theory can be translated into economically sound full scale production.

significant inventions and the resultant industrial products are more and more the results of team efforts sponsored by large corporations or the government. The individual inventor is still important, but today he finds himself at a serious disadvantage.

The continuing effort to gain new knowledge and find new ways of using it to produce new and better products is known as *research and development,* commonly referred to as R & D.

Research is a systematic and persevering effort to discover some unknown fact or principle. Some research is carried on for its own sake — to provide new knowledge without regard to its use — and is called *pure or basic research.* Most research is carried on with the intention of finding a definite, practical use for the knowledge gained from basic research. This is called *applied research.* See Fig-

ures 3–2, 3–3, 3–4.

Development is not too readily distinguished from research, but it is mainly concerned with finding the most economical means of applying the facts and principles identified in research. Basic research may reveal a new fact or principle. Applied research may then demonstrate a practical use for this information.

The development people may then enter the picture with the construction of a *pilot plant* in which the feasibility of large-scale production is evaluated. See Figure 3–5. As a result of this effort, the time between initial discovery and its appearance in a usable or commercial form has been considerably reduced. For example, 112 years elapsed between the discovery of the principles of photography and their application in the daguerreotype of the 1830's. Only 5 years were involved in developing the transistor for commercial purposes.

In 1920 fewer than 400 companies were listed in the directory of industrial research laboratories and they spent less than $30 million for research and development. Today it is estimated that over $21 billion are funneled into this effort to discover, invent, acquire, and apply knowledge. In 1960–1961, there were 10,300 manufacturing companies with R & D facilities. They employed the equivalent of 307,300 scientists and engineers. During 1960, a total of $10.5 billion was allocated for the various types of industrial R & D projects. These funds were distributed as follows: 4 percent for basic research; 20 percent for applied research; and 76 percent for development. The lumber, wood products, and furniture industries allocated $13 million for R & D in 1960. Of this amount 47 percent was for applied research and 53 percent for development.

Fig. 3–6. A career in research involves such experiences as analyzing samples of finished plywood siding for their resistance to abrasion, fading, blistering, and deterioration.

Research workers are usually scientists, technicians, or engineers who, because of their interests and abilities, have obtained the necessary preparation for such work. Many research workers have the Doctor of Philosophy (Ph. D.) degree. It is sometimes called the research degree. Earning this degree usually requires a minimum of seven years of college work. More and more technicians are being employed to assist in research. Technicians usually have two to four years of technical institute or college preparation. See Figure 3–6.

Researchers follow a logical procedure in their efforts to solve a problem. This procedure is sometimes called *"the scientific method."* In general, the following steps are involved:

1. The question to be answered or the problem to be solved is identified and defined as specifically as possible.
2. All available information and experience, if any, related to the problem is collected, carefully studied, and evaluated.
3. Hypotheses, laws, principles, propositions, or tentative solutions to the problem are formulated on the basis of the information available. This involves a thought process that moves forward from the partially known, and oftentimes confused data of experience, toward the solution; and second, a backward movement from the solution to the facts to see whether the facts verify the solution. Every solution, no matter how ridiculous it may seem, is written down or sketched as a record for possible future use.
4. The most promising solution is then selected and experimentation is begun to check its practicability. This step involves repeated trials and failures when the researcher is working with new problems. Thomas A. Edison once referred to this phase of the work as 5 percent inspiration and 95 percent perspiration.
5. When the best solution to the problem is finally determined, it is analyzed and interpreted, conclusions and generalizations are formulated, and the results reported or put to use.

Product Design

Where the problem involves the creation of an industrial product, engineers, technicians, and craftsmen cooperatively plan and produce a mock-up or prototype to demonstrate the solution. In this case, *industrial designers* or stylists might also be involved. See Figure 3–7. The

Fig. 3–7. New car styling ideas grow from sketches of all kinds in a design studio. The industrial designer presents his ideas in a rendering on colored paper. A full-size rendering or a clay and wood mock-up is then made of the approved drawing.

industrial designer is primarily concerned with the *form* or appearance of the finished product. He applies the "scientific method" (design process) to the matter of determining the most satisfactory appearance of the product. The industrial designer works closely with the engineers and craftsmen. To be most effective he must possess some of the capabilities of each in addition to those of an artist.

The designs prepared in most industries are carefully guarded secrets. The reason is that the company involved wishes to be the first to put the new designs on the market. Patents and copyrights do not effectively protect the designer's creations. They only give grounds for legal action in the courts.

Product Design in the Furniture Industry

In some of the larger furniture companies new designs are the result of the work of design or marketing committees. These committees consist of senior sales representatives, the merchandise manager, sales manager, company president, and the design staff. Jointly they decide on a design directive. The staff designers then work independently of one another for four or five weeks developing the directive. At the end of that time the sketches are reviewed by the design committee and a decision is made.

The head designer then takes charge of the project. With his assistants he develops the design in a broad range of items. Detailers (draftsmen) then prepare full-size working drawings from the sketches. Only overall dimensions are given. The drawing is measured to obtain the sizes of components (Fig. 3–8). Unlike some product drawings, furniture drawings (sometimes called "rod drawings") may have one view superimposed upon the other. Thus, the top and side views of a cabinet may be drawn on top of the front view. This facilitates drawing and saves material on reproductions, but it complicates reading the drawing (Fig. 3–9).

The design department then builds a mock-up of the new design. Mock-ups are exact in outside finish and detail, but drawers and doors may not function. Other internal details may also be omitted. The design committee may decide to make alterations in the design at this time. If so, these alterations are then incorporated into the mock-up and the drawings. After final approval of the designs, promotional brochures, sales materials, catalogs and other merchandizing aids are prepared.

In the larger furniture companies, *a pilot plant* is used to work up samples of the new designs. Tools, jigs, fixtures, and gauges are prepared and tested in the production of the samples.

These samples are then exhibited in furniture marts. The principal furniture marts are in High Point, North Carolina, and Chicago, Illinois. At this time the manufacturer distributes the sales literature and takes orders from buyers. He may also learn of design modifications from the buyers and, if possible, attempts to work these into the product before full-scale production begins. Most large manufacturers have designs on the drawing boards that evolve over a period of three to five years.

Fig. 3–8. This chest-desk, the drawing of which is shown on pp. 44 and 45, could be a mock-up, a sample, or the mass produced product you might see in a show room.

When the order to produce a given design is issued, drawings, route sheets, samples of each part, the completed product, and all of the tooling are transferred from the pilot plant to the factory where the product will be produced. In this way as much time as necessary may be devoted to the development and tooling of the product, and regular production is not interrupted for the making

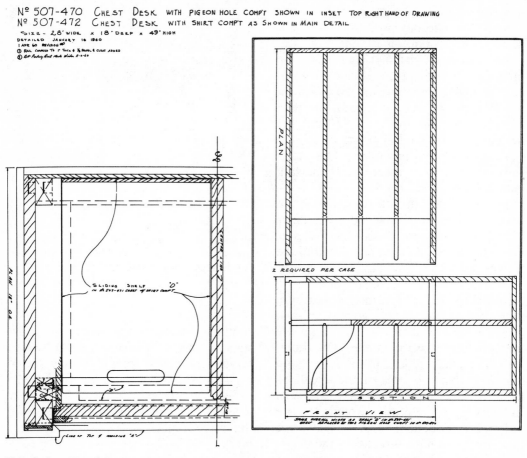

Fig. 3–9. The full-size drawing of a chest-desk is shown here reduced. Note that the side view is drawn in place of one half of the front view. Only overall dimensions are given.

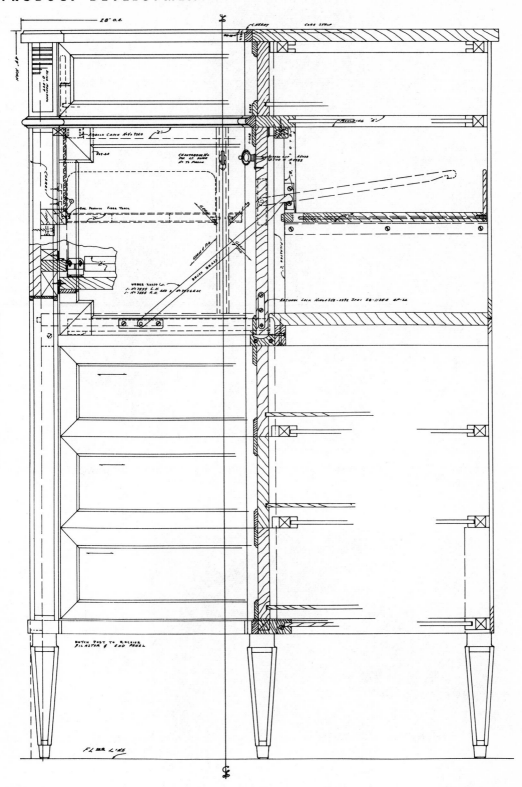

Fig. 3–10. Furniture groupings should be designed with similarities in proportion, balance, texture, and rhythm.

Fig. 3–11. This cocktail table exemplifies principles of good design.

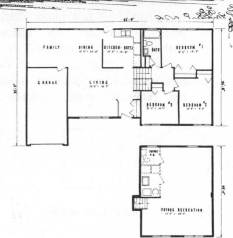

Fig. 3–12. A well-designed home should be not only functional but pleasing to the eye.

of the samples. Naturally, the pilot plant must contain duplicates of the machines used in the production plants.

When a manufacturer develops a style of furniture that becomes popular, others attempt to copy the design. Furniture with "style" remains popular indefinitely. Many designs are "fashionable" for a brief period. The general improvement in "taste" of the buying public has compelled manufacturers to consider design and quality of craftsmanship before cost. People have formed a strong emotional association with furniture. It is a close part of all life experiences. Consequently a few dollars saved is relatively unimportant when compared to design and quality.

Good design is difficult to define since it is a matter of personal taste. However, good design has functional, material, and visual characteristics that may be generalized. A well-designed product will be *functional,* i.e., useful and well-suited to its purpose. It will be made of materials that are as *durable* as is appropriate. It will be *economical* in its use of materials that are not too heavy, too costly, or that require excessively expensive fabrication techniques. The materials will be used

honestly; wood will be used for its qualities as wood, metals as metal, and plastics as plastics. The product will be *logically constructed* as function, durability, economy, and materials would make appropriate. It will have an individuality or *personality* that makes it distinctive. *Beauty* is the total organization of these characteristics and is "built in" when shape or form reflects the function of the product. See Figures 3–10, 3–11, and 3–12 for examples of well-designed industrial products.

When working on a design problem, the industrial designer attempts to achieve good design by carefully analyzing the problem and then employing several design principles in its solution. Since the function of a product must never be impaired or restricted by the form or shape given to it, the designer does have limitations imposed upon him. But, by careful and creative planning he is able to develop a product of pleasing appearance. See Figure 3–11. The design principles commonly used are:

1. *Function* determines form. Things should look like what they are. Functionalism does not mean stark simplicity, however. An automobile without a body might still be functional, but with a body it fits our notions of functionalism much better. When the basic skeleton of an

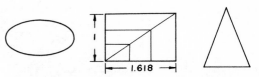

Fig. 3–14. The ellipse is more interesting than the circle. The golden mean rectangle is traditionally the most pleasing in ratio of length to width. An isosceles triangle is more interesting than an equilateral triangle.

mean rectangle are considered pleasing (Fig. 3–14). Masses should be rectangular if feasible, either vertical or horizontal. Regular shapes may be used when function so dictates. Proportions may be improved by subdividing the mass into interesting shapes or by setting areas backward

Fig. 3–13. Shapes to avoid.

object is soundly engineered, even elaborate ornamentation may be compatible with it.

2. *Proportions* must be good. Regular geometric shapes should be avoided because they are uninteresting to the eye (Fig. 3–13). The ellipse, the equilateral triangle, and the golden

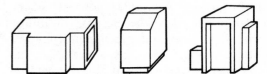

Fig. 3–16. Set areas forward or backward for function and interest.

or forward (Figs. 3–15 and 3–16). It is important to visualize objects in three dimensions.

3. *Balance* should be either formal (symmetrical) or informal (occult) and may be obtained by arranging the design elements so as to give the

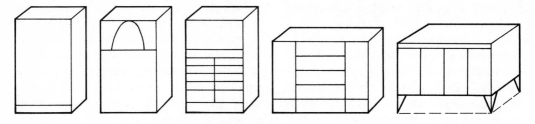

Fig. 3–15. When subdividing for function and interest, ratios of 2 to 3, 3 to 5, and 5 to 8 are best.

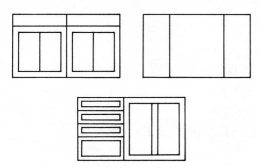

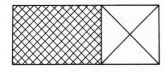

Fig. 3–17. Top two designs are examples of formal balance while the bottom one is informal.

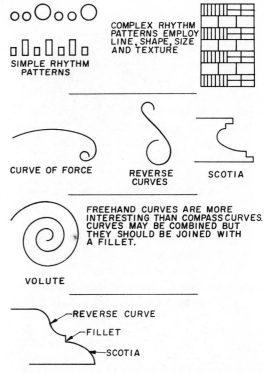

SIMPLE RHYTHM PATTERNS

COMPLEX RHYTHM PATTERNS EMPLOY LINE, SHAPE, SIZE AND TEXTURE

CURVE OF FORCE   REVERSE CURVES   SCOTIA

FREEHAND CURVES ARE MORE INTERESTING THAN COMPASS CURVES. CURVES MAY BE COMBINED BUT THEY SHOULD BE JOINED WITH A FILLET.

VOLUTE

REVERSE CURVE

FILLET

SCOTIA

Fig. 3–19. Rhythm adds interest to the design.

object the appearance of stability — of being in a state of equilibrium (Fig. 3–17).

4. *Emphasis* may be achieved by adding color, decoration, or a different texture to some area to make it a center of interest (Fig. 3–18).

5. *Unity* or harmony may be achieved by weaving everything together ac-

Fig. 3–18. Add color, decoration, or texture to emphasize a surface.

cording to a well-laid plan; by maintaining a uniformity or oneness of design that permits the eye to flow easily over the outline. See Figure 3–9.

6. *Rhythm* adds interest to the design through the use of curves, forms, textures, and colors in repeated patterns (Fig. 3–19). Progressively larger or alternating large and small elements are easily recognized. Combinations of line, shape, size, and texture may recur in rhythmic fashion

and require careful study before they are evident.

7. *Texture* of surfaces may be varied to add interest. Texture refers to the pattern of contrasts in light reflected from a surface.

8. *Color* may be used to ornament, protect, emphasize, and otherwise improve the function and appearance of the product.

The secretary (Fig. 3–20) exhibits the principles of good design. Its form is determined by its function as a place to store and display various articles and to provide a place for writing. The proportions follow the principles of rectangular shapes, subdividing, and setback. There is formal balance, and unity of outline. The color and finish add to the overall appearance.

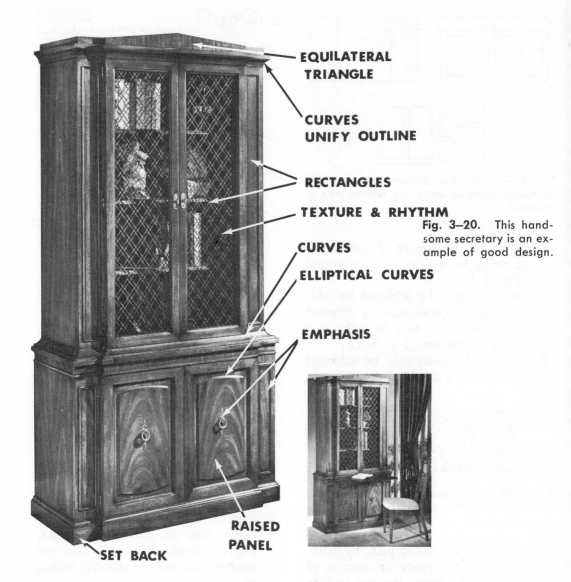

EQUILATERAL
TRIANGLE

CURVES
UNIFY OUTLINE

RECTANGLES

TEXTURE & RHYTHM

Fig. 3–20. This hand-
some secretary is an ex-
ample of good design.

CURVES

ELLIPTICAL CURVES

EMPHASIS

RAISED
PANEL

SET BACK

Product Development in the School Shop

Your school shop is an excellent place for you to learn more about the scientific method of solving problems.

First you will need to identify a problem and discuss it with your instructor. State the nature of your problem as spe-

cifically as possible, but do not state a solution to the problem. For example, suppose that you have several books at home and they deserve better care than they now receive. Your problem is to provide an attractive, useful, economical device for these books that will fit into your bedroom. You might further define the problem by stating some size, weight, and other limitations or restrictions. You might say that your problem is to design and build a bookcase. This is a solution and by predetermining that you need a bookcase, you will probably try to copy a bookcase you have seen. This would rule out the possibility of finding a better solution, if one exists.

Second, collect as many pictures, suggestions, descriptions, and as much helpful information as you can. The more ideas you find, the greater the probability that your problem solution will be most satisfactory. Make a record of all pertinent data concerning the problem such as sizes, shapes, quantities, weights, colors, and special requirements.

Third, study the materials collected and prepare some tentative problem solutions. If the problem is, to use the previous example, a device to hold books, you will want to make dozens of sketches that reflect the ideas you got from studying the materials you collected. You should make sketches showing different arrangements of structural elements, vari-

ous materials of various sizes and other combinations of the ideas your study revealed. See Figure 3–21. As you sketch an idea, try to visualize it as it will function. If it seems to be a logical solution to the problem, check back against the data you collected to see if they meet all of the requirements. Work out as many of these solutions as possible and *save each one*. Then, study the various solutions and attempt to consolidate the best features of each into one, final, most promising solution.

Fourth, experimentally determine the practicability of your solution. This may involve making full-size drawings showing *all* details. You may decide that a model or mock-up is necessary to help you finalize your thinking. See Figures 3–22 and 3–23. In any event, you will want to insure that every detail of the solution is within the limitations previously identified and also within the limitations imposed by time, school facilities, and your ability.

Finally, analyze and interpret your

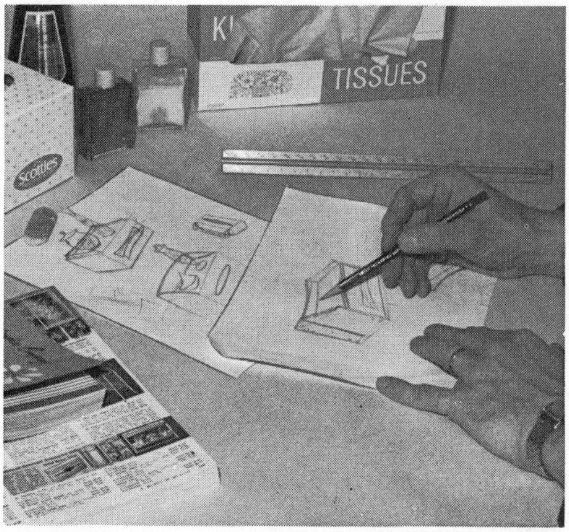

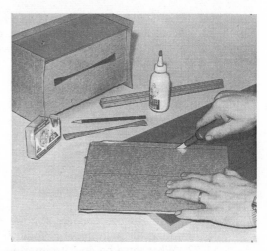

Fig. 3–21. Once you have determined what you want and gathered ideas from catalogs and other sources, begin sketching. It takes many sketches to arrive at a desirable and usable design.

Fig. 3–22. Making a mock-up. Cardboard, cut and pasted together, will give you a close resemblance to the finished product.

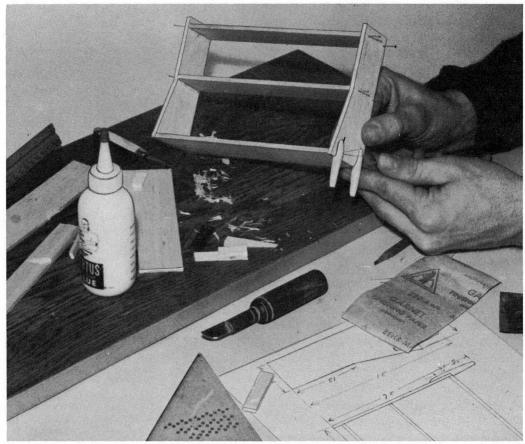

Fig. 3–23. Scale model. Products that are of large size can be scaled down and constructed of balsa or pine. Note the rough drawing the craftsman is working from.

solution, formulate your conclusions and generalizations and prepare a report of your results. Again, if the problem involved a useful device, make the necessary construction drawings, plan your procedures, construct the device as you planned it, evaluate it to see how well it serves its intended purpose, and prepare a report of the results.

DISCUSSION QUESTIONS

1. How do you account for the fact that the United States produces so many things in such quantity today?
2. What must be done to improve the economy of a nation, state, or community?
3. Define research. What do research workers do? How does one become a researcher?
4. What is the function of research and development in industry? What is the function of a pilot plant?

5. What are the steps of the scientific method of problem solving? How are they applied in designing an industrial product? How are they applied in everyday living?
6. What is an industrial designer? An engineer? A technician? A craftsman? How many kinds of engineers, technicians, and craftsmen can you name? What school subjects are useful to each?
7. What is good design? How can you recognize it?
8. What is meant by the "function" of a product?
9. What is "planned obsolescence"? What are some factors that make a product fashionable for a time and then obsolete?
10. How can good taste be developed?

SUGGESTED STUDENT ACTIVITIES

1. Plan and construct models of a:
   a) Tree farm
   b) Tree harvester
   c) Lumber mill; plywood mill
   d) Turpentine still
   e) Pulpwood chipper; digester
   f) Paper mill
   g) Gang saw; plywood lathe; planer
   h) Wharf or dock
   i) Ship or boat; car or truck; air or space craft
   j) Prefabricated home
   k) Furniture factory
2. Design and engineer, tool, and mass-produce a useful product.
3. Illustrate the botany of a tree.
4. Ascertain the chemical composition of wood.
5. Prepare a display of products made from wood.
6. Compare the characteristics, properties, uses of wood. Prepare a display.
7. Plan and construct a model of a home or other building.
8. Perform various exercises demonstrating construction practices.
9. Plan and construct jigs, fixtures, tools.
10. Plan and construct furniture, bowls, lamps, cabinets, patterns.
11. Make displays of: hardware, finishes, glues, fasteners.
12. Develop an organization chart of industry.
13. Write a report of a design project.
14. Invent or improve a device made of wood or used to process wood.
15. Visit an industry and prepare a report on your observations.
16. Select an industrial occupation and prepare a list of its advantages, disadvantages, educational, and other requirements.
17. Plan a sales program for a product that necessitates changing the public taste or buying habits.

Chapter 4 Production Planning

After a product has been designed, tested and found to meet customer requirements, the production-planning department enters the picture. In some of the smaller companies, the product-development and production-planning functions may be performed in the same department — sometimes by the same men.

The production-planning department is responsible for determining exactly how the product will be made and then creating the *plan for manufacture*. The production planner studies the drawings of the product and prepares a set of plans or directions for the production and/or procurement of every item. For new products he may first prepare estimates of the production costs to aid top management in determining whether or not the product should be produced.

During this planning phase the production planner may discover that certain revisions in the design or specifications should be made so that production costs may be held at a more reasonable level. (Savings of as little as 20 to 30 cents per unit are sufficient reason for making changes on some products such as furniture. These changes do not materially alter the design, however.) He then attempts to convince the product designer of the need for the change and, if successful, receives the necessary change orders and revisions of the product drawings.

The production planner decides which tools, machines, jigs, fixtures, gauges, and the like are needed for production. He orders them designed and either built in the plant or purchased from an outside supplier. Most manufacturers purchase machines from the approximately 900 machine tool manufacturers in this country. These machine tool builders are a most important part of our industrial picture. Small tool and die shops produce most of the specialized tools, jigs, fixtures, and gauges that are not produced in the manufacturer's tool room.

A *fixture* is a work holding device. The work is held or clamped in the fixture and then positioned in the machine for processing. See Figure 4–1. A *jig* not only holds the work, but also guides the tool to it. *Gauges* are of two types: (1) *measurement gauges,* such as micrometers, which provide a specific reading, and (2) *attribute gauges,* also called Go-No Go gauges, which are preset to specific limit dimensions and then used to determine if the part fits within the specified limits. In general, the woodproducts industries use few gauges. Because of the nature of wood, tolerances closer than plus or minus $\frac{1}{32}$ in. are seldom encountered.

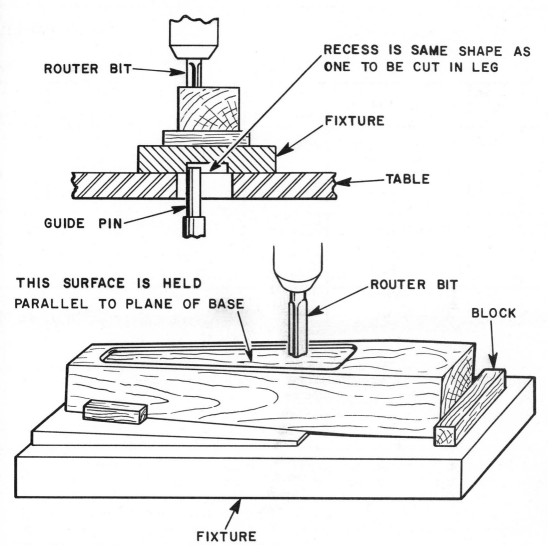

ROUTER BIT

RECESS IS SAME SHAPE AS ONE TO BE CUT IN LEG

FIXTURE

TABLE

GUIDE PIN

THIS SURFACE IS HELD PARALLEL TO PLANE OF BASE

ROUTER BIT

BLOCK

FIXTURE

Fig. 4–1. A fixture holds the work in position for processing in the machine.

Planning for Manufacture in the Furniture Industry

In furniture-manufacturing companies, the production-planning department studies the drawing and prepares a *bill sheet* as shown in Figure 4–2. From this bill sheet a *material requirements sheet* is prepared as shown in Figure 4–3. This sheet summarizes the kinds and quantities of materials needed to make one unit. The purchasing department uses this information to order the necessary materials. Finishing materials are not listed.

Utilizing the drawing and bill sheet, a *route sheet* is prepared for *each* part

PLANT NO. _____　　　　　　　　　　**DREXEL FURNITU**

BILL SHEET OF ONE　<u>CHEST DESK (WITH PIGEON HOLE COMPT.)</u>　SUITE NO. 507 - 4

PART NO.	No. Part Per Article	PART NAME	FINISH SIZE				MATERIAL		ROUGH	
			Length	Width	Thick	B.S.	Thick	Kind	Length	Wi
1	1	TOP	28	17½	13/16		4/4	POP	29	17
2	1	TOP CORE STRIP					4/4	CHERRY	29	
1-1	2	TOP RETURNS	2 15/16	13/16	11/16		4/4	"	13¼	1
2-1	2	TOP END BANDS	18	7/8	2/28		1/28	"	19	1
42	1	DROP DOOR	22 11/16	13 15/16	13/16		4/4	POP.	23¾	1.
32	1	DR. FRONT A	22 11/16	4 15/16	13/16		4/4	"	23¾	2
	2	DR. FRONTS B & C	22 11/16	6 1/16	13/16					
	1	DR. FRONT D	22 11/16	6 1/16	13/16					
84	1	DESK B TOM	25 7/8	15 1/8	13/16	25 3/8 23	4/4	POP	26 7/8	14

Fig. 4–2. A bill sheet. This sheet was prepared for the chest-desk shown in Figure 3–8. Only a part of the bill sheet is shown. The original form was printed on a tracing vellum.

of the product. These sheets are complete descriptions or plans of manufacture for each part. They accompany the material as it moves from machine to machine telling the operator what he is to do. See Figure 4–4.

At the time that the bill sheet is being prepared, the tooling people begin the task of designing, purchasing, or making all of the tools, machines, jigs, and fixtures that will be necessary for the production of the various parts of the product. When the tooling and the route sheets are completed, they are sent to the sample plant. The *sample plant* is a form of pilot plant. Here, the samples to be displayed in the furniture marts are made and the accuracy of the tooling and

the route sheets is also tested. These will be sent to a production plant later.

When the order is given to produce the piece of furniture in quantity, a complete set of route sheets is sent to the rough machine room (rough mill) of the production plant. The route sheets are sorted by species of wood and thickness. Route sheets for several different pieces of furniture may be grouped together on this basis. Thus, the machines may be set up once and like-sized rough parts for several different items cut. To insure that the proper number of rough parts for a given order are produced at the correct time, a *rough machine check-off list* is prepared. As the parts are cut to the rough size shown on the route sheet, the quantity

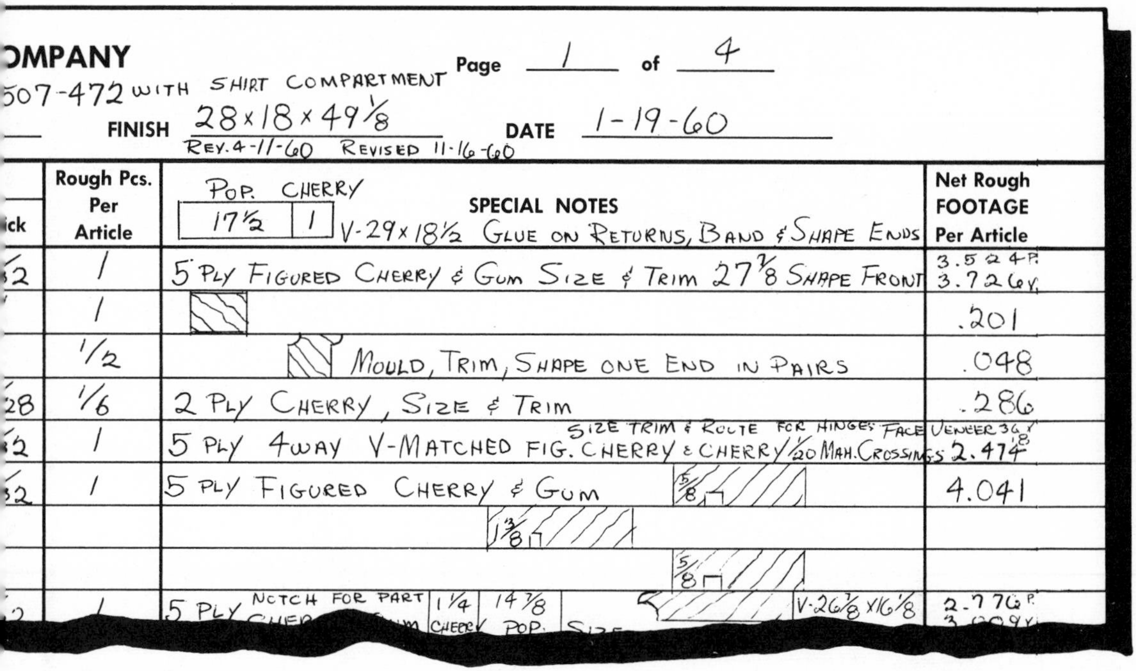

OMPANY Page 1 of 4

507-472 WITH SHIRT COMPARTMENT

FINISH 28 x 18 x 49 1/8 DATE 1-19-60

REV. 4-11-60 REVISED 11-16-60

ick	Rough Pcs. Per Article	POP. CHERRY 17½ 1 V-29 x 18½ GLUE ON RETURNS, BAND & SHAPE ENDS — SPECIAL NOTES	Net Rough FOOTAGE Per Article
2	1	5 PLY FIGURED CHERRY & GUM SIZE & TRIM 27 7/8 SHAPE FRONT	3.524 P. 3.726 Y.
	1		.201
	1/2	MOULD, TRIM, SHAPE ONE END IN PAIRS	.048
28	1/6	2 PLY CHERRY, SIZE & TRIM	.286
2	1	SIZE TRIM & ROUTE FOR HINGES FACE 5 PLY 4WAY V-MATCHED FIG. CHERRY & CHERRY 1/20 MAH. CROSSINGS	VENEER 36 1/8 2.474
2	1	5 PLY FIGURED CHERRY & GUM 5/8	4.041
		1 3/8	
		5/8	
	1	5 PLY ... NOTCH FOR PART 1 1/4 CHERRY 14 7/8 POP. ... V-26 1/8 x 16 1/8	2.776 P. ...

produced for this order is written on the check-off list. See Figure 4–5. When all of the rough parts are cut, they and the route sheets are sent to the finish machining section of the plant. The *parts control sheet* (Fig. 4–6) lists the finished size of each part and the number of the machine on which the final operations will be performed. The operations are listed from left to right in the order of their performance. The last operation for each part is in the column numbered 1. The intention is that all parts to complete a piece of furniture (case) will be completed and sent to the cabinet assembly room at one time. This arrangement is, in practice, an unobtainable ideal since many different pieces of furniture are in production at the same time and because of numerous variables in manufacture. However, it insures that the cabinet room does not begin assembling a case before all the parts are completed. When parts must be subassembled before further machining they are joined with crossed lines as shown in Figure 4–6. The remaining operations are then listed on only one of the parts.

Thus, it can be seen that production planning is the hub of the organization between product design and engineering and the manufacturing of the product. Graphically this structure appears as shown in Figure 4–7.

No. Req.	Code No.	1	ITEM, NAME & FINISH		SIZE		CAT. NO.	SUPPLIER
		2	Class / Type Mat.	Used For	Len.	Width	Footage	

MATERIAL REQUIREMENTS
ORIGINAL OR ADDITIONS

BK 12-1-61

DATE 1-20-60   49⅛ × 18 × 28

11-16-60   4-15-60
2-18-60   4-27-60
3-17-60
4-11-60

ARTICLE NO. 507-470

ARTICLE CHEST DESK (WITH PIGEON HOLE COMPART.)

No. Req.	Code No.	1 / 2	Class / Type Mat.	Used For	Len.	Width	Footage	SUPPLIER
2		1	HINGES S58-3392	B.P. 2L			SPEC. 58-1135A	NATL. LOCK
1		1	LID. SUPPORT	BRASS			LH 7555	WEBER KNAPP
1		1	LID SUPPORT	BRASS			RH 7555	" "
2		1	ESCUTCHEONS	BRASS			7556	" "
2		1	MAGNETIC CATCHES				9760 T	AMEROCK
1		1	DOOR PULL	PALAZZO	SINGLE		A 5920 DC	CHAUTAUQUA
1		1	SPEED CLIP	"			A 5038	"
1		1	STUD	"			A 4983	"
8		1	DR. PULLS	"	SINGLE		A 5918 DC– A 5919 CB– A 458	"
1			⅛" TRACK, FIBER, BLACK		5'	½"	801	ENG. PRODUCTS.
2			3/16"MOULDING , GUM		4⅜"	1¾"	D-549	KLISE

LUMBER	QUANTITY
6/4 MAPLE	
4/4 MAPLE	
6/4 CHERRY	3.109
5/4 CHERRY	1.028
4/4 CHERRY	16.456
5/4 POP.	.396
4/4 POP.	26.407
5/8 OAK	8.078
Total	**55.474**

VENEER	QUANTITY
1/28 Fig. CHERRY	10.241
1/28 CHERRY	42.082
1/16 CHERRY	12.092
1/20 MAH.	4.948
1/20 GUM.	82.693
1/8 R.C.	4.421
Total	**156.477**

PANELS	QUANTITY
3 PLY OAK 3/16	8.784
3 PLY GUM 3/16	3.835
3 PLY GUM 3/20	7.490
CHIP CORE 3/4	6.954
Total	**27.063**

Fig. 4–3. The material requirements sheet lists the materials and the quantities required for one chest-desk.

ROUTE SHEET
DREXEL FURNITURE COMPANY

	R. MILL	VENEER	R. MACH.	FIN. MACH.	SAND	ASSEMBLY	CABINET	7	
WANTED			.1287	.0506				JOB NO.	PART NO.

ARTICLES	ARTICLE NAME & NUMBER		PART NAME			
	507- 470 / 472 CHEST DESK		TOP			1

ROUGH PCS.	MATERIAL		ROUGH LENGTH	ROUGH WIDTH	ROUGH PLANE	ROUGH pcs. art.	ROUGH FT. PER ARTICLE
	KIND POP	THICK 4/4	29	17½	21/32	1	3.524

FINISH PARTS	PARTS PER		FINISH LENGTH	FINISH WIDTH	FINISH THICK	B.S.	ROUGH FT. PER PART
	ROUGH PIECE 1	ARTICLE 1	28	17½	13/16		3.524

OPER. NO.	MACHINE OR STATION	DESCRIPTION OF OPERATION		VENEER 5 PLY FIG. CHERRY & GUM
				29 × 18½ 3.726
1	1	CUT	40.2	
2	2	PLANE	—	
3	3	RIP	100.8	
4	5	SIZE 17½	26.9	
5	37	GLUE WITH 1" CHERRY	29.6	
6	2	PLANE	12.4	
7	39	5 PLY	40.0	
8	8	SIZE	19.0	
9	9	TRIM 27⅞	15.1	
10	12	SHAPE FRONT 507-4	53.7	
11		GLUE ON RETURNS & BANDS	—	
12	24	SAND 2 SIDES	16.5	
13	12	SHAPE ENDS & RETURNS 5074	66.3	
14				
15				
16				
17				
18				
19				
20				
21				
22				

(Diagram: 1" CHERRY | 17½ POP.)

SHAPE FRONT

←——— 17½ ———→

← GLUE ON RETURNS →

SHAPE ENDS

BAND

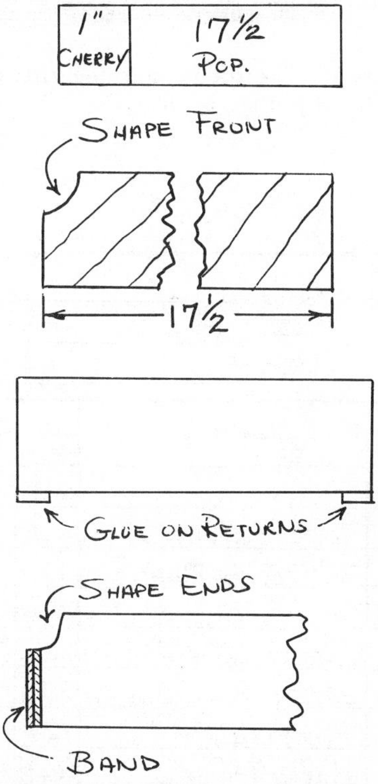

Fig. 4-4. A route sheet. The numbers .1287 and .0506 are the total man hours for producing this part in the rough and finish machining departments respectively.

ROUGH MACHINE — CHECK OFF LIST 1 OF 3   #1

SUITE NO. 507-472 470 CHEST DESK   JOB NO. _____

Amount	Part No.	Pcs. Per Case	Part Name	Length	Width	Thick	B.S.		Total
	1	1	TOP	28	17½	13/16			
	1-1	2	TOP RETURNS	2 15/16	13/16	11/16			
	2-1	2	TOP END BANDS	18	7/8	2/28			
	42	1	DROP DOOR	22 11/16	13 5/16	13/16			
	32	4	DR. FRONTS A,B,C,&D	22 11/16	4 13/16 6 1/16	13/16			
	84	1	DESK BOTTOM	25 7/8	15 5/8	13/16	25 3/8 23		
	10	1	PARTITION	12 13/16	14 11/16	13/16	12 9/16		
	47	1	BACK PANEL	26 3/8	18 11/16	3/16			
	47-2	2	COMPARTMENT BK.	10 5/16	8	3/16			

Fig. 4–5. The rough machine check-off list serves as a tally sheet to insure that the correct number of parts are cut.

Quantity Required _____ #1

Plant _____

Date _____

DREXEL FURNITU PARTS CONT

Department FINISH MACHINE

Part No.	Part Name	Dimensions				Quant. per Art.	Rip. or Size Saw	Mold. or Plane.	Feet per Part.	Class No.	16	15
		Long	Wide	Thick	B. S.							
1	TOP	28	17½	13/16		1						
1-1	TOP RETURNS	2 15/16	13/16	11/16		2						
2-1	TOP END BANDS	18	7/8	2/28		2						
42	DROP DOOR	22 11/16	13 5/16	13/16		1						
32	DR.FRONTS A,B,C,&D	22 11/16	4 13/16 6 1/16	13/16		4						
84	DESK BOTTOM	25 7/8	15 5/8	13/16	25 3/8 23	1						
10	PARTITION	12 13/16	14 11/16	13/16	12 9/16	1						
47	BACK PANEL	26 3/8	18 11/16	3/16		1						
47-2	COMPART. BK. D.	10 5/16	8	3/16		2						

Fig. 4–6. A parts control sheet for a finish machine department. A control clerk receives a daily report from each machine operator and posts the progress of each part on this sheet.

The Production Planner

A good **production planner** has a wide background and much experience in tool design and building, plant layout, motion and time study, quality control, cost estimating, and personnel supervision. He does not need to be an expert in *all* of these areas. He must be able to organize the efforts of individuals in all these areas, to communicate with them effectively, and to work harmoniously with everyone.

The importance of his work cannot be overemphasized. He primarily creates paper work on which careful planning and study can quickly correct errors. If the errors must be corrected after machines and tools have been built and placed into operation, considerable expense is involved. Many production planners have college degrees in industrial engineering or industrial management.

Production Planning in the School Shop

Planning the steps of procedure to be followed in constructing an article in the school shop is important for the same reasons it is important in industry. Whether the article is to be constructed by one student or is to be mass produced by the class, careful planning and preparation precede construction.

Plan for construction by studying the drawings of your project and making a list of all the parts, materials, etc., involved. The details necessary are indicated on the bill sheet shown in Figure 4–2. Then prepare an order form for all the materials necessary.

RE COMPANY									Article	CHEST DESK						
ROL SHEET									Suite No.	507-472 (470 above 472)						
Sheet No. 1 of 3									Order No.							

						Operations								Quant.	Delivered	
14	13	12	11	10	9	8	7	6	5	4	3	2	1	Req'd	Date	Piece
							39	8	7	12	✕	24	12			
							4^RM		10	12	✱					
										39	✱					
							39	8	9	15	18	24				
							39	25	10	8	12	23	24			
						39	8	9	12	10	11	15	24			
							39	8	9	12	10	15	24			
							39	8	9	10	15	24				
								39	8	9	8	24				
								39	8	9	10	24				

In this way the progress of production on the entire order is observed.

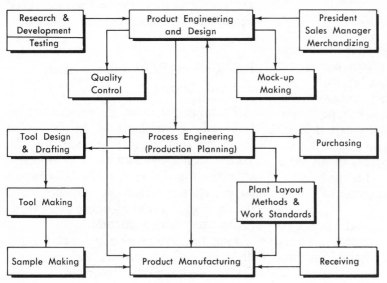

Fig. 4–7. Production planning. Product design, through engineering, to final manufacture of product.

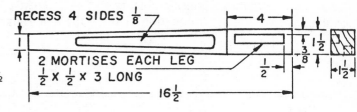

JOB PLAN
Part: Leg
Material: Maple
No. Needed: 4
Rough Size: 2 x 2 x 17
Finish Size: 1½ x 1½ x 16½
Time Start: _____
Time Finish: _____

Step	Station	Operation	Notes
1	Stock Room	Select stock	
2	Radial Saw	Cut to length — 17″	
3		Record stock used	Return unused stock
4	Jointer	Square two adjacent sides	Use push stick
5	Planer	Square to size	Place jointed surfaces down on planer table.
6	Radial Saw	Cut to length — 16½″	
7	Mortiser	Cut mortises	Lay out mortise on one leg, set stops, mark location of all mortises with an X
8	Jointer	Cut tapers	Set stop on infeed table, use push stick
9	Router	Cut recesses	Support work in fixture
10	Belt Sander	Sand all faces	
11	Bench	Break sharp corners, sand	Hand operation
12		Inspect	
13		Store	Protect until needed

Fig. 4–8. A sample job plan.

After the list is completed, prepare a route sheet for each part. Then, assemble the route sheets in the order in which the parts will be made. For example, if your project is a custom built (one of a kind) coffee table with a drawer, you would want to make the base first and then fit the drawer into the base. The top would be made last. The reasoning here is that the top would probably warp if completed first and permitted to lie around. The drawer must fit the opening in the base, and, logically, the base should be assembled before the drawer is cut and assembled. If it is necessary to process the legs while they are held in a fixture, you must design and construct the fixture first.

If, on the other hand, your classmates are mass-producing several of these tables, they would cut all the parts at one time using jigs and fixtures. Groups of students would then proceed to assemble the various subassemblies. These would finally be assembled into the finished product. Because of the various checks and controls involved in production, all parts should fit properly. The time involved should be only a few days.

In either case, however, a plan for manufacture will be necessary. This means you must identify each part of the project and list the steps of procedure for its manufacture. You should list the names of each part of your project, and under each part-name list the steps of procedure, the machine, and the operation you will perform. If your project is a table, your job plan for one of the parts might look as shown in Figure 4–8.

As we noted earlier, special tools and fixtures are necessary for the mass production of an article. You will find that it is also frequently necessary for you to make a fixture before you can accurately and *safely produce parts of your project*. The units in Part II dealing with manufacturing processes illustrate various work-holding devices that you might use to advantage.

DISCUSSION QUESTIONS

1. Define: product engineering, production planning, process engineering. What are the responsibilities of individuals in each?
2. Why are production plans necessary in industry? In the school shop?
3. What is a work-holding device? What is its use? Why are they important?
4. In what way does a fixture help to make an operation safer? Give an example.
5. For what reason might a product, once approved, be redesigned?
6. What are the qualifications of a good production planner? A tool designer? A tool maker? A machine operator? A control clerk? How does one prepare for and enter such an occupation?

SUGGESTED STUDENT ACTIVITIES

1. Plan the processes for the project you selected in Chapter III.
2. Plan the processes for an article to be mass-produced in the school shop.
3. Plan and design a jig, fixture, or tool for your shop.
4. Visit an industry, interview the production planner, and write a report describing his work, training and experience.

5. Prepare a written report on one of the following:
    a) Quality control.
    b) Motion and time study.
    c) Tool designing.
    d) Tool making.
    e) Material procurement (purchasing).
    f) Inventory control.
    g) Precision measurement, gauging, and standards.
    h) The plant superintendent.
6. Develop a production-planning chart for your school shop.

Part II MANUFACTURING

Chapter 5 Introduction to Manufacturing

The manufacturing industries today involve four basic elements, namely, men, materials, machines, and management — the four M's of an industrial enterprise. Remove any one of these elements and the chain is broken; all four are needed for success (Fig. 5–1).

This chapter will consider the machines (tools) that men control to process a material (wood) into useful products.

A quick look at the manufacuring industries shows that man's efforts, when involved in the working or processing of materials, may be (1) entirely manual as in early history and in some custom crafts today, (2) a combination of manual and machine processes as is typical of most industries today, or (3) almost completely automatic as in paper making. Automated production (automation) is becoming the rule in industries where quantity production is practiced. Several woodworking companies have already adapted some operations to automated production.

In previous chapters, you have studied the nature of wood and the manner in which industry organizes and plans for production. In this chapter you will be introduced to the basic processes involved in working wood. These processes are:

(1) measuring and laying out, (2) sawing, (3) planing, (4) drilling and boring, (5) turning, (6) shaping and routing, (7) sanding and scraping, (8) jointing, assembling, and fastening, and (9) finishing. In subsequent chapters, you will learn how these basic processes are applied in the manufacture of some of the most common products of the wood industries.

The various processes involved in the production of a product are carefully planned and organized. While no two companies may exhibit identical shop organizations and processes, there is enough similarity that a general understanding of plant layout may be developed.

Figure 5–2 shows the organization of a typical large furniture-manufacturing plant. In general, it is laid out to permit the easy flow of materials through the fabrication processes. Raw materials enter at one end of the plant and the finished product is shipped from the other. Auxiliary departments make subassemblies and introduce them into the main flow of materials as needed.

Industrial engineers are usually responsible for plant layout. They must know the sequence of operations performed in the manufacture of an article. They must also know the limitations, capabilities,

Fig. 5–1. A machine which bends, laminates, and sets veneers molded into complete wrap-around shells of various sizes and shapes within two minutes.

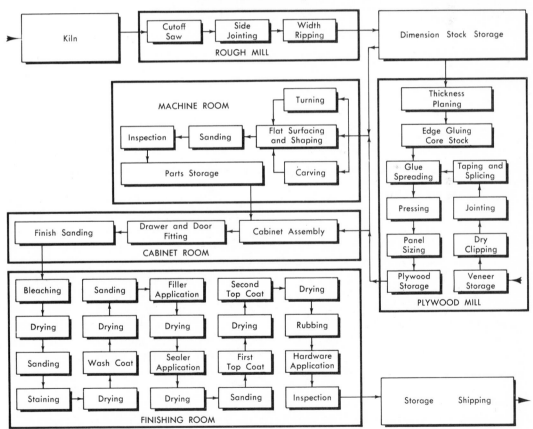

Fig. 5–2. Flow of material through manufacturing processes.

and characteristics of the various machines and be able to plan their arrangement.

In the following pages, you will learn how the basic processes of working wood have evolved, how they are performed today in industry, and how they may be performed in school shops. In some instances you will learn how some of these might be performed in the future. As you study the various segments of manufacturing and technology and experiment with the basic processes, make an effort to visualize yourself as one of tomorrow's specialized technicians or engineers, craftsmen, machine operators, managers, designers, machine builders, tooling experts, processing specialists, safety consultants, or technology teachers. Ask yourself, "What part can I play and what contribution can I make to the growth and development of technology and manufacturing?"

You will be working in tomorrow's world of technology. The chances are better than one in four that you will be employed in an occupation in the manufacturing industries. If you can equate your interests and abilities with the opportunities and requirements that exist in this industrial-technological culture, you should then be able to choose the educational preparation that will help you attain that goal.

Chapter 6 Measuring and Laying Out

Measuring is the process of determining a specific dimension, size, or capacity of a material or object. This is done with various tools and instruments that are graduated in standardized units of measurement. Closely related to measuring tools is an important group of devices which may be set or adjusted to predetermined dimensions. Tools of this type are used for making lines on the work as well as for checking the work after a certain cut or other operation has been made.

Laying out is the process of marking a designated measurement, line, location, shape, or design on the work. The information to be laid out is obtained from a drawing or from some other type of specification. When the necessary information is transferred to the work, it serves as a guide that the operator follows in making the necessary cuts. Measuring and laying out are fundamental operations which are essentially performed by craftsmen in producing custom built articles, prototypes, models, and the like. The development of standardized measurements and the various measuring devices of today are one of man's most important accomplishments.

Evolution of Measuring Processes

Crude methods of measuring were de- vised by early civilizations thousands of years ago. One of man's earliest systems for measuring lengths was based on the size of his thumb, hand, and arm. These measures were known as the "digit," "palm," and the "cubit" (Fig. 6–1).

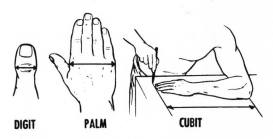

DIGIT   PALM   CUBIT

Fig. 6–1. The earliest "standards" of measurement.

Thus, the size of these measures varied as different men applied them. The cubit, based on the length of the forearm, varied as much as three inches between a short and tall man. This led to a realization of the need for a standardized system of measurement. Master cubit sticks have been found along with other artifacts that indicate that men in the Bronze Age had established such a standard. The royal cubit used in building the pyramids of Egpyt, was 20.62 in. long. These early cubit sticks were similar to a ruler. They were made of granite and had various divisions and symbols scratched

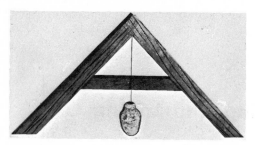

Fig. 6–2. Level.

Fig. 6–3. Plumb.

Fig. 6–4. Early Iron Age square.

on the surface. Figures 6–2, 6–3, 6–4, and 6–5 illustrate some early layout tools.

Originally the *foot* was based on the length of the human foot. Of the many standard sizes of feet used in the anicent world, the Greek foot used in building the Parthenon had the greatest influence. It measured 11.69 in. The Romans used the standard, adapting it slightly to 11.613 in. This measure spread with the Roman Empire over much of the Western world. The English foot is closely related to the Roman foot. English measurement of the yard was standardized by Henry I early in the twelfth century as the distance from the tip of his nose to the end of his thumb.

Because the early American colonies were originally under British control, the system of weights and measures used in the United States is derived from British standards. After American independence, there were certain changes in the British system that were not adopted in the United States. So the two now differ slightly.

In 1791, the French Academy devised the metric system which was intended to be based on a fractional part (1/10,000,000) of a meridian measured from the north pole to the equator. This system over the years has been widely adopted by most of the non-English-speaking countries. It is the measuring system used by scientists all over the world.

Although Congress was authorized by the Constitution to fix the standard of weights and measures, no official system was approved until 1832 when the Treasury Department adopted certain English standards. Congress gave official approval of these standards in 1836. The standard

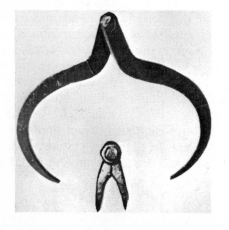

Fig. 6–5. Early Iron Age calipers.

of length was the yard defined as the distance between two points on a brass bar that had been made in England and was supposedly exactly equal to the standard English yard. In 1866, the metric system was made legal and conversion factors between that system and the American units were established. In 1893, the United States yard, which was still defined in terms of the British Imperial yard, was redefined in terms of the International Prototype meter, a unit of measure adopted by an international committee in 1875.

In 1901, the National Bureau of Standards was established to set standards for weights and measures. These are now enforced by the Federal Trade Commission, which protects the interests of the consumer.

Measuring and Laying Out Tools

The majority of measuring tools that are used in woodworking are graduated in inches. They have eight, sixteen (Fig. 6–4), thirty-two, and in some cases, sixty-four divisions to the inch. Measuring to accuracies closer than $\frac{1}{32}$ in. is seldom necessary since wood is not a dimensionally stable material.

Rules (Figs. 6–7 and 6–8) are used for making linear measurements. They are made of either wood or metal, in a wide range of types, widths, and lengths. The most commonly used rules are:

1. **Wooden bench rules** (Fig. 6–6). These rules are available in either 1-, 2-, or 3-ft. lengths. They are used for measuring and as straight edges. The 2-ft. size is widely used in the school shop. This has four graduated edges. Two are divided into sixteen divisions to the inch

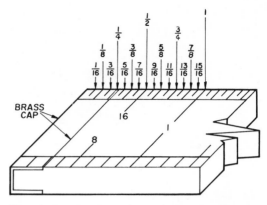

Fig. 6–6. Portion of a wooden bench rule showing the common divisions of an inch.

and two into eight divisions. The better rules have brass caps on each end to protect against damage and wear.

2. **Folding rules** (Fig. 6–7). These rules are of either wood or metal construction. They have hinged joints, some of which lock into a rigid position by means of a spring device. Folding rules open to 4 to 12 ft. in length. They are frequently used by carpenters and commonly known as the zig-zag rule. In general, folding rules are not considered as reliable or accurate as other types of rules; after extended use, some degree of wear or play develops at the joints.

3. **Rigid steel rules.** The most common steel rule is the one-foot rule that

Fig. 6–7. Folding spring-joint rule.

Fig. 6–8. A pull-push tape.

is used in conjunction with the combination square set illustrated in Figure 8. Other types of rigid or semi-flexible steel rules include the *pocket rule* and *shrink rule*. Shrink rules are used exclusively by patternmakers. They are similar in appearance to a standard steel foot rule except that the graduations are expanded slightly to compensate for the shrinkage of the different metals used in castings. For example, a 12-in. shrink rule used when making a pattern for a brass casting actually measures $12\frac{3}{16}$ in. When the molten brass freezes (solidifies) in the mold, it shrinks to the correct size.

4. **Tape or pull-push rules** (Fig. 6–8). These are made of thin spring steel, have various width blades, and range from 6 to 12 ft. in length. This type of rule is accurate and convenient. The flexible blade may be bent around curved surfaces. The blade is coiled inside a compact case which usually has an outside dimen-

sion of 2 in. The pull end of the blade has a sliding hook which is self-adjusting to permit making inside or outside measurements.

5. **Board rules** (Fig. 6–9). These rules are also called lumber scale rules. They are not rules in the usual sense. They determine the board measure of lumber. Rules of this type are not used for layout work. Board rules are 3 ft. in length and constructed of hickory or spring steel. They have three scales marked on each side which measure boards

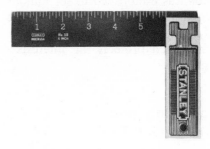

Fig. 6–10. Try square.

6, 8, 10, 12, 14, and 16 ft. in length. The rule is laid across the width of a board of known length and its board measure is read directly from that length scale.

Squares are used for measuring, laying out, and for checking right angles. Squares are also used as straightedges to test surfaces for "flatness." There are 3 basic kinds of squares used in woodworking. These are:

1. **Try squares** (Fig. 6–10). These have

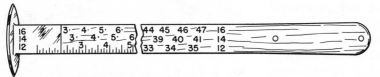

Fig. 6–9. Board ruler used for finding the number of board feet in lumber.

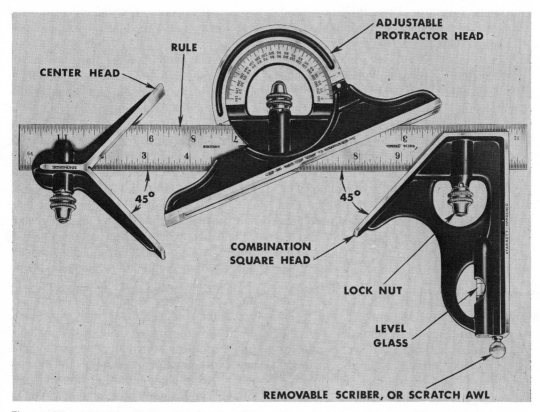

Fig. 6–11. Combination square set.

metal blades graduated in ⅛-in. divisions. Blades range from 6 to 12 in. in length. They are made with either wood or metal stocks (handles). Some stocks have a 45-deg. angle at the blade end to facilitate laying out and checking miter cuts. Try squares of this type are referred to as *miter try squares*.

2. **Combination squares** (Fig. 6–11). The combination square consists of a rigid steel, 1-ft. rule and a head which makes a 45 and 90-deg. angle to the rule edge. A combination square may be used as a rule, a try square, a miter square, a level, or a depth gauge. A small pointed scriber is stored in the square head. The head moves along a groove in

the rule and may be secured at any point by means of a lock nut.

Two other accessories that are often used with the combination square are the protractor head and the center head. The *protractor head* (Fig. 6–11) is adjustable to any

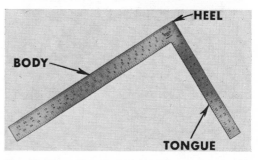

Fig. 6–12. Carpenter's steel square.

angle from 0 to 180 deg. and is used for marking and checking operations. The *center head* (Fig. 6–11) consists of a 90-deg. angle which is bisected when attached to the rule. The center head is primarily used for locating centers on the ends of round or cylindrical objects.

3. **Steel squares** (Fig. 6–12). These are the largest in size. They are made in one piece which consists of two basic parts, the body and the tongue. The tongue is the shorter of the two and ranges from 8 to 18 in. on squares of different sizes. The body ranges from 12 to 24 in. in length. The most popular size has a 24 by 2-in. body and a 16 by 1½-in. tongue. Squares of this size and type are commonly called *carpenter's* or *framing squares*. The tongue and the body are graduated in inches and divisions thereof on both surfaces. Some steel squares are also marked with the following tables:

Rafter framing table. This is used to determine the length of various kinds of rafters and the angle at which they must be cut.

The *essex table*. This is used for determining board measure.

The *octagon scale*. This is used to lay out a member having 8 equal sides.

The *brace table*. This gives the length of a brace to form the third side of a triangle or the diagonal of a square or rectangle.

The *hundredth scale*. This has an inch divided into 100 equal divisions. With the aid of a divider, fractions may be converted into decimals without mathematical calculations.

The **sliding T-bevel** (Fig. 6–13) is used to measure or transfer any angle between 0 and 180 deg. The blade generally ranges from 6 to 12 in. in length and is not usually graduated. The blade may be located at any angular position. The handles are made of either wood or machined cast iron.

The *angle divider* (Fig. 6–14) is used for bisecting or dividing angles. It is especially useful for laying out miters when fitting trim, molding, flooring, and similar jobs. This tool consists of two steel arms that pivot in unison and may be locked at any desired angle. The center or body section is graduated; it serves as a handle and is used as a center line when laying out one member of the miter joint.

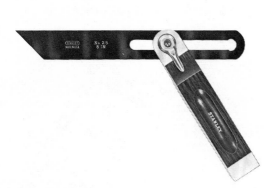

Fig. 6–13. Sliding T-bevel.

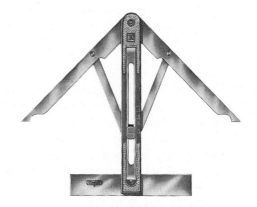

Fig. 6–14. Adjustable angle divider.

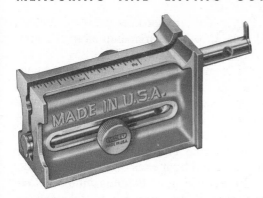

Fig. 6–15. Butt gauge of metal construction.

The **marking gauge** is used for marking parallel lines on wood. It has an adjustable head (Fig. 6–16) which may be set to any location along the length of the beam. At one end of the beam is a sharp pin which scribes a fine knife mark as the gauge is pushed along the work edge. Marking gauges are made of either hardwood or metal. The beam is generally graduated in 16ths for 6 in. of its length.

Another type of marking gauge is known as the **butt gauge** (Fig. 6–15). This has 3 spurs or points on the end of the adjustable beams. This permits marking inside corners. It is primarily used by carpenters for laying out butt mortises when hanging doors. This tool is made of metal and the body is graduated in 16ths for 2 in.

Dividers (Fig. 6–17) are used for laying out circles and arcs, and for dividing lines and angles. A divider has two hardened steel points which may be adjusted to a desired radius. Dividers are made in various sizes and types. The type illustrated in Figure 6–17 is a combination divider and compass. One leg may be removed and a pencil installed in its place.

Trammel points (Fig. 6–18) consist of two metal points which can be attached to a straight bar or stick. They are used for marking circles and arcs that are too large to be handled with a divider or a compass.

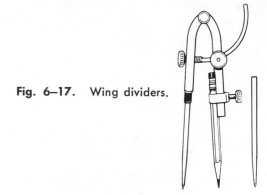

Fig. 6–17. Wing dividers.

Fig. 6–16. Standard marking gauge made of wood.

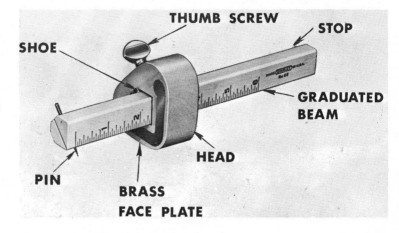

SHOE

THUMB SCREW

STOP

GRADUATED BEAM

HEAD

PIN

BRASS FACE PLATE

Fig. 6–18. Trammel points, **note:** the socket designed to hold a carpenter's pencil.

Calipers are used to transfer measurements. Calipers are of two basic types outside and inside. The *outside caliper*

(Fig. 6–19) is used to measure outside distances, particularly diameters of round work. *Inside calipers* (Fig. 6–20) are used to measure inside distances or openings. Both types are available in different sizes. They are available with various kinds of adjusting devices. The calipers shown in Figure 6–19 are of the thread-spring type of construction. They are adjusted by means of a screw and nut.

Levels are used to determine whether a surface is in a true horizontal or vertical position. The earliest types of levels used were based on the principle of the *plumb* (a weight attached to a line) as shown in Figure 6–3. The water level came into existence in 1600 B.C. Modern levels consist of a glass tube containing a special liquid. This tube is mounted in a frame of aluminum or wood. The glass vials (tubes) are slightly curved so an air bubble in the liquid will float to the high point, the exact center of the arc. When the level is in a true horizontal (or plumb) position, the air bubble will come to rest between two marks on the vial.

Levels generally have two or more vials positioned at 90 deg. to one another. The vial used for checking vertical positions is referred to as the "plumb vial."

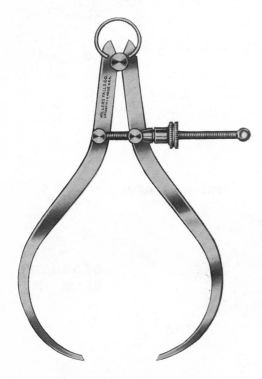

Fig. 6–19. Outside caliper.

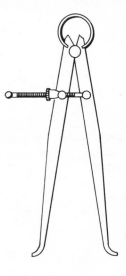

Fig. 6–20. Inside caliper.

Levels are available in a variety of sizes and special types. Three common types of levels are: (1) the 24-in. *aluminum level* with 6 vials (Fig. 6–21); (2) the *torpedo level* with a third vial set at 45 deg. (Fig. 6–22); and (3) the *line level* with only one vial (Fig. 6–23).

The **plumb bob** (Fig. 6–24) is simply an accurately machined weight that is made of steel and/or brass. It is attached to one end of a string or cord and suspended to indicate a true vertical position. Plumb bobs are used on transits. They are also hung independently to check vertical members such as corner posts and other frame work in building construction.

Chalk line (Fig. 6–25) is a mason's line or cord that is coated with chalk (usually blue) and used to lay out long straight lines. The chalk is transferred from the string to the work by the snap method, as shown in Figure 6–25. Chalk lines are also available in manually operated reels. These have a felt gasket inside, which distributes a coating of chalk

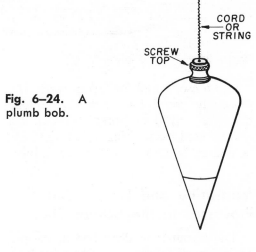

Fig. 6–24. A plumb bob.

to the line as it is withdrawn from the reel case. Chalk lines are generally available in 50-, 100-, or 300-ft. lengths.

Material markers. Chalk, crayon, or the carpenter's pencil (Fig. 6–17) may be used for marking measurements on boards. When more accurate layout marks are required, they are made with a hard lead pencil (such as a 4H) or a knife, such as the *sloyd* knife shown in Figure 6–26. The *scratch awl* (Fig. 18)

Fig. 6–21. 24″ aluminum level.

Fig. 6–22. A torpedo level.

Fig. 6–23. Line level.

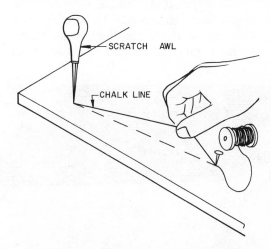

Fig. 6–25. Snapping a chalk line tightened between two points produces a straight line on the work.

Fig. 6–26. A sloyd knife.

is also a useful tool for layout work. It is especially useful for marking the locations for drilled or bored holes. It can also be used for scribing a line on plastic laminates, hardboard, and other surfaces.

Measuring and Laying Out Processes in the School Shop

The layout tools described in the preceding parts of this unit are used for many routine operations. The instructions given in the remaining pages of this unit deal with the basic uses of these tools in checking and making measurements and layouts.

Using rules (Figs. 6–27 and 6–28). To measure hold the rule on edge as shown in Figures 6–27 and 6–28. This places the graduations in contact with the material and precludes errors due to parallax (differences in viewing point).

When possible, use a rule or tape longer than the distance to be measured. This avoids errors resulting from having to move the rule several times to cover

the distance. For example, a 6-ft. tape or folding rule will be faster and more accurate than a 1-ft. rule for measuring a 5-ft. distance.

Marking lines at 90 deg. (Figs. 6–29a, 6–29b, and 6–30) to an edge or surface is often necessary when squaring stock. For this class of work, use either a combination square (Fig. 6–29a), a try square, or a framing square. Figure 6–29b shows a recommended method of marking measurements on duplicate parts. This technique is often employed when laying out identical mortises, ten-

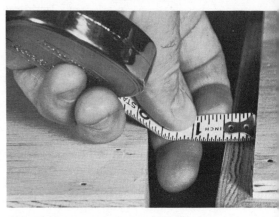

Fig. 6–28. Using a measuring tape in a restricted area. The tape is tilted slightly to place the graduations as near the material as possible.

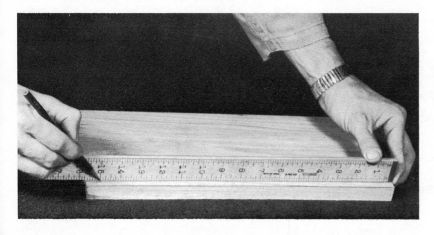

Fig. 6–27. The rule is placed on edge for maximum accuracy in measuring and laying out.

Fig. 6–29. Using squares to mark the work pieces at 90 degrees: (a) scribing a mark with a knife.

(b) With one setting of the square, the same measurement is marked on several pieces. This insures that all pieces will be alike.

ons, holes for edge-to-edge dowel joints, and similar jobs. Figure 6–30 shows a method of marking a wide panel.

Checking surfaces and corners with a square (Fig. 6–31, 6–32, and 6–33). Use the blade of the square as shown

Fig. 6–30. Scribing a line for squaring the end of a wide panel. Measurements were first made from the end of the panel and marked at each edge. Then the line is scribed along a straightedge to connect the marks.

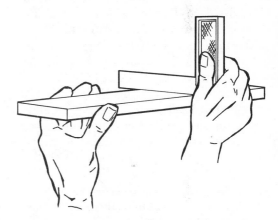

Fig. 6–31. Testing a flat surface with a square.

in Figure 6–31 when checking a surface to see if it is flat. To test for right angles on outside corners (Fig. 6–32) and inside corners (Fig. 6–33), hold the handle firmly against one surface. When possible, hold the square and the work toward a source of light. Any light visible between the blade and the work indicates a surface that is out of square.

Laying out and checking miters and angles is done with the bevel square, combination square, T-bevel, or the pro-

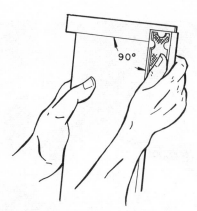

Fig. 6–32. Testing an outside corner with a square.

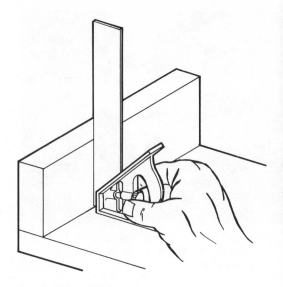

Fig. 6–33. Testing an inside corner with a square.

tractor head (Fig. 6–34) of a combination square set. Common methods of checking a 45-deg. miter and a bevel are shown in Figures 6–35 and 6–36.

Gauging parallel lines (Figs. 6–37a, 6–37b, and 6–38) may be done in the following ways:

1. *Using a marking gauge* (Fig. 6–37a). Set the head at the desired distance from the pin. Check this measurement with a rule. Hold the gauge head against the work edge with the

pin tilted so it will not dig into the wood as it is pushed forward. See Figure 6–37a. The point of a marking gauge will score the surface. If this is undesirable, as when gauging a line for a bevel or chamfer, use a pencil as described below.

2. *Gauging with a pencil* (Fig. 6–37b).

Fig. 6–34. Laying out a flat miter cut with a protractor head and rule. The head is held firmly against a true edge.

Fig. 6–35. Checking a 45-degree miter cut with a combination square.

Fig. 6–36. Checking an angle with a T-bevel.

With a little practice, this method is reasonably accurate, and does not score the wood. It is useful along irregular edges or when a high degree of accuracy is not required. *Caution*: The edge of the board should be smooth and free of slivers.

3. *Gauging with the combination square* (Fig. 6–38). This requires the use of both hands; one to guide the head

Fig. 6–37a. Gauging a parallel line with a marking gauge. The pin is tilted so it will not dig into the wood.

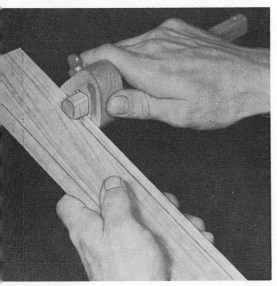

of the square against the work edge, and the other to hold the pencil point against the end of the rule.

Measuring diameters of round stock may be done with an outside caliper and a rule. To find a diameter, adjust the caliper so it will just slip over the work (Fig. 6–39). Then measure the opening between the legs of the caliper with a rule as shown in Figure 6–40. When using the caliper to check the progress of turnings, set it to the desired size and then turn the work until the caliper slips over the part. Using the calipers requires a "feel" as you slip it over the work. Avoid forcing the tool (springing the legs apart). This is a source of error.

Locating centers of round stock is most easily done with the aid of the centerhead and rule as shown in Figure 6–41. Hold the work so it is firmly against the centerhead. Mark a fine line along the blade. Turn the work 90 deg. and mark another line. The center of the work is at the intersection of these lines. To find the *center of square stock*, draw diagonal

Fig. 6–37b. Gauging a parallel line with a pencil is necessary to prevent scoring of wood fibers.

Fig. 6–38. Center gauging is a means of finding the approximate center of the work by gauging parallel lines an equal distance from each edge.

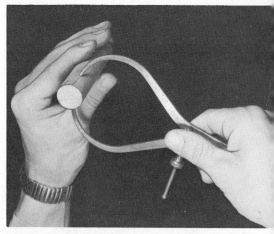

Fig. 6–39. Using outside calipers. Adjusting the caliper to slip over the work.

lines from corner to corner. See Figure 6–43.

Marking centers (Fig. 6–42) for drilling and boring is performed with a scratch awl. Sink the point into the surface of the work to provide a starting point for the bit.

Marking circles (Fig. 6–43) **and arcs.** Adjust the points of either the compass, dividers, or trammel points to the desired radius. Swing the tool to make the desired mark. Avoid excessive pressure on

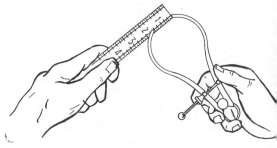

Fig. 6–40. Measuring the opening between the caliper legs. Note that one leg is on the end of the rule.

Fig. 6–41. Using a centerhead on the end of round stock to locate the center.

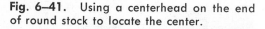

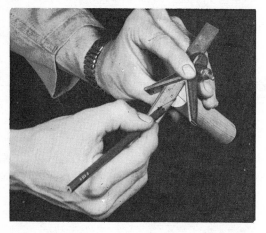

the pivot point. If a mark or indention is objectionable use tape, cardboard, a piece of rubber, or some other material to prevent the point from penetrating the surface.

Laying out irregular lines. Certain layout jobs cannot be handled by any of the methods previously described. Depending upon the nature of the pattern, the work can usually be marked by employing one or a combination of the following methods:

1. Transferring by the *graph-square method* (Figs. 6–44a and 6–44b). Briefly, this is done by drawing one set of squares over the design to be

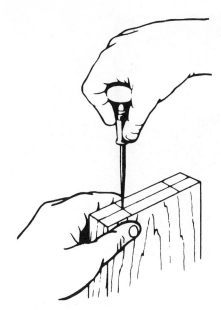

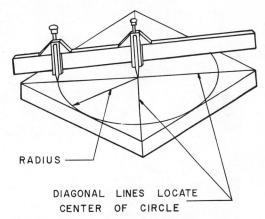

RADIUS

DIAGONAL LINES LOCATE
CENTER OF CIRCLE

Fig. 6–43. Laying out a circle on square stock.

Fig. 6–42. Using the point of a scratch awl to mark the centers for bored holes.

reproduced (Fig. 6–44a) and another set of squares (usually larger) on paper or the work itself (Fig. 6–44b). The size of the latter group of squares depends upon the desired ratio of the enlargement. Figure 6–44 shows a 1 to 4 ratio; in other words, the plan designed is being enlarged four times. Copy each point of the original pattern on the graph squares. Then connect the points with the aid of a french curve or straightedge. Use carbon paper to transfer the paper pattern to the workpiece.

2. *Transferring with a templet* (See Fig. 6–45). This is a widely used method when two or more identical parts must be laid out. A templet is a full-size pattern or outline of a design. For symmetrical designs (those that may be divided into two identical halves), a *half pattern* or templet as shown in Figure 6–45 is

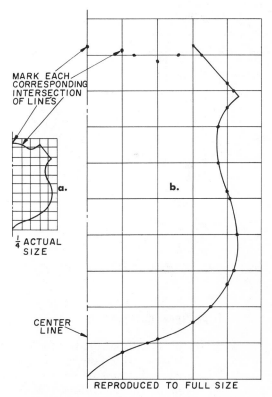

MARK EACH
CORRESPONDING
INTERSECTION
OF LINES

a.

b.

¼ ACTUAL
SIZE

CENTER
LINE

REPRODUCED TO FULL SIZE

Fig. 6–44. Enlarging a design with graph squares: (a) the original design. (b) method of locating the points for the enlarged pattern.

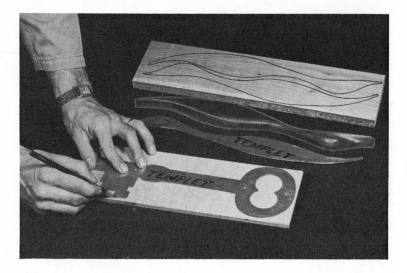

Fig. 6–45. Marking designs with templets. Two members were laid out on one piece of stock in order to conserve material.

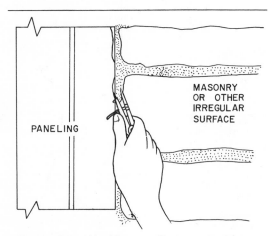

MASONRY
OR OTHER
IRREGULAR
SURFACE

PANELING

Fig. 6–46. Marking a line to match an irregular surface.

recommended. Make templets from heavy cardboard, plywood, hardboard, or sheet metal as dictated by your needs. Simply hold the templet firmly to the workpiece and trace around it with a sharp pencil. With a half templet pattern, flip it over on the center line and complete the layout of the second half in the same manner.

3. *Marking a line to match an irregular surface.* This may be accomplished with the aid of a divider or compass as shown in Figure 6–46. Commercially made devices are available for jobs of this type. Generally speaking, they are more accurate than the above method.

REVIEW QUESTIONS

1. What early methods were used for measuring?
2. Which civilization was the first to define the foot?
3. What divisions of an inch are found on most rules? What tolerance is permitted on dimensions laid out on wood?
4. What are the basic kinds of rules used in woodworking?
5. What are some of the principal uses of a combination square set?
6. What information is often found on the steel carpenter's or framing square?
7. What tools are primarily used for layout work in building construction?

8. What is a sloyd knife? What is its use in laying out?
9. How may irregular patterns be transferred to the stock?

SUGGESTED STUDENT ACTIVITIES

1. Make a full size templet for a shop project.
2. Refer to books on drafting, metalworking, and electronics and make a list of tools and instruments which are used for measuring.
3. Devise as many ways as you can for laying out the following shapes: (1) diamond, (2) ellipse, (3) star, (4) octagon, (5) hexagon, and (6) a heart shape.
4. Devise a water level and demonstrate its use.
5. Consult a local building contractor to learn how he lays out the foundations of a house.
6. Design and construct a device for determining the elevations of a plot of ground. Make a topographic map of the plot.

Chapter 7 The Evolution of Sawing
Processes and Machinery

Introduction to
Sawing Processes

Sawing is one of several processes for giving shape to a material. Sawing processes involve both hand- and power-operated tools. Sawing tools have a row or continuous series of teeth that separate or divide the material by cutting a narrow path through it. The path made by the saw is referred to as the *kerf*.

Industrial sawing may be divided into two basic classifications, *log-mill* and *industrial-plant* sawing. Sawing is employed to fell or cut down a tree in the forest. It is the first and one of the most important of all the manufacturing processes associated with the shaping of wood.

The primary function of the saws used in the mills is to cut logs into rough lumber. In this class of work, the equipment used is very large and most of the cutting is done parallel to the grain.

In industrial plant sawing, cutting with the grain and cutting across the grain are of equal importance. The wood is usually dry, and in most cases it has been surfaced smooth. The saws used are much smaller than saw-mill equipment.

The widest range of different sawing applications is found in the industrial plants and shops where lumber and other materials are manufactured into useful products.

One major deficiency in sawing is that a great amount of wood is wasted in the form of sawdust. Efforts are being made to develop processes that produce no waste or that produce a more usable form of waste. Very small jets of water under great pressure, intensified light beams, ultrasonic energy, and rotary slicing knives have been tested. All of these produce little or no waste. Newly designed saw teeth produce chips or shavings that permit their use for pulp.

Still, cutting wood with sawing machines remains the most widely accepted method. The continuous cutting action provided by the circular and the band sawing machines has led to their use in all phases of industrial sawing.

Sawing processes have changed more rapidly within recent years than in the entire previous history of woodworking.

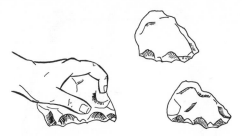

Fig. 7–1. Rough flint stones, one of man's earliest tools.

Fig. 7–2. A crude saw made of flaked flint used by man in the Old Stone Age, 200,000 B.C.

The development of high speed saws, long-wearing carbide saw teeth, and modern production machines have virtually eliminated manual sawing methods.

In order to understand better the sawing processes that industry uses today, let us review their evolution beginning with the first saws devised by prehistoric man.

The Development of Hand Saws

Archaeologists know that stone and flint instruments were used by prehistoric man half a million years ago. Early man labored to abrade or wear down a piece of wood with muscle power and a rough stone (Fig. 7–1). In time, he learned that he could shape flint by chipping and flaking and thus produce an edge that enabled him to cut. When he learned to move this edge back and forth on the material being cut, he developed the first saw. Evidence of a flint saw was

found in the remains of Neanderthal man, who lived in Europe 130,000 years ago (Fig. 7–2). In New Mexico, ancient tools and weapons with roughened edges were found recently. These were made of flaked flint similar to the early saws found in Europe. New Stone Age man developed a sickle type saw with a series of polished stone flints held in a wooden frame with pitch (Fig. 7–3). These were used between 6000 and 3500 B.C.

The Bronze Age (4500–1500 B.C.) brought about the world's first metal saws. Some of these were cast in sand or clay molds. One of the most interesting is the Egyptian saw (Fig. 7–4). Note that the Egyptian saws have the teeth pointing

Fig. 7–3. A sickle saw developed by New Stone Age man, 6,000 B.C. to 3,500 B.C. This saw was made of a series of sharp polished flints held in a wooden frame by pitch.

Fig. 7–4. This bronze pull saw was used by the Egyptians from 3,-200 B.C. to 500 B.C. with little change in its design.

backward. This requires the application
of pressure on the pulling instead of the
pushing stroke as is common in this
country. This type of hand saw is still
used today in much of the Far East.
Bronze saws were used until 500 B.C.,
well into the Iron Age, which began with
the development of iron smelting about
1500 B.C.

The Romans designed and fabricated
saws and many other tools as we know
them today (Fig. 7–5). The framing
saw, turning saw or buck saw, strained
by a tight cord, was also developed in
ancient times (Fig. 7–6). Not until the
discovery of steel were saws formed into
the more efficient cutting instruments of
today. One of the saws of the iron age
that led to the development of the modern hand saw is shown in Figure 7–7.

Many of the early settlers coming to
the New England Colonies in the seventeenth century brought along the tools
of their trade. These craftsmen included
coachmakers, wheelwrights, coopers, ship-
wrights, carpenters, joiners (cabinetmakers), chair builders, stair builders, patternmakers, and plane makers. All of
these early craftsmen prospered because
of the demand for their handmade products. Most of the early tradesmen imported their saws and other tools from
England and Europe. However, some of
the craftsmen designed and made their

Fig. 7–6.   The buck saw.

own tools from pig iron produced in the
foundries which appeared on the East
Coast as early as 1630. Most of these
early saws had wooden frames and handles because metal was scarce and difficult to fashion.

One of the earliest saws used in this
new land was the *pit saw* (Fig. 7–8).
This was a two-man wooden framed saw
that was used for ripping out boards and
planks from logs supported over a pit.
The blade, about 5 or 6 in. wide and 6
to 7 ft. in length, was held in a wooden
frame. One man stood in a pit beneath
the log and the other (called the "top
sawyer") stood above as shown in the
illustration. Their output ranged from
100 to 200 ft. of board per day. This
same process is still employed to some

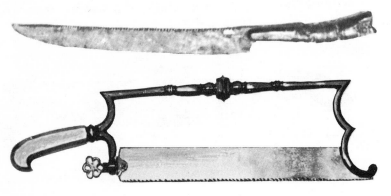

Fig. 7–5. The Romans,
the first efficient tool-
makers, used iron for
saws with regular shape
and set.

Fig. 7–7. One of many
special purpose saws
used by the craftsmen
of the Middle Ages in
Europe.

extent in Syria, Austria, China, and Central Africa. A somewhat smaller version of the pit saw was the *coachmaker's saw*. It was used for sawing the heavy timbers and planks for the construction of coaches and wagons.

Other special saws were developed by the early planemaker, who hand-made woodworking planes to be used by other craftsmen. These planes were made entirely of wood except for the metal cutting blade (plane iron). Some of these saws had no set and were made in various thicknesses and lengths to suit the requirements of the job. Primarily, the planemaker's saws (Figs. 7–9a and 7–9b) were used to cut the openings in the body of the plane. Saws with very thin blades were used by patternmakers and cabinetmakers for making very intricate cuts in their work. These are considered to be the forerunners of the modern dovetail and back saws. They were made without a reinforcing back. See Figure 7–10.

As knowledge of metallurgy increased, the modern hand saw was developed. In 1840, Henry Disston specialized in the manufacture of hand saws in his Phila-

Fig. 7–8. The New England Colonists used this pit saw to cut their logs into boards.

delphia cellar shop. Many types of saws were designed and introduced to perform special sawing operations common to craftsmen in the various trades.

Fig. 7–9. Two saws used by Colonial plane makers for sawing the mouths (openings) in the bodies of early wooden planes for the plane irons and the wooden wedges used to hold them in place.

Fig. 7–10. An 1840 saw which is considered the forerunner of the modern dovetail and back saw.

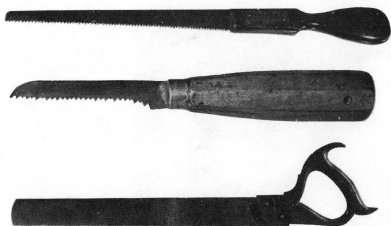

The Development of Sawing Machines

Man's effort to substitute some energy other than his own muscle power for sawing dates well back before the discovery of America. Early saw mills were powered by animals, wind, and water. Saw mills powered by water are known to have been used in the Scandinavian countries as early as the fifteenth century.

Between 1600 and 1620, the first

Fig. 7–12. The earliest type of jigsaw employed a reciprocating cutting action produced by a foot treadle. The blade was tensioned by a wooden rod attached to the ceiling.

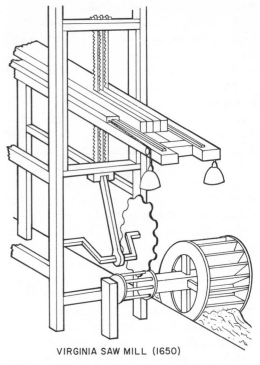

VIRGINIA SAW MILL (1650)

Fig. 7–11. A typical early American saw mill powered by water.

American saw mills appeared in Maine and Virginia. The saws used were powered versions of the two-man pit saws. They had several blades rigged in a frame and spaced to cut boards of equal width as shown in Figure 7–11.

Machines incorporating this up-and-down blade movement are called *reciprocating saws*. The actual cutting of this type of saw is done only on one stroke, usually on the downward movement of the blade. The reciprocating cutting principle was applied very early in the jigsaw and later in the gang and portable power tools used for light woodworking.

The **jigsaw** was first made of wooden parts except for the crude metal blade. The blade was strained by attaching one end to a flexible wooden rod (used as a spring) fastened to the ceiling. The blade extended downward through the table, and the other end was connected to a foot treadle near the floor (Fig. 7–12). The operator depressed the treadle to pull the blade downward and the wooden spring rod raised it again when the foot pressure was released. The first metal jigsaws made with an overarm, as we know them today, were also powered by a foot treadle mechanism. Later, the jigsaw was driven by water, steam, and then electrical energy. It soon became one of the most popular machines of the early wood industries. It was used in the furniture industry for making many of the ornate scrolls and grill work designs typical of the prevalent styles.

Circular saws are said to have been used in Holland some 100 years before Samuel Miller of England patented his successful *table circular saw* in 1777. The development of the circular saw with its rotating, toothed disk gave the world its first saw capable of delivering a *continuous cutting action*. In 1814, the first circular saw blade appeared in this country. It was of a very large size for use in a circular log mill.

Actually, there was very little improvement made to the table-type circular saw in the hundred years following Miller's invention. The early saws were made with wooden tables and supporting framework. The saw blade was mounted on an arbor and positioned so that it would extend above the table. The first method of varying the amount of blade projection was to raise the front of the table, the rear being hinged to the frame (Fig. 7–13).

The **band saw,** an endless metal band belt with teeth cut in the edge, was the second continuous sawing device to be developed. The first band saw was invented in England by William Newberry in 1808. However, his machine functioned poorly because of frequent band breakage. Methods of welding blade ends together to form the band loop still had to be perfected. A French woman of extraordinary mechanical talent, Madamoiselle Creping, is given credit for developing the first successful band saw in 1846 (Fig. 7–14).

In 1869 the first log mill band saw was built. As early as 1885 the Allis Chalmers Company of Milwaukee, Wisconsin, built a very large mill band saw with wheels 9 ft. in diameter. In 1896, this company introduced another large electrically driven band saw which carried a blade 14 inches wide.

Attempts to guard the wheels and blade of band saws were first made in the early 1900's. The first direct drive motor was used on a band saw in 1901.

Throughout the years following Madamoiselle Creping's invention, improvements in sawing machinery came rapidly. The three basic types of sawing action

Fig. 7–13. An early wood frame table saw. The hinged table is adjustable to obtain the desirable amount of blade projection.

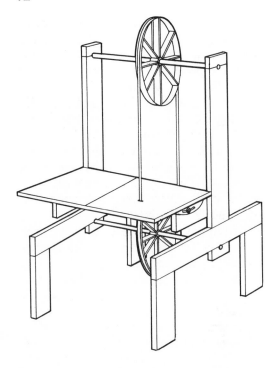

Fig. 7-14. The first successful band saw.

introduced in the earlier machines (recip-rocating, rotary, and band sawing) continued to be developed. The use of one-piece cast iron frames about 1850 gave all types of sawing machines the necessary rigidity.

The first saws used in woodworking factories received their power from water wheels through long line shafts. The shaft usually extended the length of the plant along the ceiling or the floor. Each machine was belt-driven from the line shaft. This arrangement continued in use when the steam engine and later the electric motor were introduced. Some plants did not abandon the line shaft drive until the 1930's. Small electric motors with belt drives for individual machines were introduced in the early 1900's. The direct drive motor came into use between 1910 and 1920.

About the time of World War I, the general design of woodworking equip-

Fig. 7-15. An improved table saw with a tilting arbor.

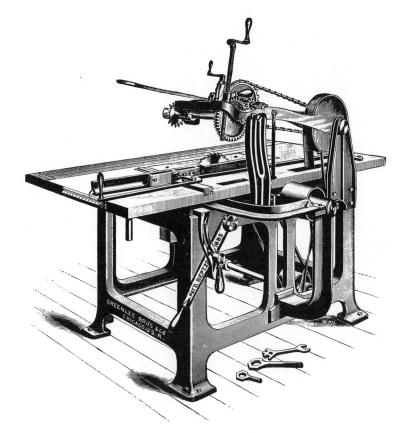

Fig. 7–16. The first saw to feature a power feed mechanism. This spur, self-fed rip saw was introduced in 1881.

ment changed. The first tilting-arbor saw was introduced by Baxter D. Whitney and Son about this time (Fig. 7–15). Ball bearings replaced babbit bearings on most machines.

The **development of power-fed saws** is perhaps the most significant of the many contributions leading to automatic production sawing in the wood industries. Before these saws came into use, ripping was done on hand-fed table saws. Generally, two or three men were required to handle the stock. It was a dangerous operation because the equipment was poorly guarded. In 1881, Ralph and Robert Greenlee introduced a self-fed power rip saw (Fig. 7–16). Although this ma-

chine was poorly guarded according to present-day standards, it was then considered to be the ultimate in sawing safety and efficiency. It also reduced the number of men needed to attend to the business of handling stock at the rip saw.

In 1911, the Hermance Machine Company of Williamsport, Pennsylvania introduced a new type of machine.* It incorporated an idea conceived by a mechanic, A. W. Nelson, of using an endless chain feed on an over-cutting rip saw. This machine came to be the forerunner of nearly all the modern types of straight line rip saws in use today.

* See page 123, Chapter 9, for a description and illustration of a modern chain feed machine.

Development of Portable Power Saws

Portable power saws first came into existence during the 1920's. The first type introduced was a portable circular saw driven by a small electric motor. This type of saw came into broad use during World War II when it was readily accepted by contractors and carpenters. Later, air-driven, portable circular saws were introduced and proved to have advantages in some industrial applications. Within the past two decades, gasoline-engine and electric-motor-driven chain saws have been developed for forest and woodland harvesting. They have largely displaced the ax and the one or two man manual crosscut saws for both felling trees and bucking tree trunks into logs. Recently, a small gasoline engine has been applied to power a portable circular saw of the type used by carpenters and construction workers. Its primary advantage is that it may be used at construction sites located at a distance from conventional power sources.

Fig. 7–17. The first radial-arm saw was developed in 1922.

The first **radial-arm saw** (Fig. 7–17) was developed by Raymond E. De Walt in 1922 and added more versatility to circular sawing equipment. Within a year or two, this machine was being manufactured by a company bearing De Walt's name, and machines of this type have grown in popularity ever since.

Sawing machines today have improved in speed, accuracy, and provision for the safety of the operator. Advances in metallurgy, improved power sources, and greater attention to overall design and engineering have brought about new machines with remarkable production rates and accuracy.

The small reciprocating portable saw known as a saber saw was first developed in Switzerland and found its way to this country around 1945. Metallurgists had produced flexible steel blades that would stay sharp, resist breaking, and withstand the heat of friction. These blades plus the wartime development of small but powerful electric motors permitted the development of this versatile saw. Today, other types of portable reciprocating saws are available.

The family of portable powered saws also includes a small band saw, but its use is primarily limited to metalworking operations such as cutting off rods, pipe, and similar materials.

Chapter 8 Hand and Portable Powered Saws Today

Hand Saws

Some of the hand saws used in the nineteenth and early twentieth centuries are still manufactured and used today. The descriptions of the different saws that follow include some that may be considered uncommon. However, some are still in existence and are used for specialty sawing as well as woodland and timber work.

The **crosscut and the rip saw** (Fig. 8–1) are the two most commonly used hand saws. Crosscut saws are designed to cut across the grain, and rip saws are for cutting with the grain. Both cut on the push stroke. A fundamental understanding of the nomenclature and cutting principles of the crosscut and the rip saw may be applied to all hand saws.

The *blade* of a good crosscut or rip hand saw is taper ground. It is thinnest at the back edge of the point, and gradually becomes thicker as it approaches the handle; the tooth edge is of uniform thickness along the full blade length (Fig. 8–1). The tapered blade provides clearance and free movement in the kerf. The *length of a blade* is measured from the point to the butt along the cutting edge. Crosscut saw blades are made 20, 22, 24, or 26 in. in length. Rip saws usually have 26-in. blades.

Points to the inch (Fig. 8–2) is a term used to designate the size of teeth on a saw. The number of teeth per inch is one less than the number of points per inch. Saws with a greater number of

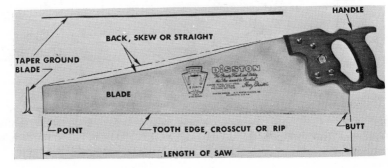

Fig. 8–1. Nomenclature of a hand crosscut and rip saw.

HANDLE

BACK, SKEW OR STRAIGHT

TAPER GROUND BLADE

BLADE

POINT

TOOTH EDGE, CROSSCUT OR RIP

BUTT

LENGTH OF SAW

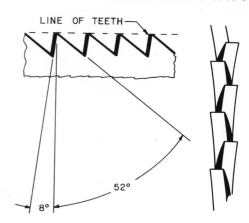

Fig. 8–2. The size of saw teeth are specified in points per inch. At the left, 8-points and 7-teeth; at the right, 5½ points and 4½ teeth.

points per inch make smoother cuts, but they cut more slowly than those with fewer points. Generally, crosscut saws have 8 to 12 points per inch and rip saws have 5½ or 6 points per inch.

The **set** of a saw is the alternate, outward bending of the teeth to make them cut a "kerf" wider than the thickness of the saw blade (Figs. 8–6 and 8–4). The amount of set is determined by the nature and character of the wood to be cut. Green (wet) wood requires more set and coarser teeth than dry wood. Softwoods require more set and coarser teeth than hardwoods. Generally, the amount of set for a rip saw is about one third of the thickness of the blade. Crosscut teeth are set to about one fourth of the thickness of the blade.

Crosscut saw teeth are shaped like a row of sharply pointed knives (Figs. 8–5 and 8–6). The front face of a cross-

Fig. 8–3. Left, enlarged rip teeth: Right, tooth edge of rip saw showing chisel-like teeth set alternately right and left.

cut tooth makes an angle of 15 deg. with a line perpendicular to the line of the teeth. The back of the tooth makes a 45-deg. angle with this line, as shown in Figure 5. The cutting edge of the tooth is usually filed to a 24-deg. bevel. The cutting action begins with a series of slicing cuts (like knives) which sever the grain fibers on each side of the kerf (Fig. 8–6).

Rip-saw teeth resemble a series of small chisels (Figs. 8–3 and 8–4). The

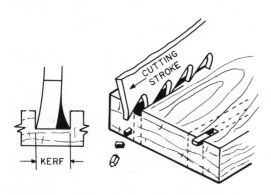

Fig. 8–4. Left, cross-section of rip teeth (note the "set"). Right, the cutting action of a rip saw.

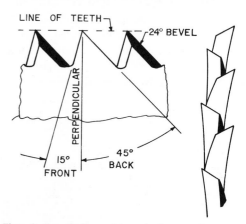

Fig. 8–5. Left, enlarged shape of crosscut teeth. Right, tooth edge of crosscut saw showing knife-like teeth.

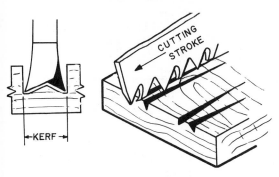

Fig. 8–7. Back saw.

Fig. 8–6. Left, cross-section of crosscut teeth (note the "set"). Right, the cutting action of a crosscut saw.

front of a rip-saw tooth makes an angle of 8 deg. with a line perpendicular to the line of the teeth. The back makes an angle of 52 deg. Note that the total included angle of a crosscut and rip tooth are both 60 deg. The cutting edges of rip saw teeth are square instead of beveled. This produces a cutting action (Fig. 4) like that of many small chisels.

The **back saw** (Fig. 8–7) has fine crosscut teeth, 12 to 16 points per inch, and a thin blade supported by a stiff back which gives this saw its name. Lengths range from 12 to 20 in. The back saw is used for fine, accurate work in finish carpentry, cabinet, furniture, and

patternmaking. Larger sized back saws are often used in a miter box as shown in Figure 8–8.

The **miter box** (Fig. 8–8) is a device used to hold the work while it is cut at an angle. It is widely used by cabinet and finish carpenters and other skilled craftsmen in custom manufacturing. The back and base frame are usually constructed of cast iron. Most types are equipped with automatic catches which hold the saw in an elevated position (Fig. 8–8) so that both hands may be used to place the work. Adjustable stops are used to cut duplicate pieces to length and to a specific depth. The saw may be swiveled up to 50 deg. right or left. Automatic locking positions are usually provided at 0, 9, 22½, 30, and 45 deg. to the right and left.

Fig. 8–8. Miter box.

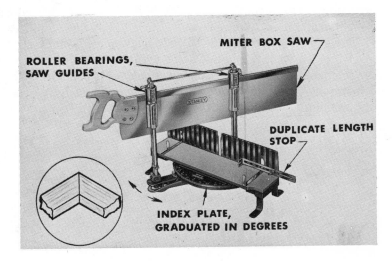

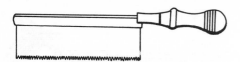

Fig. 8–9. Dovetail saw.

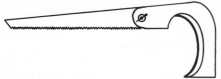

Fig. 8–10. Compass saw.

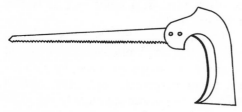

Fig. 8–11. Keyhole saw.

The **dovetail saw** (Fig. 8–9) has an extra thin tapered blade (about .032 in. or less), thinnest at the supported back. It is similar to, but narrower than the back saw, has fine teeth (15 to 20 points), usually no set, and a round handle. This saw is designed for very accurate cutting of joints such as the dovetail and tenon. Today, it is primarily used in patternmaking and model construction where smooth sawing of light-weight material is required.

The **compass saw** (Fig. 8–10) has relatively coarse (8 to 10 points) saw teeth. It is characterized by a pointed blade which may be inserted into a bored hole for making a cut that will permit the insertion of a crosscut or rip saw. The point may be forced through wallboard to make cutouts for receptacles.

The **keyhole saw** (Fig. 8–11) is similar to the compass saw, but the blade is narrower. It has 10 points to the inch. This saw is used for cutting frets and other inside designs. The saw is started in a hole that is first bored in the work.

The **nest of saws** (Fig. 8–12) is used for cutting a variety of materials. The open-grip, wooden handle will hold any of 3 interchangeable blades. The plumber's (metal cutting), compass, and key-hole saw blades are most commonly furnished.

The **coping saw** (Fig. 8–13) is some-times referred to as a hand scroll saw. The blades have either loop or pin ends and 15 points per inch. Spiral cutting blades are available. The steel frame is usually nickel-plated. The blade may be inserted to cut on either the push or pull stroke. It is tensioned by turning the handle, and it may be rotated 360 deg. The narrow blade permits this saw to cut sharp curves and make inside cuts. This saw is also used for cutting fine fret-work or scrolls. Carpenters use this saw to shape the end of a piece of molding to fit the face at inside corners in what is called a coped joint.

Stair-builder's saws (Fig. 8–14) have crosscut teeth, 10 points per inch, and a 1¾-in. blade width which may be ad-justed for sawing to various depths. Ear-lier styles were called *trenching saws*. This saw was used by stair builders for

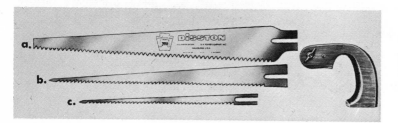

Fig. 8–12. Nest of saws. The interchange-able blades are: (a) plumber's, (b) compass, (c) keyhole.

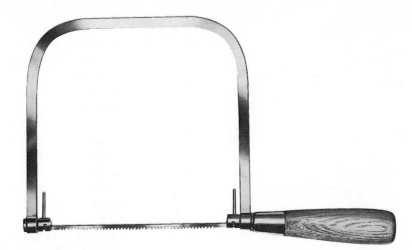

Fig. 8–13. Coping saw.

cutting dadoes and similar joints. It finds limited use today.

Flooring saws (Fig. 8–15) have crosscut teeth, usually on both edges of the point, with one tooth edge curved. It is designed for sawing into surfaces without chiseling or drilling a starting hole. This saw has been replaced with the various portable electric saws. It was once a popular saw used by remodeling and repair service craftsmen.

The **docking saw** (Fig. 8–16) has a 24 to 30-in. skew back blade with coarse-cutting (4½ point) peg teeth. It is used for fast, rough cutting around lumber-yards, farms, mines, railroads, shipyards, and docks.

The **crosscut saw** (Fig. 8–17) has a taper ground blade, 20 to 15 gauge (.038 to .070 in.) thickness and from 2½ to 5 ft. in length. This saw is available in the two-man type with handles at each end of the blade. It is used for fast cutting of green wood when felling, limbing, or bucking logs and for sawing timbers to length. This saw was once popular for use in the construction of log buildings and for woodland harvest of firewood and lumber. It has been replaced by the modern chain saws.

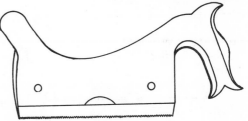

Fig. 8–14. Stair-builder's saw.

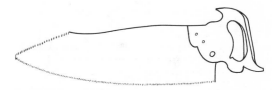

Fig. 8–15. Flooring saw.

Fig. 8–16. Docking saw.

Fig. 8–17. Crosscut saw.

Fig. 8–18. Curved pruning saw.

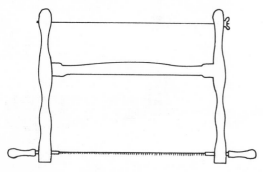

Fig. 8–19. Web saw.

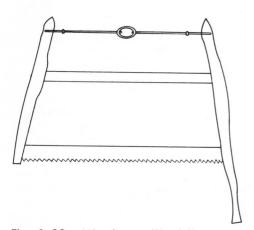

Fig. 8–20. Wood saw, "Buck."

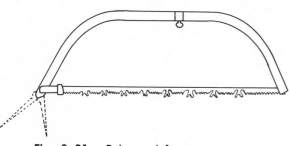

Fig. 8–21. Pulpwood frame.

The **curved pruning saw** (Fig. 8–18) was designed for fast cutting of green wood. It is much smaller than the crosscut saw. It usually has 7 or 8 points per inch and ranges in length from 14 to 24 in. Other styles of pruning saws are available with straight blades and draw-stroke cutting teeth. This saw is used today by landscapers for trimming tree limbs and hedges. Smaller folding styles are becoming popular camping accessories.

The **web saw** (Fig. 8–19) is also referred to as a "turning" or "turning web" saw. Earlier versions of this saw were used by colonial chairmakers and wheelwrights. It is made with a varnished hardwood frame and a steel rod with an adjustable wing nut to tension the blade. It holds a narrow rip tooth blade, 14 to 24 in. in length. This saw is usually used with a pull cutting stroke. Although it is not in popular use today, it is sometimes useful for cutting curves in heavy stock.

The **wood saw** (Fig. 8–20) is often called a buck saw. It has a hardwood frame, a threaded rod, and a turnbuckle to tension the blade. This saw holds blades of various widths. Blade lengths are generally 30 in. with 5 points per inch. It is a lightweight saw, used primarily for utility and firewood cutting on the farm.

The **pulpwood frame** (Fig. 8–21) is adjustable for 39- to 40-in. blade lengths. It is used in woodland cutting of pulpwood, firewood, general trimming, and land clearing.

Portable Power Saws

Within the past decade or two portable power saws have been developed. They have replaced most of the special purpose hand saws previously used in the building trades. Some of the more com-

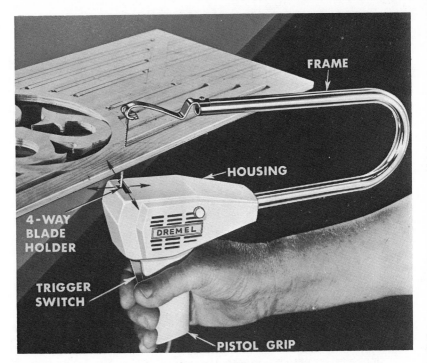

Fig. 8–22. Electric scroll saw.

FRAME

HOUSING

4-WAY BLADE HOLDER

TRIGGER SWITCH

PISTOL GRIP

mon types of portable power saws used today are described below.

The **electric scroll saw** (Fig. 8–22) is a lightweight reciprocating saw used for freehand cutting by hobbyists and craft classes. It is a safe tool to use. It may be equipped with a 3-in. combination wood- and metal-cutting blade. It may be used for sawing thin nonferrous metals, plastics, and wood up to ¾ in. thick. Widths are limited to the depth of the throat (distance from blade to frame). The saw is used for purposes similar to a coping saw.

The **saber saw** (Fig. 8–23) is powered by a small electric motor. Several sizes

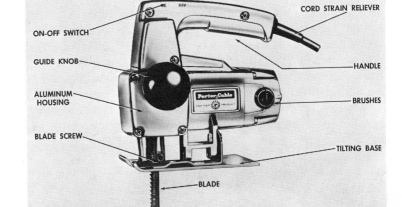

Fig. 8–23. Saber saw

CORD STRAIN RELIEVER

ON-OFF SWITCH

GUIDE KNOB

ALUMINUM HOUSING

BLADE SCREW

HANDLE

BRUSHES

TILTING BASE

BLADE

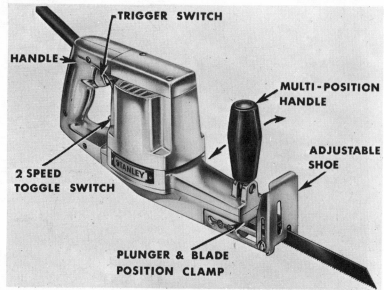

TRIGGER SWITCH

HANDLE

MULTI-POSITION HANDLE

ADJUSTABLE SHOE

2 SPEED TOGGLE SWITCH

PLUNGER & BLADE POSITION CLAMP

Fig. 8–24. Reciprocating all-purpose saw. Note the opening in the shoe which allows sawing with the blade in various positions.

are available. This tool incorporates a mechanism which converts the rotary motion of the motor into a reciprocating saw blade motion. The blade moves at a rate of about 3000 to 4500 spm (strokes per minute). Most types have a 1-in. stroke and are designed to cut on the upstroke. This short cutting stroke presents a distinct safety feature over portable electric circular saws. Saws of this type are not as fast cutting as portable circular saws.

Most manufacturers of this type of saw provide a ripping and circle-cutting gauge and a throat insert that minimizes splintering. Beveled cuts may be made by tilting the base. It may also be used for *plunge cutting,* that is, starting a cut in the surface of a board without first boring a starting hole.

With the proper blade,* this saw can be used for continuous cutting operations on ferrous and nonferrous metals, pipe, plastics, paper, leather, rubber, lumber up to 2 in. thick, and large plywood sheets. It can be used for fine intricate

---

* For information concerning blades used in portable reciprocating saws turn to page 132 ff.

scrolls, smooth curves, straight line, and angle cutting. Some models incorporate such features as: (1) orbital blade action; (This means the blade moves into the stock on the upstroke, and backs away on the downstroke. It speeds sawing, reduces splintering, and lengthens the blade life.) (2) two or three speeds for metal and wood cutting; and (3) a built-in light and an air nozzle to remove sawdust and improve visibility.

The **reciprocating or all-purpose saw** (Fig. 8–24) is a heavy duty bayonet-type saw that employs a reciprocating motion similar to that of the portable saber saw. Builders, plumbers, remodelers, electricians, and heating and air conditioning contractors use this saw for such work as cutting heavy gauge metal plate, nails embedded in lumber, and fine intricate scroll work in plastics and wood. The design and construction vary from one manufacturer to another, but generally they have the following basic features:

1. A ¾- or 1-in. pull cutting stroke with two speeds, the top speed being 3000 spm.

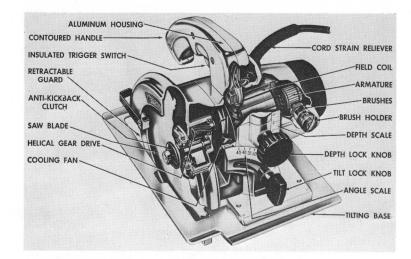

ALUMINUM HOUSING
CONTOURED HANDLE
INSULATED TRIGGER SWITCH
RETRACTABLE GUARD
ANTI-KICKBACK CLUTCH
SAW BLADE
HELICAL GEAR DRIVE
COOLING FAN

CORD STRAIN RELIEVER
FIELD COIL
ARMATURE
BRUSHES
BRUSH HOLDER
DEPTH SCALE
DEPTH LOCK KNOB
TILT LOCK KNOB
ANGLE SCALE
TILTING BASE

Fig. 8–25. Portable electric circular saw.

2. Provisions for clamping the blade in three different positions — the teeth pointing up, down, or sideways. The shoe is similarly adjustable.

3. Interchangeable blades* similar to those for jig and saber saws, ranging from 3½ to 12 in. in length, and suitable for cutting a wide variety of materials. An allen wrench is used to tighten the blade-locking screw.

The **portable circular saw** (Fig. 8–25) is often referred to as the portable cut-off saw. Saws of this type are rapidly replacing the hand saw for most cutting jobs in building construction. Masons also employ this saw, with an abrasive blade, for cutting concrete and similar ceramic materials.

Today, portable circular saws are either electric-powered (Fig. 8–25), pneumatic (air-driven) (Fig. 8–26), or gasoline-engine-driven (Fig. 8–27). They are manufactured in various sizes to take blade diameters ranging from 4 to 12 in. The 8-in. blade is the most popular and allows cuts up to 2¾ in. deep. The blade*

cuts upward from the under side of the work. The size of the saw is determined by the diameter of the blade recommended for the saw. All good saws available today have a built-in friction-type clutch which allows the blade to slip, in case it binds. This safety feature reduces

* For information concerning blades used in portable circular saws turn to page 140.

Fig. 8–26. Portable pneumatic circular saw being used to make a 45-degree cut.

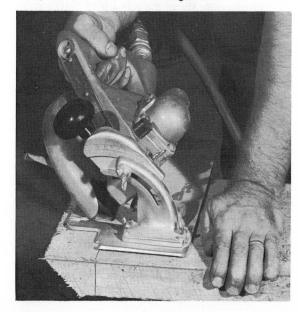

* For information concerning blades used in portable reciprocating saws turn to page 132 ff.

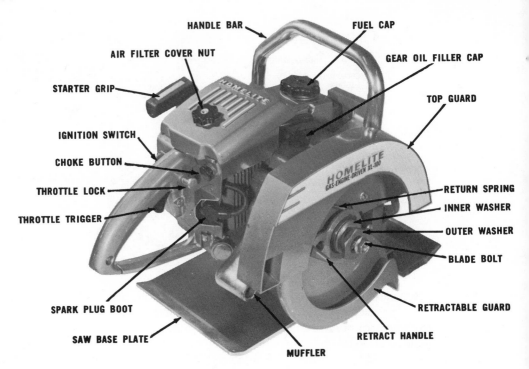

Fig. 8–27. A portable gasoline-engine-driven circular saw.

kickbacks, prevents overloading the motor, and protects against motor burnout.

The *portable electric circular saws* (Fig. 8–25) have 1- to 2-hp motors and generally operate at speeds up to 6400 rpm. The *air powered portable circular saws* (Fig. 8–26) are used in shipyards, for bridge and dam construction, and in mines for heavy-duty cutting of such materials as wet, resinous woods and masonry. This type of saw is driven by an air-operated motor that is activated by the flow of air through ½- or ¾-in. hoses from air compressors. A pressure between 80 and 100 lb. per square inch is required for operation. Without a cutting load, air-powered saws have an arbor speed of 1600 rpm on some 12-in. saws, up to 4600 and 8000 rpm on 6- to 8-in. saws. The *gasoline-driven portable circular saw* (Fig. 8–27) has useful applica-

tions at construction sites where electric power is not available and where portable air compressors are impractical. The two-cycle gas engine has a clutch which allows the engine to run (at an approximate idle speed of 2600 rpm) without the blade rotating. The blade is activated by the throttle trigger. Full speed is 4100 rpm. Although the gasoline-powered saw has certain advantages in portability, a good deal of attention must be given to lubrication, fuel-mixing requirements, cleaning of spark plugs and air filters, and other maintenance jobs common to gasoline engines.

The **chain saw** (Fig. 8–28) is used by home owners, sportsmen, farmers, and woodland tree harvesters. Chain saws (either gasoline-engine or electric-motor powered) are made in many different sizes and have various-shaped guide bars

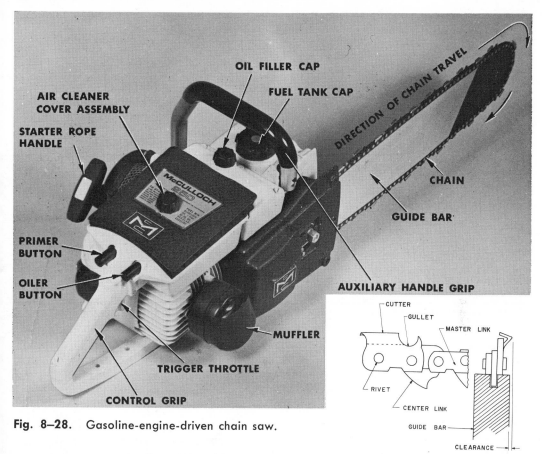

Fig. 8–28. Gasoline-engine-driven chain saw.

for different cutting jobs. Generally, the gasoline engine makes for a more powerful saw. It usually reaches a speed of 8000 rpm with a 6-hp, 2-cycle, air-cooled engine. A centrifugal clutch stops the chain motion when the trigger switch is released, allowing the engine to idle.

Chapter 9   Sawing Machines in Industry

Reciprocating Saws

Reciprocating saws utilize a very narrow blade that reciprocates (moves up and down) vertically. They are primarily used for sawing irregular shapes. Sawing machines of this type are more commonly known as either *jigsaws* or *scroll saws*. The saw blade* cuts on the downward stroke. Today, as in the past, wood industries still use jigsaws constructed to cut with the blade held vertically by an overarm or a device fastened to the ceiling.

Overarm jigsaws (Fig. 9–1) are made with heavy cast-iron frames in one or more pieces or with lightweight, pressed-sheet steel frames. The cutting capacity is determined by the distance from the blade to the column. This distance, called the *throat opening,* determines the size of the machine. The 24-in. model shown in Figure 9–1 is one of the more popular sizes. Machines of this type are found in toy plants, exhibit and display shops, patternmaking shops, and factories specializing in novelty items that incorporate inlaying, scroll, and pierced designs.

Overhead strained jigsaws (Fig. 9–2) are, for all practical purposes, limited only in the thickness of the material they will cut. They are used in industrial plants for work that is larger than can be handled on the overarm type jigsaws. This type is used for sawing large decorative figures, sign letters, large irregular contours, and for making inside openings in large-sized panels, as shown in Figure 9–2.

The *driving mechanisms* incorporated in jigsaws to provide the reciprocating motion are of several different types. The two most common are the *eccentric drive* and the *wheel and pitman drive* mechanism. Both types convert rotary motion to a reciprocating motion, as shown in Figure 9–3a and 9–3b.

With either system, the power of the motor is transferred directly (or by belt and pulley) to the driveshaft. Belt-driven machines (Fig. 9–1) have step cones or split pulleys which provide speeds ranging from around 600 to 1700 spm. Motors are usually ¼ to ⅓ hp, 1750 rpm. Light-duty machines are powered by electric motors (which drive a rocker mechanism) or by electromagnetic, vibrating motors. The latter develop cutting speeds up to 7200 spm.

Generally, industrial types of jigsaws

---

* For information concerning saw blades, turn to page 132 ff, Chapter 10.

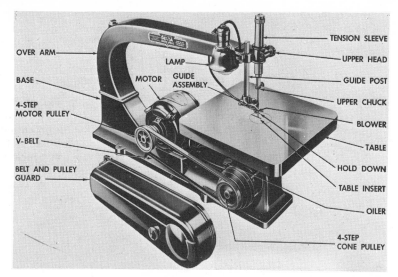

Fig. 9–1. Nomenclature of a 24-inch belt-driven jigsaw.

OVER ARM

BASE

4-STEP MOTOR PULLEY

V-BELT

BELT AND PULLEY GUARD

LAMP

MOTOR GUIDE ASSEMBLY

TENSION SLEEVE

UPPER HEAD

GUIDE POST

UPPER CHUCK

BLOWER

TABLE

HOLD DOWN

TABLE INSERT

OILER

4-STEP CONE PULLEY

are driven directly by motors that are mounted in the lower frame or base of the machine. The motors are 1 to 2 hp and turn at about 1200 rpm. The maximum thickness of stock the machine will cut ranges from 2 to 5 in. depending on the size, type, and manufacturer of the machine. The upper-blade straining spring is contained inside a tube with a plunger and the upper-chuck assembly.

Tables of the large jigsaws are made of smoothly machined cast iron. A tilting device is provided for making beveled cuts. The table also has a machined hole

Fig. 9–2. Making cutouts in large panels using an industrial jigsaw with an overhead blade straining device. Note the practically unlimited capacity of the machine and the casters on the worktable that facilitate movement of the work.

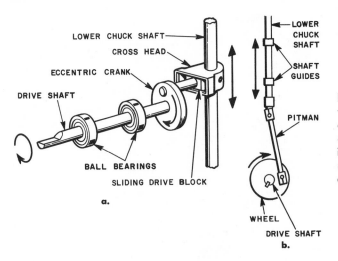

Fig. 9–3. Methods by which rotary motion is converted into reciprocating motion: (a) Eccentric drive system, typical of that used in bench model jigsaws with belted motors, (b) The wheel and pitman drive system.

Fig. 9–4. View of a saber saw blade with the upper and lower blade guides in position. When overarm is removed, the lower blade guide supports the blade.

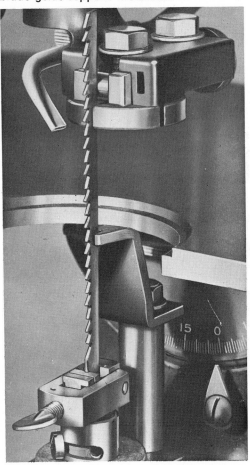

with a recessed edge in which an aluminum insert (throat plate) fits flush with the surface.

The *upper blade guide assembly* (Fig. 9–4) employs a roller and slotted disk to support the blade when the stock is fed into the saw. The guide is adjustable for blades of various widths and slotted for various thicknesses. The assembly is fastened to a vertically adjustable guide post. A spring *holddown* (Fig. 9–1) prevents the upward stroke of the blade from lifting the work off the table.

The *chucks* usually provide two positions for clamping the blade, either in line with the overarm or at right angles to it. Variously shaped files and sanding devices may also be held in the lower chuck.

Since the overarm limits the size of work that can be handled on the jigsaw, provision is made on some models to increase the capacity. This is done by removing the overarm, installing a lower-blade guide and a saber-saw blade as shown in Figure 9–4. This arrangement also facilitates making piercing cuts.

Gang reciprocating saws usually employ several saw blades held rigidly in a frame that moves up and down to make the cut. They are used to saw logs or cants into boards in saw mills.

Circular Saws

The production of a wooden product involves crosscutting and ripping lumber, plywood, and other materials to size. This is accomplished on a variety of machines using circular saw blades. The following pages will introduce you to them. You will learn of their important features and the range of sizes. You will also discover how they function and become acquainted with some of their applications in modern industry.

Table saws (Fig. 9–5) are among the most useful saws today. The basic characteristics of Samuel Miller's invention have persisted throughout the years. Sometimes table saws are referred to as *circular saw benches* or *circular saws*.

The table saw is one of the most popular and versatile of all sawing ma-

chines. It will perform a wide range of sawing operations such as: crosscutting, ripping, angle cutting, beveling, dadoing, and grooving. This hand-fed machine is often used to perform certain repetitive operations in small-scale production. It is used by skilled craftsmen in making patterns, models, and prototypes of work that will later be produced with production machinery. Often the table saw is used for sawing and joint-making work demanded by small orders. This saw is favored by many of the smaller plants and cabinet and custom shops, because it can quickly be changed from one class of work to another.

Table saws may be grouped into two classes: (1) *tilting-arbor* and (2) *tilting-table*. The tilting-arbor saw is the most popular type in use today. The saw arbor, motor, and blade are supported in a yoke which tilts for making bevel cuts. They are raised and lowered to adjust the depth of cut. The table remains station-

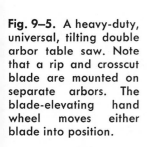

Fig. 9–5. A heavy-duty, universal, tilting double arbor table saw. Note that a rip and crosscut blade are mounted on separate arbors. The blade-elevating hand wheel moves either blade into position.

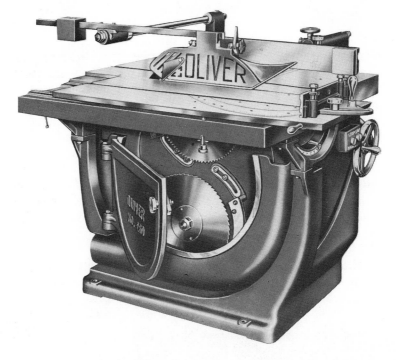

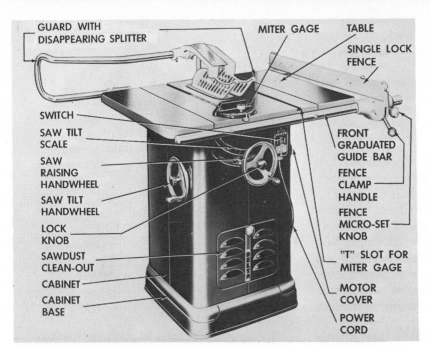

GUARD WITH DISAPPEARING SPLITTER — MITER GAGE — TABLE — SINGLE LOCK FENCE

SWITCH
SAW TILT SCALE
SAW RAISING HANDWHEEL
SAW TILT HANDWHEEL
LOCK KNOB
SAWDUST CLEAN-OUT
CABINET
CABINET BASE

FRONT GRADUATED GUIDE BAR
FENCE CLAMP HANDLE
FENCE MICRO-SET KNOB
"T" SLOT FOR MITER GAGE
MOTOR COVER
POWER CORD

Fig. 9–6. A medium duty 10" tilting-arbor table saw, typical of those used in industry and school shops.

ary at all times. Tilting-table saws are not too common today. The saw blade, motor, and arbor are mounted in a fixed position. The table is tilted from its horizontal position to make bevel cuts. The table is raised and lowered to adjust the depth of cut.

Table saws may have either one or two saw arbors. A table saw with one arbor is called a *variety table saw* (Fig. 9–6); a machine with two arbors is called a *universal table saw* (Fig. 9–5). The universal type is set up with a different blade on each arbor (usually a rip and a crosscut blade*). Each arbor has its own motor. Only the saw blade above the tables operates. This type of machine is well suited to cabinet shops and small industrial plants with insufficient space or production demands to justify individual rip and crosscut machines.

The *size* of a table saw is determined by the maximum diameter of blade which the machine is designed to carry. Light-

duty and home shop table saws range from 8 to 10 in. in size (Fig. 9–6) and are belt-driven with ½- to 1-hp motors. School and custom manufacturing shops generally use sizes ranging from 10 to 16 in. They employ 1- to 5-hp motors. Larger, industrial machines will carry blades from 12 to 20 in. in diameter with 3- to 5-hp direct-drive motors. Motor speeds are usually 3600 rpm. The basic parts of the table saw are illustrated in Figure 9–6.

The cabinet encloses the motor, blade-tilting and raising mechanism, and it also supports the heavy, cast-iron, machined table. The opening in the table, called the *throat,* allows the blade to project above the surface of the table.

The *arbor* is a threaded shaft on which the blade is mounted. The arbor and nut have a left-hand thread. This is a safety feature since a loose nut will tend to tighten when the saw arbor starts to turn. Tilting arbors are adjustable by means of a hand wheel from a 90-deg. vertical position to a 45-deg. angle with the table. Arbors are either belt-driven or

---

* For a discussion on circular-saw blades, turn to page 140.

they are extensions of the motor arbor (direct drive). Most medium-duty saws are belt-driven by two or more matched belts. The better direct-drive table saws feature an automatic safety brake that quickly stops the revolving blade when the power is shut off.

Most of these saws are equipped with a miter gauge for making angular cuts. The *miter gauge* fits into the slots in the table which are milled parallel to the blade. Better machines have inverted T-shaped slots. These hold the miter gauge in position even when the head is not resting on the table. The miter gauge is used to support and guide the work into the blade when crosscutting and cross-grain machining. It is adjustable for use in making miter cuts. Compound miter cuts are made by tilting the blade and setting the miter gauge to an angle.

The *rip fence* is used to guide the work while ripping. It is usually used on the right side of the saw but may be moved to the left side on some models. The fence is normally used in a position parallel with the blade. However, some authorities specify slightly more space ($\frac{1}{32}$ in.)

at the rear of the blade. It is claimed that this makes for less friction with the blade and minimizes splintering or feathering and the tendency to kick back.

Guards and safety devices (Fig. 9–7) are provided as standard equipment for the protection of the operator. Injuries may result from contact with the cutting blade or from *kickback*. Kickback refers to stock being thrown back by the saw blade. The *guard* is a device usually made of cast aluminum or transparent plastic which encloses the exposed portion of the saw blade. The *splitter* is located behind the blade and directly in line with it. It has the very important function of keeping the kerf open, thus preventing a board from pinching the back of the saw blade and kicking back. The splitter cannot be used on operations such as rabbeting, grooving, and dadoing because the blade or cutters do not cut through the full thickness of the stock. *Anti-kickback dogs* (or fingers) are a safety device provided to hold the stock against the table and prevent it from being thrown back toward the operator.

The general design of table saws varies

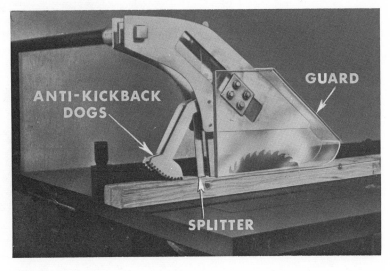

Fig. 9–7. The basic safety devices used on table saws.

Fig. 9–8. A heavy-duty table saw. Note the two miter gauges, left side sliding table and the table extension to the right. It also features an electro-hydraulic system to control saw tilting and elevating.

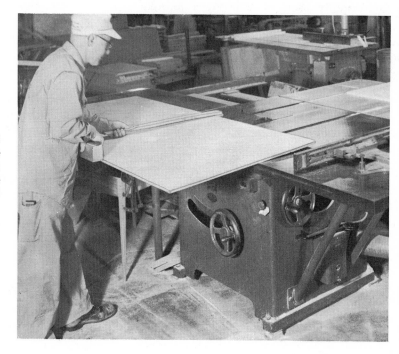

Fig. 9–9. A skilled craftsman uses a large capacity saw with an auxiliary sliding table to cut a plywood panel to size.

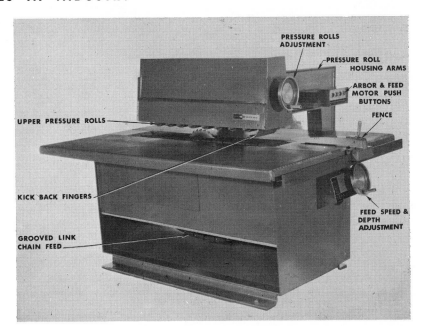

PRESSURE ROLLS ADJUSTMENT

PRESSURE ROLL HOUSING ARMS

ARBOR & FEED MOTOR PUSH BUTTONS

FENCE

UPPER PRESSURE ROLLS

KICK BACK FINGERS

FEED SPEED & DEPTH ADJUSTMENT

GROOVED LINK CHAIN FEED

Fig. 9–10. A modern straight-line rip saw with a chain feed.

from one manufacturer to another. The table saw (Fig. 9–8) shows some features found only on larger industrial saws. Some machines are provided with 2 miter gauges and an inverted U-shaped connecting yoke. This clears the saw blade and allows the two miter gauges to be operated in unison. Some saws have table extensions for the right, left, and rear. Extensions are also available for most smaller-size table saws. The sliding-table section at the left of the saw (Fig. 9–8) facilitates machining wide stock. The sliding table is provided with a locking device to hold it in place when the table is used as a solid unit. An extension sliding table is shown in use in Figure 9–9.

Straight-line rip saws (Fig. 9–10) have been developed to meet the need for continuous, heavy-duty rip sawing of wide stock into narrower widths. They have a chain feed mechanism that carries the stock into the revolving blade. The operator merely positions the stock in the feeding device.

Straight-line rip saws are classed as overcutting and undercutting types. The *overcutting type* has the saw arbor above the table surface. The *undercutting type* has the saw arbor located below the table. The saw blade projects through the table to cut the stock. The advantage claimed for the overcutting type is that thinner and smaller-diameter saw blades may be used. The thickness of the table requires a larger blade diameter on the undercutting type to cut the same thickness of stock. However, most machines in use today are of the undercutting type because the direction of blade rotation tends to hold the stock down on the table more effectively than does the direction of rotation of the overcutting types.

There are several variations of these machines. *Twin* or *gang rip saws* carry

Fig. 9–11. A close-up view of the straight-line rip saw chain feed. The photo insert illustrates the bottom of a link. The "V" grooves in the link match the grooves in the races.

two or more blades on one arbor. *Glue-joint rip saws* carry a special rip blade which produces an edge sawed so smooth that the stock may be glued immediately after coming off the saw.

The *chain-feed mechanism* (Fig. 9–11) feeds stock in a straight line regardless of irregularities in the board edge. It is composed of a series of metal links, grooved on the bottom to match V ways or *races* over which the chain passes. Most machines have two identical chains, one passing on each side of the saw blade. The chains are uniformly driven by a toothed sprocket. The links and races are automatically lubricated by an oil reservoir that leads to a felt pad over which the chains pass.

The machine shown in Figure 9–10 is equipped with push-button controls for starting and stopping the saw-arbor and feed-chain motors. The speed of the feed chain and the raising or lowering of the saw arbor is controlled by the handwheel below the table. The feed-chain speeds are changed by pulling out the handwheel and turning it; the arbor

adjustment is made by pushing the hand wheel in and turning it for the desired amount of blade projection. A soft-metal throat plate (insert) fits into the gaps between the blade and the chain on each side. This prevents slivers from jamming between the blade and the chain links.

A series of rollers in a vertically adjustable housing above the table holds the stock down on the moving feed chain. These are called *pressure rolls*. The first and last rollers are usually solid (one piece) and the center rolls are divided so the saw blade can pass between them. The ball bearing supported rollers are made of cast iron, machined for perfect balance, and spring-loaded so they may individually yield up to 1 in. for variations in stock thickness. The pressure rolls allow stock as short as 9 to 12 in. in length to pass through the saw safely. The pressure-roll housing is supported by two sturdy cast-iron arms attached to the base. These arms limit the width of stock that can be cut between the arm and the saw blade. Generally, this distance is about 24 to 25 in. Special *wide-arm rip saws* are made with a full 48-in. capacity for the accurate sizing of 4-in. wide panels.

Straight-line rip saws generally have variable feed rates up to 250 fpm (feet per minute). The feed chain is driven by a 2-hp motor. A 10, 15, or 20-hp motor is coupled directly to a 2-in. diameter saw arbor and rotates at 3450 rpm. Saw-blade diameters vary from 12 to 18 in. Saw blades usually require *stiffening collars* (large washers) for support. At least ½ in. of the blade extends above the work. The maximum thickness of stock the machine will handle is about 4 in. The large tables of these saws are about 80 in. in length and average about 5 ft. in width.

The short *fence* is also a width gauge. It is used to guide the stock into the chain drive. Some machines provide a foot switch for the operator to adjust the fence for different cuts.

An unusual device is used to determine the desired line of cut on a board before it is placed into the feed mechanism. A taut wire is mounted overhead and in line with the saw blade. A light is positioned above it in a reflector. The shadow of the wire cast on the board provides a guide line so that the operator may position the work for the best line of cut.

A variation of the straight-line rip saw is the *twin straight-line rip saw*. In this machine, two sets of saws and feed works are combined in one table. The sets operate in opposite directions. This saw is used to rip extra wide stock into several narrower pieces. The stock is passed through one saw and returned through the second saw. The machine requires two operators, but time and motion are saved by eliminating the usual merry-go-round handling of stock.

Gang rip saws (Fig. 9–12) are generally about the same size as straight-line rip saws, but they mount more than one saw on the arbor. They are often called *multi-rip saws*. Some machines of this

Fig. 9–12. A gang rip saw with power driven corrugated roller and spur type feed works.

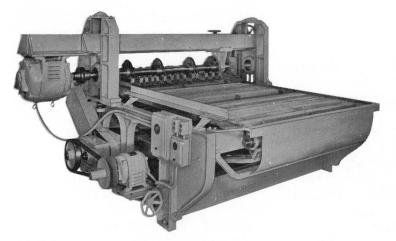

Fig. 9–13. A multiple rip and grooving machine with a slat bed feed assembly. Note the saws and groovers mounted on the collars of the long arbor. Separate motors drive the saw and feed systems.

type saw with precision glue-joint accuracy. The feed mechanism may be either the chain type used on the straight line rip saw or one composed of several overhead corrugated drive rollers with a lower, divided, adjustable spur roller positioned between the saw blades. The saw blades are held at the desired width of cut by combinations of *spacers*. The saw blades and spacers are mounted on a *quick change sleeve* so that they may easily be removed from the arbor for changes in set-up. Saw blades range from 12 to 24 in. in diameter. The sleeve hole is keyed to prevent the blade from slipping. The arbor is directly driven by a motor ranging up to 50 or 75 hp. The feed motor is generally 1½ or 2 hp, and the feed rate is variable from 50 to 300 fpm on heavy-duty machines.

Special-purpose sawing machinery is also used today. On some, a combination of operations is performed simultaneously as the work passes through the machine. An example of such a machine is the multiple-rip and grooving machine shown in Figure 9–13. This machine is widely used by furniture and cabinet manufacturers. The one shown in Figure 9–13 is set up with a gang of saw blades and grooving cutters for the machining

of drawer fronts. It rips the material to finished width and at the same time cuts the groove to receive the drawer bottom. Machines of this kind may have either a slat-bed or roller feed mechanism. Some are made to handle stock up to 24 ft. in width. These large machines are designed for the multiple sizing and machining of panels. The arbor drives and the feed mechanisms are usually powered separately by motors of various sizes. The arbor is adjustable vertically.

Radial saws (Figs. 9–14a, 9–14b, 9–15, and 9–16) are also versatile circular saws. They are widely used for custom building by carpenters and cabinetmakers and they have many important applications in mass production. In industrial plants, they are used primarily as cut-off saws. Sometimes they are equipped with a power feed attachment for ripping operations.

Several features distinguish the radial saw. (1) The saw blade is mounted over the work and is pulled across it to cut. (2) The saw may be swiveled 360 deg. and tilted through 105 deg. (3) The arm on which the saw travels may be pivoted through 90 deg. or more. (4) The blade rotates downward and away from the operator and tends to hold the work on

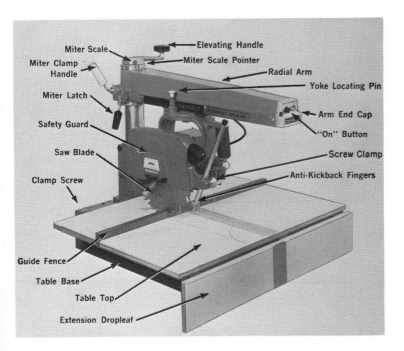

Miter Scale
Elevating Handle
Miter Scale Pointer
Miter Clamp Handle
Radial Arm
Yoke Locating Pin
Miter Latch
Arm End Cap
"On" Button
Safety Guard
Screw Clamp
Saw Blade
Anti-Kickback Fingers
Clamp Screw
Guide Fence
Table Base
Table Top
Extension Dropleaf

Fig. 9–14. Nomenclature of the single-arm type radial saw showing the controls: (a) on the left side, and (b) on the right side.

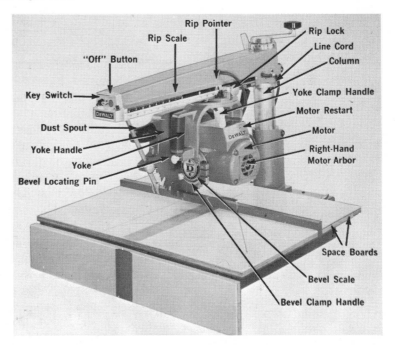

Rip Pointer
Rip Scale
Rip Lock
Line Cord
"Off" Button
Column
Key Switch
Yoke Clamp Handle
Motor Restart
Dust Spout
Motor
Yoke Handle
Right-Hand Motor Arbor
Yoke
Bevel Locating Pin
Space Boards
Bevel Scale
Bevel Clamp Handle

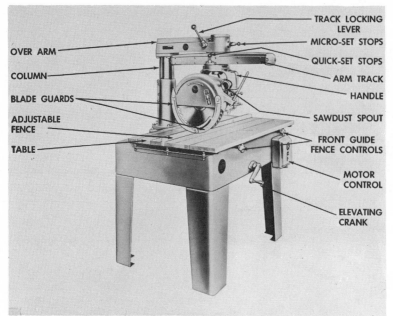

OVER ARM
COLUMN
BLADE GUARDS
ADJUSTABLE FENCE
TABLE

TRACK LOCKING LEVER
MICRO-SET STOPS
QUICK-SET STOPS
ARM TRACK
HANDLE
SAWDUST SPOUT
FRONT GUIDE FENCE CONTROLS
MOTOR CONTROL
ELEVATING CRANK

Fig. 9–15. The double arm type radial saw.

the table. This is in direct contrast to the table saw where the blade rotation tends to throw the work toward the operator.

Radial saws are designed to crosscut, rip, dado, groove, plough, miter, and compound-miter. Shaping, molding, and boring may also be performed with the appropriate tools installed.

Radial saws may be classed as follows:

1. The *single-arm* type (Figs. 9–14a and 9–14b). The motor is supported in a yoke which slides back and forth on rollers inside the horizontal arm. The major parts and controls typical of these machines are illustrated in Figure 9–14.

2. The *double-arm* type (Fig. 9–15). A short overarm supports the arm track which swivels 360 deg. The arm track guides the yoke and motor along its length.

3. The *sliding-arm* type (Fig. 9–16). The motor and elevating assembly are attached to the front end of a telescoping ram. The arm and column are a one-piece casting which swivels as a unit to make angle cuts. The saw always enters the work from the same point on the table. It is primarily used in industrial plants.

The *size* of a radial arm saw is determined by the blade diameter specified for the machine and the horsepower of the motor. Motors range from 1 hp on small machines to 10 hp on large industrial equipment used for cutting timbers. Saw blade diameters generally range from 10 to 16 in., but blades up to 36 in. are used on some special industrial machines. The saw blade is mounted directly on the motor arbor, which turns at a speed of approximately 3450 rpm. The maximum thickness of stock which can be cut in one pass ranges from 2 to 12 in. Generally, a machine which delivers 2 hp with a 10-in. blade will cut through stock 3 in. thick.

The *table* is usually made of stabilized

Fig. 9–16. A heavy duty industrial radial saw with a telescoping ram.

hardwood, or plywood. It is fastened to a metal base or stand. Jack screws permit adjusting the table height so that the saw cuts to the same depth at all points. Auxiliary tables are often used on the right and left of the saw table to facilitate handling long stock. They also have graduated bars with adjustable stops for cutting boards to predetermined lengths (Fig. 9–20). The *guide fence* is a strip of wood. It can be moved to different locations between the movable *space boards* so as to increase ripping capacity (Figs. 9–14a and 9–14b). An automatic or mechanical brake which stops the revolving blade in seconds after the power has been shut off is available for most models.

A *hood-type guard* is standard equipment on most machines; it encloses the upper half of the saw blade. Usually it is adjustable in that it may be rotated to a point just above the work. A *lower "free-floating guard"* (Fig. 9–15) is also available. This guard rises and falls, adjusting itself automatically to the thickness of stock being cut.

Radial arm saws may be equipped with a *positive saw-return device*. This is either a spring return device, or a line, weight, and pulley system which automatically returns the saw to the back of

Fig. 9–17. Air-operated pistons control these radial arm saws used in a plant manufacturing houses. These remotely controlled saws operate in unison to cut over 800 rafters per hour.

the table when it is released. Some saws also have a *cushioning device* and locking handle at the rear of the arm to prevent rebound when the yoke is returned.

Anti-kickback fingers (Figs. 9–14a and 9–14b) are provided on most machines for use when ripping. *Splitters* are also available for ripping operations. The best anti-kickback devise is a powered roll feed mechanism with sufficient power to prevent the stock from being thrown back. The *sawdust spout* is a safety device which is set to direct the sawdust away from the operator or into a dust collecting system if available. A *key switch lock* is a safety device especially

desirable where unauthorized people may have access to the machine.

Figure 9–17 shows three large pneumatically fed sawing heads being controlled by push buttons. They are cutting the bird mouths and lengths of common rafters for the manufacture of houses. Figure 9–18 shows two operators using radial arm saws to size and remove defects from stock which will be used to make large panels. The stock is conveyed from the saws into a high-speed wide belt sander.

Single cut-off saws (Figs. 9–19, 9–20, and 9–21) are used to cut lumber to length. They are of two general types:

Fig. 9–18. Two hand-fed radial arm saws used to remove defects from stock. The stock is moved to the saws on a conveyor cut-off, and then carried into a high-speed sander.

Fig. 9-19. A swing type cut-off saw.

Fig. 9-20. Suspended link cut-off saw which can also be used for angle cuts up to 45 degrees.

namely, the *swing* and the *ram*. Both types support the work on a table while the saw is moved into it to make the cut. The first type to be developed for this purpose was the swing saw. The earliest types were similar to the one of modern manufacture that is illustrated in Figure 9-19. Swing saws of this type are generally considered to be low-production machines.

The **swing saw** is suspended from either the ceiling, a wall, a column, or from a vertical support that is part of the machine itself as shown in Figure 9-19. The arbor is suspended in such a way that the saw swings in an arc as it is pulled across the work. A spring or counteracting mechanism automatically returns the saw to its original position at the rear of the table when it is released.

The **suspended link cut-off saw** is another kind of swing saw (Fig. 9-20). The saw moves in a straight line, parallel to the surface of the table. It gets its straight-line movement from the link mechanism which unfolds to bring the saw forward as the operator pulls on the feed handle. This saw may be equipped with an hydraulic feed mechanism. The

Fig. 9-21. Sliding ram cut-off saw.

length of stroke is adjustable and may be set to operate automatically by push button control. The model shown in Figure 9–20 may be swiveled to make angular cuts up to 45 deg.

The **ram cut-off saw** (Fig. 9–21) is a straight-line machine. It may be set to cycle automatically or it can be controlled by a foot switch or valve. Machines of this type are equipped with blades up to 20 in. in diameter mounted directly on the motor arbor. They rotate at 3450 to 3600 rpm. Motors are usually 7½ hp.

The saw carriage is moved forward hydraulically or pneumatically. The length of the stroke is adjustable up to about a 23-in. maximum. As the length of the stroke is shortened, the number of stokes possible per minute is increased. As many as 55 short strokes per minute are feasible on some machines. A limit switch at the end of the over-arm starts the automatic return of the saw. The head has a vertical adjustment of 3 in. The maximum thickness that may be cut is 5 in. In many industrial installations, the cut pieces of stock are placed on conveyors and passed through wide belt sanders, straight-line rip saws, surfaces, or jointing machines.

Double end cut-off saws (Fig. 9–22) have two circular saw blades that cut off the stock simultaneously at both ends. One end of the machine is adjustable for changing to work of different lengths. The one shown here is equipped with two 10-hp and two 7½-hp motors. It will carry saw blades up to 20 in. in diameter and various special purpose cutters. Stock 8 in. thick and up to 22 ft. in length may be handled. It has a maximum feed rate of 500 fpm. The work is carried into the saws by power-driven, rubber-padded, chain links and feed lugs.

The machine shown in the photo was designed for use in the manufacture of pre-fab and pre-cut home components. It makes the angular cuts at each end of a rafter and the bird's mouth notches. Various attachments permit it to perform dadoing, tenoning, panel sizing, and other operations simultaneously.

Panel saws (Figs. 9–23 and 9–24) were developed to meet the need for a fast, accurate, and easy method of cutting large panels. Panel saws are of two

Fig. 9–22. A double cut-off saw. This machine is similar in appearance to a double-end tenoner. It is set up to angle cut and notch rafters in the production of pre-cut house components.

basic types: *horizontal* (Fig. 9–23) and *vertical* (Fig. 9–24). Some are equipped with manually or electrically operated devices that feed the saw into the work.

The vertical type has several advantages. In addition to conserving floor space, less time and energy are required to maneuver the panels into position for cutting. The weight of the panel automatically positions it on the supporting base. Hand-fed versions of the vertical type are used in lumberyards to cut panels to customer specifications. These have an upright frame with a movable carriage to hold portable electric circular saws (Fig. 9–25).

Horizontal panel saws are essentially radial arm saws with sufficient capacity to permit handling sheet materials (Fig. 9–23).

Band Saws

There are a number of different kinds of band saws which are being applied to many different classes of sawing. At one time the band saw was used only to cut irregular shapes and curves in flat stock. In addition to this, industries today use power-fed band saws for straight sawing operations in full-scale production. There are various sizes and design modifications of each type of band saw, but they all may be grouped within four distinct classifications. They are: (1) the *band scroll saw* (Fig. 9–26); (2) *band resaws* (Fig. 33); (3) *band bevel saws* (Fig. 35); and (4) *band mill saws*.

Band scroll saws (Fig. 9–26) range from 14 in. to 42 in. in size. They are used in school shops and industrial plants where the majority of the work involves cutting irregular contours or curves in stock. They carry blades from ⅛ to 1¾ in. in width. Cutting operations involving straight ripping, beveling, and resawing

Fig. 9–23. Using an over-cutting type, horizontal panel saw to make a long miter cut on a laminated kitchen counter top. Note the chain feed drive.

Fig. 9–24. An undercutting, vertical panel saw. Push-button controls activate the saw travel.

Fig. 9–25. A hand-fed panel saw. The saw is moved vertically to crosscut a panel. The work is pushed into the saw to rip it.

may also be performed on the scroll band saw.

The *contour band saw* (Fig. 9–27) is designed for sawing and filing metals and other hard materials. Cutting speeds from 50 to 1700 fpm are available through a variable speed drive. It operates as a band scroll saw and has some important applications in woodworking plants. Figure 9–27 shows a production set-up with a fixture being used for accurate resawing of laminated plastic and wood core materials. With this set-up, the tip and tail core components used for the manufacture of skis are uniformly band-sawed to shape. This type of band saw is used for such work because the speed may be reduced to avoid burning the plastic. Furthermore, it produces smooth and accurately matched surfaces for the final fusing together of the laminations and sawed components.

Fig. 9–26. Nomenclature of a 14-inch band scroll saw.

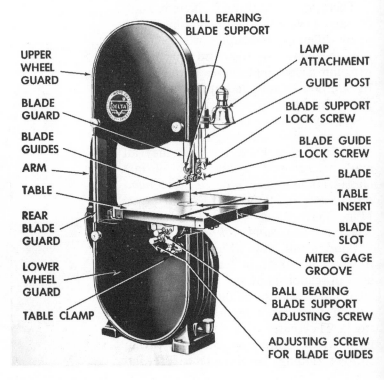

UPPER WHEEL GUARD

BLADE GUARD

BLADE GUIDES

ARM

TABLE

REAR BLADE GUARD

LOWER WHEEL GUARD

TABLE CLAMP

BALL BEARING BLADE SUPPORT

LAMP ATTACHMENT

GUIDE POST

BLADE SUPPORT LOCK SCREW

BLADE GUIDE LOCK SCREW

BLADE

TABLE INSERT

BLADE SLOT

MITER GAGE GROOVE

BALL BEARING BLADE SUPPORT ADJUSTING SCREW

ADJUSTING SCREW FOR BLADE GUIDES

Fig. 9–27. A variable speed contour band saw set-up for production cutting of tip and tail core components of skis.

Fig. 9–28. A band resaw is used here to resaw built-up stock into thinner thicknesses suitable for core materials.

Band resaws (Fig. 9–28) are used to saw stock to thickness. Saws of this type are similar to the band scroll saw except that the resaws are larger and heavier. They are available in various sizes. Band resaws are used in furniture plants and box factories and by laminated-truss manufacturers and sash and door fabricators for reducing stock in thickness. The resaw feed mechanism is power driven. Feed speeds may be set according to the size and sawing characteristics of the stock.

Fig. 9–29. A band bevel saw. The tilting blade facilitates handling large bevel sawing work often encountered in the ship building industries.

Automatic resaws (Fig. 9–30) saw successive straight slices of uniform thickness from a block of material clamped to the table. They can cut identical slats as thin as $3/32$ in. thick. The stock is carried back and forth past the saw blade without the attention of an operator. The saw

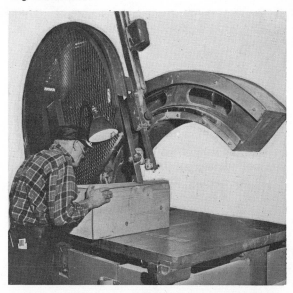

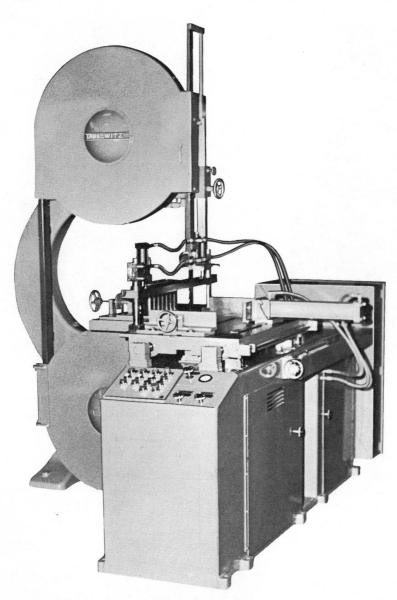

Fig. 9–30. This automatic band resaw will automatically take successive cuts from a block of wood without the attention of an operator.

stops in the event of blade breakage, wheel slippage, or loss of blade tension. The machine automatically stops the feed mechanism and releases the clamps at the completion of the last cut.

Generally, band resaws are used only for this one operation. However, machines of about the same size as the resaws are also used for ripping opera-

tions. In this case, they are referred to as *band rip saws*.

The **bevel band saw** (Fig. 9–29) has many applications in the ship and boat building industries. It is used to make curved and straight bevel cuts on heavy timbers and laminated frames used in the construction of large vessels. Most band saws have tilting tables, but this machine has a tilting blade. The horizontal table permits better control of large, heavy work.

The main frame is constructed in a "C" shape. The band wheels are mounted on another one-piece frame called the main *head rig*. This slides along the accurately milled "C" frame to provide the necessary angle of tilt up to 45 deg. right or left. Band saws of this type employ a 1-hp motor and a variable-speed drive to tilt the head rig. This permits the head rig to be slowly tilted so that the bevel angle may be changed during the course of a cut. A scale and pointer indicate the rate of angling. A friction clutch slips in case of an overload or if the blade binds. Some machines also have power-driven feed rollers in the table to move the work into the saw. These rolls are fluted, or corrugated, to give traction. The feed mechanism is also powered by a 1-hp motor with a variable speed drive.

Other machines of this type may have only manual tilting and feed controls. Bevel band saws generally have 38- or 40-in. wheel diameters and carry blades 1½ to 3 in. in width. Usually they have one speed, direct-drive motors mounted to the lower band wheel. Blade speeds of 5000 to 7000 fpm are common.

Band mill saws are becoming widely used to convert logs into lumber. They have wheels 6 to 10 ft. in diameter and blades 7 in. or more in width. These large band saws have replaced circular saws in lumber mills because the thinner blades produce less sawdust waste. These huge band saws are installed in the mill with the lower wheel (drive) below the floor level. They are equipped with a carriage for moving the log into the blade. The carriage track rests on the floor. The carriage movement and mechanisms are operated by the head sawyer from a remote control booth.

The horsepower requirements for band mill saws range from 50 to 150. The speed of the motor is adjustable so that the blade travels at a speed of about 10,000 fpm. Some blades have teeth on both edges of the blade so they may cut on both the forward and backward movement of the log carriage. This is not common, however.

The *size* of a band saw is determined by the diameter of the wheels. The *cutting capacity* is determined by the maximum stock thickness that may be cut and the throat clearance. The *throat clearance* (also called throat capacity) is the distance between the blade and the column or arm. On most industrial plant saws, this distance is about ½ in. less than the diameter of the wheels. This is due to the fact that ½ in. is taken up

Fig. 9–31. View of band wheels. Note the upper guide assembly with roller guide wheels.

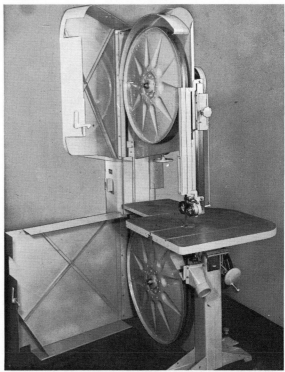

by a guard over the blade on the column side of the machine. The stock *thickness capacity* is the maximum distance between the table and the upper guide. The 14-in. band saw generally has about a 6-in. thickness capacity as compared to a 20 to 24-in. thickness capacity of a 36-in. band saw.

The *frame* on which the wheels are mounted either is a hollow, one-piece casting or is made of formed and welded steel plates. The wheels (Fig. 9–31) are constructed of cast iron, aluminum, or electrically welded, reinforced steel disks. Wheels are always carefully balanced. They are equipped with rubber tires, cemented in place, or with demountable steel rims with a reinforced rubber face. The tires are also balanced. The rubber tires cushion the blade, provide traction, and protect the set of the teeth on the side of the blade which is in contact with the wheels.

The *lower wheel* drives the band saw blade. The power is applied to the lower wheel by one of these three methods:

1. *Direct Drive* — the lower wheel is mounted directly to the motor shaft which produces a single speed.
2. *Single* (or step cone) *standard pulley* and belted drive system with 1 to 5 speeds.
3. *Variable speed drive* — by means of a split pulley or a 3-speed transmission drive system. These provide a wide range of speeds from very slow to very fast.

The motor horsepower ranges from ⅓ to 1 hp on the light-duty machines up to 5 and 10 hp on the larger machines. Motor rpm's vary from 600 to 1725. The *rim speed,* which is also the *blade speed,* is indicated in fpm. This speed ranges from 50 to 15,000 fpm. The wheels rotate on tapered roller bearings or ball bearings.

The *upper wheel* has a vertical adjustment which raises or lowers the wheel to strain the blade. The correct tension is indicated by a scale or pointer which is calibrated for the various blade widths the machine will accommodate. The upper wheel also has a device which *tilts* the wheel in or out to keep the blade tracking on the center of the wheel rims. Both wheels are enclosed in *guards* which have either completely removable panels (Fig. 9–26) or hinged doors (Fig. 9–31). Many machines are equipped with foot-operated mechanical brakes. Some have automatic hydraulic brakes. The latter operate when the motor is switched off. They also automatically stop both wheels in case of blade breakage.

The blade travels through an *upper* and *lower guide assembly* (Figs. 9–32 and 9–33). The upper guide assembly is adjustable vertically. Each guide is made

Fig. 9–32. Upper guide assembly is composed of a back blade support wheel and guide blocks.

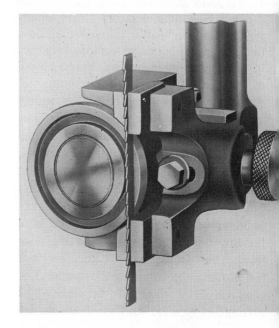

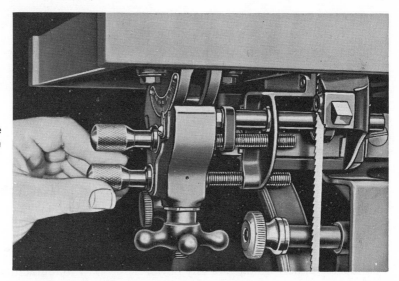

Fig. 9–33. Lower guide assembly of a 14-inch band saw.

up of two adjustable *guide blocks* (or ball bearing roller wheels) located on each side of the blade to keep it from twisting and vibrating. Adjustable ball-bearing wheels, called *back blade supports* (Fig. 9–32), are located behind the blade in both the upper and lower guide assembly. Their primary function is to keep the blade from being forced off the wheels when the work is fed into it.

The *table* is usually made of cast iron with reinforcing ribs on the underside. A slot for a miter gauge is provided on some models. The table usually tilts 45 deg. to the right and 5 deg. to the left. Some band saws are also equipped with a rip fence.

Chapter 10 Saw Blades

The successful performance of any power-sawing operation is dependent upon selecting the correct blade for the intended use. Furthermore, the blade must be well sharpened and cared for so that it will cut effectively.

Saw manufacturers supply specially designed blades that feature hard teeth for longer life, thin gauges (thicknesses) for reducing kerf waste, and special tooth designs to cut the newer construction materials efficiently.

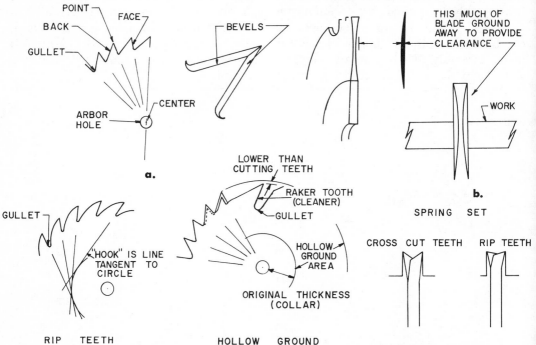

Fig. 10–1. (a) Nomenclature of circular saw blades: at top is the crosscut, at the lower left is the rip, and at the right is the combination; (b) a comparison of the blade clearance resulting from hollow-ground blades and flat-ground blades with set.

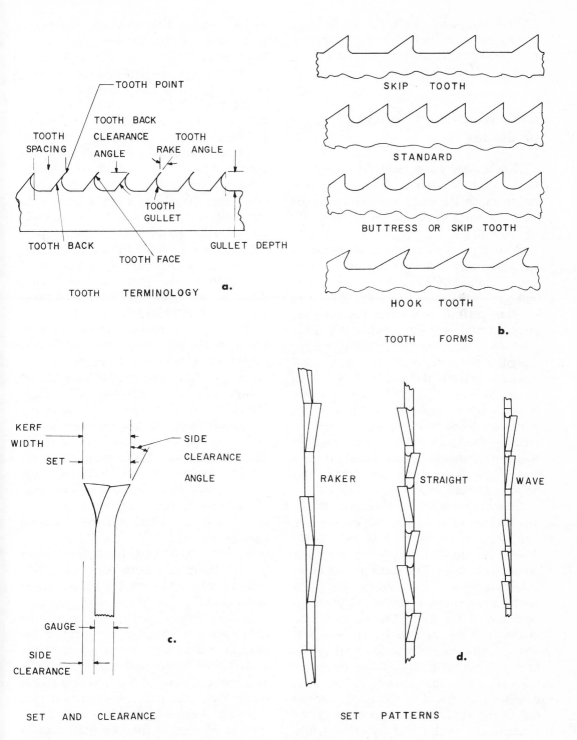

Fig. 10–2. Basic features of reciprocating and band saw blades.

This unit deals with the basic characteristics of blades and the factors to be considered for selecting reciprocating, band, and circular blades.

General Characteristics of Blades

How a saw tooth cuts. The teeth of blades that are used in sawing machines cut in much the same manner as do the teeth on hand saws. (Refer to page 95, Chapter 8.)

Basically, saw teeth are designed to cut either *across the grain* (crosscut) or *with the grain* (rip). Either tooth design will cut both across or with the grain, but they perform best when used for their intended purpose. To provide a general purpose blade, saw manufacturers have designed a tooth form that is a compromise between the two and is known as a "W" or "V" combination tooth. Figures 10–1a and 10–2a identify the parts of a tooth and illustrate certain details of the various blades discussed in this unit. It should be noted that all teeth have these four parts: (1) face, (2) point, (3) back, and (4) gullet.

Crosscut teeth (Fig. 10–1a and 10–1b) are filed with two bevels, one on the face and the other on the back of each tooth. The bevels are filed in opposite directions on adjacent teeth. The teeth are set alternately right and left. When the point contacts the wood, it severs the fibers on one side of the kerf. The beveled face of the tooth acts as a wedge (chisel) that lifts the chip away from the wall of the kerf and pushes it toward the center of the cut. The chips (sawdust) are then caught in the gullet of the tooth, carried out of the kerf, and thrown clear of the blade. If the work is fed very slowly into the saw blade, only the point is involved

in the cutting. The optimum feed rate is that which involves the point and most of the face in the cut. The benefits are more rapid cutting, longer periods between sharpenings, and less point burning.

Rip teeth (Figs. 10–1a and 10–1b) are designed to cut with the grain. They do not have face and back bevels. The points are filed square and shaped similar to the cutting edge of a wood chisel. (NOTE: some users file the back of the chisel edge [Fig. 10–1a] to a slight bevel.) As the tooth contacts the wood, it makes a cut as wide as the cutting edge of the point. When the tooth moves farther into the wood, the chip curls along the face of the tooth to the gullet and is thrown clear of the blade as the tooth clears the work. See Figure 10–7.

Both rip and crosscut teeth are combined on the type "U," "S," and planer *combination* blades. Clearance is provided by either setting the teeth or by hollow grinding the blade. (See Figs. 10–1a and 10–b.)

"Tooth form" is a term used to describe the shape or profile of a tooth. Most circular saw blades have either rip or crosscut formed teeth similar to those on handsaws. However, several variations of these tooth forms are found on circular saw blades. These will be discussed later in this unit.

Reciprocating and band-saw blades have a basic rip tooth form. The two most popular styles are the *standard* and *buttress* (Fig. 10–2b). The standard style has deeper gullets for maximum chip removal. Usually, the greatest variety of widths and points per inch are available on blades with this tooth form. The buttress form (also called skip-tooth) has a shallower gullet. This means that more metal exists in the blade and, therefore, more tension may be placed upon it. This blade makes relatively smooth cuts and is recommended for cutting thick wood and plastics. The hook tooth provides even faster cutting. The teeth literally pull themselves into the work and thus require minimum feed pressure.

The **spacing of teeth** is sometimes referred to as the *pitch*. On reciprocating and band-saw blades, the pitch is indicated as the number of *teeth per inch* or the number of *points per inch*. (There is always one more point per inch than teeth per inch.) On circular saw blades the tooth spacing is specified as the total number of teeth around a blade of a given diameter.

Generally, for thicker work, a coarser pitch blade is used for a faster cutting action. When sawing very thin materials with reciprocating saws or band saws, a blade with finer pitch (more teeth) should be used. The actual pitch required is determined by the thickness of the material to be cut. As a general rule, reciprocating and band-saw blades should have at least two teeth engaged in the work at all times (Fig. 10–3a). If a coarse pitched blade (Fig. 10–3b) is used to cut thin materials, it is likely to make rough cuts or strip the teeth from the blade.

The sizes of blades. Reciprocating blades are sized by thickness (gauge), width, length, the number of teeth (or points) per inch, and the tooth form. Band-saw blades are similarly sized except that the length refers to the circumference of the blade.

The sizes of circular saw blades are indicated by the diameter in inches, thickness (gauge), tooth form, and arbor hole diameter. The *gauge* refers to the body thickness of the saw blade. The gauge numbers may be interpreted in thousandths of an inch — the larger the gauge number, the thinner the blade. For example, most band-saw blades generally

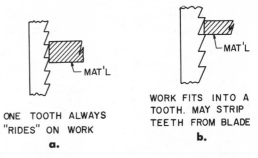

ONE TOOTH ALWAYS "RIDES" ON WORK

a.

WORK FITS INTO A TOOTH. MAY STRIP TEETH FROM BLADE

b.

Fig. 10–3. For some types of work, the number of teeth contacting the material is important. (a) Two or more teeth engaged in the work; (b) when only one tooth is engaged in the work broken blades or bucking may result.

range from 25 gauge (.020 in.) to 20 gauge (.035 in.). Circular saw blades generally range from 18 to 8 gauge (.049 to .165 in.) in thickness. In general, large diameter blades are made in the heavier gauges. To saw large, thick material, a heavier gauge blade will do the job better because it is stiffer.

The width of a reciprocating or band-saw blade is usually specified in inches or fractions of an inch. However, the width and thickness of very narrow reciprocating blades are usually indicated in thousandths of an inch. The width of both reciprocating and band-saw blades determines their ability to make circular cuts. The narrower the blade, the smaller the radii that can be cut. See Figure 12–9 in Chapter 12.

Beam strength is a term that describes the ability of reciprocating and band-saw blades to remain straight or to resist bending under the force caused by feeding the work against the blade (Fig. 10–4). This quality is determined by the combination of the blade width and thickness, and the amount of tension applied

NARROW   WIDE
BLADE   BLADE

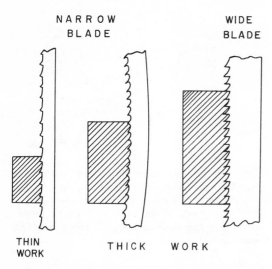

THIN   THICK   WORK
WORK

Fig. 10–4. If the beam strength of a blade is insufficient it will bend under the pressure of the cut.

to the blade. Sufficient beam strength in a blade is necessary in order to cut at a maximum feed rate with a minimum of breakage and inaccuracy.

Blade clearance (or side clearance) is the distance between the side of the blade and the wall of the kerf. See Figures 10–1b and 10–2c. All saw blades cut a kerf that is wider than the thickness of the blade. This clearance is provided so that the body of the blade will not rub against the sides of the cut. Rubbing would cause the blade to burn the stock, pinch, overheat, warp, and lose its temper and cutting edge.

Three different methods used for obtaining clearance on saw blades are:

1. *Swaging.* The tooth is flattened by up-setting or spreading the point to make it wider than the rest of the blade (Fig. 10–5). This is often done on rip teeth of larger circular saws, the inside cutters of dado heads (Fig. 16–26), and on very

wide band-saw blades. As a rule, reciprocating blades do not have swaged teeth.

2. *Setting.* The teeth are alternately bent right and left. See Figures 10–1b, 10–2c, and 10–2d. The actual amount of set on different kinds and sizes of blades varies. As a general rule, the amount of set on a circular blade is about 2 or 2½ gauges on each side of the blade, depending upon the moisture content of the wood to be cut. Wet wood requires more set than dry wood; soft wood more than hardwood. Blades used in portable circular saws should have 2½ gauges set on each side of the saw because they are generally used for rough work. For example, a 16-gauge circular saw (.065 in.) with 2 gauges set on each side would make a saw kerf of 12 gauge or .109 inch in dry softwood.

There are no definite rules for the amount of set on reciprocating or band-saw blades. Generally, they are

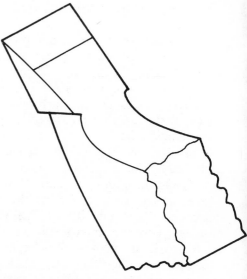

Fig. 10–5. A swaged rip tooth.

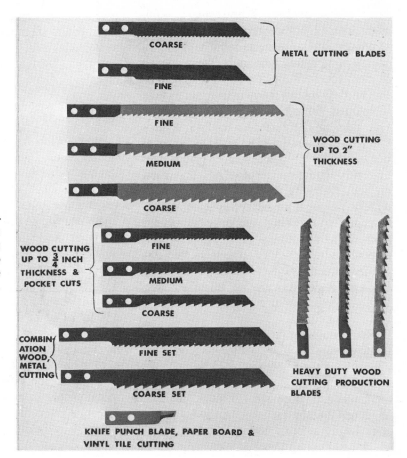

Fig. 10–6. An assortment of blades used in portable reciprocating saws. Blades must also be chosen to fit the chuck of the saw in use.

COARSE

FINE

} METAL CUTTING BLADES

FINE

MEDIUM

COARSE

} WOOD CUTTING UP TO 2" THICKNESS

WOOD CUTTING UP TO 3/4 INCH THICKNESS & POCKET CUTS {

FINE

MEDIUM

COARSE

COMBINATION WOOD, METAL CUTTING {

FINE SET

COARSE SET

HEAVY DUTY WOOD CUTTING PRODUCTION BLADES

KNIFE PUNCH BLADE, PAPER BOARD & VINYL TILE CUTTING

set according to the job at hand. A small amount of set cuts slower and smoother than the same blade with more set. However, with more set, the blade will cut shorter radii. A uniform amount of set is essential for smooth and easy cutting with all saw blades. If one tooth is set too far out, it will produce a rough, ragged sawed surface.

There are different patterns of set that are common to both reciprocating and band-saw blades (Fig. 10–2d). They are: the *raker-set pattern* (used on some band-saw blades), the *straight-set pattern,* and the *wave-set pattern.* The latter is used primarily on metal-cutting blades, but it has applications in cutting hard non-metallic materials such as plastic laminates and hardboards.

3. *Hollow-grinding.* The body of the blade is ground away on both sides. This method of obtaining blade clearance is primarily used on circular saw blades (Fig. 10–1b), but some portable reciprocating saw blades are also hollow-ground. Conventional blades are referred to as *flat-ground blades.*

The **metals** used in the manufacture of

saw blades include carbon steels, alloy steels, and high-speed steels. Circular and band-saw blades are available with small pieces of tungsten carbide silver-soldered to each tooth. Tungsten carbide is one of the hardest metals known to man. It was developed during World War I by the Germans in their search to find a substitute for industrial diamonds. Industrial diamonds most successfuly grind this material. Tungsten carbide was first used on metalworking cutters, but now it is widely acepted for all phases of woodworking, outwearing carbon-steel blades from 20 to 100 times. Although carbide-tipped blades are more expensive, the initial investment is offset through smoother, cleaner, easier sawing of all materials, and with less cost in general maintenance and sharpening.

Reciprocating and band-saw blades made of carbon, alloy, or high-speed steel are the most practical for home and school-shop use. Recent improvements in the standard alloy-steel blades include hardened teeth and a spring-tempered back. This permits them to be strained more. They may not be resharpened. High-speed steel reciprocating and band-saw blades are tougher and are used for cutting a variety of materials including metals.

Reciprocating Saw Blades

In addition to the general characteristics of blades already described, the following paragraphs detail more specifically the blade types that are used in various machines.

Blades for portable saber saws are basically of the same design except for their length. Saber saw blades (Fig. 10–6) generally range from 3 to approximately 4½ in. in length. Blades for the larger all-purpose reciprocating saws range from 3½ to 12 or 18 in. in length. The recommended blades for various jobs are given in Table 10–1. Most manufacturers of blades now have their blades color coded for easier identification. For example, metal-cutting blades may be marked red, fine wood-cutting blades yellow, and coarse wood-cutting blades black. Since

TABLE 10–1   PORTABLE SABER SAW BLADES

Cutting Job	Blade Material		Clearance			Teeth Per Inch	Length in Inches
	H. S. Steel	High Carbon Steel	Set	Wave	H. Ground		
General Cutting		x	x			6 or 10	3–4
Fast or Thick Wood Cutting		x	x		x	6, 7 or 10	3–4
Nail Embedded Wood	x		x	x		14	2⅞
Fine Wood Cutting		x	x		x	6–10	3–4
Fast Scroll Cutting	x				x	6, 7, 8, 10	3–4
Veneer, Fiberglass	x			x		6, 10	3–4
Pocket		x	x			7, 8, 10	3
Ferrous metals, less that ⅛" thick	x			x		14 or 32	2⅞

TABLE 10-2
JIG SAW BLADES
All 5″ long. Either blank or pin ends.

Material Cut	Width In.	Teeth Per Inch	Blade Full Size
Steel • Iron Lead • Copper Aluminum	.070	32	
Pewter Asbestos Paper • Felt	.070	20	
Steel • Iron Lead • Copper Brass	.070	15	
Aluminum	.085	15	
Pewter Asbestos Wood	.110	20	
Abestos • Brake Lining • Mica Steel • Iron Lead • Copper Brass Aluminum Pewter	.250	20	
Wood Panels and Veneers	.048	18	
Plastics Celluloid	.070	14	
Hard Rubber	.055	16	
Bakelite Ivory • Wood	.045	18	
Wood Veneer Plus Plastics Celluloid Hard Rubber Bakelite Ivory Extremely Thin Materials	.035	20	
Plastics Celluloid	.050	15	
Hard Rubber	.055	12	
Bakelite	.070	7	
Ivory • Wood	.110	7	
Wall Board Pressed Wood Wood • Lead Bone • Felt Paper • Copper Ivory Aluminum	.110	15	
Hard and Soft Wood	.110	10	
	.187	10	
	.250	7	
Pearl • Pewter Mica	.054	30	
Pressed Wood	.054	20	
Sea Shells Jewelry	.070	15	
Metals Hard Leather	.085	12	

JIG SAW SABER BLADES
(Blank Ends)

Common Cutting Jobs:	Thick	Wide	Long	Teeth Per Inch
General cutting inside and outside curves	.028	.250 .110 .250	4½–5	7 16 20
Non-ferrous metals	.028	.110 .110	6– 4½–5	16 20

chuck designs vary from manufacturer to manufacturer, it is necessary to purchase blades to fit the particular model of saw being used.

Blades for scroll and jigsaws are made in 3 basic types: (1) the *pin type,* which has pins in each end for use in portable scroll saws; (2) the *plain or blank end* which fits most jigsaws with flat chucks, and (3) *saber-saw blades* which have either plain or notched ends and are wider and stiffer than other types.

Very narrow blades, called *jeweler's blades,* are used for very fine work. These have 20 to 30 teeth per inch, are .054 to .022 in. in width, range from .016 to .010 in. in thickness and are 6 in. long. Saber-saw blades range from ⅛ to ¼ inch in width and are generally about .035 to .025 in. in thickness and 4 to 5 in. in length. The recommended blades for the most common cutting jobs are given in the Table 10–2. Some shops use broken band-saw blades, cut to suitable lengths, for the jigsaw.

Wirelike blades with helical teeth (sometimes called drill saws) are also available. They cut in any direction, facilitating cutting very intricate patterns. The small diameter of the wire and the shallow teeth limit the usefulness of these blades on thick materials.

Band-Saw Blades

The gullets of band-saw blades are rounded to provide for greater strength and to allow for adequate chip removal during the cut (Fig. 10–7).

Band-saw blades may be classified into two groups: *wide bands* and *narrow bands*.

Wide bands range from 2 to 12 in. in width and from 14 to 19 gauge. They are used in large band resaws and band mill saws. They are available with swaged teeth and with any desired tooth shape, set, or spacing of teeth. They are generally coarse-cutting blades with teeth spaced from 1 to 2¾ in. apart.

Narrow band-saw blades are used in band scroll saws, small band resaws, and bevel-cutting band saws. The most com-

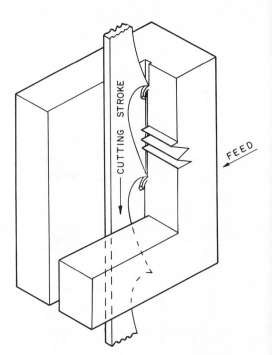

Fig. 10–7.   Band saw cutting action.

TABLE 10–3

Width	Gauge	Teeth	Width	Gauge	Teeth	Width	Gauge	Teeth
⅛″	21	6			5		20	2
	25	6		22	4			3
³⁄₁₆″	21	2			5		21	2
		3		25	4			3
		4			5			4
	22	4			6			5
		5	½″	19	2		22	3
		6			3			4
	25	5		20	2		25	4
		6			3			5
¼″	20	2		21	2	1″	19	2
	21	2			3		20	2
		3			4			3
		4			5			4
		5		22	3		21	2
	22	4			4			3
		5			5		22	4
		6		25	5			4
	25	5			6	1¼″	20	2
		6	⅝″	20	2			3
⁵⁄₁₆″	21	2		21	2	1½″	20	1
		3			3			2
⅜″	20	2			4			3
	21	2		22	4	1¾″	20	1
		3		25	5			2
		4	¾″	19	2		21	1

mon sizes available for wood cutting are given in Table 10–3. Blades for cutting wood, metal, and plastics are available with 10 to 24 teeth per inch. The heavier gauge blades are intended for use on machines with larger wheel sizes because these blades are not as flexible as those of lighter gauges. Blades may be purchased in endless, welded lengths to fit any machine. They may also be purchased in coils of 100 to 250 ft., to be cut to length and welded in the shop. (Some machines have built-in butt-welders and grinders.) The teeth are generally ground to a rake angle of 8 to 15 deg. (See Fig. 10–2a.) The points are filed perpendicular to the blade after setting.

Band-saw blades are usually folded

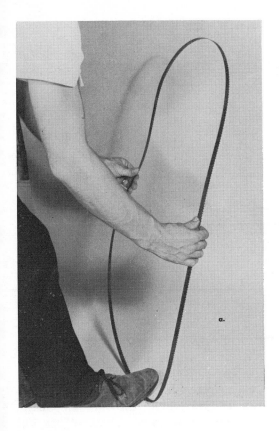

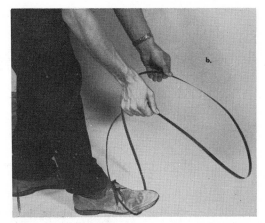

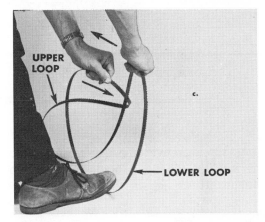

UPPER LOOP

LOWER LOOP

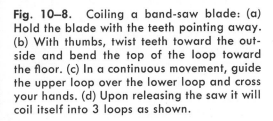

Fig. 10–8. Coiling a band-saw blade: (a) Hold the blade with the teeth pointing away. (b) With thumbs, twist teeth toward the outside and bend the top of the loop toward the floor. (c) In a continuous movement, guide the upper loop over the lower loop and cross your hands. (d) Upon releasing the saw it will coil itself into 3 loops as shown.

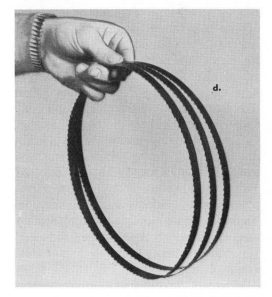

TABLE 10–4
RIP SAWS

Diam. In.	Gauge	No. Teeth	Diam. In.	Gauge	No. Teeth
6	18	36			
8	16	36			
8	17	36			
9	16	36	18	13	36
10	16	36	20	13	36
12	14	36	22	12	36
14	14	36	24	11	36
16	14	36	30	10	36

CROSSCUT (CUT-OFF) SAWS

Diam. In.	Gauge	No. Teeth	Diam. In.	Gauge	No. Teeth
6	17	100			
8	17	100	20	13	80
9	16	100			
10	16	100	22	12	70
12	14	100	24	11	70
14	14	100	26	10	70
18	14	100	28	10	70
16	13	100	30	10	70

into three or five coils for storing. One method of folding a blade is shown in Figure 10–8.

Circular Saw Blades

The selection of a circular blade, at one time, was simply a matter of choosing between a rip, cut-off, or a combination blade. These three blades generally handled all sawing requirements before the many new construction materials came into existence.

Circular-saw blades are made in many diameters and gauges, of various steels, and with various tooth forms for effective cutting of almost any type of material.

All tooth forms are basically the conventional rip or crosscut tooth, the variations being mainly in the size of the teeth. The tooth forms of the various blades available are shown in Figure 10–9.

Most circular-saw blades are purchased

flat-ground with the teeth set (Fig. 10–10). Hollow-ground circular-saw blades are also called *planer* blades. They cut so smoothly that the stock seldom requires planing before joining. In use, hollow-ground blades should project above the work an inch or more to prevent overheating, warping, and the tendency to crack or kick back. The projection for blades with set teeth is about ⅛ to ¾ in. Generally, ⅛ in. is preferred for safety reasons.

The **cut-off blade*** (Figs. 10–9, 10–10b, and 10–11b) has crosscut teeth that cut in the manner of those in the conventional hand crosscut saw. The teeth are beveled to sever (cut) the wood fibers. A cut-off blade produces finer sawdust than the same diameter rip blade because of its smaller teeth. The cut-off blade should be used only for crossgrain

* The most widely used sizes of cut-off and rip blades are given in Table 10–4.

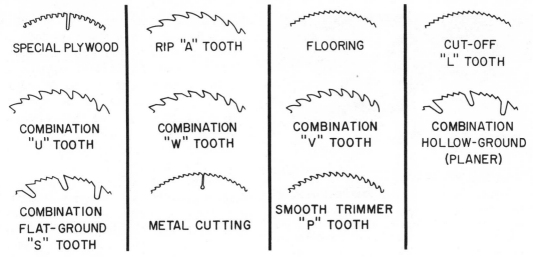

SPECIAL PLYWOOD   RIP "A" TOOTH   FLOORING   CUT-OFF "L" TOOTH

COMBINATION "U" TOOTH   COMBINATION "W" TOOTH   COMBINATION "V" TOOTH   COMBINATION HOLLOW-GROUND (PLANER)

COMBINATION FLAT-GROUND "S" TOOTH   METAL CUTTING   SMOOTH TRIMMER "P" TOOTH

Fig. 10–9. Circular saw blades.

cutting. Another type of crosscut or cut-off blade is the *smooth trimmer saw* (Fig. 10–8). It is primarily designed for cutting softwoods across the grain. It leaves a very smooth surface. The teeth generally have 45-deg. bevels that act like small knives which actually plane the end of the board while trimming it to length.

The **rip blade*** (Figs. 10–8 and 10–10a) has a larger gullet design, which allows for fast removal of the sawdust from the kerf. A rip blade is designed to cut wood efficiently in a direction parallel with the grain. Its square, chisel-like teeth are not designed to sever fibers, but to clean its own path with successive chipping (chisel-like) cuts. A special rip blade that is used on straight-line rip saws produces a finished cut so smooth that the stock may be glued without the usual jointing operation. Blades of this type are called *glue-joint rip saws*. The glue-joint rip saw is generally thinner and requires special collars to stiffen the blade and make it run true.

Combination blades are of several different tooth forms as shown in Figure

* See p. 140 *n.*

10–14a and 10–14b. They incorporate the cutting action of both the rip and the crosscut tooth.

Although combination blades are designed for general cutting, they do not rip or cut off as well as blades designed for this purpose. However, a carbide tipped, combination blade such as that shown in Figure 10–11a is a good all-purpose blade for school shop and home sawing operations.

Controlled cut blades (Fig. 10–11c) are sometimes called easy or safe feed blades. They employ a different cutting principle than the other types of blades. The back of the tooth acts as a stop which controls the depth of cut, prevents

Fig. 10–10. (a) Left, flat-ground rip blade, (b) right, a flat-ground crosscut blade.

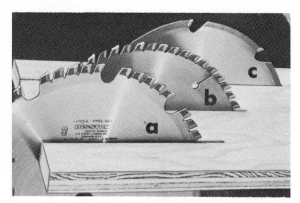

Fig. 10–11. Blades with carbide-tipped teeth. The carbide tips cut a kerf wider than the body of the blade. (a) Combination planer blade with 50 teeth, (b) a crosscut blade with 60 teeth, (c) a controlled cut (safe-feed) blade with 8 teeth.

overfeeding, and reduces the tendency for the stock to kick back. These blades have swaged teeth and are useful for general rough cutting. The advantages of a controlled cut blade are quiet operation, low cost, and easy maintenance. It is well suited for use with a portable electric circular saw. It is a relatively safe blade for use in hand-fed table and radial-arm saws.

Special plywood blades (Fig. 10–12) are designed for use in panel saws, table,

Fig. 10–12. This special plywood cutting blade is hollow-ground.

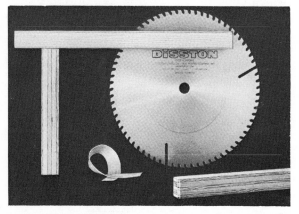

and radial-arm machines. They are usually hollow ground. They produce a smooth cut without splintering or feathering. The resulting cut is usually so smooth cut without splintering or feath-machining or processing of the plywood edge is not required. The teeth of these blades are specially hardened to resist the dulling caused by the abrasive action of the glue in plywood.

Thin-rim blades (Fig. 10–13) were designed especially for kerf-saving, free cutting of thin materials such as laminates, hardboard, thermosetting and thermoplastics, and other tough composition materials. The best blades of this type are carbide tipped. They have alternately beveled and square teeth. This blade is

Fig. 10–13. Thin rim blade with carbide tipped teeth is used to cut laminates, hardboard, and similar hard materials.

widely used by furniture manufacturers for production sawing of parts with surface laminates.

Metal-cutting blades are made of special high-speed steel alloys and are used for production cutting of materials such as aluminum, plastics, laminates, and fiber glass. Metal-cutting blades are used in the wood industries that fabricate parts which have these harder materials overlaid or laminated to wood cores.

Cut-in-half blades (Fig. 10–14) permit easy changing in gang saws, edge-trimmer saws, multiple rip saws, and other production machines with long arbors. Collars, fastened to the arbor, receive the two halves and hold them securely in place.

Concave saw blades (Fig. 10–15) are used in cooperage plants for cutting round barrel heads and in plywood plants for cutting out defects. They range from 6 to 20 in. in diameter, are generally

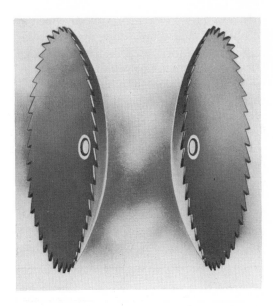

Fig. 10–15. Concave blades are used for cutting round barrel heads.

made with 44 teeth. The concave shape permits cutting almost any size circle.

The **selection of a circular-saw blade** is primarily determined by the specific machining characteristics of the material to be cut. The kinds of blades most widely used to cut most types of construction materials (under normal conditions) are summarized in Table 10–5.

Care and upkeep of circular-saw blades. Blades will accumulate deposits of pitch or gum through use. Remove the blade from the machine and clean off these deposits as they begin to accumulate. Avoid using a sharp or hard instrument such as a knife or screwdriver. Household ammonia, kerosene, turpentine, or commercial pitch removers are most effective. Scrub the blade with a stiff, short-bristle brush. Then, dry the blade thoroughly and immediately protect it by wiping it with a lightly oiled cloth.

Retoothing, gumming, and setting a

Fig. 10–14. Cut-in-half blades are used in industry to facilitate independent blade changing on multiple sawing machines.

saw are jobs for a professional. Special equipment and know-how are essential requirements for this job. Refer to page 595, which points out some of the equipment and technical requirements of this work. However, touch-up filing is often necessary in order to extend the useful life of a blade.

Dado and Grooving Heads

The **dado head set** (Fig. 10–16) contains two ⅛ in. thick outside cutters and three to seven inside chippers. Inside chippers are ¹⁄₁₆, ⅛, and ¼ in. thick.

This assortment permits cutting grooves of ⅛ in. (one outside cutter), ¼ in. (2 outside cutters), and wider sizes in increments of ¹⁄₁₆ in. up to 1 or ⁹⁄₁₆ in.

The outside cutters have a cutting action similar to a combination blade. The inside chipper blades have swaged teeth and are, therefore, thicker at the cutting edges than at the arbor hole. *The inside chippers must always be used between two outside cutters.* The outside cutters actually cut two saw kerfs, and the stock between is removed by the inside chippers. The swaged teeth of the chippers must be positioned in the gullets of the

MATERIAL			BLADE RECOMMENDATIONS								
			Comb.	Crosscut	Rip	Planer	Spec. Plywood	Carbide	Metal Cutting	Flooring	Trimme
W O O D	SOFT	General	●					★			
		Crosscut	●	○		●		●			★
		Rip	●		★	●		●			
		Miters	●	○		★	●	●			●
	HARD	General	●					★			
		Crosscut	●	○		●		●			★
		Rip	●		★	●		●			
		Miters	●			★		●			●
Occasional Nail	flooring, old lumber, etc.									★	
Fibrous, Porous Materials	acoustical tile, Celotex, etc.					★	○	●	●		
Metal	non-ferrous								★		
	Do-it-yourself aluminum			●					●		
Plastics								★			
Plywood				●		○	★	○			
Plastic	Micarta, Formica, etc.							★	●		
Hardboards	Masonite, etc.							★			
Fiberglas	Corrugated sheets			●				★		●	
Aluminum	Corrugated sheets			●				●	★	○	

● indicates blade very good for the job   ○ suggests a better blade for the job   ★ is a blade that will do the very best job possible

Table 10–5. Circular-saw blades used for various materials.

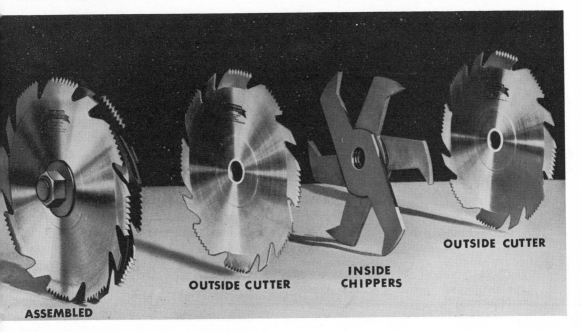

ASSEMBLED

OUTSIDE CUTTER

INSIDE
CHIPPERS

OUTSIDE CUTTER

Fig. 10–16. Standard dado head set.

outside cutters and spaced so that they do not interfere with one another. See the assembled set in Figure 10–16.

The **adjustable type dado head** (Fig. 10–17) can be quickly adjusted to cut grooves of any size from ¼ to 1¹⁄₁₆ in. without removing it from the arbor. The cutting width is adjusted by rotating the center section within its two beveled outside washers. The cutting blades are made of tool steel.

Industrial dado and grooving heads (Fig. 10–18) are made to cut a specific width. The sharp spurs on the sides sever the cross-grain fibers ahead of the knives. The cutting knives are set at an angle to produce a shearing cut. Special cutting heads like the one illustrated are made to cut a variety of widths and shapes. Specially made heads may consist of a combination dado, tenon, and trim saw head. All of these cuts are made in one pass of the stock.

Fig. 10–17. Adjustable type dado head.

Fig. 10–18. Production type dado head. These are tooled according to special product requirements.

Advances in Wood Cutting Research and Saw Design

One of the ultimate goals of research in the wood industry is to develop a method of cutting wood without waste. This waste can amount to 30 or 40 percent of the material used in the production of thin lamination strips for archery bows, slats for blinds, boat ribs, and similar thin or narrow parts.

If today's research becomes tomorrow's reality, wood will perhaps be cut with concentrated *ultra-sonic vibrations* focused to sweep through a piece of wood, eliminating the usual disturbing noise and stock waste. This process ruptures the cell structure, thus dividing the wood. Recently, high-energy light beams have been developed which might also be adapted for cutting wood. These extremely hot light beams (called *lasers*) are millions of times hotter than the surface of the sun, hotter than one million watts per square centimeter. They can vaporize any material.

Another possibility for a saw substitute is a high-velocity water jet. Wood has been experimentally severed with water jets at speeds up to 3000 ft. per second and pressures as great as 50,000 lb. per square inch. The water is forced through a small opening (nozzle) that has a diameter ranging from 0.0035 to 0.01 in. Test cuts have been made in maple up to 2 inches thick. Similar, less-powerful jets of water are being used in log mill operations for the debarking of logs.

Slicing is another experimental method for cutting without waste. This principle has been used for some time in cutting veneers by both the rotary and guillotine slicing methods. A gang of thin circular knives, spaced according to the thickness of the strip to be cut, are mounted above the machine table with a similar gang mounted directly underneath. This lower gang of knives projects above the machine table a small distance, about $\frac{1}{8}$ in. The distance between the two sets of knives is the thickness of the stock to be cut minus twice the projecting distance of the lower knives. The knife arbors are rotated by power, and as a board is fed between the two sets of knives, they form shallow slits in the upper and lower faces of the board. The direction of rotation is such that the knives pull the board forward. This set of knives is followed closely by additional sets with each set tracking exactly in the slits made by the first. The vertical gap between the knives is reduced for each set, and results in progressive deepening of the slits from both surfaces until the stock is separated. Provisions are also made to prevent the stock from spreading as the slits are deepened. The original machine was constructed to produce $\frac{1}{4}$ by 1 in. boat ribs from 1 in. thick boards.

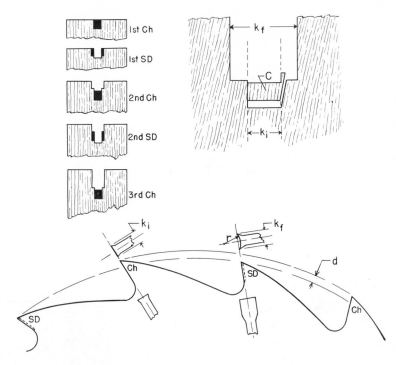

Fig. 10–19. A Duo-Kerf rip saw. Lower, the design characteristics of the blade; upper left, the sequence of cuts made by the two types of teeth; upper right, a chip breaks out with the grain.

Studies at Forest Products Laboratory, Madison, Wisconsin, have resulted in a blade with an unusual tooth design. This blade appears at the present time to be the most practical approach to producing a minimum kerf with minimum power consumption. The blade is called the *Duo-Kerf* saw (Fig. 10–19). Although it does not reduce the kerf loss to zero, it has some distinct advantages. In the near future, it may become more widely used on mill and smaller circular blades. Basically, it is designed to cut a thinner kerf, make a smoother cut, and require less power than conventional saw blades. This blade is unusual in that it combines, on one blade, teeth for chipping and for side dressing. The swaged chipper tooth cuts a very narrow kerf. The side dresser tooth is shorter, but wider and cuts (planes) only on the side of the kerf made by the first tooth, making the kerf

wider and smoother. The total amount of sawdust taken out of the kerf is considerably reduced with the Duo-Kerf saw when compared to other types of circular saws.

Figure 10–19 illustrates the cutting action of this new blade design. *The chipper teeth* (Ch) cut the first (narrow) kerf. The shorter *side-dresser* teeth (SD), with parallel sides and a concave face, widen and smooth the kerf. The progressive cutting action as the stock is fed into the saw is shown in the upper left of Figure 10–19. The upper right sketch of Figure 10–19 shows a chip that a chipper tooth partly lifted from the cut. The chip is sheared from the kerf along the line of the grain. Note that the run-out of grain at the right side of the chip ended in the bottom of the final kerf (k_f) instead of tearing into the kerf wall.

Chapter 11 Hand and Portable Sawing Processes in the School Shop

Hand Sawing

Suggestions for selecting a hand saw. Select a coarse-toothed (fewer teeth per inch), well-set saw for fast cutting of green and softwoods. For hardwood, use a fine-toothed saw. To saw large pieces select a saw with a longer blade. This permits longer strokes and decreases the time and energy required. Smaller-sized pieces may be more easily cut with light-weight, shorter saws. For example, a coping saw, dovetail saw, or a small back saw is better to use than a hand saw for cutting molding and other light stock.

Some Suggestions for Sawing

1. Lay out the line of cut on the work with a sharp pencil or a knife.
2. Clamp or hold the work securely. Support large workpieces on saw horses (Fig. 11–1). Smaller sized work may be held more conveniently in a vise. When sawing irregular curves with a coping saw, hold the work in a vise or on a saddle as shown in Figure 11–2a.
3. Hold the saw handle with the fore-finger extended along the side of the

Fig. 11–1. Crosscutting with a hand saw. Note the approximately 45-degree cutting angle and the operator's balanced position for comfort and saw control.

blade as shown in Figures 11–2b and 11–3. Use your free hand to support the work or the saw as necessary.

4. Place the saw on the edge of the work on the waste side of the line to be cut.

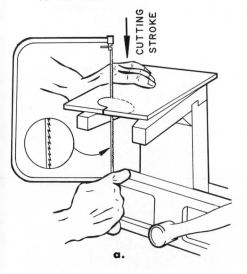

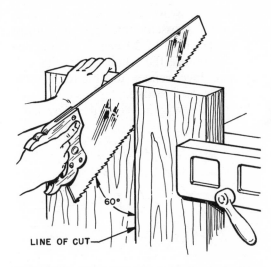

Fig. 11–3. Ripping is best performed when the saw makes a 60-degree angle with the stock. This position is awkward when the work is held in a vise.

5. Start the cut with a *backward stroke*. Use your thumb as a guide to steady the blade (Fig. 11–4). Keep the saw, your forearm, and your shoulder in line with the layout line (Fig. 11–5).
6. Use just enough pressure to keep the saw cutting. Relieve the pressure on the back stroke.
7. Saw with long, steady strokes.
8. When crosscutting lumber, hold the saw so the tooth edge makes a 45-deg. angle with the work (Fig. 11–1). For ripping, a 60-deg. angle is best (Fig. 11–3).
9. If internal stresses in the lumber cause the board to pinch the saw, insert a wooden wedge into the kerf to keep it open.
10. When sawing prefinished paneling or plywood with one good side, keep the good side up (Fig. 11–6).

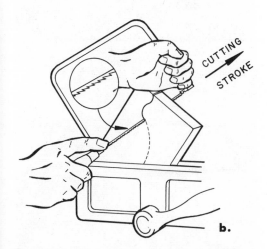

Fig. 11–2. (a) Using a coping saddle to support the work. The blade is inserted to cut on the downward stroke. (b) Sawing an irregular curve with the work held in a vise. The blade is inserted to cut on the push stroke.

11. When sawing any type of plywood, use a crosscut saw and a cutting angle of 20 to 30 deg. This practice will reduce the tendency for the bottom face veneer to splinter on the downward stroke.

12. If the saw starts to drift away from

the line of cut, twist the handle slightly on the cutting stroke to bring it back to the line of cut.

13. When sawing an irregular outline with a coping saw, hold the blade at 90 deg. to the surface of the work. This will help to produce a sawed edge that is at right angles to the face. See Figure 11–2.

Fig. 11–4. Starting a cut with a hand saw. The thumb is used to keep the blade in position until the cut is started.

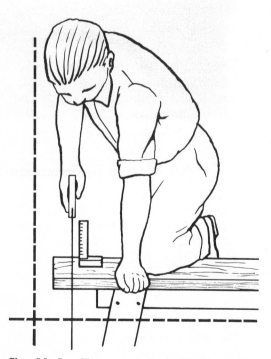

Fig. 11–5. The proper position permits observation of the line of cut and the saw; forearm and shoulder are in a plane perpendicular to the work.

Fig. 11–6. Using a hand crosscut saw to cut a 4' x 8' piece of wall paneling to length. The prefinished side is face up. The low cutting angle prevents excessive splintering on the back side.

14. To make piercing (inside) cuts, drill or bore a hole within the waste area of the work large enough to insert the blade of a coping saw or the point of a keyhole or compass saw.
15. For greater accuracy in joint making, use a miter box or a piece of scrap with a straightedge to guide the saw. See Figures 11–7, 11–8, and 11–9.
16. When finishing a saw cut, support the piece being cut off. If the piece is not supported, it will break off as the cut nears completion and split the underside of the work.
17. Keep saws sharp. Usually it is better to have saws sharpened professionally; refer to page 596 which shows some special sharpening equipment.
18. When saws are not in use, store them so the teeth do not become damaged. Wipe them with oil to prevent rusting. Lay saws on the bench top carefully so they do not touch other tools or work.

Fig. 11–8. A strip of wood clamped to the blade acts as a stop for making cuts to a uniform depth. This technique may be used for sawing dadoes, grooves, rabbets, tenons, and the like.

Portable Power Sawing in the School Shop

Portable power saws and many other types of electric tools are becoming increasingly popular. Before using any kind of portable electric tool, be sure that you understand and follow the various safety precautions as they apply to each. The general safety rules below pertain to almost all portable electric tools.

Fig. 11–7. A straight board clamped to work guides the back saw in making a shoulder cut.

Fig. 11–9. A homemade wooden miter box may be used with a fine-toothed saw for making accurate angle cuts.

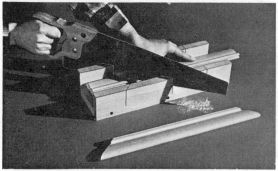

Safety Precautions for Portable Power Saws

1. Always disconnect the cord from the power circuit whenever changing blades, making adjustments, or inspecting or servicing the tool.
2. Use only an unfrayed, approved, grounded 3-wire cord (and extension) and receptacle to guard against shock. Using an ungrounded electric tool could result in a fatal electrical shock, especially if it is used while touching damp ground, concrete, or another electrical ground.
3. Clamp or hold the stock securely.
4. Use only sharp blades.
5. Always carry and lift the tool by the handle, never by the cord.
6. Store power tools in appropriate containers to protect them from dust, moisture, and damage.
7. Always disconnect the cord when the tool is not in active use.

Fig. 11–10. Using a saber saw and guide for ripping.

Using Portable Saber Saws

The saber saw is useful for a variety of purposes, especially for sawing large panels and boards that cannot be handled easily on the jigsaw or band saw. It is much safer to use than the portable electric circular saw. It may be used for making both curved and straight-line cuts.

The correct speed should be selected if the tool offers a choice of cutting speeds. Use a high speed for all crosscutting and ripping in wood, plywood, and composition materials. Use a slow speed for cutting harder and tougher materials such as metal. Select the appropriate blade for the work at hand (refer to page 136, Chapter 10). The blade must be sharp. Dull blades may pinch, slow down the work, or overload the saw and cause permanent damage to the motor. In all of the following operations, the shoe or base of the tool should be held firmly against the stock to insure safe cutting.

Straight line sawing involves crosscutting, ripping, and angle cuts. These may be performed free hand. However, a ripping guide should be used for long ripping cuts (Fig. 11–10). For crosscutting and other straight-line cuts, clamp a straightedge to the work so that the base or shoe of the tool can be guided against it.

Cutting curves generally requires narrower blades than those used for making straight-line cuts. For very sharp curves, a series of relief cuts (saw cuts made radially to the line of cut) will prevent pinching the blade. Holes may be drilled for the blade when starting inside cuts. To make circular cuts, circle guides may be used as shown in Figure 11–11. To cut larger diameters than allowed by these commercial guides, the base of the saw may be fastened to a long stick with

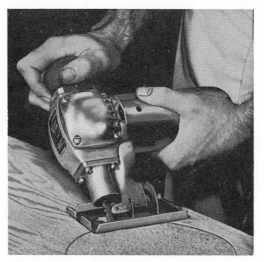

Fig. 11–12. Bevel-sawing a curve.

Fig. 11–11. Cutting circles with the aid of a circle-cutting guide.

a nail driven through it at one end to provide a pivot point.

Bevel cutting (Fig. 11–12) is accomplished by adjusting the base to the desired angle. Straight-line cuts, curved cuts, and compound-angle cuts may be made with the base tilted (Fig. 11–12).

Pocket or plunge cutting (Fig. 11–13) involves cutting through the surface of the stock without the aid of a previously drilled starting hole. The shorter length blades are recommended for this operation and the cut is usually made in the following manner:

1. Hold the saw with both hands and place it on the work as shown in Figure 11–13.
2. Place the tip of the blade on the line to be cut. Hold the saw firmly in this position.
3. Start the saw and slowly pivot it downward, letting the saw blade cut

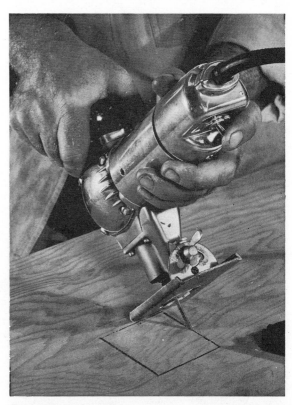

Fig. 11–13. Starting a plunge cut to make an inside opening.

itself through the stock. It is important that the base be kept in contact with the work as the blade is lowered into it.

4. After the blade penetrates the work, continue pivoting the saw until the blade is perpendicular to the work and the base is pressed against it.

Cutting With Portable Circular Saws

Before using the portable circular saw, refer to the general safety rules on page 152 and also observe the safety precautions listed below.

Safety Precautions for Portable Circular Sawing

1. Always use sharp blades of the appropriate type for the job at hand. Inexpensive, disposable blades are available.
2. For most work, adjust the blade so that the teeth project only about ⅛ in. through the material to be cut.
3. Always push the saw. Never pull the saw backward to make a cut.
4. When making long, straight-line cuts clamp a straightedge to the stock for a guide.
5. When making freehand cuts be careful not to twist the saw in the kerf, pinching the blade.
6. Do not attempt curved cuts with a portable circular saw.
7. For easier control and safer operation, always keep the widest part of the base on the work.
8. Wear goggles when cutting hard materials.
9. If the saw binds, pull it back in the cut until it regains speed. Releasing the switch will permit the saw to stop abruptly and place a severe strain on the machine.

Changing a blade (Fig. 11–14). Depending upon the make of the saw, one of several methods must be employed to

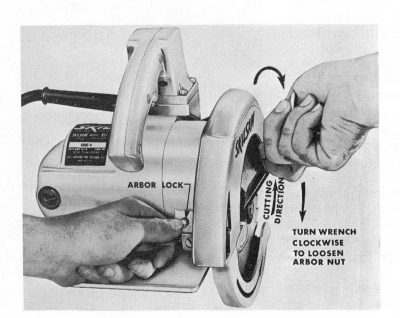

Fig. 11–14. Changing a saw blade. Here the saw shaft is locked by pushing a button while the nut is loosened.

remove and tighten the arbor nut when changing blades. If the saw is provided with an arbor lock, simply engage it and loosen the nut as shown in Figure 11–14. Some saws require the use of two wrenches: one to turn the arbor nut and the second wrench to hold either the arbor itself or the washer (which in turn holds the shaft) steady. In some cases, a nail may be slipped through a hole in the blade or through the tooth gullet and held so it bridges the opening in the saw base, thus keeping the blade steady.

With the arbor nut and washer removed, retract the lower guard and remove the blade from the arbor. Wipe the bearing surfaces of the washers and blade clean. Install the new blade with its teeth pointing upward toward the front of the base. Turn the arbor nut counterclockwise to secure the blade.

Crosscutting, Ripping, and Plywood Cutting

1. Before starting the motor, rest the front of the saw base on the work and line up the blade with the cutting line.

Fig. 11–15. Using a cut-off gauge saves time when straight, miter, or bevel sawing.

2. Do not let the teeth touch the work until the saw is at full speed. Push and guide the saw with firm pressure, but do not force it.
3. Use a guide when making miter cuts (Fig. 11–15).
4. For rip cuts, use the fence attachment set to the desired width of cut, as shown in Figure 11–14.

Fig. 11–16. Ripping to width using an accessory guide to insure a parallel cut.

Fig. 11–17. Cutting a large sheet of pre-finished plywood paneling. The finished side is placed down to minimize splitting on the good side.

5. When ripping a long board, be sure that the stock is well balanced and supported.
6. When sawing plywood (Fig. 11–17), place the good side down. Since the saw cuts upward, splitting is least likely on the good side in this position.
7. Shut off the motor after a cut is completed.

Pocket Sawing

1. Set the blade to the desired cutting depth.
2. Rest the toe of the base against the work, tilting the saw forward to clear the guard.
3. Retract the lower blade guard with the lever provided for this purpose.

4. Position the saw so the blade is in line with the layout mark.
5. Start the motor, gradually lower the saw (Fig. 11–18) until the base rests flat on the work. After the cut is well started, release the lower-blade guard lever.
6. Advance the saw along the cutting line as usual and lift the saw out of the cut before releasing the switch.

Bevel Sawing

1. Adjust and lock the base to the desired angle of cut.
2. Adjust the depth of cut.
3. Saw with the same procedure as used in straight-line cutting. NOTE: Pocket cutting should never be attempted with the blade in this position.

Fig. 11–18. Pocket cutting. The toe of the base is held firmly against the stock as the blade is slowly lowered into the work.

Chapter 12 Jigsawing and Band-Sawing Processes in the School Shop

The jigsaw and the band saw are among the safest machines to operate in the school shop. They are widely used for "freehand" sawing of curved outlines. *Freehand* sawing refers to operations in which the operator moves the work, without the aid of a gauge or fence, so that the cut is made along the waste side of an irregular layout line. The downward cutting action of the blades on both the jigsaw and the band saw keeps the work safely down on the table, allowing free feeding of the work. However, it should be remembered that they are power tools and should be handled carefully. Some of the basic operations performed on the band saw may also be applied to the jigsaw. The jigsaw is introduced first because it is the safer of the two machines to operate and is generally the first sawing machine that beginning students use.

Using the Jigsaw

Cutting speeds for various materials. In general, high speeds are used when cutting softwoods and other soft materials. Medium speeds are used for hardwoods and for sawing intricate patterns in thinner work. Slow speeds are used for cutting metal and plastics. A coarse-toothed blade and a slow speed should be used for cutting plastics to minimize friction, which causes heat and melting.

General Suggestions and Safety

1. Use the correct type and size of blade for the work at hand. Refer to page 162.
2. Insert the blade in the chuck(s) with the teeth pointing forward and downward.
3. Tighten the chuck(s) (finger tight); do not use pliers.
4. Adjust the guide block to support the blade properly.
5. Use a medium blade tension.
8. Adjust the spring holddown for the thickness of the work.
7. Adjust the belt and pulleys for the desired speed. On machines with variable speed adjustments the motor should be running while this adjustment is made.
8. Put all guards in position.

Fig. 12–1. Sawing an outside curve. The relief cuts permit sawing around short radius arcs with a wide blade. Note that two pieces of work are nailed together to produce identically sawn parts.

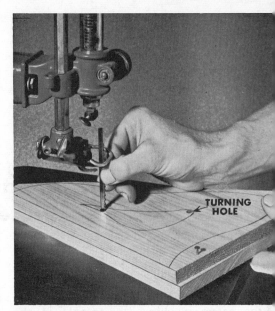

Fig. 12–2. Installing a blade through a starting hole. Note the "turning hole."

9. Check all adjustments before starting the power.
10. Keep your hands and fingers out of the line of cut.
11. Feed the work so as to keep the saw cutting; do not force it.
12. Always cut on the waste side of the layout line.

Cutting Outside Curves

1. Where several short-radius cuts are involved, use a narrow blade.
2. With wide blades, make a series of relief cuts as shown in Figure 12–1.

Piercing or Inside Cuts

1. Drill a hole through the waste part of the stock.
2. Remove the blade and raise the upper guide assembly. (If the guide can be raised high enough to clear the blade, it does not have to be removed from the lower chuck.) Position the stock on the table and reinstall the saw blade through the drilled hole (Fig. 12–2).
3. Adjust the spring hold-down and guide assembly.
4. Saw as usual.
5. Reverse the above order of procedure to remove the blade.
6. When many piercing cuts are to be made, it is sometimes advisable to convert the jigsaw to a saber saw (Fig. 12–3). Use an additional lower guide and saber blade as shown on page 108.

Band Sawing in the School Shop

Feed rates and blade speeds. Feed rate refers to how fast the work is moved into the saw. The most efficient rates vary with the thickness and kind of material being

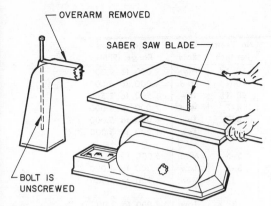

Fig. 12–3. With the overarm removed and a saber saw installed, large work may be pierced. Small work may be pierced by merely removing the guide assembly.

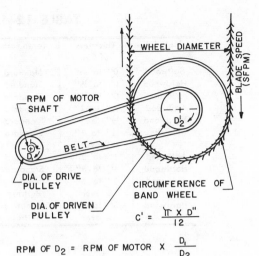

$$C' = \frac{\pi \times D''}{12}$$

$$\text{RPM OF } D_2 = \text{RPM OF MOTOR} \times \frac{D_1}{D_2}$$

Fig. 12–4. This diagram illustrates the factors involved in calculating the blade speed of a belt and pulley driven band saw.

sawed. *Blade speed* refers to the distance a point on the cutting edge of a blade travels in one minute. It is measured in feet per minute. Both the feed rate and the blade speed directly affect the smoothness and the accuracy of a saw cut. Increasing the feed rate beyond its optimum value reduces the surface smoothness of the cut, overloads the saw, and may result in damage to it. In general, a slower feed rate or a finer-toothed blade will produce a smoother sawed surface when the blade speed remains constant. Increasing the blade speed while holding the feed rate constant also results in a smoother cut. A slow feed rate is necessary when using a narrow blade or one with fine teeth. Band saws found in most school shops are either the single speed, direct-drive type, or the kind which is powered by a belted motor and pulley. In either case, the blade speed in fpm can be calculated easily.

Determining the blade speed of a direct-drive band saw. Multiply the motor rpm (given on a plate fastened to the motor) by the circumference of the band

saw wheel calculated in feet. The circumference is found by multiplying π (3.14) by the wheel diameter in inches and dividing the product by 12 to change it to feet; or, $C' = \dfrac{\pi \, D''}{12}$. Following is the formula for finding the blade speed of a direct-drive band saw:

Blade Speed in FPM $= \text{rpm} \times C'$

Determining blade speeds of belt-driven saws. Measure the diameter of the driving (D_1) and driven (D_2) pulleys and the band wheel. See Figure 12–3. Calculate the wheel circumference in feet as above. Substitute these values in the following formula:

Blade speed in FPM $= \text{rpm} \times C' \dfrac{D_1}{D_2}$

Symbol meanings:

$D_1 =$ diameter of driving pulley
$D_2 =$ diameter of driven pulley

See Table 12–1 for optimum band-sawing recommendations:

TABLE 12–1

Material	Thickness of Cut	Tooth Form	No. Teeth Per Inch	Feed Rate	Blade Speed Range (FPM)
Softwood	0″ to ½″	Standard	10–14	High	7,000 to 9,000
Hardwood	0″ to ½″	Standard	10–14	Med.	4,000 to 6,000
Plastics	0″ to ½″	Standard	10–18	Low	1,500 to 2,500
Softwood	½″ to 1″	Standard	4–7	Med.	7,000 to 8,000
Hardwood	½″ to 1″	Standard	4–7	Low	4,000 to 5,000
Plastics	½″ to 1″ & over	Standard	8–10	Low	1,200 to 3,000
Softwood	1″ to 3″	Standard	3–6	Med.	6,000 to 7,000
Hardwood	1″ to 3″	Standard	3–6	Low	3,000 to 4,000
Softwood	3″ to 6″ & over	Standard or Buttress	3	Med.	4,000 to 5,000
Hardwood	3″ to 6″ & over	Standard or Buttress	3	Low	2,000 to 3,000

Band Sawing Safety Precautions

1. Use only sharp blades. Dull blades are the major cause of band sawing accidents.
2. Select a blade width that will permit cutting the necessary radii. See Figure 12–9.
3. Install and tension the blade according to its width. Ensure that the blade is tracking correctly.
4. Set the upper guide about ⅛ to ¼ in. above the stock to be cut before the power is turned on.
5. Always let the machine reach its full speed before feeding the work into the blade.
6. Keep your hands and fingers away from the line of the saw cut.
7. Use a push stick when necessary.
8. Stop the machine if the blade or work binds. Then back the blade out of the cut. This will prevent pulling the blade off the wheels.
9. Cylindrical stock should be clamped in a work-holding fixture or jig to keep it from rotating under the downward thrust of the blade.
10. Remove deposits of gum or pitch immediately.

Changing a saw blade (Fig. 12–5) is generally accomplished as follows:

1. Disconnect the power; open the upper and lower wheel guards. Remove the throat plate and the table pin.
2. Release the blade tension (by turning the control shown in Figure 12–6) so the blade will slip off the wheels. Carefully remove coil, and store the blade.
3. If the new blade is of a different gauge and width than the one removed, back off the blade support and increase the opening between the guide blocks (or wheels) on both the upper and lower blade guide assemblies.
4. Install the new blade, putting it through the table slot with the teeth pointing downward (Fig. 12–5), and place it over the upper and lower wheels.
5. Tension the blade, just enough to hold it.
6. Hand-rotate one of the wheels to track the blade in the center of the wheel rims. If the blade does not track properly, tilt the upper wheel in or out as necessary with the tilt adjustment knob (Fig. 12–5).
7. Tension the blade fully according to its width.

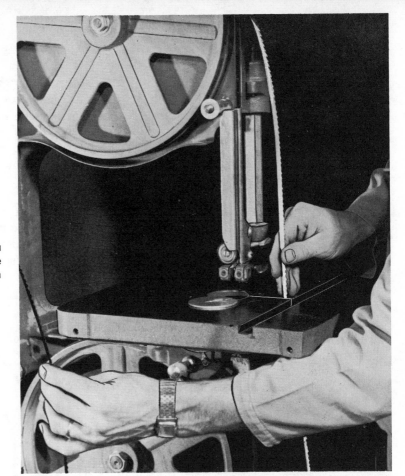

Fig. 12–5. Inserting a blade through the table slot. Note that the teeth point downward.

8. Adjust the guide blocks (or wheels) of the upper and lower guide assemblies. The correct space may be obtained by placing a piece of notebook paper between the blade and guide block on each side. This space is sufficient to keep the blade from contacting the blocks or twisting while cutting.

9. Loosen the blade roller support. Move the guide block assembly to a position where the front edges of the blocks are just behind the gullets of the saw blade (Fig. 12–7).

10. Move the upper and lower blade roller supports to a position $\frac{1}{64}$ in. behind the back edge of the blade as shown in Figure 12–7. The blade should bear against the roller sup-

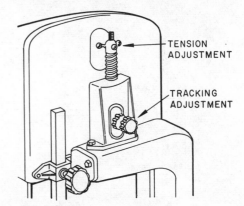

Fig. 12–6. Two adjustments are made on the upper band-saw wheel.

ports only when it is actually cutting.

11. Check all the adjustments by revolving the blade by hand once more.

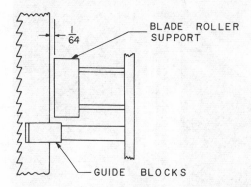

Fig. 12–7. The relationship of correctly adjusted back blade supports and guide blocks.

12. Replace the upper and lower wheel guards, the throat plate, and the table pin.
13. Check the table adjustment to be sure it is at right angles to the blade (Fig. 12–8).

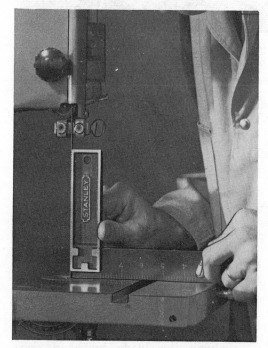

Fig. 12–8. For most sawing jobs, the table must be at right angles to the blade.

14. Adjust the upper guide, start the saw, and observe its operation.
15. Make a trial cut on scrap stock.

Sawing curves. Before cutting, study the layout on the work to determine the best path to follow. The best path is the one that will not bind the work against the column of the saw or get the blade trapped within a complex cut. The following tips will be helpful:

1. Use the widest blade possible for any given radius. Refer to Figure 12–9 which indicates the smallest

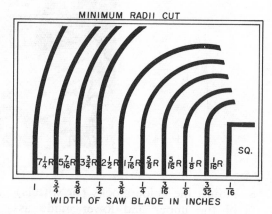

Fig. 12–9. Minimum radii cuts for different widths of blades.

radii that blades of different widths can cut.
2. Consider the capacity and limitations of the band saw when marking the layout lines on the work. Many times trapping the work against the column can be avoided by marking the layout lines on an opposite surface of the work.
3. Sharp curves and radii can be sawed by making a series of relief cuts, as shown in Figure 12–10a.
4. When the work requires cutting sharp concave curves with a wide

blade, bore "turning holes" as shown in Figure 12–10b.

5. Complicated cuts should be roughed out first, cutting about ⅛ or ¼ in. outside of the layout line (Fig. 12–10c). The final cut is made with a combination of shorter cuts.

6. When cutting rectangular openings, use any of the methods shown in Figure 12–10d to cut the inside corners. Be careful when back-tracking.

Fig. 12–11. Freehand, multiple, straight-line sawing of veneered panels in an industrial plant.

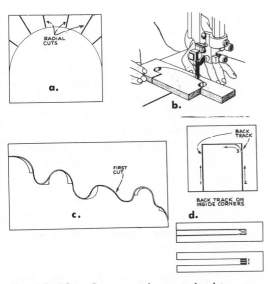

Fig. 12–10. Care must be exercised to prevent trapping the blade in a cut.

Straight sawing may be performed freehand as shown in Figure 12–11 or with the aid of a rip fence. Taper sawing is often performed on the band saw with the aid of a tapering jig. Refer to page 182, Figure 13–31, which shows an industrial application of taper sawing. The band saw may be used freehand to straighten irregular edges of boards prior to jointing and ripping. The fence cannot be used for this particular type of work. The band saw may be used to cut stock to length, but its capacity is limited by the distance between the blade and the column.

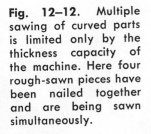

Fig. 12–12. Multiple sawing of curved parts is limited only by the thickness capacity of the machine. Here four rough-sawn pieces have been nailed together and are being sawn simultaneously.

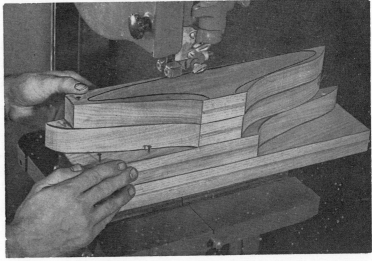

Multiple sawing (Figs. 12–11 and 12–12) is a practical way to cut duplicate parts. This is done by stacking several workpieces on top of each other and sawing them all at the same time. Several methods can be employed to hold the workpieces together. These are:

1. Nail into the waste part of the work (Fig. 12–12).
2. If the work has two or more bored holes, hold the parts in line with wooden dowels.
3. Tape the pieces together.
4. Hold large pieces together with clamps.
5. Make a special box jig similar to the example shown in Figure 12–13.

Bevel sawing (Figs. 12–14 and 12–15) involves straight or curved cuts made on the band saw with the table tilted to the desired angle. Straight bevel cuts should be made with the aid of a fence. Cuts may be made in this manner to chamfer the corners of squares when preparing stock for turning in the lathe.

Making compound cuts (Figs. 12–16) on the band saw is the process involving

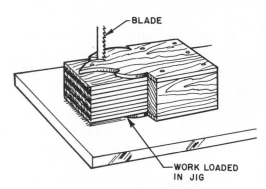

Fig. 12–13. A box jig constructed to facilitate sawing of duplicate parts.

cutting on two or more sides of the work piece. Cabriole legs (Fig. 12–16) for period furniture may be band sawed to shape by this method. Compound sawing methods are also useful for removing the waste portions of turning stock before mounting it in the lathe. The basic procedure for compound sawing is as follows:

1. Lay out the cuts on two adjoining surfaces of the work with a templet (Fig. 12–16).

Fig. 12–14. Bevel band sawing a part to shape.

Fig. 12–15. Bevel ripping is more safely performed on the band saw than on any other machine.

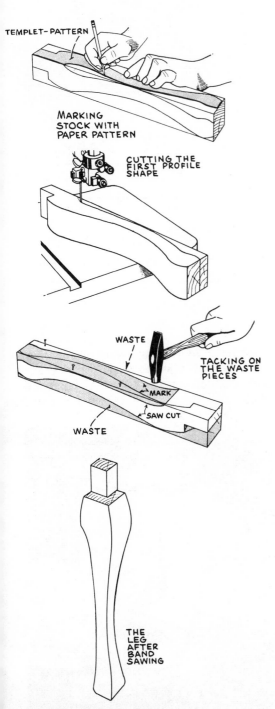

TEMPLET-PATTERN

MARKING
STOCK WITH
PAPER PATTERN

CUTTING THE
FIRST PROFILE
SHAPE

WASTE

TACKING ON
THE WASTE
PIECES

MARK

SAW CUT

WASTE

THE
LEG
AFTER
BAND
SAWING

Fig. 12–16. The steps involved in compound sawing.

2. Saw the first profile shape as shown in step two of Figure 12–16.

3. Replace the waste pieces in their original location on the work. This is necessary to provide a flat working base and to show the layout lines. The scrap pieces may be taped back to the workpiece, or nailed (Fig. 12–16) in the waste portion of the work.

4. Saw the second profile to shape in the same manner as the first. *Caution:* Always be sure that the work is adequately supported on the table; the downward force of the blade could cause poorly supported work to twist and snap the blade.

Sawing disks (Fig. 12–17). Disks may be sawed on the band saw with the aid of an auxiliary plywood table clamped to the band saw table. A pivot point is made by driving a nail into the wooden table at the desired radial distance from the blade as shown in Figure 12–17b. The nail is cut to protrude about $\frac{1}{8}$ in. and filed to a point. The correct location of the point is of prime importance. The point must be located at right angles to the blade and on a line with the points of the teeth.

To use the fixture, the stock is set against the blade and pressed down to seat the pivot point. With the saw running, the work is then slowly rotated on the pivot until the cut is completed. A sharp blade, evenly set, is required for successful results. If any adjustments are required, the auxiliary table may be shifted and reclamped to the machine table.

When sawing circles it is usually best to start the cut on the end grain. The reason for this is that cuts started parallel to the grain of some woods have a tendency to follow the grain direction rather than the intended path of cut.

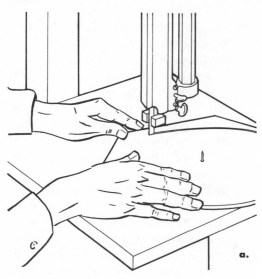

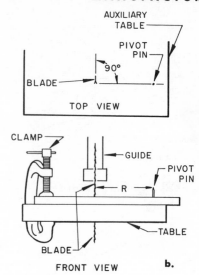

Fig. 12—17a. Bandsawing disks with an auxiliary table.

Fig. 12—17b. Setting up for the operation.

Resawing (Fig. 12–18) stock to thickness on band saws offers an advantage over circular saws in that the saw kerf is much narrower. Thereby, less stock is wasted. Accurate resawing on the band saw requires a wide, sharp, evenly set, and well-tensioned blade. A band-saw blade can be quickly tested for equal

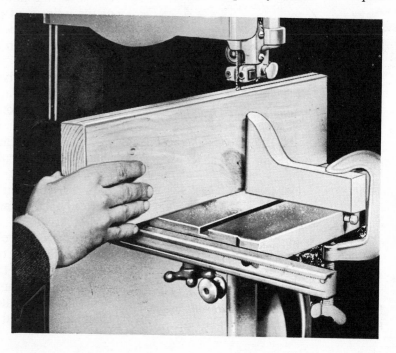

Fig. 12–18. Resawing stock to thickness using a round nose pivot-support block.

set by attempting a ripping cut using the fence as a guide. If the blade tends to drift, it is not set accurately. Resawing may be performed in either of two ways. (1) A round nosed guide such as is shown in Figure 12–18 is clamped to the table. The round nose of the guide must make a right angle with its base. The guide serves to gauge the thickness of the cut and to keep the work perpendicular to the table. The rounded nose permits guiding the work if the blade tends to drift. (2) Start the resaw cuts on the table saw, cutting into both edges of the stock, as shown in Figure 13–13, page 175. Then complete the resawing on the band saw using the round nose pivot block as shown in Figure 12–18. Commercial resaw guides are available for the larger, high-speed band scroll saws. These consist of spring-loaded rollers which hold the work against a short fence.

Chapter 13   Table Sawing Processes
in the School Shop

The table saw is used to perform basic ripping, crosscutting, and mitering cuts. It is also used to machine joinery cuts involving dadoing, grooving, rabbeting and other specialty cuts. The area of special cuts and complex joint-making procedures as they apply to particular products is far too broad to be included in this or any other book. However, the ability to solve these special problems as the future need arises largely depends upon the operator's knowledge of the functioning of the machines as described in Chapter 9 and his ability to perform the basic operations presented in this unit. The more complicated joinery cuts generally involve a combination of several of the basic operations. Industry uses special jigs and work-holding devices for safer production sawing. These are adaptable to use in the school shop. Some of these devices are presented and illustrated in this unit.

Safety Precautions for the Table Saw

1. Use the guard, splitter, and anti-kickback devices whenever possible. Refer to Figure 13–6, page 172.

2. Always use the correct blade for the type of work to be done.
3. Use only sharp blades; dull blades are the major cause of accidents. Serious kickbacks may result.
4. Keep an evenly balanced stance with your weight on both feet. Stand so that you are not in line with the saw blade.
5. Always keep your hands out of the line of the blade.
6. Always use the rip fence for ripping operations; and always use the miter gauge for crosscutting operations. *Caution*: Do not combine the use of these two devices for crosscutting unless a clearance block is used on the fence as shown in Figure 13–18, page 177.
7. Always check the stock to be sure it is free of loose knots or pieces which may come free during the cut and be thrown from the saw.
8. Hold the stock firmly. Feed it into the blade at an even, continuous rate without forcing or overloading the saw.
9. Use a push stick for ripping stock that is narrower than 6 inches wide.
10. Wait until the blade stops before removing scraps from the table.

11. When ripping long stock, obtain a helper to serve as a tailman to hold and remove the stock from the saw.

12. Always have your instructor check and approve any setups, especially operations which require removing the guard or any of the safety devices.

13. Crosscut long pieces into shorter lengths before ripping whenever possible. Table-saw crosscutting operations on boards of long lengths is a dangerous practice. It is even more dangerous when it is attempted without the aid of a helper.

14. Many basic operations become very dangerous if they are performed on work of small size. Try to foresee possible hazards. Analyze the operation beforehand. The job may be made safer by constructing and using a work-holding fixture.

15. Whenever you are in the slightest doubt about an operation or procedure, ask your instructor for help. Never risk injury to yourself or others because of being uninformed of the correct, safe procedure.

Table saw speeds and feeds (Fig. 13–1). A saw that is in good condition and rotating at the right speed should cut the stock easily. The operator should not overload the saw; that is, he should not feed the work into the saw faster than it can efficiently cut. Normally, circular saws operate at a rim speed of 10,000 ft. per minute. A 12-in. diameter blade, rotating as 3600 rpm has a rim speed of more than 120 mph. This speed when applied in kickback, makes a deadly missile of a piece of wood. Saw tables and blades are designed for specific size and speed limits which must never be exceeded. The following formula is used to determine the rim speed when the rpm is known.

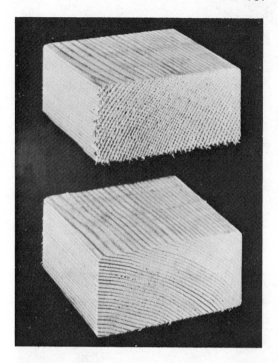

Fig. 13–1. These two blocks were cut from the same blade. The upper block was cut at too fast a feed rate.

Rim speed in feet per minute =
$$\frac{3.14 \times \text{dia. in inches} \times \text{rpm}}{12}$$

The sound (hum) of the machine when it is free running (not cutting) will change only slightly when the stock is hand-fed at the correct speed. The stock should always cut with ease. You should learn to listen to any machine and be able to recognize one that is operating properly. If the stock is fed too fast, you will damage the blade and the motor. In addition, the cut will be poor, and a kickback may result and cause an injury.

Basic Table Saw Operations

Changing a saw blade (Figs. 13–2a, 13–2b, and 13–2c). Because there are

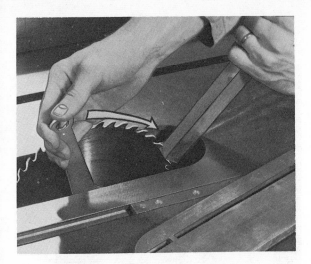

Fig. 13-2. (a) Removing a saw blade.

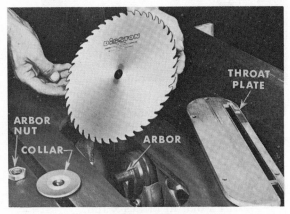

ARBOR
NUT

COLLAR

ARBOR

THROAT
PLATE

Fig. 13-2. (b) Mounting a blade on the saw arbor. Note the direction of the teeth. (c) Tightening the arbor nut.

different types of blades recommended for various cutting jobs, changing a saw blade is a routine job and an important one to do correctly. This is the recommended procedure:

1. Disconnect the power source. Swing the guard out of the way and lift out the throat plate. Throat plates are usually removed by depressing them on one end so that the other end may be grasped. Some have holes for a finger grip.

2. Place the wrench (do not use pliers) on the arbor nut. Disengage the nut (left-hand thread) by pulling on the wrench in a clockwise direction while holding a scrap of wood wedged against the blade as shown in Figure 13-2a.

3. Remove the arbor nut and the collar (Fig. 13-2b) being careful not to drop them in the sawdust (or dust collector) in the base of the machine.

4. Since the arbor holes of saw blades are slightly larger than the arbor itself, blades should be mounted on the arbor in the same position each time. Install the saw blade with the teeth pointing toward the feed (front) side of the saw. Place the manufacture's trademark up. If this practice is followed when the saw blade is jointed (refer to page 594 of Chapter 33), it will always run perfectly "round" with each tooth exactly the same height.

5. Slide the collar against the blade and thread on the arbor nut.

6. Hold the blade with the thumb and fingertips of one hand while turning the arbor nut up "snug" with the wrench as shown in Figure 13-2c. The arbor nut will not come loose. Because of the left-hand thread, the nut tends to tighten itself if the blade tends to slip on the arbor.

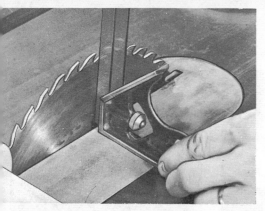

Fig. 13–3. Raise the blade to check and adjust it for squareness with the surface of the table. Then make and check a trial cut on a piece of scrap.

Fig. 13–4. The rip fence is in alignment when distance "B" is equal to "A." Some operators prefer that "B" be ½" greater than "A."

7. Replace the throat plate and the guards. Reconnect the machine to the power source.

Ripping applies to making cuts with or parallel to the grain of wood. It is important to know the different methods of ripping wide and narrow stock, cutting off thin edgings, and handling long work. Always use a rip or combination blade. When ripping, the miter gauge should be removed from the table. The edge of the work that is to be guided against the

fence must be straight (jointed true) in order to make safe and accurate cuts. Be sure that the blade tilting mechanism is adjusted and locked at right angles to the table (Fig. 13–3).

Adjusting the rip fence. The first requirement for safe and accurate ripping is to be sure the fence is properly adjusted. The fence may be checked by measuring from the front and back of the blade, at points A and B, respectively, as shown in Figure 13–4. If the fence needs adjust-

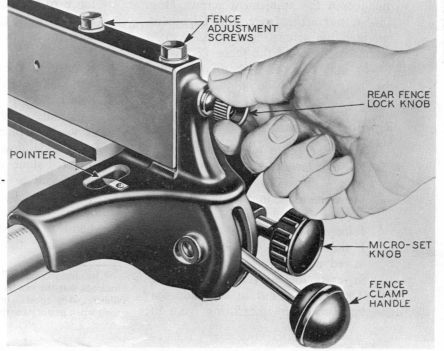

Fig. 13–5. Fence controls and adjustments.

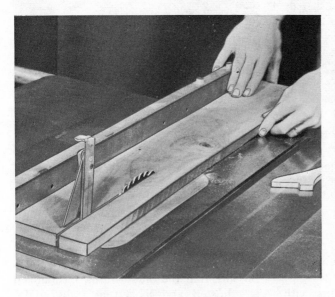

Fig. 13–6. *Note the position of the hands and the availability of the push stick. The function of the splitter and kickback fingers in ripping is also shown.

Fig. 13–7. *Using a roller top device to support long stock when ripping. Note the position of the operator's hands.

ing, loosen the adjustment screws (Fig. 13–5), move the fence into alignment, retighten the screws, and then check it again. The back of the fence (B in Fig. 13–4) may be open $\frac{1}{32}$ in. more than the front or it may be equidistant.

Ripping Procedures

1. Move the guard out of the way.
2. Raise or lower the blade until it projects $\frac{1}{8}$ in. above the stock.
3. Move the fence into ripping position, and set the lock (Fig. 13–5).
4. Joint one edge of the stock.
5. If the stock is to be jointed on the sawed edge, allow about $\frac{1}{16}$ to $\frac{1}{8}$ in. extra for the jointing operation. The width of cut to be made may be checked by measuring from the

fence to the point of a tooth which is set toward the fence. This measurement is made at "A" in Fig. 13–4.

6. Reposition the guard, splitter, and anti-kickback devices.
7. Select a scrap piece of suitable size and make a trial cut. If the stock is warped, place the concave (hollow) side down against the table. Twisted stock should be face-jointed to provide a flat surface before it is cut on the table saw.
8. Start the machine. Use the right hand to support and advance the work into the saw. The left hand

---

* Illustrations identified with an asterisk (*) indicate that the saw guard has been removed for illustrative purposes only. The guard should be used when performing these operations in the shop.

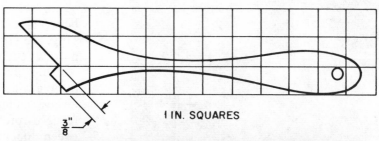

I IN. SQUARES

$\frac{3"}{8}$

Fig. 13–8. (a) Design for a push stick. (b) * The push stick is used for safe ripping of narrow stock.

should be slightly forward holding the work down and guiding it against the fence (Fig. 13–6).

9. When nearing the completion of the cut, move the left hand a safe distance away from the blade. *Caution:* Do not lean over the saw; use a push stick instead. Push the stock through with the right hand alone, letting the stock fall onto an off-bearing table. *Caution:* Pulling the stock backward between the fence and blade is a very dangerous practice. The blade may kick the stock from the saw.

10. Shut off the machine.

11. *Caution:* When ripping long lengths of stock, be sure to have a roller top to support the work, or a student

helper (tailman) to hold up the stock (Fig. 13–7). When ripping stock which is extra long, it is also helpful to have a roller top support the work in front of the saw.

12. *Caution:* When ripping stock with less than 6 in. between the saw and fence, *always* use a push stick (Fig. 13–8a) to feed the work as illustrated in Figure 13–8b.

13. When ripping wide stock to width, position yourself to the right of the saw blade rather than to the left. Feed the stock steadily into the saw and keep it firmly against the ripping fence (Fig. 13–9).

14. When ripping edgings or narrow strips from wide stock, set the fence so that the greatest distance is kept

Fig. 13–9. *Ripping wide stock to width. Note the hand position of the operator.

Fig. 13–10. * Whenever possible set the fence so the widest part of the stock is between the fence and the blade.

Fig. 13–11. * Bevel ripping narrow stock with the aid of a feather board.

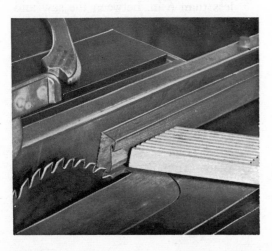

between the fence and the blade (Fig. 13–10). Avoid ripping very narrow edgings between the fence and the blade. When it is necessary to rip a wide board into narrow strips, always clamp a filler board to the fence to provide a safe distance between the blade and the fence.

15. Bevel cuts are made with the blade tilted to an angle and completed in the same manner as the other ripping cuts described above. See Figures 13–11 and 13–12.

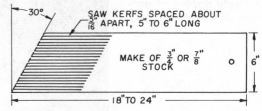

Fig. 13–12. Design for a feather board.

Resawing (Fig. 13–13) is the process of cutting one thick piece of stock into two or more thinner pieces. Narrow boards can be resawed to thickness with just one pass through the saw. Wider boards require two passes, one cut along each edge of the board. In order to resaw wide boards, they must be of a width that is not greater than twice the height of the projecting saw blade. Generally, a 10-in. saw blade will project a little over 3 in. above the table. Thus, a board which is 6 in. wide can be resawed. *Resawing is one of the most dangerous table saw operations.* It generally requires having maximum blade exposure and is often impossible to guard com-

* Illustrations identified with an asterisk (*) indicate that the saw guard has been removed for illustrative purposes only. The guard should be used when performing these operations in the shop.

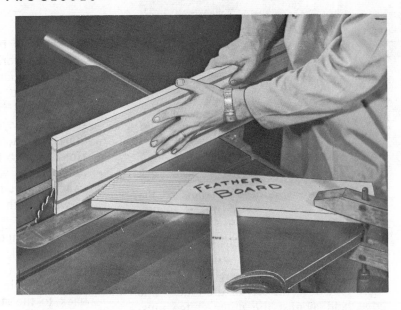

Fig. 13–13. Resawing a wide board. Here the first cut is being started. Note the feather board for hold-in, and the support used to keep the feather board in position. The guard cannot be used.

pletely. *Always* obtain the permission of your instructor and request his supervision or assistance for this operation.

Resawing Procedure

1. Remove the guard (and the splitter) if necessary.
2. Move the fence into position. Measure the distance between the fence and blade to equal the desired thickness of cut. Lock the rip fence.
3. Raise the blade to a little more than half the width of the stock for the first cut. Resawing hardwoods may require several successive passes, raising the blade before each pass.
4. Set the stock against the fence. Clamp the feather board (Fig. 13–12) to the table in a position which will press against the stock at a point in front of the blade (Fig. 13–13).
5. Start the saw. Feed the stock slowly but steadily into the machine.
6. Finish the cut by using a push stick. It is a good idea to have a helper

to remove the stock at the rear of the saw. *Caution:* Never reach over the saw blade!

7. Flip the board end for end (being sure that the same face is placed against the fence) for the second cut.
8. Hold the board securely. Feed it at an even rate. Complete the second cut with a push stick. NOTE: A helper at the rear of the saw is especially desirable to remove the pieces upon completion of the second cut.
9. When a board is too wide to be completely resawed with two cuts made along the opposite edges, then it may be necessary to finish the cut on the band saw.

Crosscutting is the process of sawing wood across the grain. A crosscut or combination blade should be used, with the choice dependent upon the desired finish and the kind of material to be cut. The work to be cut is always held against the miter gauge, and both the work and gauge are advanced toward the blade.

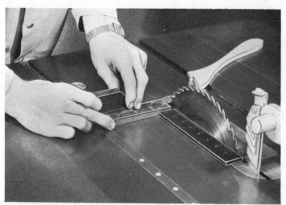

Fig. 13–14. Check the squareness of the miter gauge and the blade with a square. Then make and check a trial cut on a piece of scrap.

The miter gauge is preferably used in the table groove to the left of the blade. The edge held against the miter gauge must be jointed true. Also, the miter gauge must be accurately set to the desired angle of cut (Fig. 13–14). Any cut which is not perfectly square is a miter cut. It is a good idea first to make and check out a trial cut using scrap stock of suitable size.

1. Check the blade-tilting adjustment and miter gauge to be sure they are set square. Also, make and check a trial cut.
2. Move the ripping fence well off to the right of the table or remove it from the machine.

3. Set the saw blade to project ⅛ in. above the work.
4. Place the guard in position.
5. Line up the stock to the blade so the cut will be made on the waste side of the layout line.
6. Start the machine.
7. Hold the work securely against the miter gauge with the left hand. Advance the gauge and feed the work forward with the right hand (Fig. 13–15).
8. *Keep* both hands on the miter gauge and the work. Slide the stock slightly to the left (away from the blade) before drawing the work and gauge back to the starting point.
9. Turn off the power with one hand while holding the work with the other.
10. *Caution*: Always wait until the saw blade stops revolving before removing the scrap or cut-off piece from the table.
11. Crosscutting stock that is very wide can often be accomplished by reversing the miter gauge in the table groove as shown in Figure 13–16. Hold the stock in position on the

Fig. 13–15. Crosscutting. Note the position of the operator's hands.

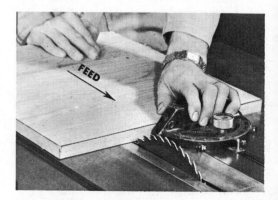

Fig. 13–16. * Crosscutting wide stock with the miter gauge reversed.

miter gauge with the left hand. Use your right hand to hold the work firmly against the miter gauge while advancing the stock into the saw.

Devices for cutting duplicate parts to length. When crosscutting two or more pieces of stock to the same length, several stop devices may be used with the miter gauge. These devices save time and produce pieces of identical size. The devices commonly used are:

1. *A miter gauge stop rod* (Fig 13–17). The *positive measurement* (which is the length of the desired workpiece) is made between the blade and the stop.

2. *A clearance block*. A block clamped to the fence *in front of the blade* is necessary to provide sufficient clearance for the cut-off pieces (Fig. 13–18). This prevents them from becoming wedged or pinched between the blade and the fence and being thrown back from the saw. The positive measurement is made between the block and the point of the tooth closest to the block. An alternate method is to clamp a block or length of stock directly to the table. It should be located in front of the blade so that as the work is advanced it will not bind between the block and the blade.

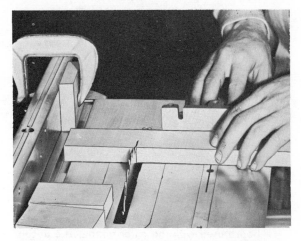

Fig. 13–18. * Crosscutting stock to identical length, using a clearance block clamped to the fence. Note the location of the clearance block and how the cut-off pieces lie freely between the blade and the fence.

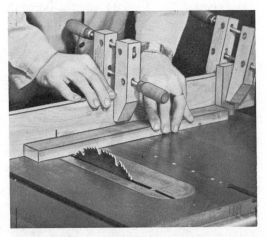

Fig. 13–19. An auxiliary facing board that is clamped (or screwed) to the miter gauge assures accurate cutting of duplicate parts. The saw guard must be raised high enough to clear the facing board for this operation.

Fig. 13–17. * Using a miter gauge stop rod for cutting duplicate pieces to length.

* Illustrations identified with an asterisk (*) indicate that the saw guard has been removed for illustrative purposes only. The guard should be used when performing these operations in the shop.

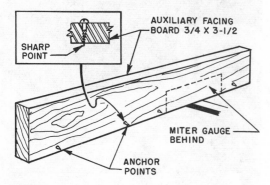

SHARP POINT

AUXILIARY FACING BOARD 3/4 X 3-1/2

MITER GAUGE BEHIND

ANCHOR POINTS

Fig. 13–20. Detail of an auxiliary facing board used with the miter gauge. The anchor points are used when cutting miters. At other times they are retracted.

3. *An auxiliary facing board.* A straight board clamped or screwed to the miter gauge is often used to support the work safely (Fig. 13–19). The board (Fig. 13–20) should be long enough to extend beyond the right side of the blade. This will then carry the cut-offs, trimmings, or scraps safely out of the way, pushing them beyond the back of the revolving blade. Using an auxiliary board

Fig. 13–21. * Making a miter cut on picture frame stock. Here the auxiliary facing board is fastened to the miter gauge with a C-clamp. The guard must be elevated for this operation.

will also serve to eliminate possible chipping or splintering of the work as the cut is completed because the stock is fully supported around the path of the blade.

Cutting flat miters involves nearly the same procedure as for crosscutting, but the miter gauge is set and locked at a predetermined angle. The miter gauge may be used in either of the two table grooves, whichever is more convenient. The most common problem confronted when cutting miters is the tendency for the stock to creep (slide) along the miter gauge during the cut. A stop rod or block may be used to prevent creeping. Many craftsmen use the auxiliary miter gauge facing board (Figs. 13–20 and 13–21). It has two or more sharp pointed screws

Fig. 13–22. * Using adjustable hold-down attachment for making a flat miter cut.

* Illustrations identified with an asterisk (*) indicate that the saw guard has been removed for illustrative purposes only. The guard should be used when performing these operations in the shop.

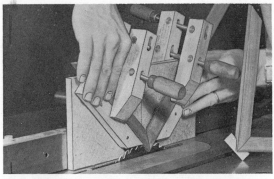

Fig. 13–23. A sliding fixture holds the work for making accurate miter cuts. When the work is cut through, the fixture is pulled back to the starting position.

Fig. 13–24. Using a fixture to hold flat mitered parts in alignment while cutting a kerf for a feather. An assembled mitered corner is shown at the right.

protruding slightly through the face side to anchor the stock and thus prevent creeping. Commercial clamping devices, which fit on the miter gauge, are adjustable for stock of different thicknesses (Fig. 13–22).

Many shops with special miter requirements make their own fixtures. One device used for cutting miters is the home-

made sliding table (Fig. 13–23). Two hardwood guide strips, fastened to the underside, slide in the table grooves. A kerf for a feather may be cut with the fixture shown in Figure 13–24.

Cutting edge bevels and spline kerfs. Straight bevel or edge miter-joint cuts require tilting the blade to the desired angle (Fig. 13–25). Usually the cuts

Fig. 13–25. * Cutting edge miters as shown here produces pieces of equal length. The guard must be elevated for this operation.

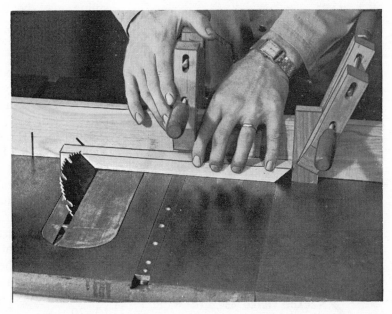

Fig. 13–26. Left: Splined miter joint assembled. Right: Parts before assembly showing blind kerfs and spline. The kerf is cut in one piece by backing it into the saw.

Fig. 13–29. Making the last cut for a rabbeted miter joint.

Fig. 13–27. A rabbeted miter joint.

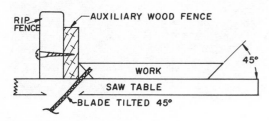

Fig. 13–28. This setup is used to cut kerfs for a spline miter joint.

are made at 45 deg. on components which are fitted together to make up mitered corners for boxes, cases, and cabinets. There are many different kinds of edge miter joints. These are illustrated in Chapter 14, page 194. The spline and rabbeted miter joints are two popular joints (Figs. 13–31 and 13–32). The spline may be either a small piece of ⅛-in. plywood or a solid piece of hardwood cut so that the grain is running across its width rather than its length. Tempered hardboard, ⅛ in. thick, also serves the purpose well. Use an outside cutter of a standard dado head set to cut a ⅛-in. kerf. The method of cutting a spline kerf for miter joints is shown in Figure 13–28. Industrial plants use a special thin (22 gauge) blade that will cut kerfs for metal fasteners called clamp nails. A clamp nail draws the two parts together as it is driven in the kerf. Refer to mechanical fasteners, page 432.

The last cut of a *rabbeted miter joint* is made with the saw set up in much the same manner as when making a kerf cut for an edge spline miter. See Figure 13–29.

Rabbet cuts (Figs. 13–30a, 13–30b, and 13–30c) require two ripping cuts at right angles to each other. There are several different methods used to machine rabbets on the table saw. A rip or combination blade should be used. The following procedure is one of the most common:

1. Mark the size of the rabbet (width and depth) on one end or edge of the work.
2. Remove the splitter and the guard, if necessary.
3. Set the fence so the first cut is made on the waste side of the layout line with the stock positioned on its edge.
4. Adjust the saw blade to the correct depth of cut.
5. Make the first cut with the face of the stock against the fence (Fig. 13–30a). NOTE: It is advisable to use a feather board located in front of the blade to hold the stock against the fence.
6. Reset the blade depth and the fence position so the second cut may be made with the stock resting flat on the table as shown in Figure 13–30b. This is the preferred method since there is less danger of the waste piece kicking back.
7. Complete the second cut.
8. Sometimes it is necessary to make the second cut by the alternate method as shown in Figure 13–30c. This is particularly true when cutting rabbets in large panels. *Caution* must be exercised. At the completion of the cut, the waste piece is trapped between the blade and the fence and it is likely to be thrown out of the saw with great force.
9. When a quantity of duplicate rabbet cuts must be made, it is often advisable to use a dado head. This permits cutting the complete rabbet with just one pass through the machine.

See Figure 13–39 and the paragraph regarding the use of the dado head on page 144. NOTE: The above method can be applied to make tongue cuts, simply by cutting two rabbets along the same edge.

Making taper cuts (Fig. 13–31) requires the use of a wedge-shaped fixture

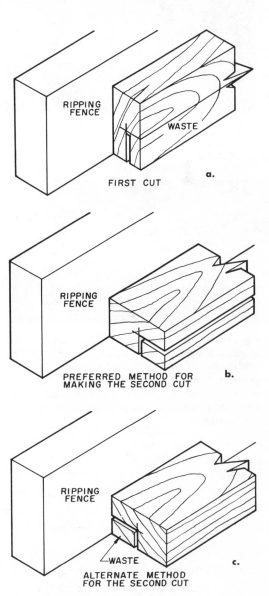

Fig. 13–30. Cutting a rabbet.

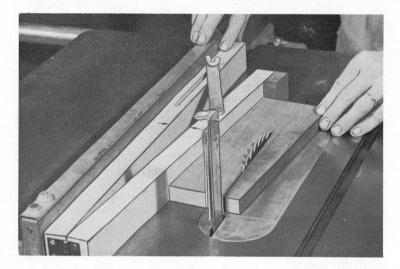

Fig. 13–31. * Using an adjustable tapering jig to cut a tapered part. The ripping fence should be set to cut ⅛ in. oversize so the edge may be jointed smooth.

* Illustrations identified with an asterisk (*) indicate that the saw guard has been removed for illustrative purposes only.

Fig. 13–32. *This improvised sliding table is guided by a hardwood strip riding in the table groove. It is especially constructed to produce tapered gusset plates of ½-in. plywood for use in making roof trusses. Only one cut is necessary to produce eight identical gussets.

Fig. 13–33. Cutting a cove by making shallow diagonal passes over the saw blade. The push stick is used to complete each pass.

between the fence and the stock. The operator pushes the fixture, which holds the stock in position as it is fed into the saw.

Many shops make their own adjustable tapering fixtures. They can be set to enable sawing different tapers (Fig. 13–31). For unusual jobs, a special fixture may be constructed according to the requirements dictated by the job. A good

example is shown in Figure 13–32.

Cutting a cove (Fig. 13–33) is the process of making a concave cut in stock. Coves are cut on the saw by guiding the stock obliquely (not parallelly) into the saw blade. The stock must be held against a fence and a number of successive shallow cuts must be made on the workpiece until the desired depth is obtained. The angle of feed and the final depth of cut determine the shape of the completed cove. Shapes of various coves that result from feeding the work at different angles to the blade are illustrated in Figure 13–34. This illustration shows that the final shape of a cove is not perfectly round, but is elliptical or oblong. Figure 13–34 shows that as the feed angle increases, the shape of the cove becomes closer to a semicircular shape. However, feed angles greater than 45 deg. are seldom used because then the work must be fed in a direction that is more nearly perpendicular to the blade. Consequently, less stock can be removed with each pass and chances of burning the work are increased. A larger diameter saw blade will cut a more nearly round cove than a small saw blade with the same feed angle and depth of cut. Briefly, the general procedure for setting up the machine and cutting a cove is as follows:

1. Determine depth and width of the desired cove.
2. Install a heavy gauge saw blade and project it above the table to the final depth of the cove desired (Fig. 13–35).
3. Find the angle of feed. This angle will produce the desired width of the cove. A simple method of obtaining the feed angle and cove width is accomplished with a homemade parallel rule shown in Figure 13–35.
4. Mark a line on the table indicating the feed angle and clamp a fence (straight board) parallel to this mark to locate the position of the cut from the edge of the work.
5. Lower the blade so it projects just enough for the first cut. This should be around ⅛ in. for softwoods or ¹⁄₁₆ in. for hardwoods.
6. Slowly feed the stock as shown in Figure 13–33, listening for an overload of the blade. Complete each pass with a push stick.
7. Make the necessary number of passes raising the blade ¹⁄₁₆ to ⅛ in. between each pass. Use a very shallow cut and slow feed for the final pass to finish the cut surface.
8. When a number of coves must be cut, time and wear on the blade will be saved if the work is first roughed

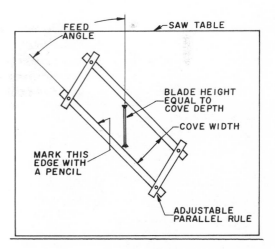

Fig. 13–35. Making the setup on the saw for cutting a cove of predetermined width and depth. The parallel rule shown here may be made of four strips of wood and four nails. The joints must pivot for adjustment.

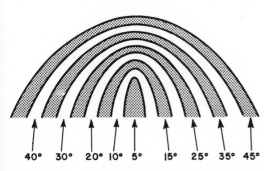

40° 30° 20° 10° 5°   15° 25° 35° 45°

Fig. 13–34. The angle at which the stock is fed to the saw blade determines the shape of the cove.

to shape by cutting grooves with a dado head.

Grooving and Dadoing With the Table Saw

A **groove** is a cut which does not go completely through the wood, and is made with the grain of the wood. A *dado* is a similar cut made across the grain. Cutting grooves and dadoes are fundamental operations in the machining of many kinds of joints. There are different kinds of cutters available for dadoing and grooving operations on the table saw. These cutters are usually referred to as *dado heads,* but they may also be called *grooving heads.* Refer to page 145, which describes different types of dado heads.

When using the dado head, a special dado throat plate must be installed in the saw table. Remember the following tips when assembling a standard type dado set that is composed of inside and outside cutters:

1. The inside chippers (cutters) must

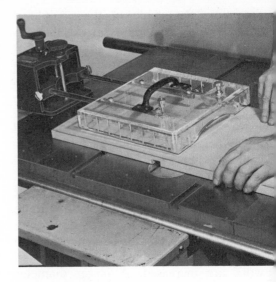

Fig. 13–37.   Dadoing with a guard over the cutterhead.

always be used between two outside cutters.

2. The swaged teeth of the chippers must be positioned in the gullets of the outside cutters and staggered to ensure a true width of cut. See Figure 13–36.

Use a guard whenever possible. An example of a good guard for this work is shown in Figure 13–37. Always check the set-up with your instructor. Make a trial cut on a piece of scrap stock of suitable size to check the width and depth of cut. *Caution:* Never cut dadoes or grooves on small pieces.

Grooving and dadoing operations are performed in much the same manner as ripping and crosscutting with a standard blade. However, a dado head must be respected more. In dadoing, feed the work slower because a bigger bite is taken out of the work than is removed with a standard blade. The fence may be used when cutting dadoes and grooves with the miter gauge. It is always a good idea

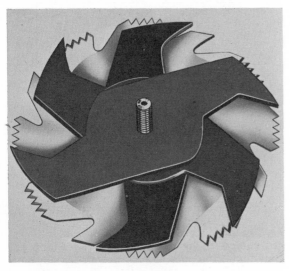

Fig. 13–36.   The correct assembly of inside chippers of a dado head.

to use an auxiliary facing board clamped to the miter gauge when dadoing. This will prevent possible splintering of the edge at the completion of the cut.

Cutting equally spaced dadoes (Fig. 13–38). It is often desirable to make a series of evenly spaced dado cuts for shelves, drawer rails, or frames in two or more workpieces. This may be easily and accurately accomplished with a stop fastened to the auxiliary facing board used with the miter gauge. The first dado is made by cutting to a layout line marked on the work. The auxiliary facing board is also cut. The stop is made to the same width as the dado and fastened (glued) into the dado cut made in the auxiliary facing board. The auxiliary facing board is then repositioned so the stop is a distance from the dado head that equals the spacing between dadoes. The next dado cut is made in the stock by setting the first dado over the stop. Each successive dado is located by placing the preceding dado over the stop as shown in Figure 13–38.

Making rabbet cuts with the dado head (Fig. 13–39) is much faster than making two cuts with a saw blade as described on page 181 of this chapter. The dado head makes cutting rabbets much easier, especially when the cut is to be made on large panels. It is advisable to use an auxiliary board fastened to the fence for this operation as shown in Figure 13–39. With the wooden fence, the blades may be positioned against the fence, cutting into the wood to some extent if necessary.

Tongue and tenoning cuts are also quickly and easily produced with the dado head. Refer to Chapter 23, Tenoning, which presents more specific information about cutting tenons on the table saw.

Cutting stopped or blind dadoes and grooves (Fig. 13–40). Depending upon the particular workpiece or pieces involved, cuts of this kind require the operator to lower the stock over the revolving dado head. This in itself is a dangerous practice as one can easily visualize. However, with the correct procedure (which makes use of stops to keep the work from being thrown back), this class of work can be accomplished with a reasonable measure of safety.

Cuts of this type are widely used in furniture and cabinetmaking. They are best suited to the table saw when the workpieces are of larger sizes. Smaller work should be cut with a router or with hand tools. In some cases, a fixture for

* Illustrations identified with an asterisk (*) indicate that the saw guard has been removed for illustrative purposes only. The guard should be used when performing these operations in the shop.

Fig.13–38. * Making equally spaced dadoes. Here the operator is positioning the dado over the stop prior to cutting the third one.

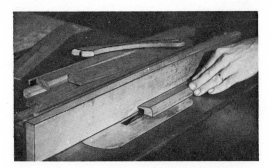

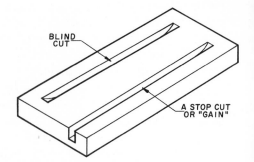

BLIND
CUT

A STOP CUT
OR "GAIN"

Fig. 13–39. * Making a rabbet cut with a dado head. Note the auxiliary board fastened to the rip fence and the push stick in position, ready for use.

Fig. 13–40. These cuts are made by lowering the workpiece onto the revolving saw blade. Stops clamped to the fence determine starting and finishing points.

the table saw may be constructed to keep your hands away from the revolving dado head and enable you to hold the stock firmly while lowering it over the cutters. Work that requires cuts of greater width and depth also requires additional precautions since the possibility of kickback increases because there is more of the dado head exposed to grab and throw the stock. Be sure to check this operation with your instructor. The procedure for setting up and cutting blind dadoes and grooves with a dado head is as follows:

1. Install the dado head set for the desired width of cut and elevate it

above the table equal to the depth of cut desired.
2. Clamp or screw an auxiliary board to the rip fence.
3. Move the fence against the dado head. Mark each end of the cutting arc of the dado head where it projects through the table as shown in Figure 13–41.
4. Reset the fence so the cut will be

* Illustrations identified with an asterisk (*) indicate that the saw guard has been removed for illustrative purposes only. The guard should be used when performing these operations in the shop.

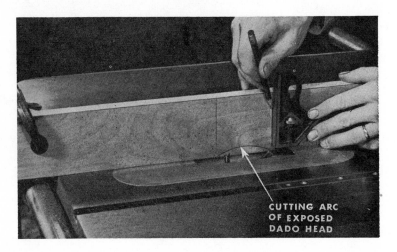

CUTTING ARC
OF EXPOSED
DADO HEAD

Fig. 13–41. With the fence set close to the dado head, the limits of the cutting are marked on it.

Fig. 13–42. The work is positioned so that the mark (arrow) indicating where the cut is to begin is in line with the rear mark on the fence. A stop (hand screw clamp) is fastened to the fence to establish this position.

made the desired distance from the edge of the workpiece.

5. Mark the locations indicating where the cut is to start and end on the top of the workpiece (pieces) as shown by the arrows on the stock in Figure 13–42.

6. Fasten stop blocks to the fence so as to limit the length of cut. Blind cuts require two stops; one to stop the feed and an additional stop to prevent the work from being thrown back when starting the cut. The location of this stop in relation to the work is shown by the clamp in Figure 13–42.

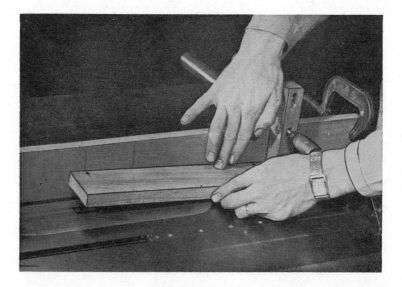

Fig. 13–43. Lowering the work over the revolving dado head. Note the work is held against the stop as well as against the fence.

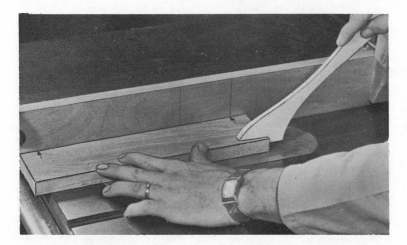

Fig. 13–44. The stock is fed to a second stop block clamped to the fence or to the arrow indicating where the cut is to end. If the cut is to run through, use a push stick as shown to complete the cut.

7. Turn on the power.
8. Place the edge of the work against the fence, and put one end on the table, holding the end against the nearest stop (Fig. 13–43). Gradually lower the work over the revolving dado head.
9. When the stock rests flat on the table, feed it forward until the end of the cut is reached. This point is reached when the corresponding marks on the fence and the work line up (Fig. 13–44) or the end of the work hits the second stop.
10. Hold the work down on the table (with pressure against the fence and the stop), and turn off the power.

NOTE: The illustrations here show the steps of procedure for grooving. The same general procedures are followed (using stops) for stop dadoing except that the miter gauge may also be used to keep the work at a right angle to the line of cut.

Chapter 14 Radial Arm Sawing in the School Shop

The radial arm saw is sometimes referred to as the *radial saw*. It is used for a multitude of sawing operations. Basic operations such as crosscutting, ripping of large stock, and cutting bevels, miters, or compound angles are easily performed on this machine. With a dado head, the usual grooving and dado cuts may also be made. Several accessories are available to convert this machine for a variety of woodworking operations.

Safety precautions for radial saws. Safe use of the radial saw requires an understanding of the hazards involved, the correct procedures and the setups for the various operations. Observe the following safety rules.

1. Use the correct blade for the job. Mount it so the teeth point in the direction of the arrow marked on the guard and motor (Figs. 14–1 and 14–2).
2. Adjust the saw depth so that it cuts into the table about $\frac{1}{16}$ in.*
3. Check all guards, anti-kickback, and locking devices before starting the

---

* A piece of ¼-in. hardboard tacked over the table at the corners will preserve the surface. The hardboard is replaced when necessary. This eliminates the eventual replacement and adjustment of a new table surface.

motor.
4. Position the stock firmly against the guide fence. Stock should rest firmly on the table.
5. Never reach across the line of the cut.
6. Return the saw to its starting position at the rear of the table after completing the cut.
7. Remove stock from the table only after the saw is returned to its starting position.
8. When ripping, ploughing, or grooving, be sure that the saw blade rotates against the direction of feed.

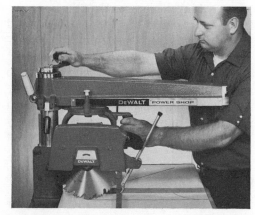

Fig. 14–1. The depth of cut is adjusted by raising or lowering the arm.

Fig. 14–2. Mounting the saw blade. The teeth must point in the direction of motor rotation.

1. Raise the arm sufficiently (Fig. 14–1) to bring the blade out of the kerf in the table surface.
2. Remove the guard.
3. Hold the arbor with one wrench and loosen the arbor nut (left-hand thread) with another wrench. Or, place a block between the saw teeth and the table and break the nut loose with a wrench.
4. Remove the arbor nut, outside collar, and the blade from the arbor.
5. Mount the new blade (or cutters) with the teeth pointing downward (trademark up) in the direction of the arbor rotation. This is indicated by an arrow on the motor and guard.
6. Replace the collar (with the recessed side against the blade), tighten the arbor nut by turning it in a counterclockwise direction while holding the arbor.
7. Replace the guard assembly.
8. Lower the arm to place the teeth about $\frac{1}{16}$ in. below the table surface.

Use the anti-kickback fingers and splitter whenever possible (Fig. 14–12).

9. Always keep guards in place. Anti-kickback fingers are *not* used for crosscutting. They should be set to clear the work and guard the exposed edge of the saw blade. In this position the blade will "sweep" away anything in its travel path.
10. *Always* shut off the machine and *wait until the blade stops before making any adjustments* in the setup.
11. Before changing from crosscutting to ripping, angle cuts, or other setups, always be sure to elevate the arm *before* moving it. This is necessary to raise the blade out of the kerf in the table.

Basic Operational Procedures

Changing a saw blade (Fig. 14–2) or mounting other cutters is accomplished as follows:

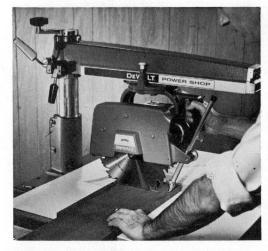

Fig. 14–3. * When the longest part of the stock extends to the left, it is held against the fence with the left hand. The right hand pulls the saw through the cut.

Fig. 14–4. The left hand feeds the saw when the longest length of the stock is to the right of the saw. The stop clamped to the graduated bar permits cutting identical lengths. Note the roller table extension and the dust hood at the rear. (Guard removed for illustrative purposes only.)

GRADUATED BAR

STOP BLOCK

Crosscutting (Figs. 14–3 and 14–4) is the most widely performed operation on the radial-arm saw. Use the following procedure for setting up and performing crosscutting operations:

1. Use a crosscut or combination blade.
2. Set the arm at right angles to the guide fence. The arm is positioned with the latch shown in Figure 14–5 and then locked with the clamp handle.
3. Place the work firmly against the fence.
4. The kickback fingers are not used for crosscutting. Set them about ⅛ in. above the stock so they are out of the way.
5. The layout line, if used, should be lined up with the saw kerf in the fence. If stops are used, set them at the proper distance from the blade.
6. Hold the stock with either the left or the right hand. If the greater

length of the work is on the left side of the blade, hold the work with your left hand (Fig. 14–3). Use the right hand to pull the yoke handle. However, if most of the stock extends to the right of the blade, hold the work with your right hand and use the left hand to pull the saw through the work (Fig. 14–4).

7. Turn on the power and let the motor reach its full speed.
8. Grip the yoke handle firmly, and pull the saw steadily through the work to make the cut. *Caution:* When cutting heavy stock, hold the handle very firmly. If not the saw may walk too rapidly into the work and tend to jump forward toward you. Therefore, you should be prepared to resist the forward travel of the saw.
9. At the completion of the cut, immediately return the saw to the rear

Fig. 14–5a. Releasing the clamp and lifting the latch allows the arm to swing horizontally to any angle.

Fig. 14–5b. The motor is tilted by releasing the bevel clamp pulling out the bevel locating pin.

of the table and turn off the power.

10. To cut off more than one piece to the same length, clamp a stop block to the table or use the graduated bar as shown in Figure 14–4.

11. Stock too thick to be cut in one pass of the blade may be cut as follows: (1) raise the blade to cut a little more than half the thickness; (2) set a stop block to the length of the cut; (3) make one cut; (4) turn the stock over; and (5) complete the cut on the other side.

12. To make a miter cut, use the same set-up and procedure as for cross-cutting, but tilt the motor to the desired angle (Fig. 14–5).

13. To make *dado* (Fig. 14–6) and end *rabbet* cuts (Fig. 14–7), use the

Fig. 14–6. The radial saw is ideally suited to making stopped dadoes because the layout marks are clearly visible. (Guard removed for illustrative purposes only.)

same procedure as for crosscutting. Always make a trial cut to be sure that the cutters are set to the desired depth and width. The cut can be made to any width by moving the stock for successive cuts. A stop clamped to the fence will position the stock when several pieces must be cut in an identical manner.

Flat and compound mitering (Figs. 14–8 and 14–9) are performed in much the same manner as crosscutting except that the arm is first set and locked to the desired angle on the miter scale. As when cutting miters on the circular saw, you must be aware that the work has a tendency to "creep." To prevent this, use stops clamped to the fence or use anchor points. A nail or screw with the

Fig. 14–7. Using the dado head to simultaneously make end lap joint cuts on 2 pieces of stock. (Guard removed for illustrative purposes only.)

Fig. 14–8. Cutting a flat miter. The arm is locked at the 45-degree position. (Guard removed for illustrative purposes only.)

Fig. 14–9. Sawing a compound angle cut on a jack rafter. The set-up is made by tilting motor and swinging the arm to the desired angles. (Guard removed for illustrative purposes only.)

Fig. 14–10. The hooded upper guard is lowered to a point just above the stock when ripping. Always use a push stick to complete the cut.

point protruding through the fence makes a good anchor point.

Cutting miters. Follow this procedure for setting up and making miter cuts:
1. Raise the arm slightly so the blade will clear the table.
2. Release the miter clamp and miter latch. Swing the arm and lock it at the desired angle.

3. Start the motor and lower the arm until the teeth run about $\frac{1}{16}$ in. below the table top.
4. Return the saw to the rear of the table and stop the motor.
5. Place the stock on the table and cut it as in normal crosscutting (Fig. 14–8). NOTE: It is always a good idea to make a trial cut on a scrap piece of stock, checking the angle for accuracy.
6. To make compound angle cuts (commonly called bevel miters), the saw blade must be tilted and the arm set at an angle (Fig. 14–9). Table 14–1 provides the settings for both the miter-angle setting of the arm and the blade tilt for various compound-angle cuts.

For example: To cut a 4-sided picture frame with the sides tilting outward at 45 deg. (the work angle), the machine settings are: blade tilt — 30 deg.; arm setting — 35¼ deg.

Ripping (Figs. 14–10 and 14–11) is

Work Angle (Degrees)	4-Sides Blade Tilt (Degrees)	4-Sides Arm Setting (Degrees)	6-Sides Blade Tilt (Degrees)	6-Sides Arm Setting (Degrees)	8-Sides Blade Tilt (Degrees)	8-Sides Arm Setting (Degrees)
5	44¾	5	29¾	2½	22¼	2
10	44¼	9¾	29½	5½	22	4
15	43¼	14½	29	8¼	21½	6
20	41¾	18¾	28¼	11	21	8
25	40	23	27¼	13½	20¼	10
30	37¾	26½	26	16	19½	11¾
35	35¼	29¾	24½	18¼	18¼	13¼
40	32½	32¾	22¾	20¼	17	15
45	30	35¼	21	22¼	15¾	16¼
50	27	37½	19	23¾	14¼	17½
55	24	39¼	16¾	25¼	12½	18¾
60	21	41	14½	26½	11	19¾

Front View — 4-Sides — 6-Sides — 8-Sides

Table 14–1. Blade tilt and arm settings for compound angle cuts on the radial arm saw or the table saw. Use the values given in the columns marked blade tilt, and move the miter gauge from a right angle setting the number of degrees indicated in the arm setting columns.

not the safest and easiest of the basic radial arm operations. It requires extra precautions and a thorough knowledge of the correct machine setup and sawing procedure. Be sure that each step is thoroughly checked out. Remember this most important rule for radial-arm ripping: *The stock must be fed against the direction of blade rotation.* Study Figure 14–10. Failure to observe this rule of feed direction can be disastrous. If the work is fed in the same direction as the saw's rotation, it will pull the work out of the operator's hands and throw it violently.

Rip cuts are made by swiveling the motor and yoke so that the saw blade is parallel to the fence (Fig. 14–12). Stock may be ripped from either the right or left of the machine so long as the rule of feeding into the blade rotation

Fig. 14–11. Release the yoke clamp and then lift the locating pin to swivel the motor and yoke right or left for ripping.

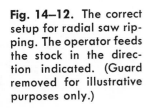

Fig. 14–12. The correct setup for radial saw ripping. The operator feeds the stock in the direction indicated. (Guard removed for illustrative purposes only.)

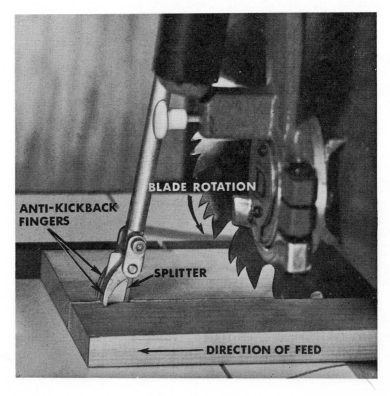

BLADE ROTATION

ANTI-KICKBACK FINGERS

SPLITTER

DIRECTION OF FEED

Fig. 14–13. A front extension increases the ripping capacity of the radial arm saw.

is followed. The setup and cutting procedure for radial arm ripping is as follows:

1. With the arm in the crosscut position, raise it so that the blade will clear the table.
2. Revolve the yoke so the blade is

parallel to the fence (Fig. 14–12). Preferably, set the blade so that the feed is from the right of the machine as shown in Figure 14–11.

3. Lock the carriage on the arm where it will give the desired width of cut between the fence and the saw blade.
4. Lower the arm so the blade is below the surface of the table $\frac{1}{16}$ in.
5. Rotate the hooded guard down until it just clears the stock on the in-feed end and lock it.
6. Position the splitter and anti-kick-back fingers on the opposite end of the guard as shown in Figure 14–10.
7. Start the machine and feed the stock with slow, even pressure. Do not stand in line with the blade.
8. Always use a push stick, one that is at least 12 to 18 in. long, to complete the cut, *no matter how wide* the cut is (Fig. 14–10).
9. Bevel ripping cuts may be made following the above procedure with the blade tilted to the desired angle.
10. Large panels (wider than the normal capacity of the saw) may be ripped on machines equipped with a front

Fig. 14–14. Cutting simulated louvered doors with a two-knife shaper head attachment on the radial saw.

Fig. 14–15. Another example of the flexibility of radial saws. The edge of a lip type cabinet door is shaped in one pass with a shaper cutter mounted on the saw arbor.

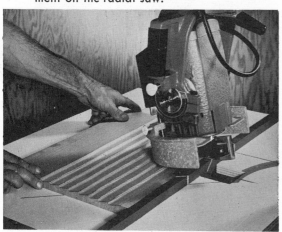

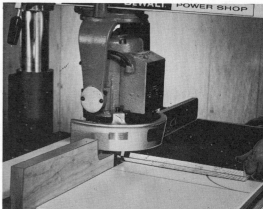

table extension. The fence is removed and the stock is guided against the raised lip on the front extension (Fig. 14–13).

NOTE: The radial-arm saw may be used for other machining operations with the aid of appropriate attachments. Figures 14–14 and 14–15 show the machine performing shaping operations.

REVIEW QUESTIONS

1. What are the two broad classifications of all industrial sawing processes?
2. What types of saws were used by the early settlers of this country?
3. What is a pit saw? What is the significance of the term "top sawyer"?
4. What are the three basic types of cutting action employed with machine saws?
5. Who is credited with the invention of the first successful circular saw?
6. Who invented the first successful band saw?
7. What is a mill band saw? What is its principal use?
8. What materials were used in the construction of machines before the 1800's?
9. Who developed the first tilting-arbor saw?
10. List some of the disadvantages or limitations of early woodworking machinery.
11. What is a self-feed saw? Who developed the first self-feed power rip saw? How did the feeding mechanism function?
12. Who developed the first radial-arm saw? How long has it been in use?
13. How are portable saws powered?
14. Explain the differences in the design and cutting action of the rip and crosscut saws.
15. What is meant by the term "points per inch"?
16. What are the advantages of sawing with a miter box?
17. What kinds of saws may be used for cutting green wood?
18. List the various types of portable reciprocating saws.
19. What types of driving mechanisms are embodied in the construction of jigsaws?
20. What are the two basic kinds of circular saws?
21. How are the sizes of circular saws specified?
22. What is a variety saw? a universal saw?
23. What part of the table saw is used for crosscutting operations?
24. What is the rip fence? How is it used?
25. What is the "splitter" of a table saw?
26. What is the advantage of a saw table with a roll or sliding section?
27. Compare the difference in the cutting action of table saws and radial-arm saws.
28. What is a cut-off saw?
29. What types of saws are used for production ripping processes?
30. How is the shadow of a wire employed in industrial ripping operations?
31. What types of machinery are used to saw large sheet materials?
32. What are the four basic types of band saws?
33. How is the size of a band saw determined?
34. What sizes are typical of band mill saws?
35. What is a saw kerf?
36. In what three ways is clearance provided between the blade and the kerf?
37. What materials are saw blades made of?
38. What is the function of the "gullet" of a saw tooth?

39. What types of circular-saw blades are commonly found in the school shop?
40. What is a glue joint rip saw?
41. What are the various devices by which dadoes are cut?
42. What kind of teeth are found on the inside chippers of a standard dado head set?
43. What steps are being taken in saw blade design to improve the smoothness of the sawn surface?
44. List several ways in which wood may be cut in the future.
45. What general rules should be observed when cutting plywood with band and portable saws?
46. How is a hand saw guided when starting a cut?
47. What safety rules should be observed when using portable power saws?
48. What is pocket cutting?
49. What is "freehand" sawing?
50. Explain how inside cuts are made with the jigsaw.
51. How is the speed of a band-saw blade determined?
52. What is a "relief cut"?
53. How is the width of band-saw blades related to the minimum radii of curves that may be sawn?
54. Describe several methods of cutting identical parts on jigsaws and band saws.
55. In what ways may the band saw be used to prepare stock for turning on the lathe?
56. List several work examples that may be handled by compound sawing operations on the band saw.
57. Explain the procedure for resawing on the band saw.
58. List three acceptable ways in which a stop is used for crosscutting parts to identical length on the table saw.
59. List five hazardous situations in which a kickback may occur.
60. Explain how to set the table saw fence for cutting stock to 4-in. widths.
61. What is a "feather board"?
62. Describe the function and use of a tapering jig.
63. What is the rim speed of an 8-in. circular saw?
64. Calculate the blade speed in surface feet per minute of the band saw in the shop.
65. What are the advantages of using an auxiliary board clamped to the miter gauge?
66. How are kerfs cut for splines or clamp nails of miter joints?
67. List the procedures involved to set up and cut a ⅜ by ⅜-in. rabbet in a ¾ by 18-in. panel.
68. How are these cuts made on the table saw: cove, taper, groove, dado, stopped dado?
69. What kinds of safety equipment are recommended for radial-arm saws?
70. When ripping with radial-arm saws, how should the stock be fed in relationship to the rotation of the blade?
71. Explain the specific safety precautions that must be observed when crosscutting with the radial-arm saw.
72. What is meant by the term "creeping" when applied to miter sawing operations?
73. What operations other than sawing may be performed on the jigsaw, band saw, table saw, and radial-arm saw?

SUGGESTED STUDENT ACTIVITIES

1. Make an enlarged model of rip, crosscut, and combination saw teeth.
2. Demonstrate one method of coiling a band saw blade.
3. Make a model of a wheel and pitman mechanism.
4. Design a push stick or jig for ripping stock to ⅛-in. widths in quantity.
5. Make a jig for sawing finger joints on the band saw.
6. Construct a circle sawing jig for the band saw.
7. Make a wooden model of a jigsaw with a treadle drive and a wooden spring pole.
8. Design a jig for a 10-in. table saw that will permit accurate crosscutting of panels 24 in. in width.
9. Prepare a paper dealing with the history of sawing tools.

Chapter 15 Planing

Planing is the process by which a thin layer of stock is removed in order to obtain a flat, true surface. Planing is performed with many different types of hand and machine tools. In *hand planing,* the cutter is supported in a block or frame. The design of the tool enables it to cut a continuous shaving as it is moved over the stock. In *machine planing,* several cutters or knives are fastened in a cylindrically shaped cutterhead, which rotates at high speed and discharges a series of short shavings.

Planing is an important machining operation. Most boards, after being sawed, are planed at some stage in their fabrication into a finished product.

The Evolution of Hand Planes and Machinery

Several hundred thousand years ago, prehistoric man discovered that the same sharp stones which cut his feet could be used to cut wood and bone. Thus, man's first cutting tools were completely fashioned by nature. Later in the Old Stone Age, man chipped or flaked flints to a shape that could be held more comfortably in his hand (Fig. 15–1a). Archaeologists refer to this early tool as a *hand axe*. Early man used this hand axe as a weapon to kill animals, as a knife to cut meat, and to scrape hides for clothing. It was also used as a multipurpose woodworking tool for making clubs, spears, arrows, and the like.

It was well over 50,000 years ago that Old Stone Age man applied the principle of mechanical leverage to his hand axe. He did this by tying a handle to his axe with rawhide or fiber lacings. Later in this same period, flints were shaped to resemble knives, chisels (Fig. 15–1b) and other tools. In this manner, man developed the basic tools for slicing, scraping, chipping (Fig. 15–2), and chopping. This marked the beginning of man's continuing efforts to make and re-

Fig. 15–1. Prehistoric tools made from stone; (left) hand axe, (right) chisel, wedge shaped with a sharp cutting edge.

Fig. 15–2. A polished flint chipping tool fixed to a bone handle was used in the New Stone Age.

Fig. 15–3. Bronze Age axe.

Fig. 15–4. Bronze Age knife.

fine tools to solve his technical problems.

Out of the Bronze Age, 4000 to 6000 years ago, evolved improved forms of cutting tools such as the axe (Fig. 15–3), the adze (Fig. 15–4), the knife (Fig. 15–5), and the chisel (Fig. 15–6). All of the cutting implements which developed in the Bronze Age (with the exception of the saw) incorporated a cutting edge shaped like a wedge.

Many of the boards and timbers that were used in the construction of early implements and buildings were chopped to the desired shape directly from the log. This chopping process, known as *hewing,* was accomplished with the adze (Fig. 15–7) and the axe. The adze was used to make crossgrain cuts in roughing a round log to a more usable shape. Then the log was smoothed and made true with the broad axe (Fig. 15–8). The broad axe was beveled only on one side to give it a cutting action similar to that of a modern wood chisel. This permitted the axe to be laid flat against the surface of the work for final smoothing (or planing).

An iron adze was one of the major tools used by Colonial carpenters and shipbuilders. This adze had a long or short handle. Some were made with

Fig. 15–5. Bronze Age Egyptian adze.

Fig. 15–6. Bronze Age wood chisel resembling the modern cold chisel used in metalwork.

Fig. 15–7. The short handled adze was used in the process of squaring logs for making boards, beams, and rafters.

curved cutting edges for gouging out logs to be used as boats, troughs, and rain gutters. The adze was a very hazardous tool. Its blade was at right angles to the handle (similar to a garden hoe) and swung dangerously close to the craftsman's feet as he hacked away at the work. The adze is still used to some ex-

Fig. 15–8. A broad axe of the late Iron Age.

Fig. 15–9. This early Roman plane with a metal-covered base dates between 50 B.C. and 300 A.D.

tent in the shipwright trades for fitting heavy timbers. The modern axe is made in many different sizes and shapes, but today it is considered a tree-felling tool rather than a planing or construction tool.

The first **hand planes** had a cutting edge (plane iron) supported in a wood block and are known to have been used by the ancient Romans. It has not been definitely determined that these early planes were fitted with a wooden body rather than a metal shoe-type base as shown in Figure 15–9. However, it is certain that planes made during succeeding centuries had wooden bases. The thirteenth-century Chinese plane and the *hog* plane of the late 1700's are typical of early wooden-base planes. See Figures 15–10 and 15–11. The early Chinese planes were pulled toward the operator, unlike present-day planes which are pushed. To pull, rather than push, is still the custom in the Far East. It is interesting to note that in these two examples of early planes, the plane iron was held

Fig. 15–10. A Chinese plane of the 1200's.

in place with a wedge jammed against a cross pin.

Many of the European and Colonial American craftsmen who practiced a specialized trade made their own planes. Consequently, a great many of them were designed to perform special types of planing. See Figures 15–12, 15–13, 15–14, 15–15, and 15–16. Some of these planes were crude and rough hewn. Others were expertly crafted and beautifully carved, exemplifying the craftsman's pride in his work (Fig. 15–16).

The sheer wealth and variety of these special planes prohibit a detailed presentation here. Suffice to say, they include a wide variety of *molding planes* with cutting edges and bases shaped to the desired style. *Rabbet planes, curved base planes* and *toothing planes* are other classifications of early special purpose planes. *Spokeshaves* were developed for both

Fig. 15–12. An early European smoothing plane.

Fig. 15–13. This old plow plane incorporated threaded adjustments and was used for cutting grooves in the edges of boards.

Fig. 15–11. A one- or two-man hog plane used by Colonial craftsmen of the late 1700's. When used as a 2-man plane, a rope was attached to the side pins, and it was usually pulled by a boy apprentice, as the master craftsman pushed.

Fig. 15–14. This early chisel plane was used for planing into corners. It is one of the forerunners of the modern bullnose plane.

Fig. 15–15. Cooper's jointer plane, the largest of all early types of planes. Wood was pushed over this inverted plane in much the same manner that stock is pushed over a modern machine jointer.

Fig. 15–18. This coachmaker's spokeshave was used to cut tenons on wagon wheel spokes.

shaping and planing operations. They are classified as a form of plane because of their construction and cutting action. Originally, the spokeshave was designed and used by early wheelwrights and carriage and coach makers to shape spokes for wooden wheels. Three early styles

of spokeshaves are shown in Figures 15–17, 15–18, and 15–19.

Early planing machines. Evidence of man's efforts to develop planing and surfacing machines to replace laborious hand methods date back to the 1700's. The first planing machine pushed or

Fig. 15–16. A handsomely carved jointer plane. Similar planes of longer lengths were known as flooring planes. The cross pin has been eliminated and a carved opening has been made for the wedge grip.

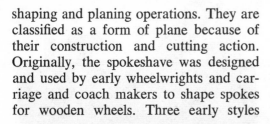

Fig. 15–17. A convex cutting spokeshave which was used for shaping round spokes by the early coachmaker.

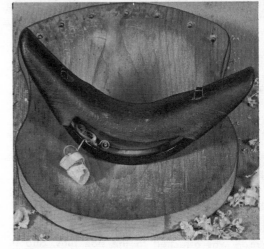

Fig. 15–19. An early spokeshave used to cut the concave shape in chair seats.

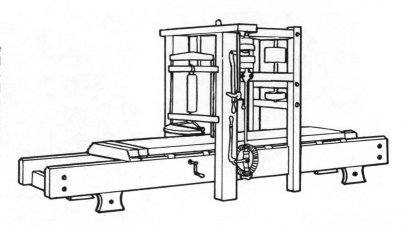

Fig. 15–20. A late model of the improved traverse or Daniels planing machine. The wood frame was copied from the design of a metal cutting planer that had a carriage feed and planed in both directions of carriage travel.

pulled a hand plane across the work. In 1776, a machine based on this principle was patented in England. It had several plane irons rigged with pulleys so they could be moved over the stock which was clamped to the table. The next machine to appear was the *fixed knife planer*. It was equipped with a stationary knife, resembling that of a large hand plane, supported in a frame over a set of powered feed rollers. The top surface of the stock was planed as the feed rollers carried it under the fixed cutter.

A mechanical genius named Samuel Bentham invented many machines and tooling processes from 1791 through 1793 while in charge of an English shipbuilding yard. Bentham contributed much to the development of woodworking machinery and manufacturing techniques. Among his inventions are the planer, jointer, matcher, molder and numerous cutting processes, most of which employed a rotary cutting action. Today's production machines still operate on this principle.

In 1802, a *traverse planing machine* was invented by Joseph Bramah, a young associate of Samuel Bentham. Like Miller's table saw, both the Bentham and Bramah planers were crudely constructed.

They were made with wooden frames with only the cutters and bearings made of metal. The traverse planing machine employed a set of cutters attached to a disk which revolved in a horizontal plane as the stock passed under it on a carriage (Fig. 15–20).

A machine similar to the traverse planer appeared soon after in this country. This American made machine was the *Daniels planer*. It had an improved roll feed device to carry the stock into the machine. In 1828, William Woodworth combined the rotary cutting head with feed rollers and obtained a patent on an improved planing machine which was a true production machine. Feed rollers moved the stock into the revolving blades and side cutters made grooves and tongues on its edges.

The first practical planing machine embodying a *cylinder type of cutting head* was built by Baxter D. Whitney in Massachusetts in 1846 (Fig. 15–21). The cylinder cutting head soon proved to be the most efficient for surfacing stock and rapidly became a standard feature of all planers. In 1866, Whitney introduced an improved planer which incorporated the first wedge bed adjustment. This planer won a silver medal award for Whitney

Fig. 15–21. The first planer with a cylindrical cutterhead.

Fig. 15–23. Whitney's first double planer, introduced in 1883.

Fig. 15–22. Whitney's famed Silver Medal Planer featured the first wedge type bed adjustment.

Fig. 15–24. The first direct motor-driven planer, introduced in 1911.

Fig. 15–25. The 1912 Whitney direct-drive double planer.

Fig. 15–26. A cylindrical cutterhead set diagonally on an improved Daniels planer. The feed rollers are swung to the side to enable the carriage to return to the position for starting another cut.

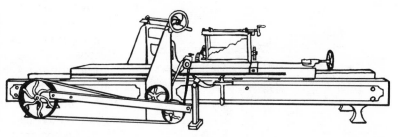

at the Paris exposition in 1867, and the machine became popularly known in the industry as the Silver Medal Planer (Fig. 15–22). The innovation of the wedge bed adjustment enabled the operator to change the thickness of the cut by raising and lowering the bed; previously, the cutter head had to be raised and lowered (See Figure 15–20). The wedge adjustment is a construction feature of heavy duty planers today. Other features of the Silver Medal Planer included four geared feed rollers capable of carrying wet or dry lumber through the machine. The speed of the rollers could be varied by means of cone pulleys. The bearings were made of a tin-and-copper alloy (bronze) which proved to be much better than the iron or Babbitt bearings previously used.

In 1883, Whitney built the first double planer (Fig. 15–23) for the woodworking industry. This planer cut both surfaces of the lumber, thereby reducing it to uniform thickness in just one pass through the machine. In 1911, Whitney introduced a direct-drive motorized planer (Fig. 15–24), and then followed with a direct-drive double planer in 1912 (Fig. 15–25).

Another significant development in the evolution of planing machinery was the introduction of a diagonal cutting head (Fig. 15–26). This improvement was brought out by the S. A. Woods Machine Co. in the 1880's. The feature of having the cutterhead set at an angle to the direction of stock travel eliminated much of the chipping and tearing of cross-grained wood. The diagonal cutterhead is still used on some heavy machinery, particularly in lumber-planing mills.

Planing machines were quickly accepted in the early lumber mills and woodworking factories for the surfacing of boards and timbers. Vertical spindle cutterheads were later added to both the single and the double planers for cutting

Fig. 15–27. A planing and matching machine used in the late 1890's. A top planing head, vertically adjustable, and two side matching heads could work stock on three sides at the rate of about 34 feet per minute.

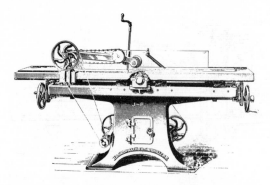

Fig. 15–28. A belt driven hand planer or jointer with a power feed attachment that dates to the late 1800's.

lumber on one or both surfaces and both edges with one pass through the machine. Machines of this type became known as *planing and matching* machines (Fig. 15–27). The vertical cutterheads, called *matching heads* or *side heads,* were also used to cut tongues and grooves on the board edges while it was being planed. Planers and matchers that were used strictly in the production of flooring products soon became known simply as *flooring machines.* Another similar machine with its cutterhead knives ground

to cut a wide variety of narrow cross-sectional shapes, such as interior trim and stair railings, became known as a *molder.* Because of the narrow sticks usually handled by these machines they were also called *stickers.* Molding machines are now common. They may have as many as six cutterheads and are used to machine higher-grade materials and to produce smoother finishes than planing and matching machines.

The early **hand planers or jointers** were developed to do the work previously done with hand planes (see Fig. 15–15). These machines understandably became known as either jointers or hand planers. The first jointer is credited to Samuel Bentham in 1793.

The early jointers were made with wooden frames. The transition to iron frames or bases was made in the 1850's. The first jointers to be made with cast iron bases were similar in appearance to the jointers made today. However, they lacked many of the refinements and safety features of today's machines. For example, guards were not provided to cover the rotating cutterheads, the drive

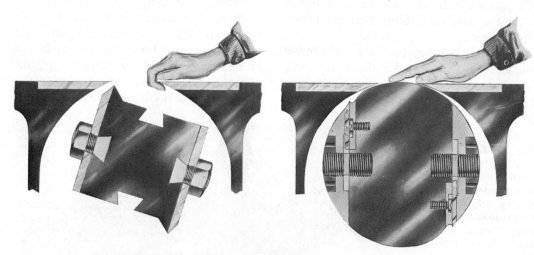

Fig. 15–29. The change from the square jointer cutterhead to the cylindrical cutterhead, was made in 1908.

belts or the pulleys. Even today, with their improved guards and other safety devices, the jointer remains one of the most dangerous pieces of equipment to operate. This is due largely to the fact that most jointers are hand-fed machines.

In the late 1800's, the H. B. Smith Machine Co. introduced a power-feed attachment for their jointers (Fig. 15–28). Today, industry uses various power-feed devices on jointers which are used to plane the edges of boards to be glued into larger panels. The power-feed jointer provides maximum protection for the operator.

The first jointer cutterheads were square. This type of cutterhead was replaced by a cylindrical cutterhead developed in England. The Oliver Machinery Co. introduced this feature in this country in 1908. The evident safety features of the cylindrical cutterhead are shown in Figure 15–29.

Chapter 16 Hand and Portable Powered Planes

Hand planes and the modern versions of the special-purpose hand planes have limited use in mass production. They are, however, still used by skilled workers such as carpenters, cabinetmakers, model and patternmakers, and other craftsmen in custom manufacturing. Portable powered planes are being used in some industries to supplement the regular production equipment. They are also gradually replacing some of the hand planes used by the custom builders.

The Common Hand Planes

The hand planes available today are much improved over the crude tools of yesterday. The body of the plane is now machined cast iron. The *cutter,* which is also called a *plane iron,* is not made of iron but of high quality tool steel which retains a sharp cutting edge much longer than its old iron counterparts.

The names of the basic parts of a hand plane are shown in Figure 16–1. The

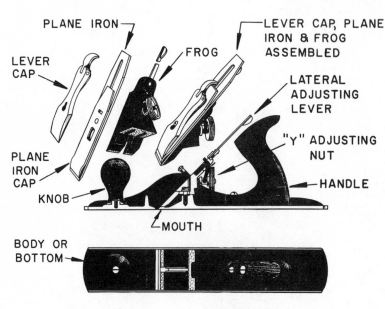

PLANE IRON — FROG — LEVER CAP, PLANE IRON & FROG ASSEMBLED

LEVER CAP — LATERAL ADJUSTING LEVER — "Y" ADJUSTING NUT

PLANE IRON CAP — KNOB — MOUTH — HANDLE

BODY OR BOTTOM

Fig. 16–1. The parts of a hand plane.

210

plane iron does the cutting. The *plane iron cap* reinforces the plane iron and breaks the chip. The *lever cap* clamps the plane iron and the plane-iron cap securely to the *frog* by means of a cam. Most planes have a screw mechanism to control the depth of cut. This is composed of a knurled, brass thumb nut and a Y-adjusting lever which raises or lowers the plane iron. The plane iron projects through a narrow opening, called the *mouth,* in the bottom of the plane. The *lateral adjusting lever* moves the plane iron so that the cutting edge may be aligned with the bottom of the plane, permitting a uniform thickness of cut.

There are five hand planes which are generally considered as the *common planes.* These are the smooth, jack, fore, jointer, and block planes. See Figure 16–2. They are more widely used than other types of planes. Although they were designed for specific classes of work, they are sometimes used interchangeably. All other kinds of planes are made for special planing operations and therefore are grouped as special purpose planes.

Smooth planes (Fig. 16–2a) range in length from 7 to 10 inches. They are used for finishing work, usually after the surface has been made straight and true with one of the larger planes. They have either a 1¾- or 2-in. wide plane iron. The *scrub plane* is similar in appearance to the smooth plane. It is used for rough work, such as removing dirt, grit, paint, or for roughing stock to size. It generally lacks the usual blade adjustments and has a narrower blade, about 1¼ in.

The **jack plane** (Fig. 16–2b) is the most popular and widely used of all hand planes. It is used for both rough- and finish-planing operations. Because of its capacity for doing almost any kind of planing job, it was originally named a "jackass plane." Jack planes are made in

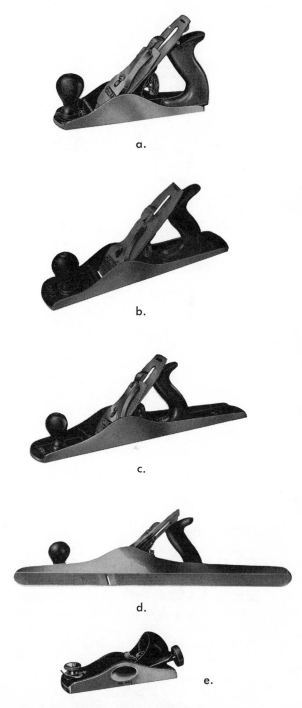

a.

b.

c.

d.

e.

Fig. 16–2. The common hand planes; (a) smooth plane, (b) jack plane, (c) fore plane, (d) jointer plane, and (e) block plane.

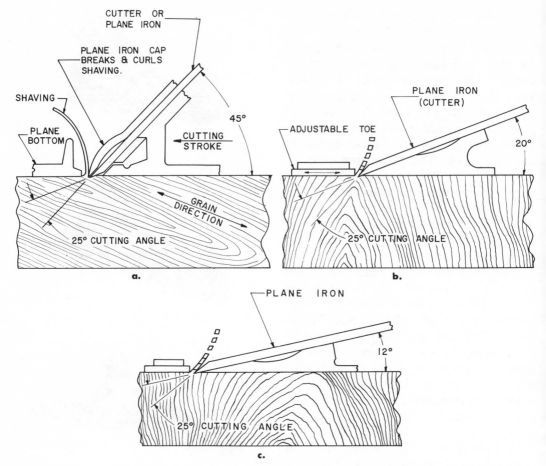

Fig. 16–3. Illustrating the cutting action of block planes, and other common planes.

lengths ranging from 11½ to 15 in. The most common size is the 14-in. model. The 11- and 12-in. models of this type are known as *junior jack planes*. The large jack planes have 2-in. wide plane irons; junior jack planes have plane irons 1¾ in. wide.

The **fore plane** (Fig. 16–2c) has an 18-in. body length and a plane iron 2⅜ in. in width. Its long length and wide plane iron make it especially suitable for edge planing extra long boards and surfaces or edges that are wider than normal.

The **jointer plane** (Fig. 16–2d) carries a plane iron 2⅜ in. wide and is made in lengths of 22, 24, and 30 in. Originally, jointer planes were used to plane exceptionally large or long surfaces, such as flooring, table tops, and similar types of work. Today, the jointer plane is used where its longer length facilitates edge jointing and surface truing.

The **block plane** (Fig. 16–2e) is primarily designed for planing end grain. Although it is not equipped with a cap to break the shaving, its small size makes it a handy plane for removing sharp corners and performing some of the conventional operations on work of smaller sizes. Block planes are 6 or 7 in. in length; plane irons are 1⅜ or 1⅝ in., respectively. They are made in two models, each having the cutter seated at a different angle. The 20-deg. angle type is used for general work. The 12-deg. angle type is intended for end-grain planing of hardwood.

The *cutting action* of the plane iron is illustrated in Figures 16–3a and 16–3b. The cutting action of the block plane is somewhat different from that of the other planes. The plane iron is ground to a bevel of 25 to 30 deg. for all hand planes. This is the usual cutting angle for planing both hardwoods and softwoods. The angle at which the plane iron is seated on the frog (tilted to the work) is 12 to 20 deg. on block planes (Fig. 16–3b) and 45 deg. on the others (Fig. 16–3a). The sharper "seating" angle of the plane iron on block planes enables it to cut off end-grain fibers more smoothly than other types of planes. In order to achieve the low "seating" angle on block planes, the plane iron is mounted with the bevel up, as shown in Figure 16–3b. Since the block plane cuts end-grain fibers, the shaving generally breaks itself into small chips as it strikes the bevel of the plane iron.

Planes which have the plane iron mounted with the bevel down are fitted with a plane-iron cap. They are normally used to cut a shaving from the work "with" the *grain* of the wood (Fig. 16–3a). They may also be used to plane stock with irregular grain (running in both directions), and sometimes against the grain. However, the results usually are disappointing. As the shaving passes through the mouth of the plane it is curled upward as it strikes the plane-iron cap. If the shaving is cut from cross-

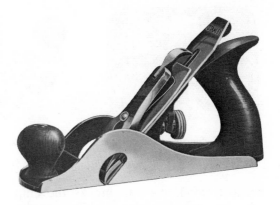

Fig. 16–4a. Bench rabbet plane.

Fig. 16–4b. Bullnose rabbet plane.

Fig. 16–4c. Duplex rabbet plane.

 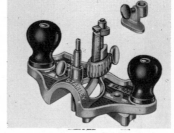 

Fig. 16–5. Small router plane. Fig. 16–6. Open-throat router Fig. 16–7. Combination plane.
plane.

grained wood, the cap breaks the chip off, thus reducing the tendency of the shaving to tear below the level of the cut. The plane cuts hard and irregular-grained wood best when the plane-iron cap is set $\frac{1}{64}$ in. to $\frac{1}{32}$ in. from the cutting edge of the plane iron. For soft-woods, this distance should be $\frac{1}{32}$ in. to $\frac{1}{16}$ in.

Special Purpose Hand Planes

Rabbet planes (Figs. 16–4a, 16–4b, and 16–4c) are specialty planes. There are many different kinds of rabbet planes, but the most common are: the *bench rabbet plane* (Fig. 16–4a), the *bullnose rabbet plane* (Fig. 16–4b), and the *duplex rabbet plane* (Fig. 16–4c). Rabbet planes, as the name implies, are primarily used for planing rabbets. They are also used for cross-grain planing such as trimming the shoulders or cheeks of tenons, smoothing large recesses, and fitting lap joints. The plane iron in all three of these planes is sharpened to a 25- to 30-deg. angle and installed with the bevel down. Each type of rabbet plane is best suited to a particular kind of rabbeting operation.

Bench rabbet planes (Fig. 16–4a) are made in 9- and 13-in. lengths. The 2⅛-in. plane irons are fitted with both a plane-iron cap and lever cap. They are especially suited to cutting or smoothing large rabbeted surfaces on patterns and models. Adjustments are similar to the common hand plane.

Bullnose rabbet planes (Fig. 16–4b) range from 4 to 6½ in. in length. Plane iron widths range from ¾ to 1³⁄₃₂ in. The position of the plane iron in the body of this plane permits its use in corners or other places that are hard to get at with conventional planes. Shorter bull-nose rabbet planes are often referred to as *cabinetmaker's rabbet planes* (not illus-trated) because they are ideally suited to this type of work. These, however, are usually of a special design. The front is removable, providing a form of *chisel plane*. With the cutting edge of the plane iron at the front, this plane is able to plane up to an obstruction.

The **duplex rabbet plane** (Fig. 16–4c) combines features of the bench and bull-nose rabbet planes. It has only one cutter, but two seats for it. One seat is used for regular work; the forward seat is used for bullnose work. It is equipped with an adjustable fence which can be used on either side of the plane. A small knife edge attachment severs the wood fibers to prevent tearing when rabbeting across the grain.

Router planes (Figs. 16–5 and 16–6) are used to surface the bottom of grooves, gains, dadoes, and other depressions. The *open-throat* type router plane (Fig. 16–6) comes with ¼ in., ½ in. and V cutters for various work requirements. Router planes are also used for inletting work and making recesses of equal depth in straight, concave, or convex surfaces.

The **combination plane** (Fig. 16–7) is similar to a rabbet plane, but is used to cut rabbets, dadoes, grooves, and moldings. Forty-five to fifty cutters of different sizes and shapes are available. It is equipped with two adjustable fences and an adjustable depth gauge. It is about 9 in. in length. A simpler version of this plane is known as a *plow plane*. Another plane, similar in function to the plow plane, is the *tongue and groove plane*. This has two cutters and two handles which permit a cutting stroke in either direction.

The **circular plane** (Fig. 16–8) is used for planing both concave or convex surfaces. The sole or base of the plane is made of flexible steel which may be adjusted to the desired curve by turning the center adjustment screw. This novel tool has a 1¾ in. wide plane iron and its length is about 10 in.

The **spokeshave** (Fig. 16–9). The cutting action of the spokeshave places it in the plane family. It is used to square, smooth, and shape convex or concave edges. It uses a cutter sharpened like a plane iron. Spokeshaves are available with either a flat or convex bottom. The convex bottom is used on concave edges which have a small radius. The straight-bottom type is used to cut flat or large radius curved surfaces. Spokeshaves measure about 9 or 10 in. between handle tips. They use a cutter 1¾ or 2 in. in width. They may be either pushed or pulled over the work.

NOTE: For information concerning the adjustment and use of the more

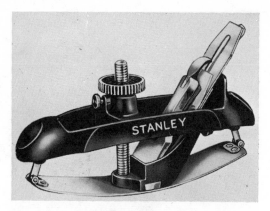

Fig. 16–8. Circular plane.

Fig. 16–9. Spokeshave.

widely used kinds of hand planes, refer to page 238, "Hand and Portable Planing Processes in the School Shop." Sharpening and maintenance of planes is discussed on page 576.

Portable Electric Planes and Portable Power Planers

Small, lightweight, portable electric planes and larger portable hand planers are relatively new. They developed because of the wide acceptance of the plane attachments for portable electric routers (Fig. 16–10). Portable electric planes are finding innumerable uses in many areas of woodworking where hand planes and jointers were previously used.

Portable electric hand planes (Figs. 16–11 and 16–12) are basically motor-driven cutters mounted in an aluminum housing. A part of the housing is adjust-

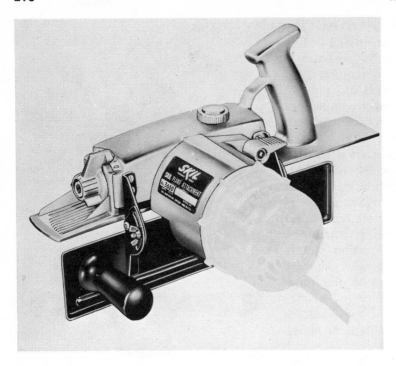

Fig. 16–10. This plane attachment is used with a router motor. A spiral cutter is mounted in the motor chuck.

Fig. 16–11. The parts of a portable electric plane. This plane uses a spiral type cutter. Because the motor is mounted on the side, this plane may be used for edge planing only.

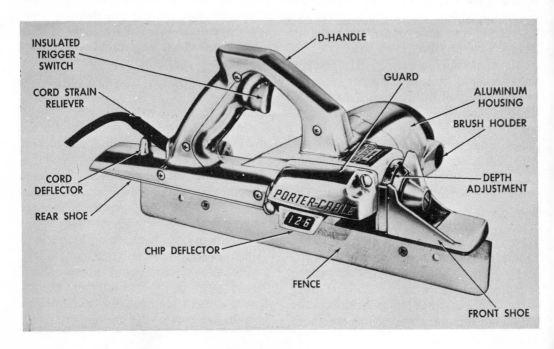

able so as to control the depth of cut.

There are two basic kinds of portable electric planes. The essential differences involve the type of cutter employed and the means by which the cutter is driven. Drives are either direct or belted. Cutters are of two types, the spiral or the cylinder.

The *spiral type cutterhead* (Fig. 16–13) is mounted on an arbor that fits into a chuck on the motor. This type of cutter is usually used with the plane at-

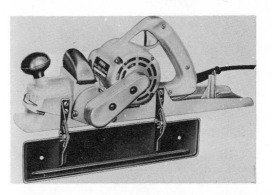

Fig. 16–12. A portable power plane that will plane edges and flat surfaces. It embodies a cylindrical two-knife cutterhead that is belt driven.

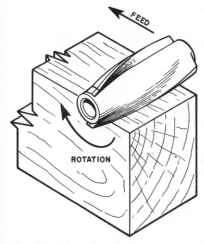

Fig. 16–13. A spiral cutter.

tachment for a router. See Figure 16–10. The motor is removable for use in a router base. These motors generally range from ¼ to 1¼ hp and produce a cutter speed of 22,000 or 23,000 rpm. The maximum width of cut is about 2¼ in. Because of its construction, this type of power plane is limited to performing edge planing operations such as trimming doors, windows, and similar work. Figure 16–11 shows a plane with similar features, except that the motor is permanently affixed. These planes cannot be used for planing the surface of wide boards.

The *cylinder-type cutterhead planes*

Fig. 16–14. Cut-away drawing showing a two blade cylinder type cutterhead and drive belt.

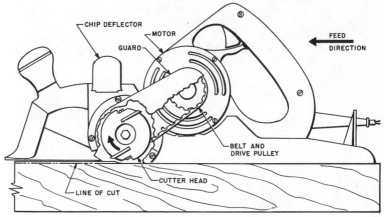

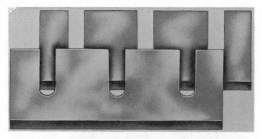

Fig. 16–15. Blades for a cylindrical type cutterhead.

(Figs. 16–12 and 16–14) will do both edge and surface planing operations. The cutterhead mounts two or three knives (Fig. 16–15) that are sharpened to a 45-deg. bevel. The knives are held in the cutterhead with three hex-head locking screws and an adjusting screw that doubles as a safety device. The motor is posi-

tioned above the line of cut and permits free movement of the plane over a surface of any size. Motor power is as high as $1\frac{1}{2}$ hp. Cutterhead speeds of 13,500 rpm are obtained through a toothed belt and pulley. A 3-in. wide cut is normal.

Both types of power planes have a depth capacity of $\frac{1}{8}$ in. They can be easily set to remove as little as $\frac{1}{64}$ in. of stock. They generally range from 16 to 18 in. in length and come equipped with adjustable fences for planing bevels and chamfers.

The **power block plane** (Fig. 16–16) is about 7 in. in length. It may be held and operated with one hand. It has a $1\frac{1}{4}$-in. diameter, spiral cutter which is belt driven at 21,000 rpm. The shoe is adjustable to a maximum cutting depth of $\frac{1}{64}$ in.; it will cut to a width of $1\frac{3}{4}$ in. It can be used for surface planing opera-

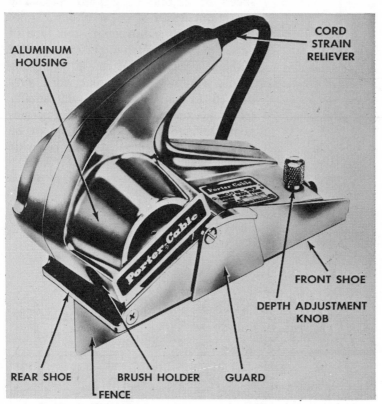

ALUMINUM HOUSING

CORD STRAIN RELIEVER

REAR SHOE   BRUSH HOLDER   GUARD
FENCE

FRONT SHOE

DEPTH ADJUSTMENT KNOB

Fig. 16–16. A power block plane. This tool embodies a spiral type cutter that is belt driven.

Fig. 16–17. This portable surface planer with a cylindrical cutterhead is driven by a flexible shaft from an electric motor. It is being used to plane a laminated member for a ship frame.

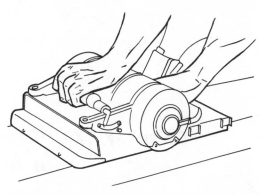

Fig. 16–18. This heavy-duty portable surface planer embodies a direct drive motor. It will plane up to ⅛ inch in depth by ten inches in width.

tions with the fence removed. When the guard is raised out of the way, it will make rabbet cuts.

Portable electric surface planers (Figs. 16–17 and 16–18) are found in wood fabricating plants. They are used on very large work, such as laminated beams and trusses and on boat timbers where other types of surface planers would be impractical. Portable surface planers are made in several different sizes. The cylindrical cutterhead is driven by either a flexible shaft from an electric motor (Fig. 16–17) or by a direct drive motor (Fig. 16–18).

The planer shown in Figure 16–17 is a large, heavy-duty type with a 3-hp motor. It weighs over 50 lbs. and measures about 19 in. in length and 14 in. in width. It will take cuts up to ⅛ in. deep and 10 in. wide. It has a built-in automatic brake to stop the large rotating cutterhead when the power is turned off. A base is available for this machine to convert it into a stationary surface planing machine.

Chapter 17 Planing Machines
in Industry

Planers are machines designed to produce straight and true surfaces on lumber. They may be classified as jointers, surfacers, and matchers and molders. The latter are capable of producing surfaces with a variety of shapes.

Jointers

The several different kinds of jointers found in the woodworking industries are primarily used for planing a surface or edge straight and true, and for planing a surface square with an adjoining surface. The jointer may also be used in custom production work for planing tapers, bevels, chamfers, and rabbets. However, the jointer is not used to perform these operations on a mass production basis.

The jointer is widely used for planing a board out of wind (straightening a surface). This operation trues one surface

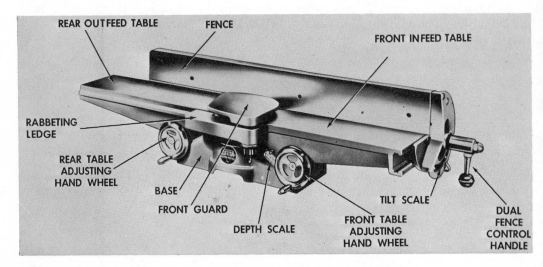

Fig. 17–1. The parts of a six-inch belt-driven bench model jointer.

Fig. 17–2. This 8-inch jointer mounted on an enclosed cabinet is typical of those found in many shops.

of the stock so that it may be planed flat and to uniform thickness with the surface planer.

Most jointers are hand fed. For this reason it is one of the most dangerous machines to operate. Although the cutterhead is normally covered by a self-adjusting guard, the nature of some operations limits its effectiveness.

The **size** of a jointer is determined by the length of the knives carried in the cutterhead. Jointers range from 4-, 6-, or 8-in. bench models (Figs. 17–1 and 17–

2) to the larger, heavy-duty floor models (Fig. 17–3) that are from 12 to 30 in. in size. The 8-, 12-, and 16-in. sizes are most common in pattern and cabinet shops. All jointers are similar in mechanical function and construction. The major parts of a jointer are the cutterhead, table, base, fence, guard, and motor.

The *cutterhead* and the cutting action of a typical jointer are illustrated in Figure 17–4. The cutterhead is a cylinder of steel and rotates on ball bearings. It contains machined slots which hold either 2, 3, 4, or 6 straight knives. The knives are made of carbon steel, *high-speed steel, solid tungsten carbide,* or they are tipped with tungsten carbide. They are generally ground to a *cutting bevel* (CB of Fig. 17–4) of 30 to 40 deg. The *cutting angle* (CA of Fig. 17–4) is the angle between the face of the knife and a line perpendicular to the surface of the work at the cutting point. As a general rule, a 25-deg. cutting angle is used for planing both hardwoods and softwoods. Where hardwoods are continuously planed, a cutterhead with slots that produce a 20-deg. cutting angle is often used. For continuous planing of softwoods, a cutterhead

Fig. 17–3. A 16-inch floor model, heavy-duty jointer with a direct drive motor. The outfeed table is equipped with a device that permits making spring joints.

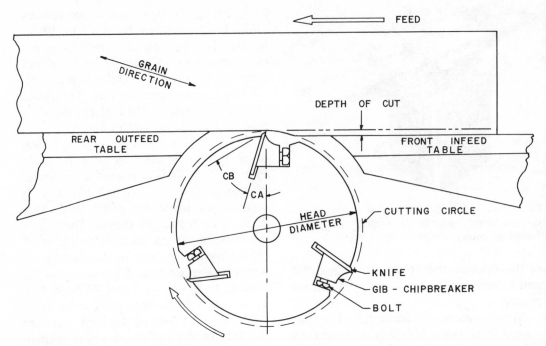

Fig. 17–4. How the jointer functions. CB is the cutting bevel of the knife and CA is the cutting angle of the knife. Note the grain and feed direction of the stock and the position of the tables in relation to the line of cut.

with a 30-deg. cutting angle is used. However, industry has found that some fuzzy grain conditions can be corrected by changing from a 30- to a 10-deg. angle. In other cases, a 5- or 10-deg. cutting angle has been determined the best for planing hardwoods such as hard maple. Changing the cutting angle may be accomplished by grinding a *back angle* on the knife as shown in Figure 17–5.

There are several different methods employed to hold the knives in place in the cylinder. A tapered *gib* is most common. It is held securely in the slot in the cylinder head by means of a square-headed machine bolt, as shown in the diagram (Fig. 17–4). All cutterheads make provision for raising or lowering each knife so that the cutting edges may extend to the cutting circle.

The diameter of the cutterhead (and cutting circle) directly affects the size of the mill marks produced on work by the jointer and other planers. As the work is fed into the rotating cutterhead, each knife takes a shallow, concave cut out of the work. The resulting ripples are known as *mill marks*. See Figure 18–35, Chapter 18. All planed surfaces have these mill marks. With a constant rate of feed and equal cutterhead speeds, a larger diameter cutterhead will leave shallower mill marks than one with a smaller diameter. Furthermore, increasing the number of knives in a cutterhead or its speed results in more cuts per inch of feed with a corresponding reduction in the size of mill marks.

The *tables* (Fig. 17–1) of jointers are heavy iron castings with accurately machined surfaces. There are two tables, one in front of and one to the rear of the cutterhead. The planes of their surfaces are parallel in order that a straightedge may be jointed. Each table may be raised or lowered independently of the other. They move on dovetailed inclines on the base. The rear table is called the *outfeed table*. It is adjusted so its surface is tangent to the cutting circle of the cutterhead. See Figure 17–4. The front table is called the *infeed table*. It is the only one that is adjusted to change the depth of cut. The amount it is lowered below the surface level of the outfeed table equals the depth of cut. This adjustment is made by means of a screw mechanism that is controlled by the infeed table adjustment handwheel. On some larger machines (Fig. 17–3) the infeed table is controlled by a large handwheel located on the back side. The depth of cut is usually indicated on a graduated *depth scale* located on the side of the infeed table.

A *rabbeting ledge* (Fig. 17–4) is part of the infeed table. It extends around the end of the cutterhead to support the work. The edge of the outfeed table is rabbeted so that the uncut part of the stock will not hit this table during rabbet cutting. Refer to page 243, Figure 18–12. which shows the rabbeting operation. In some instances, the tables of the jointers are fitted with extensions to facilitate handling extra long lengths.

The *fence* (Fig. 17–4) is an iron or aluminum casting that is attached to one of the tables or to the base of the machine. It is adjustable from 0 to 45 deg. for beveling and chamfering operations, and may be locked at any desired angle. Some jointer fences have a system of stops that quickly locate it at 45 and 90 deg. (Fig. 17–6).

The fence can be moved and locked at

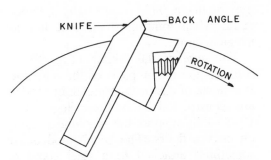

Fig. 17–5. A modified cutting angle may be required to continuously cut certain species of wood. This is accomplished by grinding a back angle on the knife.

any desired position across the width of the tables. Some jointers feature a fence that may be set diagonally with the axis of the cutterhead so that a shearing cut

Fig. 17–6. View showing the control handle and 90-degree tilt stop on the fence of a typical jointer. Here one control handle is used for the crosswise and bevel adjustment of the fence.

may be made. This is especially advantageous when jointing stock that has an irregular grain.

The *base* of the jointer (Fig. 17–1) supports the major parts of the machine. It is made of cast iron. Some floor models are constructed with three legs (Fig. 17–3) that support the machine steadily on uneven floors. The bench models are sometimes attached to a steel stand or cabinet (Fig. 17–2).

The *motors* that drive the cutterhead range from ½ hp on 6-in. machines up to as much as 7½ hp on the largest machines. Generally, 1- to 2-hp motors are used on 8-in. machines, and 5-hp motors are used to drive 12- to 16-in. jointers. Jointers with direct-drive motors generally operate at 3600 rpm. Belt drives run the cutterhead at speeds up to 6000 rpm.

The *guard* (Figs. 17–7a, 17–7b, and 17–7c) is a very important part of the jointer because of the hazard of the high-speed cutterhead. The guard is usually kept in place automatically by means of a spring. There are many different kinds and shapes of guards available, but generally they fall into two classifications. The most common is the "leg of mutton" type, which is shown in Figures 17–1,

17–2, 17–3, and 17–7a. This type pivots away as the work is fed between the guard and the fence. It is satisfactory for work such as jointing an edge. When jointing the surface of a board, this type of guard leaves much of the cutterhead exposed, especially when the work passes over the cutterhead at the completion of the cut.

The other type of guard which has received the approval of safety officials is the "vertical and horizontal" moving guard (Figs. 17–7b and 17–7c). During planing, this type of guard is automatically raised over the top of the work (Fig. 8–b) and is dropped down to cover the cutterhead after the stock has passed. When jointing an edge, this guard moves horizontally like the leg of mutton type, as shown in Figure 17–7c.

A second guard is normally provided to cover the part of the cutterhead that is exposed on the back side of the fence. As the fence is moved across the tables (toward the rabbeting ledge), the cutterhead is dangerously exposed unless some guarding device is provided. A sliding metal shield is often used here or provision is made for mounting another leg-of-mutton guard.

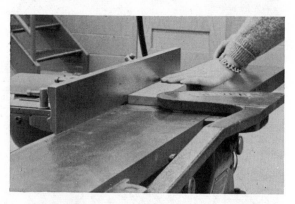
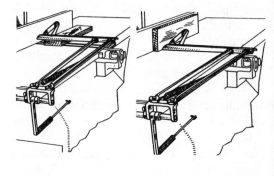

Fig. 17–7. The function of jointer guards: (a) the leg-of-mutton guard exposes much of the cutterhead when jointing a surface; (b and c) the vertical and horizontal automatic guard during (b) surface jointing and (c) edge jointing.

Power feed jointers (Fig. 17–8) are used in industry to joint edges prior to gluing. On some machines the stock receives an application of glue on the planed edges of the work as it is passed through the machine. Machines of this type are referred to as *glue jointers*. The stock is carried into the machine at feed rates up to 100 fpm. An endless feed chain is composed of linked, steel blocks that are sprocket-driven by 5-hp motors. Pressure is maintained on the feed chain by coil springs. The machine illustrated in Figure 17–9 has two cutterheads, one on each side of the machine, that are directly driven by 5-hp motors. The stock may be fed simultaneously from both ends. This enables one outfeed operator to turn each piece of stock over, after it has been jointed on one edge, and then feed it back into the machine for jointing the second edge. The machine illustrated has a depth capacity of ¾ in. It will

Fig. 17–8. This power-driven chain feed edge jointer features simultaneous feeding from both ends of the machine. Some models also apply glue to the planed edge.

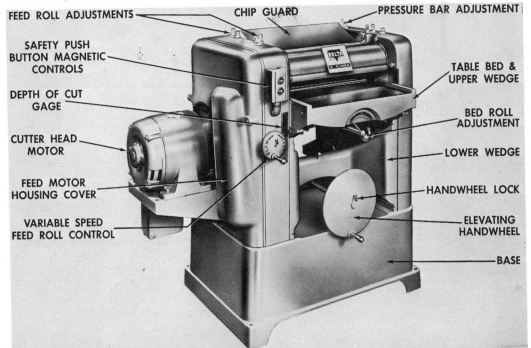

FEED ROLL ADJUSTMENTS — CHIP GUARD — PRESSURE BAR ADJUSTMENT

SAFETY PUSH BUTTON MAGNETIC CONTROLS

DEPTH OF CUT GAGE

CUTTER HEAD MOTOR

FEED MOTOR HOUSING COVER

VARIABLE SPEED FEED ROLL CONTROL

TABLE BED & UPPER WEDGE

BED ROLL ADJUSTMENT

LOWER WEDGE

HANDWHEEL LOCK

ELEVATING HANDWHEEL

BASE

Fig. 17–9. The parts of a single surfacer.

handle stock ½ to 4½ in. thick and 6 in. or more in length.

Surfacers

The surfacer (or thickness planer) is used to plane one or two surfaces of a board, in contrast to the jointer which planes the edges of a board.

There are a number of different kinds of surfacers, including: (1) the *single surfacer* (Fig. 17–9), which planes one surface but does not remove twist or cup, (2) the *facing planer,* which planes one face and removes twist and cup, (3) the *double surfacer,* which planes two surfaces to a parallel thickness in one pass but does not remove twist or cup; and (4) various combinations of the above.

All of the machines in the surfacer family are power-fed machines. They have several different types of feed mechanisms and two basic systems for adjust-

ing the depth of cut. The principles of operation are basically the same.

The **single surfacer** (Fig. 17–9) has a cutterhead similar to that of a jointer. It is located above the table and cuts the top surface of the stock as it passes through the machine. Figure 17–10 shows the relationship of the various parts of the single surfacer.

As the board enters the surfacer it passes between two infeed rolls (Fig. 17–10). The lower infeed roll has a smooth surface. It is adjusted to protrude slightly above the surface of the table. This ranges from four to six thousandths of an inch for finish work to ⅟₃₂ in. for rough work. The actual adjustment depends on the average surface condition of the stock that is to be planed. Some surfacers are equipped with a lower feed-roll adjustment that permits raising and lowering them to suit the work conditions.

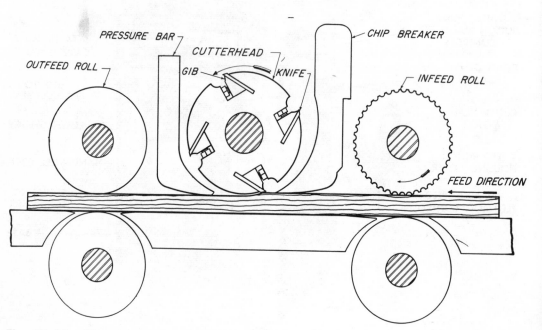

Fig. 17–10. The relationship of the parts inside a surfacer.

The *solid upper infeed roll* (Fig. 17–10) is corrugated to provide traction. It is spring-loaded and adjusted to hold the wood firmly enough to feed it through the machine without leaving visible corrugation marks on the work when light cuts are taken. The better machines have a top-corrugated feed roller that is made up of many spring-loaded segments. These segments yield independently, as much as 5/16 in., to accommodate uneven surfaces of rough boards. This type of feed roll is known as a *sectional infeed roll* (Fig. 17–11). Some larger machines, called four-roll planers, have two sectional infeed rolls above and two smooth infeed rolls below. Small machines usually have only the upper infeed and outfeed rolls powered; larger machines have all rolls powered.

The *cutterhead* (Figs. 17–10, 17–12, and 17–13) rotates against the feed direction of the stock. It is usually of the straight-blade type. The knives (3 to 6) have the same bevel and cutting angles as those used in jointers. See Figure 17–4. Two additional kinds of cutterheads may be used in surfacers. These are the *spiral-blade type* (Fig. 17–12) and the *spiral-bit type* (Fig. 17–13). The chief advantages claimed for these are that their slicing or shearing cut requires less power and produces a smoother finish on cross-grain stock than the conventional straight blade. The main disadvantage lies in the complexities of blade sharpening.

High-speed motion pictures of cutterheads in operation have shown that the knife action includes splitting as well as cutting. As the knife approaches the end of a cut, the direction of cut becomes slightly upward. Fine splits, which are visible in the surfaced board, develop just ahead of the knife edge.

To minimize the length of the splits

Fig. 17–11. A sectional infeed roll with all but two sections removed to show the springs that provide for individual yield of sections.

Fig. 17–12. A spiral knife planer head and the chip it produced on cross-grain stock as a result of its slicing cutting action.

Fig. 17–13. A planer head with spirally staggered carbide bits.

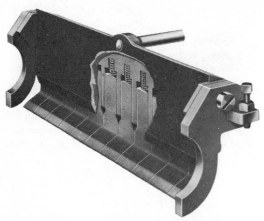

Fig. 17–14. A sectional type chip breaker showing the spring-loaded sections.

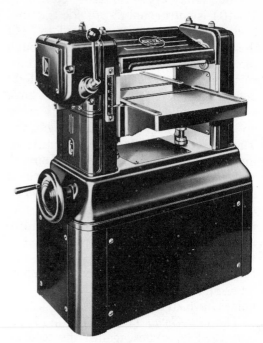

Fig. 17–15. A light-duty 13 x 5-inch single surfacer with the cutterhead and feed power supplied by one drive motor. The handle disengages the feed rolls.

produced by the knives and thus reduce the appearance of chipped grain on the planed surface, a *chip breaker* is installed just in front of the cutterhead (Fig. 17–10). It also holds the board firmly against the table to minimize vibration. The chip breaker on the smaller machines is made of a heavy one-piece steel bar. On the larger machines it consists of individually spring-loaded sections (Fig. 17–14) which automatically adjust to uneven surfaces in the same manner as the sectional feed roll does.

The *pressure bar* (Fig. 17–10) is located on the outfeed side of the cutterhead. The function of the pressure bar is to hold the surfaced board down on the table to prevent it from being gouged by the cutterhead. The pressure bar is adjusted so that its lower edge is on a line tangent to the bottom of the cutting circle.

The *outfeed rolls* are smooth. The lower outfeed roll is adjusted the same distance above the table as the lower infeed roll. The upper roll is spring loaded and is adjusted to hold the work

snugly as it feeds it out of the machine.

The *size* of a surfacer is determined by the maximum width and thickness of stock that will pass through it. Sizes range from the 13 by 5 in., light-duty machines (Fig. 17–15), 18 by 6 in. (Fig. 17–9), 24 by 8 in. (Fig. 17–16), and upward to 44 in. (Fig. 17–17) and even 72 in. on the largest production machines. All surfacers are limited in the *minimum* length of the stock that can be passed through the machine. The short stock limit is generally 6 or 8 in. on small machines. This is the distance between the centers of the infeed and outfeed rolls. The minimum length is proportionately greater on the larger machines.

The *frame* of the surfacer is made of heavy cast iron and provides the necessary rigidity for supporting the parts of the machine. (Some large machines weigh nearly 5 tons.) The bed (or table) of the planer supports the lower feed rolls. It is guided vertically along ways machined into the frame. The bed adjusts for thickness of cut by means of a handwheel. On some of the larger machines, a motor drive moves the bed up and down by push button control.

The bed is moved by means of wedges (Fig. 17–18) or screws (Fig. 17–16). The *wedge-bed planer* is noted for its accuracy. The bed moves vertically as the elevating handwheel moves the lower wedge forward or backward by means of a screw. On the *screw-elevating bed,* the handwheel turns bevel gears fixed to each of two screws. As the screws turn in their mating threads, they raise or lower the bed.

The beds are a one-piece machined casting. Some machines have the center section inserted separately. This part, known as the *platen,* is made of hardened steel to resist wear.

The *cutterhead drive* and *feed systems* on smaller, light-duty machines (12 and

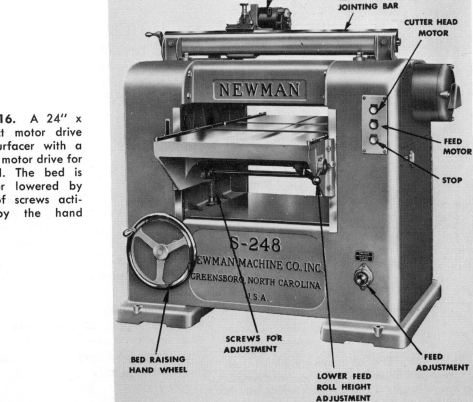

Fig. 17–16. A 24″ x 8″ direct motor drive single surfacer with a separate motor drive for the feed. The bed is raised or lowered by means of screws activated by the hand wheel.

KNIFE GRINDER

KNIFE GRINDING AND JOINTING BAR

CUTTER HEAD MOTOR

FEED MOTOR

STOP

NEWMAN

S-248
NEWMAN MACHINE CO. INC.
GREENSBORO, NORTH CAROLINA
U.S.A.

BED RAISING HAND WHEEL

SCREWS FOR ADJUSTMENT

LOWER FEED ROLL HEIGHT ADJUSTMENT

FEED ADJUSTMENT

Fig. 17–17. A heavy duty single surfacer of wedge bed construction.

Fig. 17–18. One of the two methods used to raise and lower the bed. The lower wedge raises or lowers the bed wedge which travels in vertical ways.

13 in.) have one motor that is the only source of power for operating both the feed rolls and cutterhead. On machines of this type (Fig. 17–15), a system of belts and pulleys and/or gears, sprockets, and chains drives the feed rolls and cutterhead. A clutch allows the feed roll to be disengaged without stopping the cutterhead or shutting off the machine. Most machines, however, have independent feed and cutterhead drive motors. Feed rolls are either gear or chain-driven. The cutterhead may be powered by either a belted drive system (Fig. 17–9) or by a motor mounted directly to the cutterhead arbor (Fig. 17–15). On direct drive machines, the cutterhead operates at 3600 rpm. In some cases, higher speeds are obtained through the use of frequency converters. The belted drive machines usually operate at 3600 to 5000 rpm.

The *feed rate* may be varied on most

machines. It ranges from 15 to 36 fpm on the smaller machines to more than 100 fpm on the larger machines.

The motors driving the cutterhead range from 2 hp on the single-motor, light-duty surfacers up to 40 hp on very large machines. Feed motors generally range between ⅓ and 2 hp on the small to medium planers and up to 3 or 5 hp on some of the largest machines.

Hopper feeding devices (Fig. 17–19) are used on production surfacers with conveyor or chain-driven infeed tables. The setup shown in Figure 17–19 is a chain-feed table attachment that carries the stock into the feed rolls of the machine, one piece at a time. The stock goes through the machine, and falls onto another conveyor at the exit side of the machine to be carried to another work station. At least one company makes a device that automatically sorts the surfaced stock by lengths.

Some machines do not have the usual lower infeed rollers, but are instead equipped with *traveling beds* that carry the stock under the rotating cutterhead. These are of two general types; those composed of *metal cross slats* that are sprocket-driven by two endless feed chains, and those which have wide *flexible belts* driven by two rollers. These machines do have the usual upper feed rolls and pressure bars. The traveling-bed mechanisms are designed to carry the stock to a point where it is taken by powered outfeed rolls or the traveling bed carries the board completely out the rear of the machine. Machines of this type have an advantage in that they eliminate changing the adjustment of the lower feed rolls. Traveling-bed planers are made in several different sizes. Some have a 60-in. capacity designed for planing large laminated beams.

The **facing planer** (Fig. 17–20) is a single surfacer that has another entirely different feeding mechanism. This machine is designed to produce one smooth, true, flat surface on stock that is cupped or in wind (twisted). This is not the case with conventional types of single surfacers. A board that is in wind or cupped will not be straightened to a true plane with single surfacers. The warped stock will be pressed flat by the

Fig. 17–19. A hopper feed installed on a planer.

Fig. 17–20. The facing planer shown here is designed to true the surface of a board.

Fig. 17–21. A 44-inch double surfacer powered by a 40-hp motor on the upper cutterhead and a 25-hp motor on the lower cutterhead. The push buttons control the head, feed, and table elevating motors. The micrometer dial behind the hand wheel is for bed adjustments of .001 inch.

feed rolls. If it does not crack, it will spring back to its previous shape as it comes out of the machine.

With the facing planer, however, the stock comes out of the machine with one true face. It will not be of uniform thick-

ness, but by passing it through a single surfacer the desired thickness is obtained.

On the facing planer, the usual pressure and feed roll system is missing. It has a feed mechanism made up of many spring-loaded fingers (or spikes) that protrude from an endless belt which moves above the work. The fingers adjust automatically, accommodating themselves to the "twist" or uneven surface of the stock. They are similar to the feed mechanism shown in Figure 17–24. The fingers have an action somewhat like that of the human hand feeding stock to a jointer. The pressure is firm, but not enough to take the "twists" out of the stock. This machine has grooves ground into the surface of the tables to reduce friction and maintain a positive feed. The cutterhead is mounted in the lower table. Machines of this type generally range up to 36-in. sizes and have variable feed rates of 40 to 120 fpm. They are driven by a 15-hp cutterhead and a 2-hp feed motor.

Another, not too common planing

Fig. 17–22. This special 72-inch double surfacer has a conveyor feed. The machine handles curved or straight laminated beams up to 24 inches thick.

Fig. 17–23. The infeed end of a combination facing planer and surfacer. Stock is delivered to the machine by a conveyor system.

process is handled by a special type of machine that is designed to plane very thin and highly flexible materials. These machines are similar to conventional single surfacers except that they have special platens with air holes that are connected to a vacuum pump system. The vacuum holds the stock firmly on the platen during the feeding and cutting operation. They are generally equipped with flat guide shoes on each side of the cutterhead, rubber-covered upper feed rolls, and smooth-steel lower feed rolls. The thickness of cut may be controlled to an accuracy of .001 in. The cutting width capacity is 52 in.

Double surfacers (Figs. 17–21 and 17–22) are high production machines. Their principle of operation is similar to single surface planers, but they have an upper and lower cutterhead. One cutterhead is positioned behind the other rather than directly below it. They are, naturally, much larger machines. Heavy duty machines like the one shown in Figure 17–23 have four upper feed rolls (two of the corrugated sectional type) and four smooth, lower feed rolls. As the board passes into the machine, it is first planed on the top surface by the upper cutterhead. Then it passes over the center platen of the table and is planed by the lower cutterhead. The upper and lower outfeed rolls finally roll the piece out of the machine.

Double surfacers are equipped with upper and lower chip breakers and pressure bars like those used on heavy-duty single surfacers (Fig. 17–14). The sizes of double surfacers range from 30 by 8 in. to 59 by 16 in. Special purpose machines, like the one shown in Figure 17–22, may be as large as 72 by 24 in.

Double surfacers have feed rates up to 105 fpm on the smaller sized machines with somewhat slower feed rates on the larger models. They have up to 40-hp motors for the cutterheads and up to 10-hp feed motors. The larger machines also have auxiliary motors for raising and lowering the table.

The **combination facing planer and**

Fig. 17–24. View illustrating the facing planer end of a combination facing and surfacing machine.

surfacer (Fig. 17–23) is, in effect, two machines (a jointer and a surfacer) built into one. It operates in a much different manner than the conventional double planers. This machine takes the wind out of boards producing one true surface on the bottom of the stock as it is passed over the first cutterhead (Fig. 17–24). As the stock moves on, it is planed to a uniform thickness as it passes under the second cutterhead. An example of the kind of work this machine does in just one pass is illustrated in Figures 17–25a and 17–25b.

The **feed mechanism** (Fig. 17–24) is similar to that of the facing planer. It is composed of an endless chain link belt assembly with spring loaded, rubber or hardened steel fingers. This feed assembly guides the board over the first cutterhead and directs it into the infeed rolls of the surfacer section. The feed rate is variable from 20 to 120 fpm. The machine is made in 18, 24, and 36 by 8-in. sizes.

Planer-Matchers and Molders

The planer-matcher and planer-molder are similar machines. They will cut almost any shape on four sides of lumber in one pass. Basically, they involve the same cutting action incorpo-

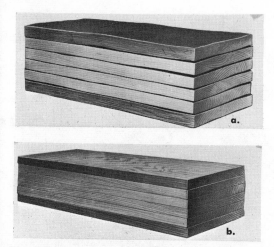

Fig. 17–25. Face jointing and thickness planing of (a) the rough and twisted boards, produce (b) true surfaces and uniform thickness in one pass.

rated in double surfacers with the addition of two or more vertical cutting heads. They are able to produce an infinite variety of shapes and patterns at very high feed rates. They are not usually found in cabinet shops or small custom woodworking plants, but are primarily used in large mass-production plants that specialize in making a volume of various

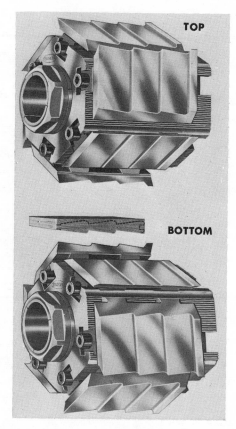

Fig. 17–27. This simulated louver is one of the many patterns produced by top and bottom profile heads.

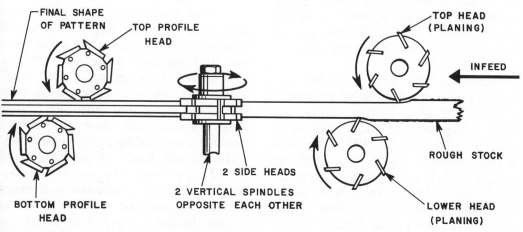

Fig. 17–26. Arrangement of cutterheads in a planer-matcher.

PLANING ZONE · · · MATCHING-MOULDING ZONE

SIDE HEADS

MOTORS

BELT TO SPINDLES

Fig. 17–28. A four-side planer-matcher-molder that has a 20 by 8-inch capacity.

shapes. Such plants make things like interior trim, flooring, church seats, broom handles, and pencils. Some of the operations involved in the manufacture of clothespins are also performed on these machines.

Planer-matchers (Fig. 17–26) are generally used for production processing of dimension stock, flooring, ceiling, and siding. They have an output rate of as much as 1000 fpm, but 300 to 500 fpm is most common. Most large machines have five or six cutterheads; namely, an upper and lower cylinder-type planer head, two round side-matching heads, and one or two profile heads.

The *side heads* rotate against the di-

rection of feed on vertical spindles. Each is independently adjustable in either a vertical or horizontal direction. They are also equipped with chip breakers and pressure shoes that have the same function as those used on single surfacers. The side heads compose the "matching" part of the machine. They cut on each side of the stock simultaneously to produce tongues and grooves, rabbets, rounded edges (easing), and other shapes.

The *profile heads* (Figs. 17–26 and 17–27) are usually the last pair of cutterheads the stock encounters as it passes through the machine. The one above is termed the *top profile* and the lower one is called the *bottom profile*. They are mounted on horizontal spindles, usually of the sleeve type that permits quickly changing cutters from one pattern to another. They make cuts such as the hollow back in flooring, various grooves, and the shape of drop siding. They are often combined with rip saws to cut a board into two or more pieces to make multiple moldings.

All of the cutterheads on modern machines are of the direct-drive type with motor sizes as follows: 40 hp on the top head, 20 hp on the side heads, and 10 to 15 hp on the profilers. These machines also have feed motors of 15 hp. The size of stock that can be handled by the planer-matcher ranges up to 8 by 24 in.

The **planer-molder** (Fig. 17–28) is generally of two classifications: *light molders* and *heavy-duty molders*. Both types have four or more cutterheads. Molders produce an infinite number of shapes, but they are generally of narrower widths than the shapes produced by planer-matchers. The cutterheads (top, bottom, and 2 or more side heads) are fitted with knives that are ground to cut any pattern desired. See Figure 17–29. Light-duty molders generally have a maximum capacity of 4 by 6 in. and have

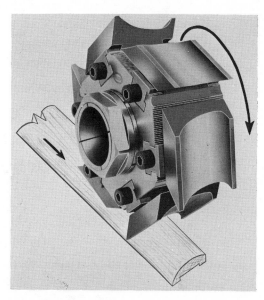

Fig. 17–29. Typical milled-to-pattern cutters mounted in a molding head used for quantity production of casing.

feed rates up to 160 fpm, with cutterhead speeds up to 7,200 rpm. Heavy molders may have as many as seven cutterheads. They have a maximum stock capacity of 16 in. and variable feed rates up to 250 fpm.

Chapter 18 Planing Processes in the School Shop

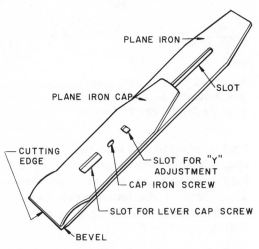

Fig. 18–1. Double plane iron terminology.

PLANE IRON

SLOT

PLANE IRON CAP

CUTTING EDGE

SLOT FOR "Y" ADJUSTMENT

CAP IRON SCREW

SLOT FOR LEVER CAP SCREW

BEVEL

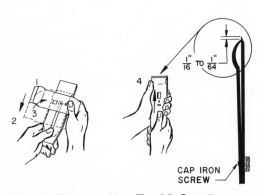

Fig. 18–2. Assembly. **Fig. 18–3.** Adjustment.

CAP IRON SCREW

$\frac{1}{16}$" TO $\frac{1}{64}$"

Planing experiences in the school shop usually involve common hand planes, some of the special-purpose planes, portable powered planes and hand-fed jointers and single surfacers.

Hand Planing

Hand planing begins with the choice of the proper plane for the task. See page 211 for a discussion of selecting a hand plane.

Adjusting planes. The first requirements for successful use of any plane are: (1) a very sharp plane iron and (2) a plane that is correctly adjusted for the work at hand. The general steps for assembling and adjusting most common hand planes are:

1. Release the lever cap and remove it from the plane. Take out the plane iron and the plane-iron cap (Fig. 18–1). These latter two devices are usually referred to simply as the double plane iron.
2. Disassemble the double plane iron by loosening the cap screw (Fig. 18–1).
3. Check the cutting edge for sharpness. This may be done by one of two methods. In the first method,

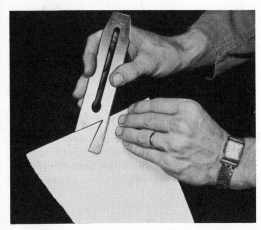

Fig. 18–4. Checking the cutting edge for sharpness.

hold a piece of paper with the thumb and forefinger and let it hang freely; place a corner of the plane-iron cutting edge on the paper and move it downward (Fig. 18–4). If the edge cuts into the paper rather than pushing it away, the edge is sharp.

The second method is based on the fact that a sharp edge does not reflect light. Look at the cutting edge while holding it up to a bright light and check it for "white spots." If there is no light reflected from the edge, it is sharp. If sharpening is necessary, refer to Chapter 33, page 576 for information concerning sharpening and honing of plane irons.

4. *Assemble the double plane iron* by holding the plane iron in the left hand with the bevel down (Fig. 18–2). Set the plane-iron cap at a right angle over the plane iron with the cap screw through the opening. See step No. 1 in Figure 18–2. Next, slide the plane-iron cap back, away from the cutting edge as shown in step 2 (Fig. 18–2). Swivel it so that it is parallel with the plane iron (step 3). Slide it forward (as in step

4, Fig. 18–3) to a point no more than $\frac{1}{16}$ in. from the cutting edge. See Figure 18–3. Leave $\frac{1}{16}$ in. exposed for most softwoods. The plane-iron cap should be set as close as $\frac{1}{64}$ in. to the cutting edge for making fine or thin cuts on hardwoods and for planing cross grain wood.

5. *Assemble the plane.* Insert the assembled double plane iron into the plane with the bevel down. The end of the Y adjustment lever (connected to the knurled adjusting nut) and the small round ring of the lateral adjustment must be in their respective slots.

6. Slip the lever cap in place, and depress the cam lever to lock the double plane iron in place. If it is too loose or if the cam lever will not snap down, make the necessary adjustment on the lever-cap screw. The lever cap may be used as a screwdriver for this purpose.

7. *Adjust the plane.* Turn the plane upside down, sight along the bottom, and move the lateral adjustment lever so that the plane-iron cutting edge is parallel to the bottom. Also,

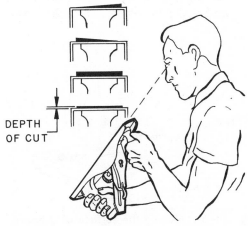

Fig. 18–5. Checking the cutting edge for depth of cut.

set the cutting edge for depth of cut (Fig. 18–5) by turning the brass adjusting nut. Make a trial cut on scrap stock to check the adjustments. A sharp plane iron in a properly adjusted plane will make a slight hissing sound as the shaving is produced. The plane should cut with little effort on any kind of wood without chattering or jerking.

General Suggestions for Using Planes

1. Develop the habit of setting the plane on its side whenever placing it on the bench. This will keep the weight of the plane off the cutting edge and avoid dulling the edge and nicking the bench.
2. When possible, fasten the work firmly so that both hands may be used to control the plane.
3. For edge planing, clamp the work in a vise; for planing a surface, it is best to clamp the work between a retractable vise dog and a bench stop on top of the bench (Fig. 18–6). To plane a surface, always clamp the board on end grain. Clamping it on edge grain will "cup" the board and make truing the surface impossible.

Fig. 18–6. Planing the surface of a board. Note the grain direction and its relationship to the direction in which the plane moves.

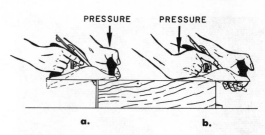

Fig. 18–7a & b. Shift the pressure from the knob to the handle to prevent rounding the work at (a) and (b). Note the position of the left hand when planing narrow edges.

Fig. 18–7c. The plane with the longer bottoms will bridge the low spots and cut off the high spots. The shorter plane follows the irregularities.

4. Take a balanced stance alongside of and a little to the rear of the work. Place your left foot forward.
5. *Plane with the grain* as shown in Figures 18–6, 18–7a, 18–7b, and 18–7c. Note that this is in an "uphill" direction.
6. Push the plane forward. Use your body weight by shifting it to your left foot as the plane moves through its stroke. Keep your head above but a little to the rear of the plane throughout the stroke.
7. Avoid rounding off each end of the board (Figs. 18–7a, 18–7b, and 18–7c). This is accomplished by applying pressure on the knob at the beginning of the stroke (Fig. 18–7a), maintaining equal pressure on the handle and the knob in the middle of the stroke, and completing the stroke with the pressure transferred to the handle (Fig. 18–7b).

8. Lift the plane slightly on the return stroke. This will reduce wearing and dulling of the cutting edge.

9. *Removing wind* from the surface of a board is accomplished by planing off the "high" areas. Use the longer length planes. See Figure 18–7c. Generally, a diagonal cut (Fig. 18–6) works best. As the work progresses, it should be checked frequently by "sighting" along the surface and by laying a straightedge diagonally across it.

10. When planing a surface, a shearing cut can be obtained by holding the plane at a slight angle to the direction of the cutting stroke. A well-honed cutting edge, a closely adjusted plane-iron cap, and a shallow, shearing cut should give good results on most cross-grained woods.

11. For finish-planing surfaces, use a sharp smooth plane. Set it for a shallow cut and plane in the grain direction rather than diagonally.

12. *Planing an edge* (Figs. 18–7a, 18–7b, 18–7c, and 18–8) square with

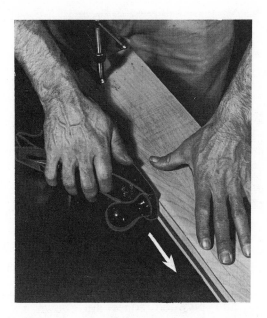

Fig. 18–9. Planing the edges of veneer clamped between two boards. Here the plane is held on its side against the flat surface of the bench top.

a surface requires holding the plane so its bottom is at right angles to that surface. This is somewhat difficult and takes practice. A good method of holding the plane for this operation is shown in Figure 18–8. The fingers below the plane help to maintain the right angle. The right hand must keep the plane in position while pushing it across the work.

13. To edge plane very thin materials, such as veneer and hardboards, clamp the work between two boards on a bench top. Lay the side of the plane on the bench top and guide it as shown in Figure 18–9.

14. *Planing end grain* (Figs. 18–10, 18–11a, 18–11b, and 18–11c) requires a shallow cut and a very sharp plane iron. Precautions must be taken to prevent the corner from splitting when the cutting edge passes over it.

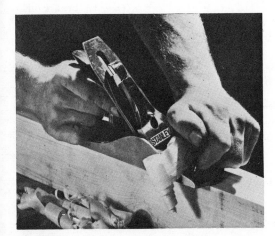

Fig. 18–8. Finish-planing an edge with a smooth plane. Note the continuous shaving of uniform width and thickness.

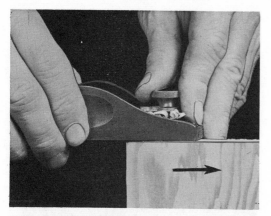

Fig. 18–10. A block plane is shown planing the edge of plywood so as to avoid splitting the corner.

Three methods of planing end grain and plywood edges are shown in Figures 18–11a, 18–11b, and 18–11c.

15. *Rabbets* (Fig. 18–12) should be started with the aid of a straightedge guide fastened to the work as shown.

First score the line of cut by drawing a knife or chisel along the guide strip to sever any cross grain fibers. The guide strip is not necessary if the rabbet plane is equipped with an adjustable fence.

16. The *router plane* (Fig. 18–13) tends to mark surfaces that have been finish planed. A hardboard or plywood base fastened to the bottom of the plane will reduce this tendency. A guide fence can be attached to this base for making straight cuts. Here again, score the grain fibers with a chisel or make saw cuts to prevent splitting the wood outside the guidelines.

17. When storing a plane, brush off the shavings, retract the plane iron to protect it, and store it in a suitable holder. Occasionally wipe the machined surfaces of the plane with a lightly oiled rag to prevent rust from developing.

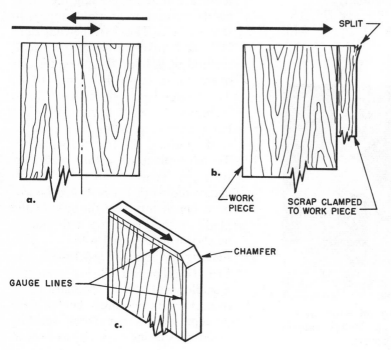

Fig. 18–11. Three methods of planing end grain to prevent splitting the corner. The heavy arrows show the direction of cutting strokes: (a) a little more than half way from each edge, (b) full length of the edge but with a scrap retaining block to hold the corner in place, and (c) full length of the edge, but with the corner previously chamfered.

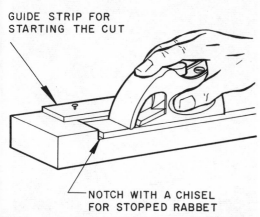

GUIDE STRIP FOR
STARTING THE CUT

NOTCH WITH A CHISEL
FOR STOPPED RABBET

Fig. 18–12. Planing a stopped rabbet with a bullnose rabbet plane. Note the guide strip for starting the cut. The notch is made first to provide clearance for the plane's nose.

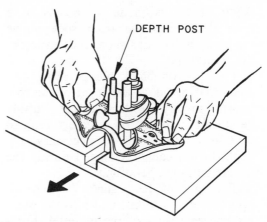

DEPTH POST

Fig. 18–13. Using a router plane to cut a dado to uniform depth.

Using Portable Electric Planes

Electric planes are generally easy to adjust* and operate. They are relatively safe to use, but as a rule they do not have a means of guarding that part of the cutterhead that projects through the bottom (shoe) of the plane. For the use of a router-plane attachment, turn to page 300, Chapter 20, which describes the general operation and care of portable routers. Before using this and the other electric planes, review the safety rules on page 152, that apply to all portable power tools. Observe the following safety precautions for the operation of portable electric planes.

Safety Precautions for Electric Planes

1. Disconnect the cord from the outlet when changing or adjusting blades

* Refer to the manufacturer's operator's manual for information dealing with the adjustment of cutterheads, their replacement, and sharpening requirements.

and when attaching or adjusting the guide fence.
2. Set the plane on its side (with the switch off) when connecting the cord to the outlet.
3. Check the condition of the stock before planing. Nails, loose knots and so on may damage the tool and cause serious accidents.
4. Keep both hands on the handles of the plane when the motor is running.
5. Keep both hands on the plane until the cutterhead stops coasting after the switch is off and before laying the tool on the bench or carrying it at your side.
6. If chips pile up in the deflector and are not freely ejected, stop the motor. Pull the plug from the outlet, remove the deflector, and dump out the chips. It is a hazardous practice to put your fingers or some object into the deflector to free clogged chips while the plane is running.

The **adjustment of power planes** for planing either an edge or a surface is basically the same. However, the router-plane attachment cannot be used for surfacing operations. The adjustment for depth of cut is made by means of a lever that raises the front shoe above the level of the rear shoe, thus exposing the cutterhead.

The shoe on block planes is a single piece that pivots at the front of the tool housing to vary the depth of cut. Cutting depths are indicated on a scale graduated in 64ths of an inch. If necessary, the depth of cut can be changed during the actual cutting operation.

The **rate of feed** generally depends upon the depth of cut and also the planing characteristics of the material. Forcing the plane overloads the motor. If the cut is too deep, the surface may be burned. On the other hand, a high rate of feed with a shallow cut will produce a poor surface finish. The best surface condition is produced by operating between these extremes. A change in the sound of the motor is generally a good indication that the feed rate is too fast or the cut is too deep. The *feed direction* is the same as when using common planes because the cutterhead rotation is against the forward motion.

Planing an edge (Figs. 18–14 and 18–15) is accomplished with the aid of a fence. This is the only operation that can be performed with the router-

Fig. 18–15. Using a power block plane on an edge.

plane attachment. Consequently, a guide fence is built into the base. The fence must be attached to the housing of the other kinds of planes. On larger planes, the fence may be attached to either the right or left side of the plane, but usually it is fastened to the left side as shown in Figure 18–14. The procedure for planing an edge is:

1. Attach the fence and check it with a square to be sure it is at right angles to the shoe.
2. Clamp the work securely.
3. Place the front shoe on the stock, but do not permit the cutterhead to touch the work.
4. Apply pressure to the front handle and start the motor. Allow the cutterhead to reach full speed, and then push the plane forward, keeping the fence against the work.
5. After the cut has been started and the rear shoe rests on the work, transfer the pressure to the rear

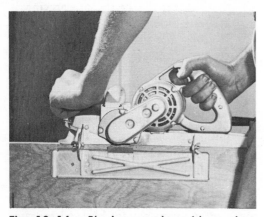

Fig. 18–14. Planing an edge with an electric plane.

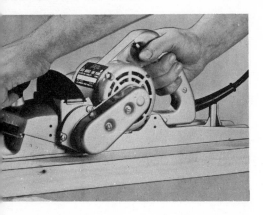

Fig. 18–16. Planing a surface with an electric hand plane.

Using the Jointer

The principal cutting operations performed on the jointer are: (1) planing an edge square to an adjoining surface, (2) planing a chamfer or bevel, (3) planing a taper, (4) planing end grain, and (5) planing a surface true. Of the above operations, the first and last are the most frequently performed.

The jointer is a relatively dangerous machine to operate. According to the National Safety Council, the circular saw and the jointer are the two most dangerous machines in the school shop. How-

handle and keep it there throughout the cut.

6. At the completion of the stroke, turn off the motor, and lift the plane from the surface.

Planing a surface (Figs. 18–16 and 18–17) may be done with either the power plane or block plane.

1. Remove the guide fence and set the depth of cut.
2. Make the first cut near the center of the work as shown in Figure 18–17.
3. Make successive cuts slightly less than the full width of the cutterhead and in a direction parallel to the first cut. Overlap each cut, and hold the plane at a slight angle so that the rear shoe rides on the surface of the previous cut as shown in Figure 18–17. This will produce a uniform surface regardless of irregularities in the surface of the unplaned area of the work.
5. *Rabbet cuts* may be made with the aid of a thin straightedge guide clamped to the work surface. The small guard over the end of the block plane cutterhead must be raised in order to make this possible.

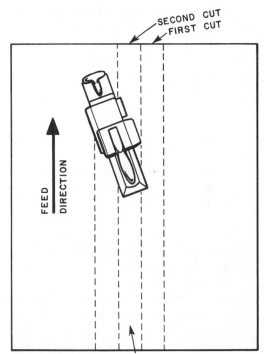

OVERLAPPING PREVIOUS CUTS PROVIDES TRUE SURFACE FOR SUPPORT OF REAR SHOE

Fig. 18–17. Procedure for planing a wide surface. Note the angled position of the plane with the rear shoe guided over the previous cut.

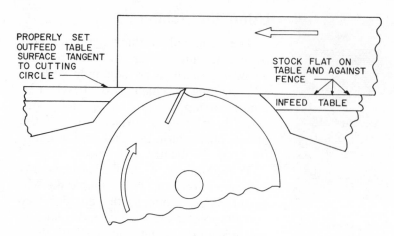

PROPERLY SET
OUTFEED TABLE
SURFACE TANGENT
TO CUTTING
CIRCLE

STOCK FLAT ON
TABLE AND AGAINST
FENCE

INFEED TABLE

Fig. 18–18. The outfeed table is properly adjusted when its surface is tangent to the cutting circle of the cutterhead.

ever, if certain safety practices are always observed, these hazards can be reduced to a minimum. Therefore, you should study and fully observe the following safety precautions.

Safety Precautions for the Jointer

1. If in doubt, always ask your instructor for help.
2. Always assume that the cutterhead is revolving. Make adjustments to either the fence or the rear table only with the power off.
3. Be sure that the jointer knives are sharp. Dull knives pound the work and resist normal feeding efforts. The revolving cutterhead can thrust the work out of the operator's hands and this potential increases sharply when dull knives are used. Refer to page 257 for information concerning the sharpening and balancing of jointer knives.
4. Keep the cutterhead guard in position at all times. (For some rabbeting operations, the guard must be removed.) Also be sure that the part of the cutterhead exposed on the rear side of the fence is guarded.

5. Be sure that shop aprons and clothing are not dangling. Tuck neckties into your shirt. Roll your sleeves to the elbow if they do not fit snugly.
6. Check the stock. Be sure it is of suitable size and in good condition, free from knots, grit, dirt, checks, nails, dried glue, and hard finishes that tend to dull cutterhead knives.
7. Stock smaller than 1 by 2 by 12 should not be jointed except with a specially made clamp or fixture approved by your instructor. Use a hand plane to work small pieces. A general rule is: joint no piece that is shorter than the jointer table is wide.
8. Always use a push stick (see Fig. 18–21) when planing the faces of boards. Stock should be more than ½ in. in thickness for face planing operations.
9. Keep the floor area around the machine free of shavings, scraps, boards, and the like that might interfere or cause slipping. (A non-slip floor covering is recommended.)
10. Be sure that the fence is firmly locked.
11. Adjust for the desired depth of cut before starting the machine. Several

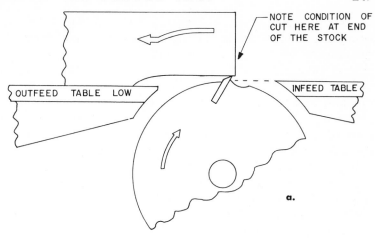

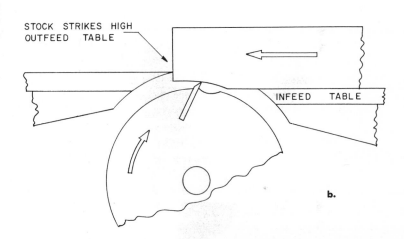

Fig. 18–19. The effects of improper adjustment of the outfeed table. (a) Low outfeed table results in undercutting, (b) high outfeed table stops forward motion of stock.

light cuts (1⁄16 in. on faces, 1⁄8 in. on edges) are preferred to one heavy cut to reduce the chances of kickback.

12. Consult your instructor before making special cuts (tapers, etc.), and when the job requires making a single cut over 1⁄8 in. in depth (1⁄16 in. on surfacing).

13. Plan the work so that jointing may be done before the stock is cut into shorter lengths.

14. Stand to the side of the jointer, and relatively close to it so that body balance may be maintained throughout the cutting operation.

15. Turn on the machine and permit it to reach full speed before feeding stock into the cutterhead.

16. Keep your undivided attention on the job at hand.

17. When the operation is completed, turn off the power and stay at the machine until the cutterhead has stopped revolving.

18. Clean the machine with a brush (not with the hands).

Adjusting the jointer. The surface of

the outfeed table must be tangent to the cutting circle of the cutting head. (See Figure 18–18.) Once the outfeed table is properly set, it does not need further adjustment. However, if it is out of adjustment it will be either too low or too high. Two conditions call for adjustment of the outfeed table. First a *low table* will result in the cutterhead taking a nip out of the trailing end of the work as it leaves the infeed table (Fig. 18–19a); second a *high table* will result in either the stock bumping into the table and being stopped (Fig. 18–19b) or in the stock being taper cut.

Adjust the outfeed table as follows:
1. Select a board with a straightedge.
2. Set the infeed table to take a cut about ¹⁄₁₆ in. deep.
3. Start the machine and feed the board about ¼ in. onto the outfeed table (Figs. 18–19a and 18–19b).
4. Shut off the machine.
5. Loosen the locking device on the outfeed table and lower it slightly.
6. Raise the table until its surface touches the surface of the cut (Fig. 18–18). Be careful not to raise the

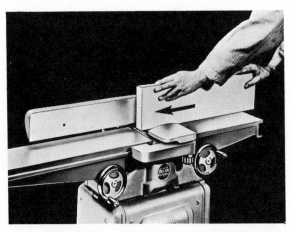

Fig. 18–20. Jointing an edge. The work is held against the fence and the table as it is fed forward. Note the position of the operator's hands.

stock off the infeed table. Always make the final adjustment by raising the table to the correct height. "Play" in the raising screw mechanism will not affect the adjustment if this procedure is followed.

Jointing an edge (Figs. 18–20 and 18–21). First, check the condition of the edge of the stock that is to be jointed. If it is radically uneven it should be rough sawed to a straight line on the band saw. If the face to be placed against the fence is rough, in wind, or cupped, it must first be planed true if the adjacent edge is to be square with it.*

1. Position the fence so that a sufficient length of the cutterhead is exposed for the cut. It is good practice to move the fence from time to time to prevent dulling the knives in one spot. Check the fence with a trysquare to be sure it is at right angles to the infeed table (Fig. 18–22). Ensure that the guard is in position.
2. Adjust the front table for depth of cut. This is generally ⅛ in. for roughing and ¹⁄₁₆ in. for finish cutting, sometimes less for hardwoods or for stock with irregular grain.
3. Ascertain the grain direction of the stock to determine which end should be the lead end.
4. If the face is cupped, place the concave side against the fence.
5. Turn on the power and feed the stock into the machine at a moderate, steady rate. Smoother surfaces are obtained with a slower feed rate because there are more cuts (smaller mill marks) per inch. The guard will move as the work is pushed against it. *Do not touch the guard with your fingers.*
6. As the cut progresses, gradually shift

---

* Refer to procedure for jointing a surface, p. 250.

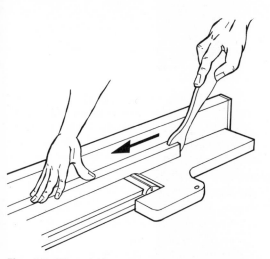

Fig. 18–21. * Use a push stick on narrow stock to keep the right hand at a safe distance from the cuttinghead.

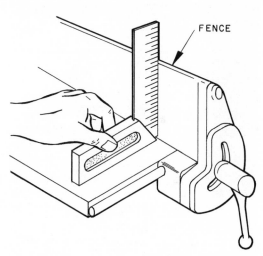

Fig. 18–22. The fence should be at right angles to the table for jointing an edge square with a face.

the weight of your body to the left foot to maintain your balance.

7. Position the hands so that they do not pass dangerously close to the revolving cutterhead.

8. Keep the stock in contact with the fence and the table with a firm pressure as it is pushed forward (Fig. 18–20).

9. Carefully shift the position of your hands so that they never pass over the cutterhead while holding the stock. As the cut is started, both hands are over the infeed table. The left hand should be moved so as to keep it over the infeed table until six inches or more of stock has passed onto the rear table. Then shift the left hand to apply pressure on the stock over the outfeed table.

10. Complete the cut with a follow-through motion. If the stock is less than 2 in. in width, use a push stick (in the right hand) to feed the trail-

ing end of the work over the cutterhead as shown in Figure 18–21.

11. At the completion of the cut, lift the work off the outfeed table. Do not pull it back over the cutterhead.

12. Shut off the power and stay at the machine until the cutterhead has stopped coasting.

End grain jointing (Fig. 18–23) should be done only on edges that are at least 12 in. long. The depth of cut must be shallow because the knives are cutting perpendicularly to the grain direction. Furthermore, as in hand planing, precautions must be taken to prevent chipping the trailing edge of the stock as it passes over the cutterhead.

The most common method employed to prevent this chipping is to make a short cut, about ½ to 1 in. long, on the edge to be jointed. Then reverse the stock, and complete the cut from the opposite direction (Fig. 18–23). This does not always prevent some slight

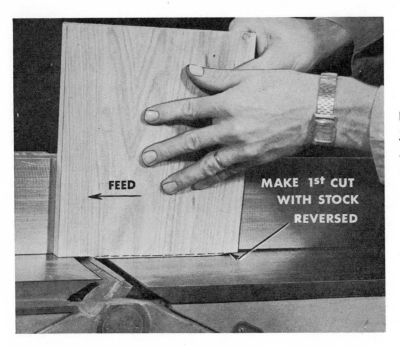

Fig. 18–23. * Jointing end grain on wide stock. The short cut is made first to prevent splitting that corner.

FEED

MAKE 1st CUT WITH STOCK REVERSED

* Illustrations identified with an asterisk (*) indicate that the guard has been removed for illustrative purposes only.

feathering. For best results, clamp a waste piece of stock to back up the trailing edge of the work. Or, where permissible, plane the end grain first and remove the

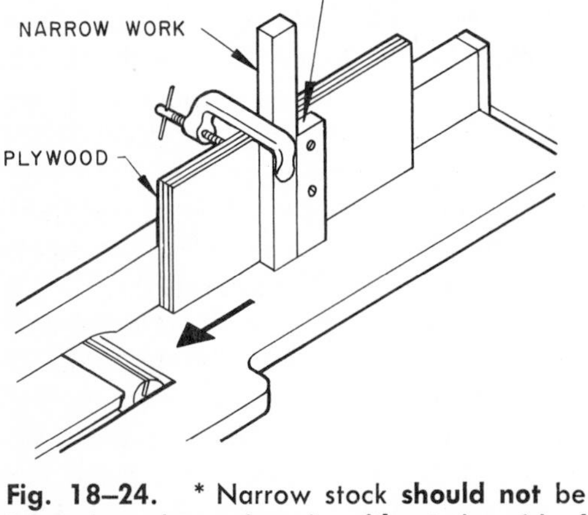

Fig. 18–24. * Narrow stock **should not** be jointed on the end grain **without** the aid of a fixture similar to the one shown here.

SUPPORTING BLOCK PERPENDICULAR TO TABLE

NARROW WORK

PLYWOOD

resulting split corner by taking a cut with the grain. This procedure does not apply to plywood.

Planing end grain on stock of narrow widths is sometimes necessary, but this class of work should be done only with the aid of a work-holding fixture. It may be designed like the one shown in Figure 18–24.

Jointing bevels and chamfers (Fig. 18–25) is accomplished with the fence tilted to the desired angle. The fence may either be tilted in (as shown) or out (the opposite way). When jointing bevels or chamfers around four edges, it is best to make the cross-grain cuts before cutting with the grain. This procedure will usually clean up any chipping or splintering caused when jointing the end grain.

Jointing a surface (Fig. 18–26) *always* requires the aid of a "pusher" to keep your hand safely away from the cutterhead as the trailing end of the work passes over the cutterhead. This operation is often referred to as *face jointing*. The maximum width that may be cut on the jointer is governed by the length of the cutterhead knives. Face jointing, or truing, involves removing wind (twist), cup, high spots, and any roughness from the surfaces of a board. Face planing on the jointer is normally done to only one surface of the work. The jointer will not, as a rule, produce a board of uniform thickness. Planing to a uniform thickness should be done on the surfacer after one working face has been planed on the jointer. Observe the following steps for planing a surface on the jointer:

1. Adjust the fence for the width of the stock. Be sure the guard is in place.
2. Adjust the infeed table for a shallow depth of cut, generally not more than $\frac{1}{16}$ in. for softwoods and $\frac{1}{32}$ in. for hardwoods.
3. Check the grain direction. Be sure that the pusher is within easy reach. Turn on the power.
4. For boards of shorter lengths, keep both hands on the pusher (Fig. 18–26).
5. Feed the stock slowly with an uninterrupted forward motion. Follow

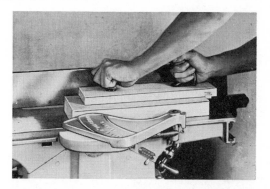

Fig. 18–26. Jointing a surface. Note that both hands are on the "pusher."

through, keeping both hands on the pusher to complete the cut.
6. When handling longer length stock, start the cut with both hands on the work over the infeed table.
7. When 12 to 18 in. of the leading end of the board have moved onto the outfeed table, shift the position of the left hand over to the outfeed table and apply pressure to the work.
8. When nearing the cutterhead with the trailing end of the board, hold the pusher in the right hand and use it to complete the cut.
9. Make successive passes (if necessary) until a true flat surface is obtained.

Rabbets may be cut on the jointer as follows (see Fig. 18–27):
1. Adjust the fence. (It may be necessary to remove the guard.) Move the fence toward the rabbeting ledge until the length of the cutterhead knives exposed equals the desired width of cut. Check the adjustment by measuring from the end of each knife in the cutterhead to the fence. The end of one knife may project further than the others. In this case, make the measurement from the knife which has the greater length exposed.

Fig. 18–25. Planing a bevel or a chamfer with the fence tilted. Full bevels at large angles, such as 45 degrees, should be made in several passes.

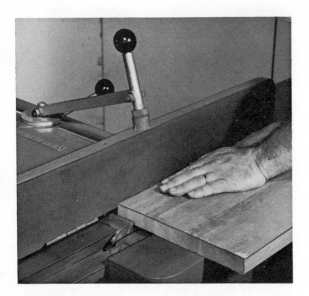

Fig. 18–27. Making a rabbet cut. The guard must be removed for work of this size.

2. Lower the infeed table to equal the desired depth of cut. Wide and deep rabbets in hardwoods should, if possible, be made in two passes rather than one.
3. Turn on the power and make a trial cut on scrap stock.
4. Make any necessary adjustments. (Be sure to stop the jointer first.)
5. Make the cut or cuts as in normal jointing.

Taper cuts (Figs. 18–28a, 18–28b, 18–28a, and lower the infeed table are made by several different procedures, depending upon the length of the cut and the amount of taper required. Gradual tapers may be cut on stock no longer than the infeed table with just one pass. This kind of taper cut is made as follows (see Figs. 18–28a and 18–28b):

1. Mark the taper as shown in Figure 18–28a, and lower the infeed table to equal the desired amount of taper.
2. Turn on the power. Hold the work

against the fence and slowly lower the leading end between the guard and the fence so that the corner of the stock rests on the front edge of the outfeed table as shown by the arrow in Figure 18–28a.
3. Feed the stock forward, maintaining a uniform pressure throughout the cutting operation (Fig. 18–28b). Use a push stick if the stock is narrower than 2 in. in width.
4. If the taper is too great for one cut, additional cuts may be taken.

Taper cuts which are greater in length than the infeed table are considered as *long tapers* and are made in two or more passes as follows:

1. Divide the length of the stock into equal divisions no longer than the length of the infeed table.
2. The depth of cut is also divided into the same number of divisions. This will be the amount of cut for each pass. For example, if a board, 40 in. long, is to be tapered ⅜ in. from end to end, the length is divided into two 20-in. divisions and the infeed table is lowered to 3⁄16 in. for the depth of cut.
3. Make the first cut. This is started by lowering the board with the mark (indicating the division of the length) over the cutterhead as shown in Figure 18–29a.
4. Complete the first pass as in normal edge planing (Fig. 18–29b).
5. Make the second cut, beginning with the lead end of the board resting on the outfeed table as shown in Figure 18–29c.
6. Complete the final pass as usual.

Taper cuts which are *short and fast* (steep) are best handled as shown in Figure 18–30. This operation is often employed to make tapered cuts near the ends of square legs. A wedge, sawed to

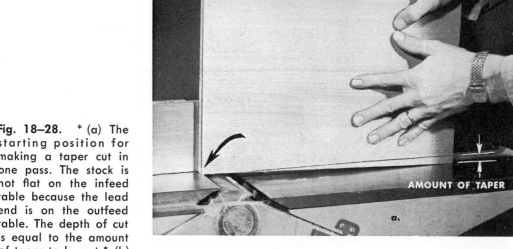

AMOUNT OF TAPER

a.

Fig. 18–28. * (a) The starting position for making a taper cut in one pass. The stock is not flat on the infeed table because the lead end is on the outfeed table. The depth of cut is equal to the amount of taper to be cut.* (b) Making the taper cut in one pass.

* Illustrations identified with an asterisk (*) indicate that the guard has been removed for illustrative purposes only.

b.

the desired taper, is used to support the work. The wedge is fastened to the stock with small brads. After each cut, the wedge is removed and used to support the next surface to be tapered. The procedure for this operation is as follows:

In the following formula which can be used to calculate the number of mill marks per inch:

1. Mark the beginning of the taper on

each surface of the stock to be tapered.

2. Fasten the wedge to the work with the apex of the wedge at this mark.
3. Lower the infeed table for the required depth of cut.
4. Fasten a stop block to the fence to help position the work at the start of the cut.
5. Start the machine. Stand behind the

outfeed table (opposite the usual position), place the work against the stop block and lower the work to the table. Apply pressure to the work

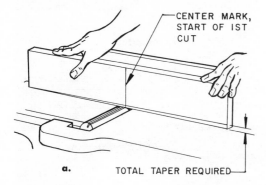

a.   TOTAL TAPER REQUIRED

CENTER MARK, START OF 1ST CUT

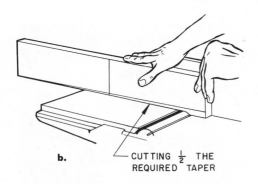

b.   CUTTING $\frac{1}{2}$ THE REQUIRED TAPER

START OF 2ND CUT

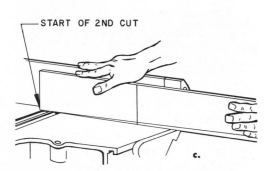

c.

Fig. 18–29a, b, c. * Cutting a taper on long stock in two passes: (a) Starting the first pass at the center, (b) the first pass cuts are one half of the required taper, and (c) the second pass starts with the lead end of the work on the outfeed table.

while pulling the stock over the cutterhead.

Using the Surfacer (Surface Planer)

The major function of the surfacer is to plane lumber to a uniform thickness. This operation will not remove cup or wind from a board. Boards in this condition should first have one surface trued on the jointer so they will lie flat on the bed of the surfacer.

Safety Precautions for the Surfacer

1. Plane stock that is no shorter than the center to center distance between the infeed and outfeed rolls.
2. Be sure that excess glue, grit, and foreign objects are removed.
3. When feeding the stock, hold it so that your fingers do not become pinched between the stock and the bed.
4. Keep your hands away from the feed rollers. Remove your hands as soon as the stock is gripped by the feed rollers.
5. Stand to one side (Fig. 18–31) of the infeed table while using the surfacer. Slivers, knots, or chips may be kicked out of the machine. *Never look into the infeed end of the machine while it is running.*
6. If two or more boards are to be planed with the machine set at one depth of cut, be sure each piece is approximately the same thickness. Otherwise, a thin board following a

---

* Illustrations identified with an asterisk (*) indicate that the guard has been removed for illustrative purposes only. The guard should be used when performing these operations in the shop.

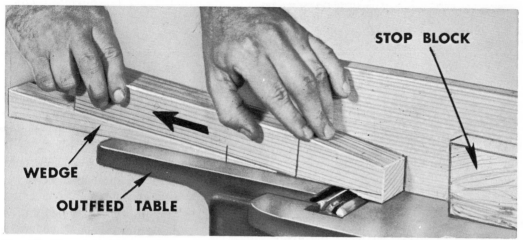

Fig. 18–30. * Making a short taper on a square table leg. The stock is pulled rather than pushed over the cutterhead.

thicker board (or side by side) will not be held by the feed rolls and may be kicked back by the revolving cutterhead.

7. Stock that is less than ⅛ in. in thickness should be planed while held in a fixture designed for the purpose. (See Figure 18–34.)

8. When making adjustments to the inner parts of the machine, be sure the power is disconnected.

9. When cleaning the surfacer, brush the chips out. *Never* put your hand inside the machine while brushing. If compressed air is used to blow the chips out, wear goggles. Caution others to stand back while blowing out the chips.

10. If pitch or other deposits collect on the rolls or bed, clean them with turpentine, mineral spirits, or kerosene. Coat the cleaned surfaces with a light film of wax or oil to prevent rusting.

11. When planing long boards, obtain the assistance of a helper to support the work.

Plane a board to thickness (Figs.

Fig. 18–31. When feeding stock into the surfacer, stand to one side. Do not permit the fingers to be pinched between the stock and the machine.

18–32 and 18–33) using the following procedure:

1. Insure that one face of the stock is true.

2. Measure the stock at its thickest point and adjust the table to remove

Fig. 18–32. Planing thin stock. The board to be planed is supported by a larger board. The feed rollers carry them both through the machine. This method would be employed for surfacing thin strips to be laminated.

$\frac{1}{32}$ to $\frac{1}{8}$ in. If the stock is to be surfaced on two sides, remove $\frac{1}{2}$ of the excess thickness from each side.

3. Determine the lead end of the stock by checking the grain direction. If necessary, take a light cut with a hand plane to ascertain the grain

Fig. 18–33. Surfacing long heavy stock. An assistant should receive the stock on the outfeed end. Note the shavings that must be contended with when a surfacer is not connected to an exhaust system.

direction. Mark the direction with a penciled arrow.

4. Adjust the feed rate for the requirements of the wood and the surface finish desired.

5. Turn on the power. Place the trued surface on the table and push the stock forward until it engages the feed rollers. Always feed the narrow end of tapered boards first.

6. If two or more boards are to be surfaced to the same thickness, run all of them through the surfacer before changing the table setting. If some of the pieces are considerably thicker than others, they will have to be planed to the same thickness first. As the stock leaves the surfacer, stack it face up and with the lead ends at the same end of the stack. This is done to keep the grain direction properly oriented.

7. When the stock has been surfaced on one side, adjust the table for the next cut. Turn the pieces over and end for end. (The grain direction is reversed on the back side.) Feed the stock as before.

8. Short pieces (no less than the distance between chip breaker and pressure bar) may be planed by butting them end to end. The last piece butted must be at least as long as the distance between the centers of the infeed and outfeed rollers. Use the slowest feed.

9. Tapers, chamfers, or bevels may be planed with the aid of a work-holding fixture similar to the one shown in Figure 18–34.

Mill Marks Produced by Jointers and Surfacers

As each knife in the cutterhead cuts through the work, it leaves a shallow, concave depression in the surface. These are known as mill marks. The size of these mill marks, and consequently the finish or appearance of the machined surface, are subject to control by the operator. He increases or decreases the rate at which he feeds the stock. Slower feed rates increase the number of knife cuts per inch. The result is a reduction in the size of the individual mill marks and a smoother surface. Faster feed rates decrease the number of mill marks, but the marks are larger and the surface is rougher.

For most species of wood, a good finish is achieved with about 20 mill marks per inch. (Fig. 18–35b). For hard maple, birch, and walnut, 30 mill marks to the inch is recommended. The number of mill marks per inch depends upon the cutterhead speed, the feed rate, and the number of knives in the cutterhead:

$$\frac{rpm \times K}{R \times 12} = M$$

rpm = rpm of cutterhead
K = number of knives in cutterhead
R × 12 = feed rate in feet times 12
M = number of mill marks per inch

Knife adjustment and sharpness. These are perhaps the most technical aspects of successful jointing and planing. The knives must not only be sharp, but they must also be jointed so that they all project the same amount. The woodworker's phrase *one knife work* (Fig. 18–35a) is often used to describe surfaces on which the highest knife in the cutterhead defines the cutting circle and consequently does all of the cutting. This produces a surface with very pronounced knife marks. Most jointers and planers are fitted with attachments for grinding and jointing the knives without removing them from the machine.*

---

* Refer to Fig. 33–8, p. 580 for an illustration of a knife grinding attachment.

Fig. 18–34. Using a fixture to plane a large chamfer. Note the base is made from plywood with strips glued to it to provide a firm support for the work.

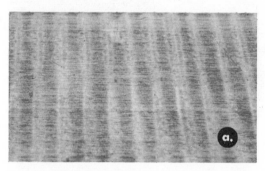

Fig. 18–35. (a) Mill marks produced when only one knife was cutting.

Fig. 18–35. (b) All knives were cutting uniformly to make this mill mark pattern.

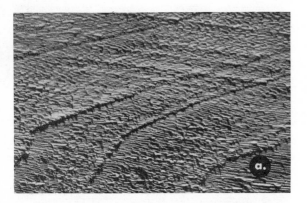

Fig. 18–36a. Raised grain.

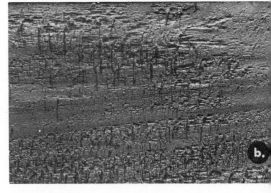

Fig. 18–36b. Fuzzy grain.

Fig. 18–36c. Chipped grain.

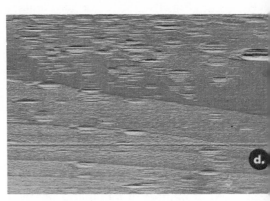

Fig. 18–36d. Chip marks.

Knife sharpness is easily detected by inspecting a cut made on the end grain of one of the lighter and softer woods. If the surface fibers are cut cleanly, the knives are sharp; if they are crushed or torn, the knives are dull and in need of sharpening. A hand lens would be useful for observing the fibers closely.

The **depth of cut** is a very significant factor to be considered for obtaining a good planed surface. Numerous tests have proved that a far greater number of defect-free pieces of stock are obtained with a $\frac{1}{32}$-in. depth of cut than with a $\frac{1}{16}$-in.

cut. Therefore, two shallower passes will produce a much better surface than one deep cut.

The **moisture content** of the wood is still another factor that affects the surface smoothness of a jointed or planed surface. The best results can be obtained on wood that contains from 6 to 12 percent moisture. The quality of the surface generally becomes poorer as the moisture content increases because raised or fuzzy grain is more likely to develop.

Refer to the machining characteristics of wood listed in the appendix. You will note that some woods have better planing qualities than others.

Although all of the functioning parts of jointers and surfacers may be in correct adjustment, there are, sometimes, certain defects which show up on planed surfaces. The *defects* (Figs. 18–36a, 18– 6b, 18–36c, and 18–36d) are generally caused by the very nature of the wood itself. The following descriptions will help you to identify the most common defects:

1. *Raised grain* (Fig. 18–36a) is a rough condition on lumber in which part of the annual ring is raised above the surface but not torn loose from it. It is caused from the pressure exerted by the surfacer rollers and other parts as the lumber passes through. The softer parts of the annual rings compress more in the planing and expand again when the pressure is removed. The more dense parts are thus left below the general level of the surface. Sharp knives and a reduction in the moisture content of the lumber tends to prevent this condition.

2. *Fuzzy grain* (Fig. 18–36b) consists of small groups of fibers that do not sever cleanly in planing, but stand up above the level of the surface. To a large degree, fuzzy grain is due to the presence of abnormal wood fibers. This condition is most common in basswood, cottonwood, and willow, and negligible in heavier woods such as ash, maple, and oak. Sharp knives and low moisture content are the best preventive measures

for this condition.

3. *Chipped grain* (Fig. 18–36c) results when very short particles are broken out below the line of cut. *Torn grain* is similar to chipped grain, but is more pronounced. Usually, chipped grain is associated with cross-grained lumber, and occurs at spots where the knives are cutting against the grain. It is often found in birch, maple, and hickory. When the grain direction in a board is crossed, this condition can not be avoided by "graining" the board, i.e., feeding it so that the knives cut with the grain. Many boards have dips or swirls, and are of such a nature that chipping is likely to occur regardless of which end enters the planer first. The most important factors in the prevention of chipping are a greater number of knife cuts per inch and a very shallow depth of cut. The spiral-knife type of cutterhead also tends to minimize this condition.

4. *Chip marks* (Fig. 18–36d) are shallow dents in the surface caused by shavings being pressed into it by the outfeed rollers. They will be most evident in shops that do not have exhaust systems or where the exhaust has insufficient capacity. A fast rate of feed may result in a bigger volume of chips than can be handled by the exhaust or ejected from the machine. Chip marks can be repaired by applying a few drops of water and waiting a few minutes. The wood fibers will swell as they absorb the water.

REVIEW QUESTIONS

1. Describe the ancient process of "hewing."
2. What early civilization was the first to use a hand plane similar to the type we use today?
3. List some special purpose planes used by early American craftsmen.
4. What did Samuel Bentham contribute to the field of woodworking?
5. Who invented the first planer with a cylindrical cutterhead?
6. What were the major features of the "Silver Medal Planer"?
7. Why is the square cutterhead more hazardous than the round cutterhead?
8. Describe the construction and use of plane iron, jack plane, block plane, jointer plane, rabbet plane, spokeshave, and router plane.
9. Which plane is designed for planing end grain? What are the features that make it suitable for this work?
10. List four methods employed to prevent splintering when planing end grain and plywood edges.
11. What are the distinguishing features of the portable power hand planes?
12. What type of cutterheads are found on portable power planes?
13. What is a joiner? What is its principal function in industry? In cabinet shops?
14. What determines the size of a joiner?
15. In a sketch, show the relationship of the cutterhead and the infeed and outfeed table for a normal jointing operation.
16. How does the rate of feed affect the number of "mill marks"?
17. What is "one-knife work"?
18. How is the joiner adjusted for depth of cut?
19. What type of guards and other safety devices are available for hand-fed jointers?
20. Identify the essential differences between a single surfacer, a double surfacer, a facing planer.
21. In a sketch, show the relationship of the infeed rolls, cutterhead, pressure bar, chip breaker and the outfeed rolls.
22. What are the three different types of cutterheads available for planers? What are the advantages and disadvantages of each?
23. Explain some causes and remedies of common planing defects.
24. What are the two principal types of mechanisms used to raise and lower planer tables?
25. What types of feeding devices are used to move or transfer stock continually into planers?
26. What type of work is produced on planer-matchers and molders?
27. What are profile heads?
28. What are the advantages of sectional infeed rollers and sectional chip breakers?
29. How are planers sized?
30. What is the "double plane iron"? How should it be adjusted?
31. Describe how to plane a surface to remove "wind" with a hand plane. With a joiner.
32. Will a single surfacer remove wind, cup, or warp from a board? Why?
33. List the safety rules that should be observed when using portable power planes, hand-fed jointers, and surfacers.

34. What types of push sticks are used for various jointing jobs?
35. When jointing, what indicates a high outfeed table? A low outfeed table?
36. Explain the procedure for jointing an edge.
37. How are surfaces of warped boards planed on the jointer?
38. What types of taper cuts may be made on the jointer? How?
39. How are rabbets cut on the jointer?
40. How is thin stock surfaced with the planer?
41. How could one taper table legs in a planer?

SUGGESTED STUDENT ACTIVITIES

1. Determine the number of mill marks per inch produced on work with the planer in your school shop.
2. Make a model to illustrate the relationship of the major parts of the single surfacer as shown in Figure 17–9 of page 225.
3. Make a fixture for machining edge bevels and chamfers with the surfacer.
4. Make a wooden hand plane similar to the type shown in Figure 15–14. Use a plane iron from a jack plane.
5. Make a wooden hand plane with a curved bottom and a plane iron sharpened to plane concave surfaces.
6. With a block of wood and a wood chisel, make a rabbet plane.
7. Design and make a model or mock-up of a power feed device for edge jointing on the jointer in your shop.
8. Design a jig for cutting round tenons on dowels with the jointer.
9. Design and construct a small plane for model work using a razor blade for a plane iron.
10. Design and construct models of screw and wedge elevated planer tables.

Chapter 19 Routing and Shaping

Routing and shaping includes many hand and machine tool processes by which wood is cut to a desired pattern or form. *Hand* routing and shaping are performed with tools that gouge, chip, or carve away excess material. Similar results are obtained in the machine processes by bits or knives that rotate at very high speeds.

Some routing and shaping machines are hand fed and some operate automatically. They function in three basic ways: (1) the stock is advanced against the cutter; (2) the work is held stationary as the cutter is moved against it; or (3) both the work and the cutter move simultaneously during the operation.

Routing includes such operations as (1) making straight or curved grooves and recesses of uniform depth; (2) "hollowing-out"; (3) piercing — cutting through the work to produce inside openings; and (4) making pattern (molding) cuts along straight or curved edges. *Shaping* includes: (1) making pattern cuts on irregular or curved work pieces such as the edges of oval table tops; (2) cutting blanks into contoured form such as a chair rocker or the curve of a chair back; and (3) cutting or shaping 3-dimensional forms such as ornate chair legs or figurines.

Routing and shaping are important processes in both the custom and mass production industries. Many consumer products, ranging from small knife or brush handles to delicate musical instruments and fine pieces of furniture, undergo shaping and routing operations at some stage in their manufacture.

Evolution of Routing and Shaping Processes and Machines

Implements for shaping and routing existed in crude form in the Stone Age. Primitive man's stone axe and later his flaked flint tools were used to shape wood by chopping, chipping, slicing, sawing, and scraping. One of the early tools developed for shaping materials was the file. Files, as we recognize them today, appeared during the Bronze Age (Fig. 19–1a). However, objects made of granite have been found that are similar in appearance to files and may have been used in the Stone Age. In many cases, it is difficult to determine whether they were actually saws, files, knives, or a combination of the three tools. Rasps (files with individually raised teeth) are known to have been used as shaping tools by the ancient Egyptians and by the inhabitants of Italy around 1200 B.C.

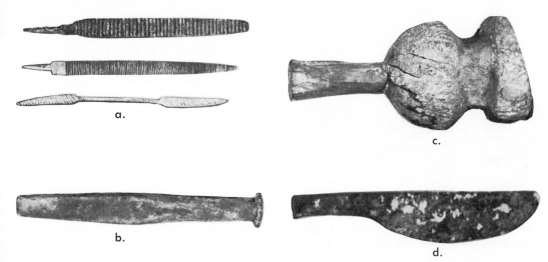

Fig. 19–1. Tools of the Bronze Age used for shaping wood to form, (a) handmade files, (b) chisel, (c) Egyptian mallet, and (d) a crude carving knife.

Recognizable chisels (Fig. 19–1b), gouges, and knives (Fig. 19–1d) date back to the Bronze Age. They were used to cut wood to shape. The early chisels and gouges had the blade and handle forged as one piece. They were generally driven into the wood with a mallet (Fig. 19–1c). Sometime later, chisels were forged with a tang that was driven into a wooden handle, or with a tapered socket into which a wooden handle could be inserted.

Better edge cutting tools came into existence with the advent of the Iron Age (Figs. 19–2a and 19–2b). Chisels, gouges, and other tools were developed to cut various shapes. The early cooper's tools included many types and shapes of chisels, the adze, the axe, the draw knife (Fig. 19–2b), and the draw shave. Some of the special-purpose planes discussed in Chapters 15 and 16 were designed to do shaping as well as planing. A typical example is the router plane which could be fitted with round or V-shaped cutters. Some early router planes are shown in Figures 19–3 and 19–4.

The **first portable electric router** was developed about the time of World War I by R. L. Carter, a patternmaker in Syracuse, New York. It was designed to replace a slow, spokeshave process for

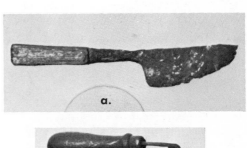

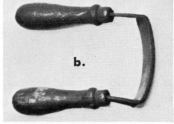

Fig. 19–2. These edge tools of the Iron Age were used for shaping wood: (a) knife with a wooden handle and (b) a well preserved draw knife used by the cooper for shaping wooden barrel staves.

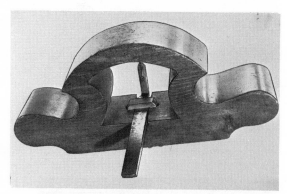

Fig. 19–3. This early hand router of German origin was used for cutting straight or curved recesses and grooves.

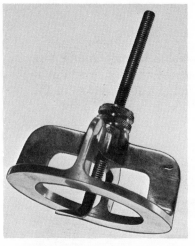

Fig. 19–4. This brass model hand router is an improved version of the hand router in Figure 19–3. Its base is similar in design to that of the portable electric router of today.

Fig. 19–5. The modern portable electric router at the left, with some of it forerunners. These evolved from the first portable shaper router.

cutting matched radii on the edges of core boxes. Carter used a worn gear from the motor of an old electric barber's clippers as a cutter. This improvised cutting bit was fastened to the shaft of a motor which was supported between two guides. The popularity of this portable tool grew quickly. Within 10 years 100,-000 routers had been manufactured by Carter. At that time they were called electric hand shapers. Eventually, the R. L. Carter Company of Phoenix, New York, became the world's largest producer of portable direct motor-driven woodworking machines. Carter's hand shaper was later improved by the addition of a chuck that could hold cutting tools such as rotary files and specially designed router bits with $\frac{1}{4}$-in. round shanks.

The original Carter router was a low performance tool with an output of $\frac{1}{4}$ hp. Its provision for depth control was essentially the same as the routers of today. The base frame and motor housing were threaded with 16 threads per inch. Thus, one revolution of the motor in the frame resulted in a depth change of $\frac{1}{16}$ in.

In 1929, Carter sold his business to Stanley Power Tools. Today, Stanley manufactures a line of routers that have been further improved but they still retain most of Carter's basic construction features (Fig. 19–5).

A **universal routing machine** (Fig. 19–6) constructed of metal parts was included in the line of woodworking machines put out by the pioneering H. B. Smith Co. of New Jersey prior to 1900. The spindle was supported from a post by an arm that moved horizontally under hand control. The spindle was adjusted vertically by a screw. This machine was also provided with a collar to ride against a pattern so that duplicate parts could be made. The wooden table of this machine could be adjusted vertically by means of screws at each end. This machine was used for cutting grooves in stair rails to receive the stiles and for other work that required stopped grooves. Routing machines that incorporate these constructional features are still used today.

The **first shaper** is credited to "the father of woodworking machinery," Samuel Bentham of London, England. It was developed and manufactured between 1791 and 1793 along with the many other kinds of machines patented at that time by the famous Englishman. The first shapers were constructed with wooden bases and frames, but these gave way to cast iron bases in the middle 1850's. The first shaping and routing machines were belt driven from line shafts powered by water wheels and later steam engines.

A typical *single spindle shaper* manufactured by the H. G. Smith Company in the late 1800's and early 1900's is shown in Figure 19–7. This machine had a reversible drive mechanism. The operator

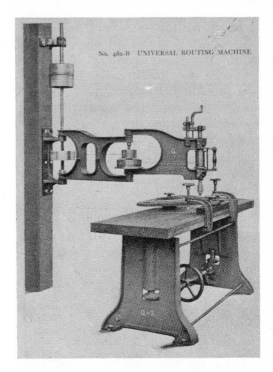

Fig. 19–6. This universal routing machine was used in the late 1800's and early 1900's.

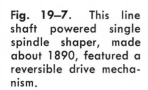

Fig. 19–7. This line shaft powered single spindle shaper, made about 1890, featured a reversible drive mechanism.

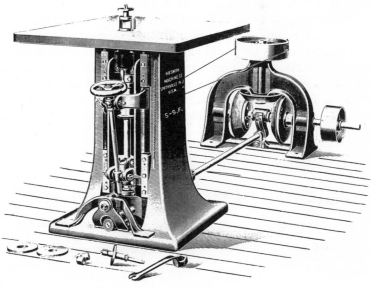

could change the rotation of the spindle as necessary to obtain the proper cutting action. The reversing mechanism was controlled by a foot treadle. The treadle disengaged one friction drive cone and engaged the other, thus quickly reversing the spindle rotation. The spindle was adjusted vertically by a handwheel. These early machines were used in furniture and piano factories to make moldings on straight or curved edges. There were no significant improvements to shapers until 1916 when Baxter D. Whitney applied the first direct drive motor to the shaper spindle. Today, however, most shapers are belt-driven by individual electric motors to obtain higher spindle speeds.

Hand Routing and Shaping Tools Today

There are many kinds of hand tools that are used to shape wood today. Briefly, they include the modern versions of the ancient chisels, gouges, files, rasps, and other kinds of shaping tools. The major areas of work in which hand shaping tools are used are: (1) for small work that is too dangerous to be shaped by machine processes; (2) by professional wood sculptors or artist-craftsmen who make patterns for metal castings and master models or patterns that will be duplicated in a carving machine; and (3) by general woodworkers, such as carpenters, cabinetmakers, students, and home craftsmen.

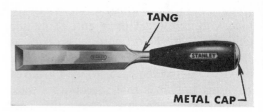

Fig. 19–9. This tang chisel with its improved design has a tang that extends through the handle to the metal cap.

Chisels (Fig. 19–8) are edge tools with blades made of carbon tool steel. They are used for chipping stock to shape and for the final trimming and fitting of joints. Chisels are classed into two groups, the *socket* (Fig. 19–8) and the *tang* (Fig. 19–9). The socket chisel gets its name from the cone shaped opening or socket that receives the handle. The socket chisel is also referred to as a *firmer* chisel. The name stems from the days of wooden handles and the fact that it could withstand heavier mallet blows than the tang type. The handle of the tang chisel is fitted over either a pointed or blunt tang on the blade. A shoulder on the tang prevents it from being driven too far into the handle.

Both types of chisels are made in various thicknesses, widths, lengths, and shapes of blades. Generally, the size of a chisel is designated by its blade width. Chisels range from $\frac{1}{8}$ in. to 1 in. in $\frac{1}{8}$-in. steps; from 1 in. to 2 in. in $\frac{1}{4}$-in. steps. Chisels may be purchased individually or in basic sets of four (Fig. 19–10) or six.

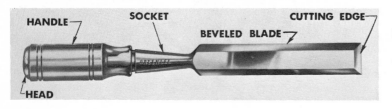

Fig. 19–8. The basic parts of a socket paring chisel.

They are available with hickory or plastic handles and either plain, leather, or metal caps.

The most common classes of chisels are:

1. *Paring chisels* (Fig. 19–8). These have thin blades with 15–20 deg. beveled sides. The blade is about 4 to 6 in. in length. They are usually used for fine hand chiseling and paring.
2. *Butt chisels* (Fig. 19–10). These have short sturdy blades varying from 2½ to 3 in. long. The sides of the blades are usually beveled.
3. *Mortising and framing chisels* (Figs. 19–11a and 19–11b). These have thick blades with either a beveled or a plain edge. They are used for heavy chiseling jobs in construction work and for prying chips out of mortises. They are available in 8-, 9-, or 10-inch blade lengths.
4. *Glazier's chisels* (Fig. 19–12). These

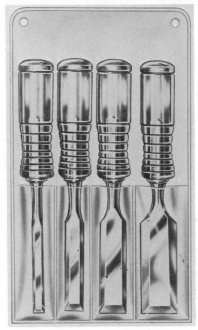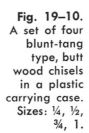

Fig. 19–10. A set of four blunt-tang type, butt wood chisels in a plastic carrying case. Sizes: ¼, ½, ¾, 1.

have a thick, 2 in. wide blade with a length of 2¾ to 3¼ in. They are used for removing window putty and cleaning out the sash. The square edge is used for driving glazier's points.

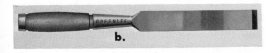

Fig. 19–11. Socket mortising and framing chisels: (a) standard bevel edge blade (b) plain edge blade. A brass ring encloses the end of the handle.

Fig. 19–13. Socket gouges: (a) Outside bevel, (b) inside bevel.

Fig. 19–12. A glazier's chisel.

Fig. 19–14. This tang type gouge with a bent shank to off-set the handle is commonly used by patternmakers.

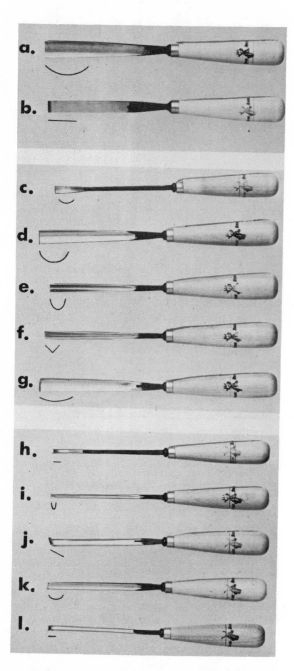

Fig. 19–15. Some of the various sizes and sweeps (forms of cutting edge) of professional carving tools.

Gouges (Figs. 19–13a, 19–13b, and 19–14) are chisels with a cross-sectional arc shape. They are available in both the socket (Figs. 19–13a and 19–13b) and the tang (Fig. 19–14) type of construction. The cutting edge may be beveled on the outside (Fig. 19–13a) or inside (Fig. 19–13b). The outside bevel gouge generally has more uses and is easier to sharpen. The inside bevel gouge is primarily used by patternmakers for making concave grooves and for paring inside arcs and circles. Gouges are available with blades that range from ¼ to 2 in. in width.

Carving tools (Fig. 19–15) are similar to chisels and gouges, but they are smaller and not intended for rough or heavy cutting. Carving tools may be purchased separately or in sets of four, six, or eight. The professional wood-carver or sculptor generally has a set of 16 or more differently shaped tools. Carving tools generally range from ¹⁄₁₆ to 1 in. in width and from 3 to 7 in. in overall blade length. The tang type of construction is predominant. Either wood or plastic handles are used. They are capable of taking light blows with a mallet, but they are not as durable as conventional chisels and gouges. Various carving tools and their "sweep" (pattern of the cutting edge) are shown in Figure 19–15. They are generally named and used as follows:

a. Wide sweep gouge — for rough cutting to depth.

b. Flat chisel — for smoothing edges.

c. Front bent or "spoon" gouge — for cutting narrow concave surfaces.

d & e. Straight gouge — for finish and rough cutting.

f. Parting tool or right angle V — for outlining the cut or design.

g. Wide sweep gouge — for general purposes.

h. Skew chisel (fishtail model) — for vertical paring.

i. Fluter — for rounding angles.

j. Corner chisel — for squaring internal edges.

k. Straight gouge — for general carving.

l. $\frac{1}{16}$ straight chisel — for carving intricate designs.

Carving knives (Fig. 19–16) are used for carving and whittling wood to form or shape. They have wood or aluminum handles in several sizes. Interchangeable blades of various shapes fit into the slotted chucks of the knife handles. They are useful for severing grain fibers, marking layout lines in joinery, and for slitting thin veneers.

The *utility knife* (Fig. 19–17) has an aluminum die-cast handle fastened together by screws. The blades are held in a flat recess between the halves of the handle by pins. Replaceable blades are stored inside the handle. This knife is useful for cutting wood, veneer, paper materials, and for general pattern work.

The *cornering tool* (Fig. 19–18) is used by patternmakers and general woodworkers for rounding sharp edges or arrises. This is a hand operation known as "easing." The tool has a different size cutter at each end. It is available with a combination of $\frac{1}{16}$- and $\frac{1}{8}$-in. cutters or $\frac{1}{4}$- and $\frac{3}{8}$-in. cutters.

The *draw knife* (Fig. 19–19) is used to rough-shape wood by pulling the tool with the cutting edge toward the operator. The blade is generally $1\frac{3}{8}$ or $2\frac{1}{2}$ in. in width, 8 to 14 in. in length, and beveled on one side. It is useful for peeling bark from poles and for rough shaping large carvings and sculptures.

The *axe, adze,* and *hatchet* (Fig.

Fig. 19–16. A set of carving knives with replaceable blades.

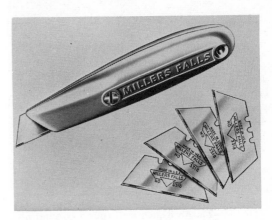

Fig. 19–17. A utility knife with replaceable blades.

19–20) may also be considered as shaping tools although their use is primarily limited to rough work as chopping on larger timbers. They are used extensively in bridge, mine, and dock work in the modern shipwright trades.

Wood files (Fig. 19–21) and rasps (Figs. 19–22a and 19–22b) are used for

Fig. 19–18. A cornering tool is used to "ease" sharp edges.

Fig. 19–19. Draw knife.

Fig. 19–20. A hatchet: the modern version of a prehistoric hand axe is sometimes useful for rough shaping and carving work.

roughing and finishing wood to shape. At times, an intricate pattern or shape can best be worked with a file. Rasps and files are essentially gangs of chisel-like teeth formed on a hardened tool steel surface. There are over 3000 different

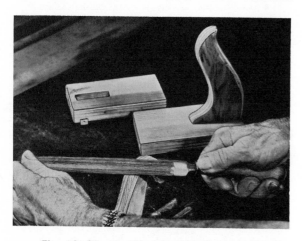

Fig. 19–21. An 8-inch half round cabinet file.

Fig. 19–22. (a) An 8-inch half round wood rasp. (b) An 8-inch half round cabinet rasp.

kinds of files available. For woodworking only a few are used.

Files and rasps are identified by four basic characteristics:

(1) The *length* (Fig. 19–23) measured from the heel to the point. Generally, the most widely used sizes of wood files or rasps range from 6 to 12 in. in length.

(2) The *shape,* which is an identification of the geometric cross-sectional shape (Fig. 19–24a).

(3) The *cut,* whether single, double, or rasp. This refers to the shape of the cutting teeth in the file or rasp.

(4) The *grade of coarseness* refers to the size of the teeth and their spacing. See Figure 19–24b. Coarseness is designated as bastard, second cut, or smooth. An 8-in. bastard double cut file has finer teeth than a 12-in. bastard double cut. This is to say that the longer the file, the larger the teeth.

The *cabinet rasp* and the coarser *wood rasp* are used to rough shape wood and other soft materials. The coarser single and double cut files may be used for fine cuts on hard woods. A file card or brush is used to clean a file or rasp.

Bent rifflers (Fig. 19–25) are files or rasps with curved ends. They are generally adaptable to wood carving, pattern-making, and gunsmithing operations.

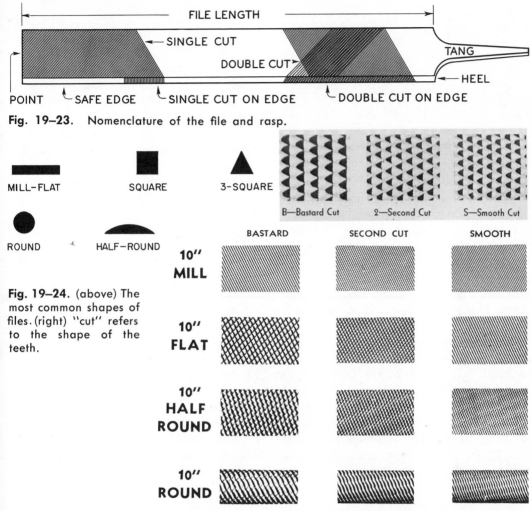

FILE LENGTH

SINGLE CUT

DOUBLE CUT

TANG

HEEL

POINT   SAFE EDGE   SINGLE CUT ON EDGE   DOUBLE CUT ON EDGE

Fig. 19–23. Nomenclature of the file and rasp.

MILL–FLAT   SQUARE   3-SQUARE

B—Bastard Cut   2—Second Cut   S—Smooth Cut

ROUND   HALF–ROUND

BASTARD   SECOND CUT   SMOOTH

Fig. 19–24. (above) The most common shapes of files. (right) "cut" refers to the shape of the teeth.

10″ **MILL**

10″ **FLAT**

10″ **HALF ROUND**

10″ **ROUND**

Fig. 19–25. A set of bent rifflers.

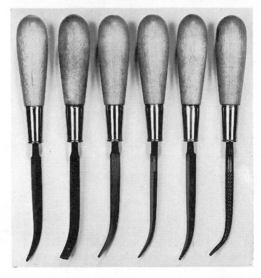

They are made in various sizes, shapes, and styles. Some have no tang. In its place is another file body with teeth of a different grade of coarseness than those on the other end.

Needle files and rasps are 5 to 6 in. long, including the integral handle. Generally, they are no more than ¼ in. at the thickest end and taper to a fine thin point. They are used for exacting work, such as smoothing inside openings of models and inletting gunstocks.

Rotary files or burrs (Fig. 19–26) are power-driven files. They are widely used

Fig. 19–26. Ball-shaped rotary files.

in wood and metal shops for finish smoothing and shaping of detailed parts. They are used in drill presses, lathes, electric or air-operated hand tools, and flexible shaft machines. They are available in a number of sizes and shapes such as oval, round, ball, cylindrical, cone, and tapered. They are usually made of high speed steel with ⅛- or ¼-in. diameter round shanks.

The **forming tools** (Fig. 19–27a) are relatively new additions to the family of hand shaping tools. The cutting portion is composed of a series of individual razor sharp teeth formed on thin, hardened tool steel. Each tooth cuts with a shearing action. The shavings are lifted and passed through the openings in the blade as shown in Figure 19–27b. The

blades are available in different shapes to fit corresponding holders. Flat blades, as shown (Figs. 19–28a, 19–28b, and 19–28c), are generally 1⅝ in. in width. When a blade becomes dull or broken, it may be replaced by removing the screws that hold the blade to the handle or frame. Forming tools are also available in half round, round (Fig. 19–28d), and drum shapes (Fig. 19–28e) with a shank that fits into a drill chuck.

Powered Portable Routers and Shapers

The **rotary carving tool** (Fig. 19–29) is used for engraving and carving wood as well as for drilling, grinding, and polishing. This lightweight tool weighs a little over one pound. It is useful for small delicate jobs such as those found in pattern and model making. The operator controls this tool freehand since it is not equipped with a base or guide as the router. It has a collet type chuck that will take any type of rotary tool with a ⅛-in. shank. It delivers a speed of 27,000 rpm.

Portable electric routers (Figs. 19–30a

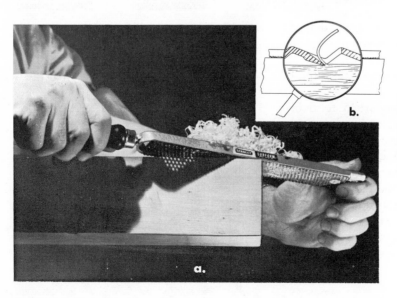

b.

Fig. 19–27. (a) The forming tools produce shavings. (b) An enlarged section drawing to show the shearing cut of the tooth.

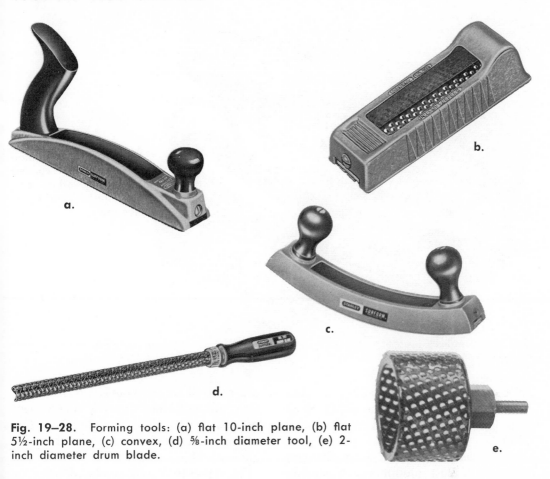

Fig. 19–28. Forming tools: (a) flat 10-inch plane, (b) flat 5½-inch plane, (c) convex, (d) ⅝-inch diameter tool, (e) 2-inch diameter drum blade.

and 19–30b) are used in all levels of woodworking, from the home workshop to the industrial plant. They operate by direct drive at high speeds of 5000 to 24,000 rpm. The size of a router is determined by the horsepower (hp) rating of the motor. Light-duty to medium sizes carry motors that range from ¼ to 1¼ to 2½ hp. Heavy-duty sizes range from 4 to 8 hp.

The modern router consists of 2 major parts. The *motor* and the *base*. The motor *spindle* is hollow so as to receive a collet. The collet grips the round shank of a bit when the lock nut is tightened on the spindle. Smaller routers have ¼-in. diameter collets; larger industrial routers have collets ½ in. in diameter. Some routers have a spindle-locking device for use when changing the bit. These locking devices are operated by either depressing a button on top of the motor or by a switch. A router with a motor shaft lock requires only one wrench to change the bit whereas a router without a shaft lock requires two wrenches.

The motor unit can be adjusted vertically in the base. This is accomplished by threads in the motor housing and base or by two pins on the motor which slide in spiral grooves in the base. Some models raise and lower by means of a rack and pinion. A clamp lever on the base locks the motor firmly to the base.

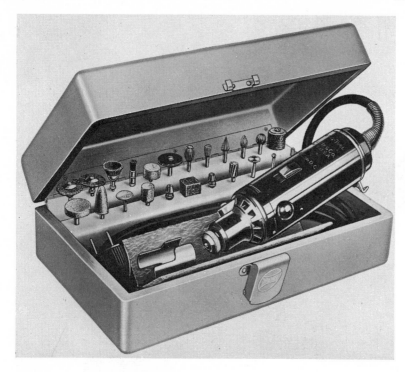

Fig. 19–29. A high speed rotary carving tool with various cutters, brushes, and abrasive tools.

Modern routers feature a built-in micrometer depth adjustment. The depth of cut is indicated in graduations of $\frac{1}{64}$ in. to .004 in.

The *router base* is generally constructed of cast aluminum. A subbase of molded fiber or plastic is often attached to the base to resist marring the work surface.

Pneumatic routers (Fig. 19–31) are used in industry. The major advantages common to all air tools are: less weight no shock hazards, less overheating, and less maintenance. Air turbine router motors require 90 PSI of air pressure and reach up to 16,000 rpm.

The **cutters or bits** (Figs. 19–33, 19–34a, 19–34b, and 19–34c) used in a router are made of high-speed steel, solid tungsten carbide, or carbide-tipped tool steel. There is a variety of bits available to cut different patterns or profiles. Generally, the cutters (Fig. 19–33)

are referred to as *one-piece bits* because they are machined from a single piece of metal. One-piece straight bits (Fig. 19–34) may be further classified as single end (Fig. 19–34a) or double end (Fig. 19–34b), and single, double, or spiral (Fig. 19–34c) flute.

One-piece bits that make pattern profile cuts along the edge of a board (Fig. 19–34b) are called *piloted bits*. The pilot is the part of the bit that rides along the edge of the work to control the horizontal depth of cut.

When the motor unit of the router is used in a shaper table (Fig. 19–40), special cutters are used. They are referred to as *shaper cutters* (Figs. 19–35a and 19–35b). Shaper cutters have a hole through their center and are mounted on arbors (Fig. 35a) between spacing collars. Many of the profiles of one-piece bits are also available in shaper cutters.

Attachments and accessories available

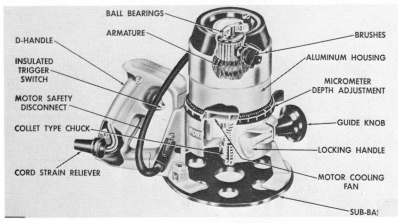

Fig. 19–30. Nomenclature of a portable electric router featuring a "D" shaped handle and trigger switch.

BALL BEARINGS

ARMATURE

BRUSHES

D-HANDLE

INSULATED TRIGGER SWITCH

ALUMINUM HOUSING

MICROMETER DEPTH ADJUSTMENT

MOTOR SAFETY DISCONNECT

GUIDE KNOB

COLLET TYPE CHUCK

LOCKING HANDLE

CORD STRAIN RELIEVER

MOTOR COOLING FAN

SUB-BAS

for portable routers are described in the following paragraphs:

1. A *guide* for straight and circular cutting (Fig. 19–36) is attached to the base of the router. The guide serves as a fence for straight cuts. A *trammel point* permits circular cuts.
2. *Templet guides* are available with

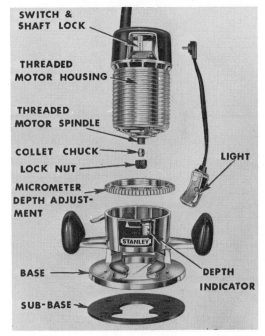

SWITCH & SHAFT LOCK

THREADED MOTOR HOUSING

THREADED MOTOR SPINDLE

COLLET CHUCK

LOCK NUT

LIGHT

MICROMETER DEPTH ADJUSTMENT

BASE

DEPTH INDICATOR

SUB-BASE

Fig. 19–31. View showing the assembly and the major parts of a router.

Fig. 19–32. A pneumatic router.

different inside openings and outside diameters. A templet guide is mounted to the bottom of the router base to permit the router to follow the contour of a templet or pattern. The bit protrudes through the templet guide to make the required cut. The method is often used to duplicate irregular contours or designs on the surface of wood.

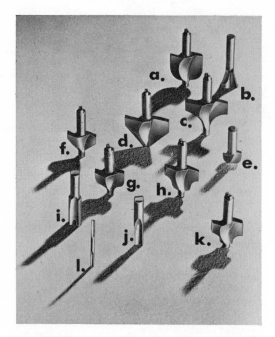

Fig. 19–33. Most common types of one-piece router bits: (a) cove, (b) dovetail, (c) corner rounding, (d) "V" grooving, (e) core box, (f) chamfer, (g-h) ogee, (i) stair routing, (j) straight, (k) beading, and (l) double end straight or veining.

It is also used with the dovetailing fixture shown in Figure 19–37.

3. *Dovetail fixtures* (Fig. 19–37) consist of a plastic templet and an aluminum base with adjustable stops to position the work. A clamp holds both members of the joint so that they may be cut simultaneously.

4. *Door and jam butt templets* (Fig. 19–38) are used in cutting mortises for butt hinges.

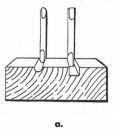
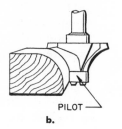

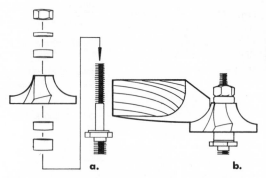

Fig. 19–35. A shaper cutter: (a) the assembly of a corner rounding cutter and the arbor, (b) making a cut.

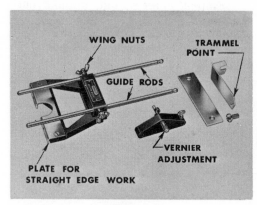

Fig. 19–36. Guide for making straight and circular cuts.

5. *Trimmers* (Fig. 19–39) are attached to the router base to guide it when trimming thin materials flush or close to another surface. With a carbide tipped bit, this attachment

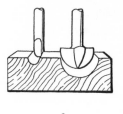

Fig. 19–34. Cuts made by basic one-piece bits. The corner rounding bit (b) used on the edge of stock is guided by the pilot.

Fig. 19–37. A dovetail fixture holds both members of the joint for simultaneous cutting with a dovetail bit.

Fig. 19–38. A door and jam butt templet.

is excellent for making straight or beveled trim cuts on plastic laminates.

6. The *shaper table* (Fig. 19–40) is used for mounting the motor of the router upside down in a stationary position so it may function as a light-duty shaper.

7. A *grinding fixture* attached to the router base is used to hold the bits as they are sharpened by a rotary abrasive wheel mounted in the collet.

8. The *power plane* is shown in Figure 16–12, page 217.

Routing and Shaping Machines and Processes in Industry

Radial arm routers (Fig. 19–41) are widely used in industry for work on large panels, such as cutting window openings in doors or cut-outs for sinks in kitchen counters. With this type of machine, the work is held stationary on a table and the router head is guided manually, either free hand or with the aid of a guide pin following in a pattern or templet.

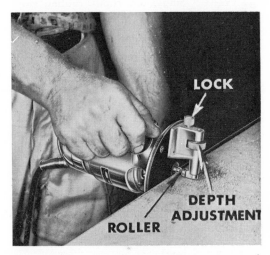

LOCK

DEPTH ADJUSTMENT

ROLLER

Fig. 19–39. Trimmer attachment as used on veneers and plastic laminates.

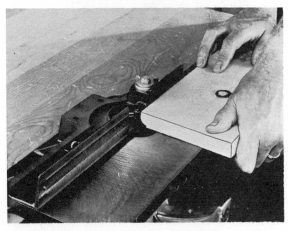

Fig. 19–40. Shaper table attachment.

Fig. 19–41. Single arm radial routing machine making multiple cutouts in stacked panels.

Radial-arm routers are made with either a *single arm* (Fig. 19–41) or a *double arm*. They have heavy semi-steel pedestal bases, which support the turret post. The arms pivot 360 deg. around the post and are jointed for a free-moving elbow action. The arm houses a mechanism that rotates the spindle head. It also contains the air cylinders, which raise or lower the router head. The *router head* on machines of this type has a spindle

with a collet chuck. The spindle revolves at 14,400 to 22,000 rpm and is driven by a 5-hp, high frequency electric* or air-turbine motor. The capacity of the radial-arm router is determined by the *reach* of the arm, which may be up to 109 in.

The **overarm routers** (Figs. 19–42 and 19–43) are very flexible industrial machines. Not only do they make cuts on the upper surface and edges of the work, but they also make internal (piercing) cuts. The basic applications of these routers are illustrated and described in Figure 19–44.

The base, column, and overarm are of heavy cast-iron construction. They house the electrical, pneumatic, and hydraulic mechanisms. The table is adjusted vertically by means of the front handwheel. It may also be raised and lowered by means of a foot treadle. The vertical travel ranges from 7 to 12 in. on the various machines. Guide pins fit into the table for feeding the work, as shown in

---

* A motor made to run at 3600 rpm at 60 cycles will run at 7200 rpm if a frequency converter is used to produce 120 cycle current.

Fig. 19–42. An overarm router with a floating head.

Fig. 19–43. A router being used to route slots in drawer sides.

Figures 19–44b, 19–44c, and 19–44f. The table may be tilted on some models.

The *spindle* is belt-driven by motors of 2 to 7½ hp. Some models employ cone pulleys to produce spindle speeds ranging from 10,000 to 20,000 rpm. Pneumatic routers operate at speeds up to 50,000 rpm. The router head is raised or lowered by hydraulic or pneumatic cylinders, energized by means of a foot pedal. The total vertical travel of the spindle ranges from 3¼ to 5 in. Generally, these machines have a throat capacity (clearance from spindle to column) ranging from 15 to 36 in.

A relatively new feature incorporated in some of these machines is a *floating head* or *floating spindle* (Figs. 19–42

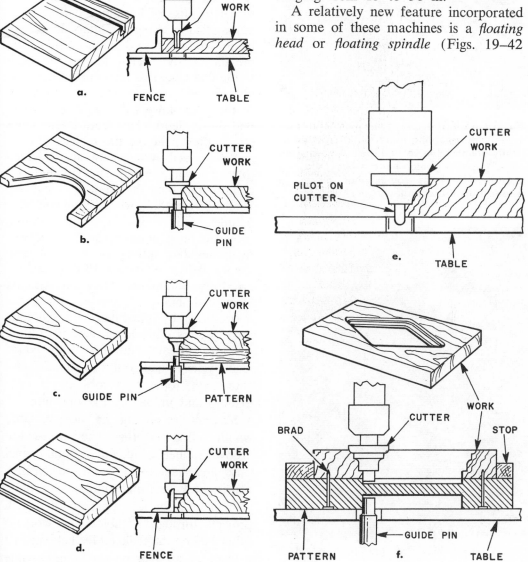

Fig. 19–44. Typical work methods of industrial routers.

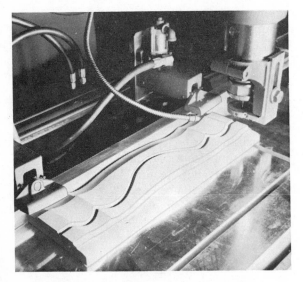

Fig. 19–45. This cut of uniform depth was made with a floating head router. A hydraulically driven table carried the clamped work piece past the router head while following a pattern and the router head moved in response to the changes in the surface.

Fig. 19–46. View of the pattern which guides the movement of a power driven table attachment on the router.

and 19–45). With this feature, the cutter can be controlled to a uniform depth over irregular surfaces (Fig. 19–45). A cushion of air above the spindle maintains a uniform pressure on the guide that rides on the work and thereby controls the depth that the cutter may enter the work.

An automatic cycling device is optional on some routers. The machine may be set to raise or lower the cutting head automatically at regular intervals. It may be preset to cut at different depths. Depressing a foot pedal lowers the head to the first level and maintains it until the pedal is released. A second depression of the pedal lowers the head to the second preset depth. This feature eliminates hand adjustments of the table.

Power feed systems are also adapted to production routers. These include air clamps that hold the work to a hydraulically driven table which is guided by a templet (Fig. 19–46). This feature, provided on a floating spindle machine, facilitates the cutting of very intricate shapes. Advanced designs of this machine are fully automatic. They are templet controlled and programed to make the desired cuts by integrated cam and solenoid systems. This design permits routing various intricate patterns. With power feed systems and fully automatic machines, the operator's job entails only loading and unloading the machine.

Shapers are among the most versatile woodworking machines. They are used to groove, rabbet, bead, flute, tenon, panel raise, and shape moldings. Basically, they consist of knives and cutters that rotate at high speed on a vertical spindle which projects through a table. The work is supported on the table and is held against a fence or a collar on the spindle while being cut. The work is applied to the rotating cutters manually or by automatic feeding devices.

Shapers are available in many sizes and types, but basically they may be grouped as follows: hand-fed *single-spindle shapers* (Fig. 19–47), hand-fed *double-spindle shapers* (Fig. 19–61), *automatic shapers* (Fig. 19–62), and *automatic profile shapers* (Fig. 19–67).

The **single-spindle shapers** are available in small bench models for home craftsmen and light industrial work. They are also available in floor models, as shown in Figures 19–47 and 19–48.

The *spindle* (Fig. 19–49) is the heart of the shaper. It rotates in bearings designed to withstand the side thrust that results during use of the machine. The spindle is driven either by a direct high frequency motor or more commonly by a belted motor. The spindle speed generally ranges from 5000 to 10,000 rpm. Some machines have spindle speeds as high as 14,500 to 18,000 rpm. Some shapers feature a reversible motor. This permits the operator greater choice of cutters and two directions of feed. The work is always hand-fed *against* the rotation of the cutter.

The spindle and motor-drive system are generally fitted to a *yoke* that can be adjusted vertically. It is raised or lowered as one unit by means of a handwheel (Fig. 19–50). The assembly has a travel

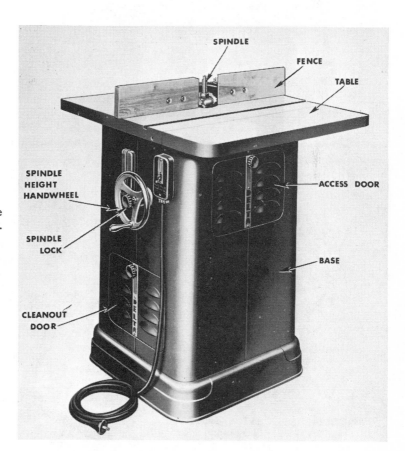

Fig. 19–47. A single spindle cabinet shaper.

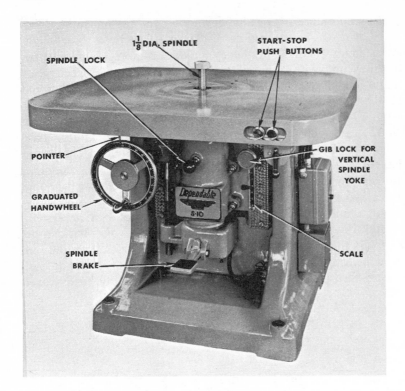

SPINDLE LOCK

$1\frac{1}{8}$ DIA. SPINDLE

START-STOP
PUSH BUTTONS

POINTER

GIB LOCK FOR
VERTICAL
SPINDLE
YOKE

GRADUATED
HANDWHEEL

Dependable

S-10

SPINDLE
BRAKE

SCALE

Fig. 19–48. A heavy-duty shaper with a 1⅛-inch diameter spindle.

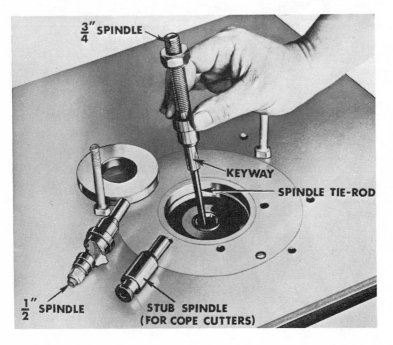

$\frac{3}{4}''$ SPINDLE

KEYWAY

SPINDLE TIE-ROD

$\frac{1}{2}''$ SPINDLE

STUB SPINDLE
(FOR COPE CUTTERS)

Fig. 19–49. Interchangeable spindles permit use of a wide variety of cutters.

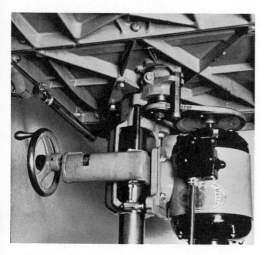

Fig. 19—50. The spindle, motor, yoke, and raising mechanism of a shaper.

of about 3½ in. on the small- to medium-sized machines, up to 6 in. on the larger machines. Spindle sizes generally range from ½ in. on the smaller shapers up to 1⅛- or 1¼-in. diameters on the heavy-duty machines. They are rotated by ½- to

Fig. 19—51. A typical setup for a solid wing cutter. Cutters are usually made of high speed steel. Some are carbide tipped.

Fig. 19—52. Profile of the many shapes of cutters available.

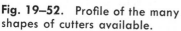

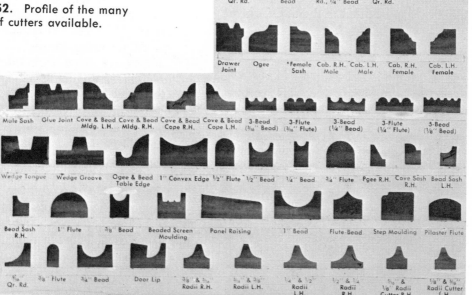

Fig. 19–53. Flat shaper knives with collars used for shaping plastic laminated table tops.

Fig. 19–54. The shape produced by the cutter shown above.

2-hp motors on small- and medium-size machines and 5- to 7½-hp motors on heavy-duty shapers. Some spindles are of hollow construction so that auxiliary spindles may be fitted to them. Others are

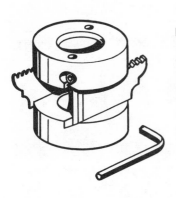

Fig. 19–55. Each knife edge is notched, engaging threads on adjusting screws in the to collar.

threaded on the upper end. These auxiliary spindles are known as *spindle tops.* They range from 6 to 12 in. in length. The spindle tops are fitted with cutters and collars of various thicknesses and diameters as desired, all held securely in position with a lock nut. When long spindle tops are used and when heavy cuts are made, an auxiliary bearing on the top of the spindle is often necessary to resist side thrust and steady the spindle. This bearing, known as the *overhead bearing* (Fig. 62), may be removed when it is not in use.

Shaper cutters are of 3 basic types:

1. *Solid wing cutters* as shown in Figure 19–51. This type is the most popular and the safest to use because it is machined from one piece of metal. It has a center hole which slips over the spindle top. Some of the many shapes of solid cutters are shown in Figure 19–52.

2. *Flat shaper knives* (Fig. 19–54). These are held in position by two slotted collars. Knives may be purchased ground to shape or in 12- to 24-in. lengths. The lengths are then cut and ground to shape as needed. It is important that both knives be the same weight to prevent excessive vibration. Safety-lock knives and collars (Fig. 19–55) reduce the danger of throwing knives.

3. The *shaper head with interchangeable knives.* Figure 19–56 shows one style of shaper head that may be fitted with most of the knife shapes shown in Figure 19–53. Shaper heads are also made square and fitted with milled knives.

Shaper collars (Fig. 19–51) range from ⅛ to 2 in. in thickness and are available in various diameters. Collars are placed above, below and, when two or more cutters are used, between them as neces-

Fig. 19–56. A shaper head with three interchangeable knives. Set screws hold the knives in place.

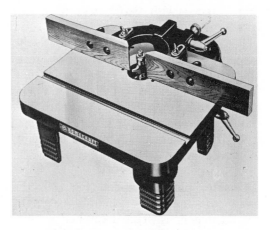

Fig. 19–58. An adjustable fence is useful for making straight molding cuts.

sary. They serve two basic functions: (1) they limit the depth to which the cutter may penetrate the work, and (2) they position the cutter(s) on the spindle. Special ball-bearing collars are used in place of the standard collars when friction would cause the wood to burn.

The *shaper table* is a heavy casting with a machined surface, machined spindle hole, bored guide pin holes, and in some cases, a machined groove to accomodate a sliding table jig (Fig. 19–57). Most machines have large spindle holes. A set of disks, or inserts, of various sizes fits into the hole to keep the

opening around the spindle and cutter as small as possible.

A *fence* (Fig. 19–58) is fastened to the table to guide straightedge work. The fence consists of a cast base or bracket and two sections that have independent screw adjustments. The fence is

Fig. 19–57. A sliding shaper jig holds short and narrow pieces by means of a clamp. The miter gauge head can be set to any angle from 0 to 45 degrees.

Fig. 19–59. An adjustable ring type guard.

usually faced with two pieces of hardwood.

The hand-fed shaper is a relatively dangerous machine to operate. A ring guard (Fig. 19–59), when positioned over the cutter, helps to protect the operator on certain operations. The guard can also be adjusted to serve as a hold-down. Spring clamps are available for use with the fence when shaping narrow work (Fig. 19–60).

Double spindle shapers (Fig. 19–61) operate on the same principle as single spindle machines. The difference is that double spindle shapers have two independent spindles which may be rotated in opposite directions. With this feature, two cutters of the same shape, one made to cut left and one right, may be mounted on the spindles. Consequently, cuts can always be made with the grain of the wood. When different cutters are mounted on each spindle, two different patterns or cuts may be made on one workpiece. Spindle-top sizes range from

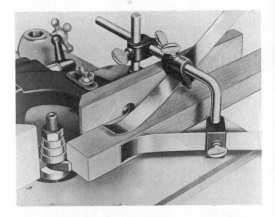

Fig. 19–60. Spring hold-downs attached to the fence hold narrow work firmly against the fence and table.

¾ to 1½ in. in diameter. Each spindle is equipped with a quick-acting brake. Spindles rotate at speeds from 7200 to 15,000 rpm. They are belt-driven by either 2-, 3-, 5-, 7½-, or 10-hp motors depending upon the size and nature of the work to be performed.

Automatic shapers are of two basic

Fig. 19–61. A double spindle shaper.

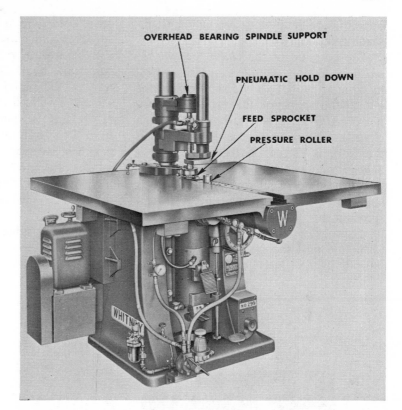

OVERHEAD BEARING SPINDLE SUPPORT

PNEUMATIC HOLD DOWN

FEED SPROCKET

PRESSURE ROLLER

Fig. 19–62. Automatic single spindle shaper.

types: (1) the stationary table, fixed spindle type as shown in Figure 19–62 and (2) the revolving table, movable spindle type as shown in Figure 19–66. With both types of machines, the work is moved past the cutterhead automatically. A guide roller bears against a pattern to position the work or the cutter. See Figure 19–63. The work is fed in the same direction as the rotation of the cutter. This is opposite to the direction in which single and double spindle shapers are fed. This type of cutting action is referred to as "back knifing" or "climb cutting." It produces a smoother cut than is possible on the hand-fed machines. The automatic feeding device prevents the cutter from pulling the work as happens on the hand-fed machines.

The duties of the automatic shaper

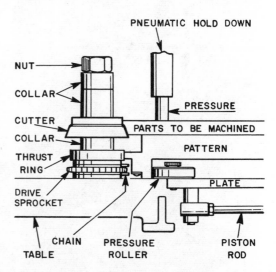

PNEUMATIC HOLD DOWN

NUT

COLLAR

CUTTER

COLLAR

THRUST RING

DRIVE SPROCKET

PRESSURE

PARTS TO BE MACHINED

PATTERN

PLATE

CHAIN TABLE

PRESSURE ROLLER

PISTON ROD

Fig. 19–63. The operation of a chain feed. The pressure roller bearing against the pattern guides the pattern against the thrust ring and the drive sprocket, bringing the work to the revolving cutter.

operator are limited to loading and un-loading the machine.

The function of the *chain feed mech-anism* on stationary table shapers is shown in Figure 19–63. A wooden pattern is cut to the shape of the proposed work pieces. The pattern is then fitted with a chain as shown in Figure 19–63. When the work is placed on the pattern, it is held by pins (pointed nails) and a pneu-matic hold-down clamp. The chain is engaged by an independently driven feed sprocket that fits around the spindle. The feed sprocket moves the work at a uni-form rate past the revolving shaper cut-ter. The pattern is held against the sprocket and cutterhead by a pneumati-cally controlled pressure roller. The pres-sure roller bears against a lip on the bot-tom of the pattern as shown in Figure 19–64. The feed motors are either ¾- or ½-hp, and the spindle-drive motors range from 5 to 10 hp on belt-driven machines. On direct-drive shapers, 4- to 18-hp motors are used which operate through high frequency generators. In general, the spindle speeds range from 6000 to 9000 rpm.

Revolving table shapers (Fig. 19–64) have the pattern bolted to the table. The

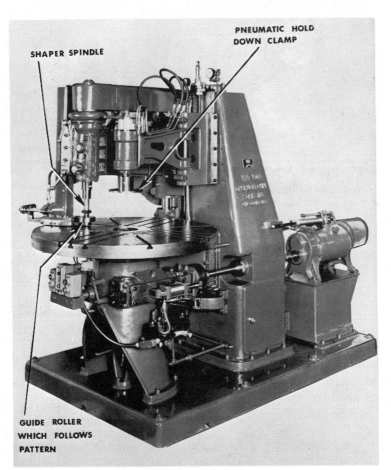

SHAPER SPINDLE

PNEUMATIC HOLD DOWN CLAMP

GUIDE ROLLER WHICH FOLLOWS PATTERN

Fig. 19–64. An auto-matic shaper with a re-volving table.

Fig. 19–65. This 72-inch automatic, revolving table shaper will mount work 84 inches in diameter. Here the operator loads and unloads blanks while the table slowly revolves. This set-up consists of 8 stations which shape 8 different parts with one revolution of the table.

work is held on top of the pattern by an overhead pneumatic clamp. As the table rotates, it carries the stock into the rotating cutters. The cutter spindle is mounted on a pneumatically loaded, movable arm that pivots from the main column. A guide roller bears against the pattern as the table and work rotate. The

Fig. 19–66. A double spindle automatic shaper of the revolving table type.

Fig. 19–67. An automatic profile shaper.

contact of the guide roller with the pattern automatically sets the depth of cut and results in the machined parts matching the contour of the pattern. See Figure 19–65.

The automatic shaper (Fig. 19–66) carries a double spindle, one on each of the two arms of the machine. This machine operates in the same manner as the smaller one shown in Figure 19–64, but it is primarily employed for shaping larger work. Automatic shapers have rotating tables with turning capacities up to 112 in. Spindle speeds range from 7500 to 10,000 rpm. They are belt-driven by 10-hp motors. The table feeds are powered by a 2-hp motor with a variable-speed control.

The **profile shaper** (Fig. 19–67) is also referred to as the contour profiler. This machining process is one of the newest concepts in automatic shaping. Machines of this type will shape serpentine drawer fronts (having contoured surfaces), chair backs, skis, simple gun stocks, some components of musical string instruments, and the like. Once the machine is set up, it will shape multiple or single parts at

a surface cutting rate up to 80 fpm. This is much faster than a skilled band saw operator can follow a pencil line.

The profile shaper has a long, heavy bed with hardened-steel ways (similar to that of a wood lathe); the bed is supported on cast-iron pedestals. The workpiece is held securely to the pattern by pneumatic clamps. The pattern is mounted on an hydraulically driven table which slides back and forth on the ways of the bed. See Figure 19–68. When the operator presses a foot pedal, the profiler table carries the work past the shaper cutter. The pneumatically controlled cutter follows the contour of the pattern under the guidance of the roller (Fig. 19–69). When the cut is complete, the cutter spindle and guide roller retract and the table returns to the starting position. At this point, the clamps release the work. The operator unloads the profiler and then positions a new work piece on top of the pattern.

Some machines incorporate two independent cutterhead spindles and are called *double-head profile shapers* (Fig. 19–70).

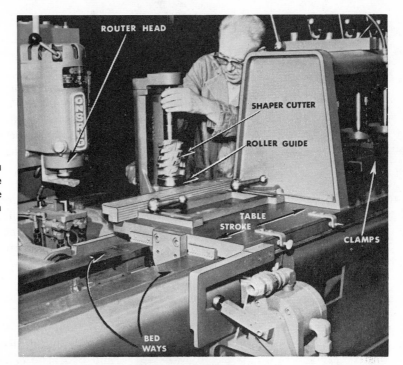

Fig. 19–68. Tooling a profile shaper. Note the staggered teeth on the cutter and the location of the roller guide.

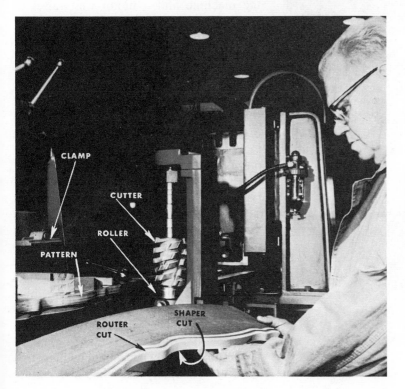

Fig. 19–69. The set-up man inspects a trial piece before releasing the machine to an operator.

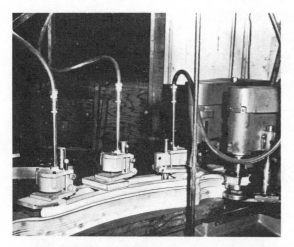

Fig. 19–70. This double head profile shaper makes two cuts in one pass of the work pieces (chair rockers) which are clamped to the pattern. The pieces are interchanged for the cut on their opposite edges.

In general, the shaping spindles of profilers are 1¼ in. in diameter and either direct-motor or belt-driven by 7½- to 20-hp motors at spindle speeds of about 7200 rpm. Profile shapers have a capacity of 84 in. in length and 10 in. in thickness. The maximum width is unlimited on single head profilers. On double head profilers, the width is generally limited to 12 in.

Pattern milling machines (Fig. 19–71) have revolutionized the job of pattern-making. These machines are used for a wide range of operations, such as grooving, recessing, routing, shaping, boring, slotting, mortising, dovetailing, molding, and tenoning. They are useful for making all kinds of wood patterns. See Figure 19–72.

Pattern milling machines consist of a heavy column, arm, head, spindle, table, and bed. The *column* carries the arm of the machine and a motor that raises or lowers the arm on the column. The arm supports the machine head which includes a 5-hp motor and spindle. The head tilts 45 deg. to the left and 90 deg. to the right by means of a worm gear. The *spindle* is belt-driven and has 8 speeds from 1480 to 4100 rpm. One end of the spindle is enlarged to receive the tapered shanks of the special cutters required for this type of work.

The table is of the compound universal type. It is mounted on a swivel carriage. The carriage is graduated in degrees and moves along the machine bed under hand or power feed. The swivel carriage is adjustable vertically. It supports the slide frame on which the table is mounted. The three motors incorporated in this machine have push button remote controls conveniently located within the operator's reach.

Multiple-spindle carving machines (Fig. 19–73) are widely used in the furniture

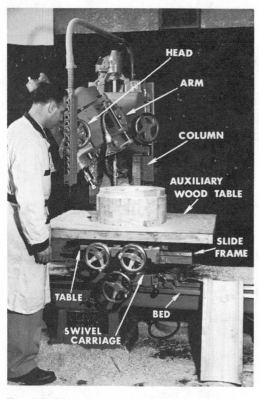

Fig. 19–71. A pattern milling machine.

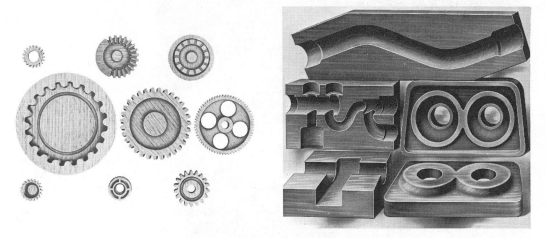

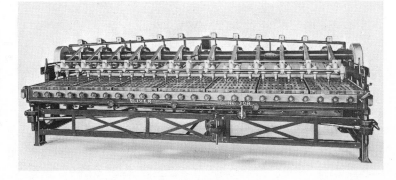

Fig. 19–72. Some examples of wood shapes (patterns) produced by a pattern milling machine.

industries. They are employed to machine workpieces with complex surface shapes. The work performed by carving machines is generally of two classifications: *flat work* and *shaped work*. Flat work includes such things as decorative plaques, frames, grills, and moldings. Odd-shaped work includes cabriole and other ornamental legs, gun stocks, figurines, and the like. See Figures 19–74 and 19–75.

Flat work blanks are fastened to removable wooden racks (Fig. 19–73) by means of clamp screws. The blanks of odd-shaped workpieces are held between live centers in the rear beam and cup

centers in the front beam. Consequently, the blanks may be slowly and simultaneously rotated. A lever located near the operator controls the rotation of the workpieces.

A pattern is positioned in the center of the machine in the same relative position as the blanks. See Figure 19–74.

A *pantograph* is located on the top of the machine. This is a carefully balanced, freely movable mechanism containing a number of belt-driven spindles and a *tracer*. Each spindle contains a router cutter with the same shape as the point of the tracer. As the operator moves the

Fig. 19–73. A multiple spindle carver with 24 spindles. This machine is ready for carving flat work. By removing the wooden racks, it may be used for carving complex shapes between centers.

Fig. 19–74. Carving gun stocks on a multiple spindle carver. Here, the blanks are supported between centers. The operator is following the pattern with a tracer.

tracer over the surface of the pattern the cutters reproduce the pattern in the blanks.

The size and capacity of multiple carvers vary. These machines may have from 4 to 32 spindles. The spindles usually rotate at 10,500 rpm. One ¾-hp motor is arranged to drive two spindles. Generally they use cutters with ¼-in. round shanks. Normally, multiple spindle carvers will handle stock which ranges from 58 to 72 in. in length. The distance between the spindle centers ranges from 7 to 14 in.

Fig. 19–75. The carving at the left is in the rough as carved between centers on a multiple spindle carver. The finished figurine is shown at the right.

Chapter 20   Routing, Carving, and Shaping in the School Shop

Hand Tool Processes

The hand tools used in the school shop for shaping wood normally include files, rasps, forming tools, chisels, gouges, draw knives, carving tools, and carving knives. Some of the hand planing tools, such as the spokeshave, block plane, and router plane described in Chapter 16 may also be used for shaping wood by hand.

Using files, rasps, and forming tools. Files and rasps should be fitted with a suitable handle to prevent the tang from injuring the hand. Whenever possible, the work should be held in a vise or clamped to the work bench. Use either a forming tool (Fig. 20–1) or rasp (Fig. 20–2) for rough cutting. Change to a finer file as the final size is approached. As with other cutting tools, the cutting stroke should be made with the grain to prevent splintering. In general, apply pressure uniformly as the file is pushed forward. By slanting the file slightly, a shearing cut

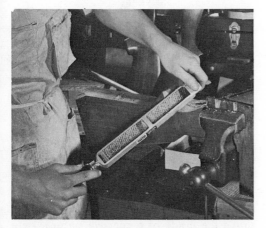

Fig. 20–1. Using a half round forming tool for rough shaping a gun stock.

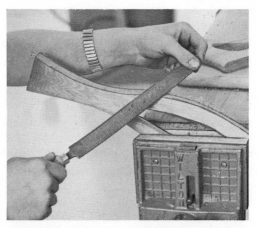

Fig. 20–2. Using the flat side of a half-round rasp to shape a convex edge.

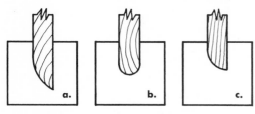

Fig. 20–3. Examples of cardboard templets that may be used for checking the work edge in shaping processes.

Fig. 20–4. Using an 8-inch round rasp to round an inside corner pattern.

may be produced. This technique prevents digging into the work and reduces the possibility of splintering.

When filing surfaces that have been rough sawed, round or chamfer the arrises (corners) slightly. This is done by sliding the file along the edge at an angle of about 45 deg. If the edges are to be rounded considerably as shown in Figure 20–2, rock and file lengthwise during the stroke. Overlap successive strokes to prevent flat spots from developing. It is a good idea to make frequent checks of the accuracy of the work with a cardboard templet (Fig. 20–3).

Use a file with a flat surface for rounding convex edges (Fig. 20–2) and a half round (Fig. 20–1) or round file (Fig. 20–4) for concave edges. Dished out, cupped, or convex surfaces, such as the inside of bowls and dishes, are best handled with riffler files or with rotary files mounted in the drill press as shown in Figure 20–5.

Chips that may become lodged between the teeth of files and rasps can often be removed by lightly rapping the end of the file on a block (not metal) to jar the chips loose. Finer files should be cleaned with a short, stiff bristle or wire brush made especially for cleaning files. This type of brush is known as a *file card*.

Files and rasps are cutting tools. Consequently, they should be used with care and stored in holders to protect the teeth

from damage caused by contact with hard objects.

The **chiseling operations** described and illustrated here include those most commonly used in making and fitting joints.

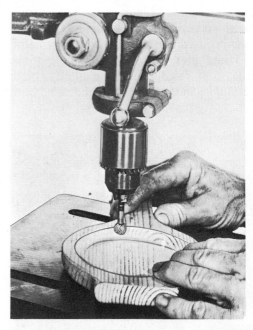

Fig. 20–5. Using a ball-shaped rotary file to shape the inside of a concave surface. Here the work is moved on the drill press table with the quill locked in position.

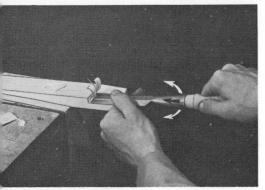

Fig. 20–6. Note the position of the hands while paring with a chisel.

In many cases, these basic principles may also be applied to the use of gouges and carving chisels.

Safety Precautions for Using Edge Tools

1. Fasten the work securely in a vise or clamp.
2. Insure that the tools are *sharp*. Refer to page 584 for the techniques of sharpening and honing edge tools.
3. *Always keep both hands behind the cutting edge.*
4. Always cut *away* from the body.
5. Use the tools only for their intended purpose.

6. Use a wood, rawhide, or a plastic head mallet for driving socket chisels, gouges, and carving tools. A metal hammer will mar the head of the chisel. These marks may cause blisters when hand chiseling.

Horizontal chiseling generally refers to the class of work that involves cutting the stock parallel to the grain. To chisel a surface flat (as in joinery work) keep the bevel of the chisel up (Fig. 20–6). If possible, cut with the grain. Hold the chisel blade between the thumb and forefinger of the left hand supported against the work. Use this hand to guide the tool. Squeeze it to control the cutting action as the tool is pushed by the right hand. (Left-handed workers reverse these hand positions.) It is often helpful to move the chisel diagonally across the surface to obtain a shearing cut. A faster cutting action may be obtained by tapping the handle with the palm of the hand or a mallet. When chiseling across the grain, work from both sides toward the middle to prevent splitting the edge.

Chiseling curves. Keep the bevel up when chiseling convex curves (Fig. 20–7). Use a mallet for making heavy cuts,

Fig. 20–7. Chiseling a convex curve.

Fig. 20–8. Starting to cut a concave curve. Blade bevel is down.

Fig. 20–9. Vertical chiseling. Here a heavy cut is started with the aid of a fiber mallet.

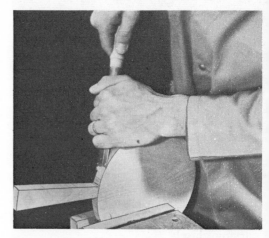

Fig. 20–10. Using a chisel with a paring action to smooth a sawn surface.

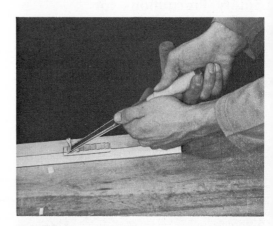

Fig. 20–11. Chiseling a recess.

Fig. 20–12. Using the chisel with the bevel down to shave off dried glue squeezed out of inside corner joints.

raising the handle with each blow. Finish the cut to the layout line with a paring or shearing cut. A concave cut is made with the blade bevel down (Fig. 20–8). To cut with the direction of the grain it is necessary to work toward the center of the cut from each end.

Vertical chiseling (Fig. 20–9) refers to cutting across the grain, thereby severing the wood fibers. A mallet is useful to supply the extra force necessary for making these cuts. For finishing cuts, a sharp chisel and a paring or slicing action is required. (See Fig. 20–10.)

Chiseling a recess for an inlay or a butt hinge is accomplished by using both the vertical and horizontal cutting methods. The outline of the recess is first deeply scored by holding the chisel vertically, with the bevel toward the waste stock, and by rapping sharply with the mallet. Then, with bevel down, a series of cuts is made as shown in Figure 20–11. Finally the waste stock is chipped and pared away.

The chisel is an indispensable tool. It has been stated that when no other tool will do the job, use a chisel. In addition to the use described here, chisels are also employed in removing dried glue from the inside corners of joints as shown in Figure 20–12. Also, chisels are used for hand mortising as shown on page 360.

Gouges and carving chisels are handled in much the same manner as wood chisels. Inside hollows, free forms, and concave shapes (Fig. 20–13) require the use of the outside bevel gouge. Shaping jobs of this type should be started by scoring the outline to avoid splintering the grain. Then the outline should be carefully grooved in the waste stock. Finally, larger amounts of waste may be removed by taking heavy cuts with the gouge and mallet (Fig. 20–14). The surface is finished by making thin paring or slicing cuts.

Wood carving. There are five basic kinds of wood carving. These are: (1) *chase carving* which merely involves cutting shallow grooves to outline the design in the surface of the wood; (2) *chip carving* which is performed by making a pattern of knife or chisel cuts on a background for purposes of decoration; (3) *relief carving,* which involves cutting away the background in such a way that a figure stands above the surface; (4) *wood sculpturing,* which is carving human figures or animals in a three-dimensional form (sculpturing skills are the most artistic and the most difficult techniques to acquire); (5) *whittling* (Fig. 20–15), which is a general term for the process of giving shape to wood with knives rather than with chisels or carving tools.

When carving, whittling, or sculpturing an object in wood, it is generally easiest to start from a rough-sawed block as shown in Figure 20–15. When using carving knives to whittle, control the knife with both hands and always cut away from your body as shown in Figure 20–16. When possible, make the first cuts across the grain to sever the fibers. Make succeeding cuts at an oblique angle so that the stock is removed by slicing.

Fig. 20–13. This tray involved many basic techniques of using gouges, forming, and shaping tools.

Fig. 20–14. Heavy gouging with a socket firmer gouge and a mallet for fast removal of stock.

Using the Portable Electric Router

The portable electric router is generally considered safer for many shaping operations than spindle shaping machines. This is due to the relatively limited exposure and small size of the cutters and bits used in the routers. With the portable router, many industrial routing and shaping operations may be performed in the school shop. Before operating the router, refer

Fig. 20—15. This carved figurine was made from a block of wood. The block was first sawn to shape as shown at the right.

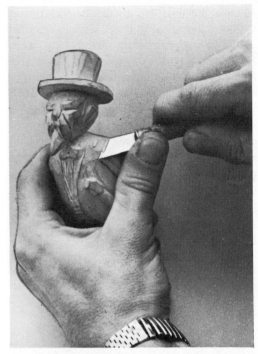

Fig. 20—16. Removing stock with cutting stroke oblique to the grain. Note the position of the fingers.

to the general safety rules on page 152 and observe the safety considerations for using the router which are listed below.

Safety Precautions for Portable Routing

1. Secure the work firmly in a vise or a fixture, or with clamps.
2. Use sharp bits and cutters. If they need sharpening, refer to page 594.
3. Disconnect the cord from the outlet before making any adjustments on the router.
4. Always use the motor unit with the base or the shaper table.
5. Be sure that all adjustments are tight before operating the router.
6. Keep your hands and fingers away from the revolving bits and cutters.

7. *Important:* Hold the tool firmly when turning on the motor to overcome the starting torque of the motor.
8. Let the motor reach its full speed before feeding the cutter to the work.
9. Take a trial cut on a piece of scrap stock.
10. Disconnect the cord when the router is not in use.

Installing bits and cutters. Select the correct bit for the job at hand. Loosen the base clamp. Remove the motor and lay it on the bench to change the bit. The shank of the bit or cutter should be inserted into the collet chuck to a depth of at least ½ inch. Tighten the chuck. See Figure 20–17. (Some routers have spindle locks and require only one wrench.) Replace the motor unit in the router base.

Adjusting for depth of cut may be done in one of two ways: (1) lower the motor unit and, with a rule, measure the length of the bit which extends through the base. Turn the motor in the base to change the setting. Lock the motor in place when the desired depth is obtained.

Fig. 20–17. Tightening a bit in the router collet.

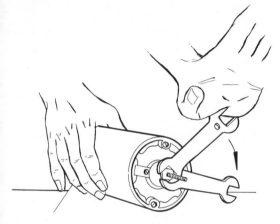

(2) Use the micrometer depth adjustment as follows:

  a. Lower the motor unit until the bit just touches the work and clamp the motor.

  b. Set the micrometer ring (and scale) to the desired depth.

  c. Release the clamp. Raise the router above the work and the motor will drop to the desired depth.

  d. Clamp the motor.

When accuracy is important, make a trial cut on scrap stock and measure the depth.

The **direction of feed** should be from left to right (Fig. 20–18) or in a counterclockwise direction as shown in Figure 20–19. The motor and bit rotate in a clockwise direction. Thus, the router is more easily controlled when the *feed* direction is *against the rotation of the bit.* This also produces the best quality of cut. When making cuts along all four edges of a workpiece, the best practice is to make the cross-grain cuts first. See Figure

Fig. 20–18. Making a rabbet cut along an edge with a pilot type bit.

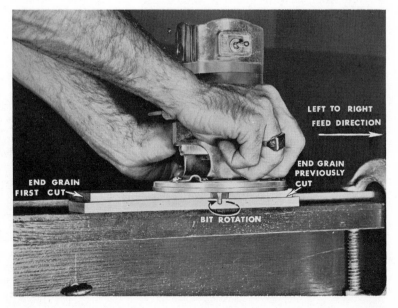

LEFT TO RIGHT FEED DIRECTION

END GRAIN PREVIOUSLY CUT

END GRAIN FIRST CUT

BIT ROTATION

20–18. If any chipping develops at the end of these cuts, it will be removed when making the cuts with the grain.

The **rate of feed** largely depends upon the width and depth of cut and the density or hardness of the wood. The optimum feed rate is that which is not so slow that the work is burned and not so fast that the motor slows down. Feeding too fast puts a strain on the motor, causes overheating, and impairs the quality of the cut. Feeding the router too slowly is likely to cause the cutter to burn the wood; the heat created may draw the temper from the bit.

The correct feed rate is generally determined by the "sound" and "feel" of the tool. For example, when feeding the router too fast, the normal high pitched sound of the motor will become lower as it loses speed and the pressure required to feed it will be noticeably increased. In some cases, as with very hard woods, it is necessary to make several passes at shallow depths until the desired depth is reached.

Straight-line routing is generally involved when cutting grooves, dadoes, recesses, chamfers, rabbets, and many other joinery cuts. Straight cuts may be

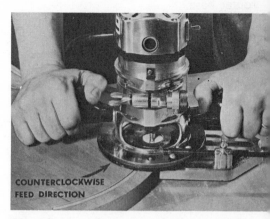

COUNTERCLOCKWISE
FEED DIRECTION

Fig. 20–19. Making a groove parallel to the edge of a circle.

made with the router in several different ways, depending upon the location or type of cut and the size of the workpiece. There are three basic methods of guiding the router for straightline cuts. They are: (1) with the aid of the router guide (Figs. 20–19 and 20–20); (2) with a straightedge (Fig. 20–22) clamped to the work; and (3) with a pilot type bit (Fig. 20–18).

To attach the guide to the base of the

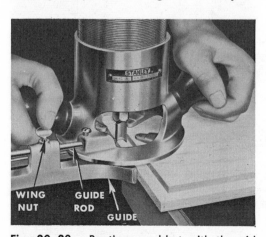

WING
NUT

GUIDE
ROD

GUIDE

Fig. 20–20. Routing a rabbet with the aid of the router guide.

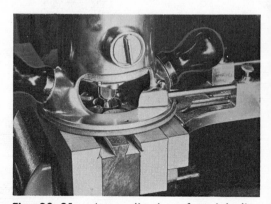

Fig. 20–21. An application of straight-line routing on narrow stock. Two blocks are clamped to each side of the work to provide a wide surface for the router base.

CATION MARKS

Fig. 20–22. Routing dadoes with a T-square guide.

router, insert the two guide rods into the base and secure them with the screws provided. Adjust the guide on the guide rods so the bit is the desired distance from it (Fig. 20–23). Tighten the wing nuts (or screws) to keep the guide in position. Make a trial cut on a scrap piece to check the location and depth of cut.

A straightedge must be used when making straight cuts that are either beyond the reach of the router guide or that are not parallel to the edge of the work. To position the straightedge in relation to the cut, measure the distance from the cutting edge of the bit to the outer edge of the router base. Clamp the straightedge parallel to the cut at this distance. Make the cut by guiding the base against the straightedge. The homemade T-square jig shown in Figure 20–22 is a useful device for cross-grain cutting. With the head positioned against the work, splintering at the edge is reduced. Also, the cut in the head aids in positioning the straightedge.

Circular cuts are made parallel to an edge with the guide used as shown in Figure 20–19. This leaves two points of contact for guiding the router along the circular edge.

For routing arcs and circles (Fig. 20–24), the *trammel-point* attachment is fastened to the guide rods. It is located the radial distance of the circle from the cutter. The point is stuck into the surface

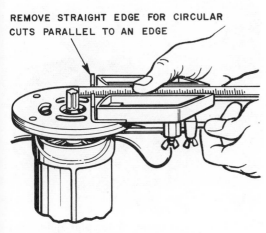

REMOVE STRAIGHT EDGE FOR CIRCULAR CUTS PARALLEL TO AN EDGE

Fig. 20–23. Adjusting the guide.

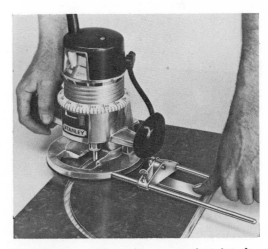

Fig. 20–24. Using the trammel point for routing arcs and circles.

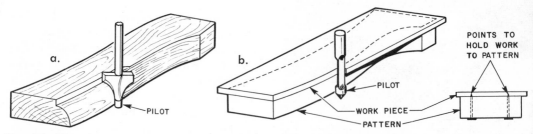

Fig. 20–25. Contour edge routing with pilot bit: (a) making a pattern cut; (b) using a straight panel bit and a pattern to cut duplicate pieces. The pilot rides against the pattern.

of the work and held there while the router is moved about the point.

Edge contour routing is generally performed with pilot-type bits as shown in Figures 20–25a and 20–25b. Provide at least ⅛ in. of the work edge for the pilot to ride against. The pilot has a tendency to score or burn the work because of its high speed.

Whenever possible, use a pattern that duplicates the contoured edge as shown in Figure 20–25b. This pattern method is also recommended for shaping several identical parts. The work may be held to the pattern by either brads or clamps.

Use a hard material such as maple, plywood, or tempered hardboard, for making patterns.

Templet routing (Fig. 20–26) is a method of duplicating patterns. Bits without pilots are used in this operation. The router is guided by a metal templet guide which is fastened to the router base (Fig. 20–27). The router bit protrudes through the hole in the templet guide and

Fig. 20–26. Routing a pattern in a surface with the aid of a ¼-inch plywood templet.

Fig. 20–27. Fastening a templet guide to the router base.

Fig. 20–28. A section drawing showing the allowance between the edge of the templet and edge of the bit which must be considered when making templets.

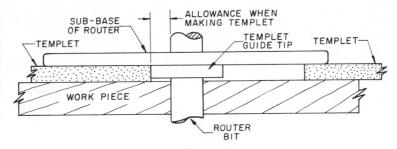

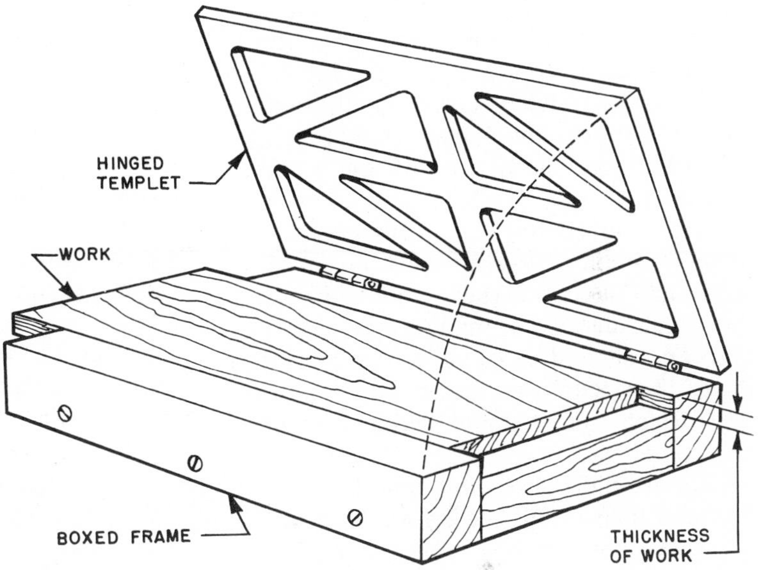

Fig. 20–29. A box type templet jig which quickly positions the work for production routing. The work is held by sharpened points in the bottom of the jig.

the side of the guide rides against the edges of the templet to make the desired cuts.

Select the appropriate size templet guide according to the size of bit and curvature of the work. The outside diameter of the guide tip (shown in Fig. 20–28) should not be greater than twice the smallest radius of any curve in the templet. The templet must be made a little larger than the work to be cut. The amount to be added on all sides is equal to the distance between the cutting edge of the bit and the outside edge of the templet guide as shown in Figure 20–28. Attach the templet guide to the work with clamps or brads, or place the work

in a simple box jig as shown in Figure 20–29.

Dovetailing (Fig. 20–30) for drawer joint construction as shown in Figures 20–31 and 20–32 is a frequent application of the router in schools and small shops. The accessories required for this operation are: (1) a commercially made templet and clamp fixture, (2) a dovetail bit, and (3) the appropriate templet guide to fasten to the router base. In dovetailing with the router, both the male and female members of the joint are cut at one time. On drawers, the female part is cut into the drawer front. Drawer fronts are normally ¾ or $1\frac{3}{16}$ in. thick. The male member of the joint is cut in the sides. The thickness of the sides of the drawers ranges from $\frac{5}{16}$ to $\frac{9}{16}$ in.

The router may be used for dovetailing both the *flush* (Fig. 20–31) and the *lip* or rabbeted (Fig. 20–32) types of drawer fronts. However, each type requires a somewhat different setup of the finger templet and clamp fixture. Consequently, the detailed instructions supplied by the manufacturer of the dovetailing fixture should be carefully followed. Once the fixture is set up for the type of joint desired and the router is correctly adjusted, any number of joints may be cut provided the workpieces are of the same thickness.

Before dovetailing the members of a drawer, prepare several short pieces of stock the same thickness and width as the front and sides, and make a trial cut. The general steps of procedure for dovetailing with the router are:

1. Attach the templet guide to the router base.
2. Insert the motor unit into the base and then install the dovetail bit into the collet chuck.
3. Adjust the bit for the depth of cut. Refer to the manufacturer's instruc-

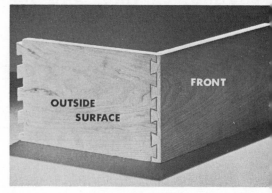

Fig. 20–31. Trial pieces assembled to test the fit for a flush type drawer.

tions. (Some recommend $\frac{19}{32}$ in. from the tip of the bit to the base.)

4. Mark the surfaces of the drawer front and sides "outside" and "inside" as appropriate. The reason for this is that the pieces are routed with the inside surfaces facing outward from the fixture.
5. Clamp the side of the drawer vertically in the fixture with the *outside* surface against the front apron and the edge against the left stop (Fig. 20–33).
6. Place the drawer front under the finger templet with the *outside* surface down (Fig. 20–33). Slide the edge against the stop and clamp the templet (with moderate pressure) to hold this piece in position. NOTE: the end of the front should be butted squarely against the drawer side. The upper surfaces should be flush with each other as shown in Figure 20–33.
7. *Important!* Before starting the router, set it on the templet with the base resting firmly on the surface of the templet (Fig. 20–34). *Never* remove the router from the templet with the motor running. If the router is lifted, the bit will cause permanent damage to the templet fingers.

Fig. 20–30. A trial cut is made prior to dovetailing drawer members.

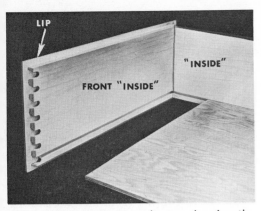

Fig. 20–32. A lip type drawer showing the female cut on the inside front.

8. Start the router and make the dove-tail cuts in both members by moving the router so the guide rides against the templet fingers (Fig. 20–34).
9. Turn off the motor.
10. *Wait until the bit stops* revolving and *slide* the router off the templet.

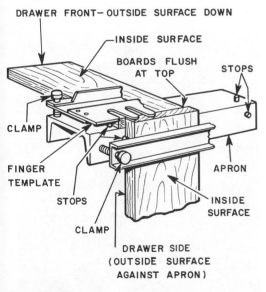

Fig. 20–33. Dovetailing a flush type drawer. The side and front are routed with their inside surfaces facing out.

11. Inspect the cut.
12. Remove the pieces from the fixture and make a trial fit (Fig. 20–31).
13. If the fit is too loose, lower the bit about ¼₄ in. or less; if the fit is too tight raise the bit slightly.
14. When the trial cuts produce satisfactory results, follow the same procedure for making the dovetails in the drawer members.

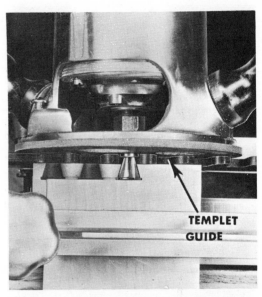

Fig. 20–34. The templet guide follows the templet. Here it can be seen why the bit would ruin the templet if the router were lifted vertically.

15. To dovetail the other drawer side and the opposite end of the drawer front, the same procedures are followed with one exception. Both members are butted against the stops on the right end of the fixture rather than on the left as was previously done.

Trimming veneers and surface laminates (Fig. 20–35) with the router requires the aid of the guide or a trimmer attachment. Straight pilotless bits may be used. However, the carbide-tipped combination bit shown in Figures 36a and 36b is recommended. This bit is especially designed to do both flush and bevel trimming (Fig. 20–36) of hard plastic laminates. To trim edge-bonded materials flush to a surface or to bevel a surface overlay, the material should be previously rough-cut to no more than ⅜ in. from the finished line of cut.

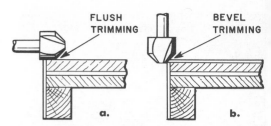

FLUSH TRIMMING   BEVEL TRIMMING

a.   b.

Fig. 20–36. (a) Carbide tipped trimming bit. (b) Application of the bit for flush and bevel triming.

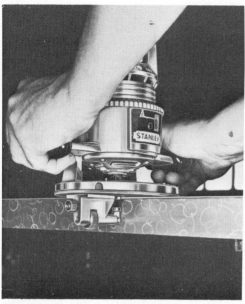

Fig. 20–35. Bevel trimming a plastic laminated surface.

1. Lower the motor unit to expose the appropriate part of the bit (Fig. 20–36b).
2. Adjust the trimmer attachment so the roller controls the horizontal depth of cut as desired. Lock it in place.
3. Start the motor, and guide the router along the work. Keep the base flat against one surface and the roller of the trimmer attachment in contact with the adjacent surface as shown in Figure 20–35.

Freehand routing (Fig. 20–37) is done without the aid of guides, templets, or patterns. This technique is occasionally used for routing signs with either raised or incised letters, for roughing out work as in making trays, removing backgrounds in carvings, and similar work. Following a layout line in this manner requires great skill and maximum control of the router. For this class of work, clamp the stock firmly, take shallow cuts, and use narrow bits whenever possible. Use both hands to guide the router. For maximum control, rest your forearms on

Fig. 20–37. Freehand routing of incised letters with a V-grooving bit.

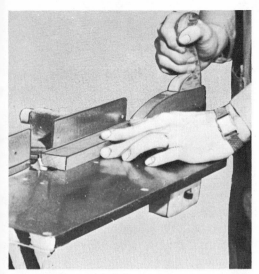

Fig. 20–38. Using the router in the shaper table accessory permits operations similar to those performed on spindle shapers.

the surface for added support. When duplicate cuts are to be made, the best results are obtained with the aid of a templet or a pattern.

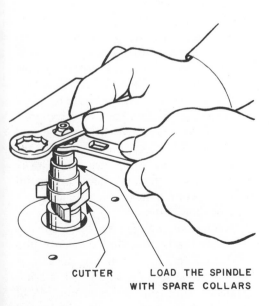

CUTTER   LOAD THE SPINDLE
WITH SPARE COLLARS

Fig. 20–39. Mount cutters as low on the spindle top as possible.

Other uses of the router include mortising (Fig. 22–12, page 361), tenoning, tonguing, and grooving. The router is also used for inlaying, carving, surface decorating, beading, and fluting of table legs, etc. For all of these operations, the basic principles described above may be applied. In some cases, it may be necessary to make special jigs, templets, or fixtures either to guide the work to the router or to guide the router in relation to the job.

The **router-shaper table attachment** (Fig. 20–38) provides for many additional applications of the router. Use either router bits or shaper cutters as dictated by the requirements of the work at hand. By tilting the motor to various angles, a wide variety of shapes may be produced with one cutter. The description of spindle shapers in the remaining pages of this unit will suggest many techniques that may also be applied.

Using the Shaper

Hundreds of different wood cutting, forming, and shaping operations may be performed with the single spindle shaper. The competent shaper operator must not only be able to make set-ups, change cutters, and operate the machine safely, but also be able to design and construct various work-holding devices for special shaping problems. In this section, you will become acquainted with the basic principles of using a single-spindle shaper.

The shaper is a dangerous machine to operate. The knives rotate at high speeds, they are sometimes necessarily exposed, and the work is normally fed by hand. However, the machine may be used safely if you observe the necessary precautions.

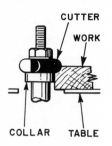

CUTTER
WORK
COLLAR   TABLE

a.

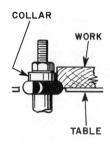

COLLAR
WORK
TABLE

b.

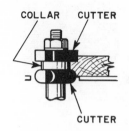

COLLAR CUTTER

CUTTER

c.

Fig. 20–40. Three ways to mount cutters and collars when shaping work against collars.

Safety Precautions for the Shaper

1. When in doubt about any phase of shaper operation, obtain the help of your instructor.
2. Disconnect the power before changing the cutters and before making any special set-ups.
3. Use one-piece, 2- or 3-wing cutters whenever possible. They must be sharp! If they are dull, refer to Chapter 33, page 593.
4. Mount the cutters on the spindle so that the cutting is done on the underside of the work.
5. Whenever possible, use the machine with a fence, the ring guard, or some auxiliary guard that covers the portion of the cutter not being used.
6. Revolve the spindle by hand before turning on the power to insure that the cutters turn freely.
7. Use guards, feather boards, hold-downs, and hold-ins whenever possible. See Figure 20–45.
8. Stock less than 2 in. wide by 12 in. in length must not be shaped unless held in a suitable fixture. (See Fig. 20–53.) Failure to observe this rule is the major cause of shaper accidents.
9. Shape end grain only when it is held in a suitable fixture.

10. Double-check all adjustments and clamping mechanisms on fixtures, forms, etc., to be sure they are secure.
11. Wear tight-fitting clothing. Be sure that sleeves are not dangling. Wear safety goggles.
12. Have all set-ups, special jigs, and fixtures approved by your instructor before using the shaper.
13. Check the condition of the workpieces. They should be free from warp, knots, splits, checks, and excessive irregular grain.
14. Avoid deep cuts; it is better to make several passes at shallower depths than one pass with a deep cut.
15. *Important!* Feed the work against the rotation of the cutters. See Figure 20–41. Feeding with the rotation is hazardous. The knives tend to grab the work and throw it from the machine. Therefore, *never* "back up" during a cut; slide the stock away from the cutter and then start again.
16. Keep your hands at a safe distance from the cutters.
17. Keep your eyes on the job. Your undivided attention and concentration during the operation are necessary.
18. When the shaping operation is complete, shut off the machine. Wait until the cutters stop revolving and cover them with a guard. Discon-

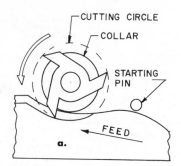 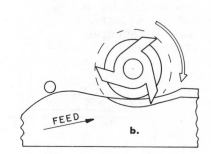

Fig. 20–41. Feeding directions when shaping with collars: (a) counterclockwise cutter rotation; (b) clockwise cutter rotation.

nect the power before leaving the machine.

19. It is recommended that shaper switches be provided with a lock to prevent unauthorized persons from attempting to operate the machine.

Changing cutters and collars (Fig. 20–39). Disconnect the power, and release the lock nut on the spindle top. Engage the spindle lock or hold the spindle steady with another wrench. Some machines require an allen wrench in the end of the spindle. On others a wrench is used to engage flats milled on the end of the spindle top.

Select the cutter with the desired profile and the collars necessary for the job. Collars may be put on the spindle above, below, and/or between cutters as shown in Figures 20–40a, 20–40b, and 20–40c. For shaping against collars, the preferred setup is with the collar (controlling the depth of cut) placed on top of the cutter. On machines that do not have reversing switches, the cutter must be installed so that it will cut with the rotation of the spindle.

On machines that are provided with reversing switches, the cutter may be installed on the spindle to cut in either a clockwise or a counterclockwise direction (Figs. 20–41a and 20–41b). The choice is determined by the desire to take advantage of the grain direction of the work

or to position the cutter so that most of the cut is made on the lower portion of the work.

Usually extra collars of smaller diameters are placed on the spindle to fill in the space under the top lock nut.

The **feed direction** (Figs. 20–41a and 21–41b) is determined by the way in which the cutters are mounted and the rotation of the spindle. The *feed* of the stock must always be *against the rotation of the spindle* regardless of the grain direction. When edge-shaping contours on circular stock, it is necessary that the feed be against the grain of the work. When shaping around the workpiece (on its four edges), it is best to shape the end grain first as shown in Figure 20–42a.

The **rate of feed** in shaping operations has the same significance as in planing and jointing operations. A slower rate of feed increases the number of knife marks per inch and produces a smoother surface. As with the jointer and other hand-fed machines, the proper rate of feed is determined by the depth of cut, the hardness of the material, and the quality of cut desired. The sound of the machine and the "feel" of the work (the force required to feed the stock) are clues for determining the best rate of feed. Too slow a feed will result in burning the work and the cutter.

BOTH FENCES ARE IN
LINE WHEN JUST A
PART OF THE WORK
EDGE IS REMOVED

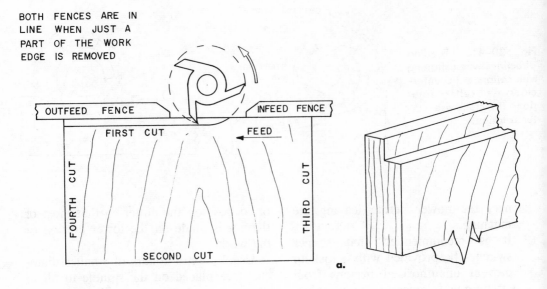

FENCE IS ADJUSTED
TANGENT TO CUTTING
CIRCLE WHEN ENTIRE
EDGE OF WORK IS
REMOVED

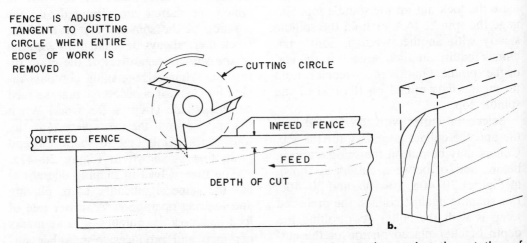

Fig. 20–42. Using the fence. The feed direction of stock must be against the rotation of the cutter as shown: (a) illustrates shaping with both halves of the fence in line; (b) the outfeed fence is adjusted to support the stock when the entire edge is cut away.

Shaping Methods. Most of the shaper operations may be classified into four general groups according to the manner in which the work is supported or guided during the cut. These four methods are:

1. Shaping *with guides*. This involves using a fence or wooden fixture clamped to the shaper table against which the work is supported and guided during the cut. This method is generally the safest and most widely used for normal school shop applications.

2. Shaping *against collars*. In this group

of operations, collars are mounted on the spindle with the cutter. The work rides against the collar which limits the horizontal depth of cut.

3. Shaping *with patterns*. Operations of this type are similar to shaping with collars except that the work is mounted above or below a pattern. The pattern, not the work, rides against the collar. This method of shaping is widely used for duplicating pieces.

4. Shaping *with fixtures, jigs, or forms*. For this class of work, various home-made devices or the sliding table jig is used to hold and support the work as it is advanced to the cut-

ters. These devices are made up as dictated by the size and shape of the work.

Shaping with a guide (Figs. 20–42, 20–42b, 20–43, 20–44a, 20–44b, 20–44c, 20–44d, 20–44e, 20–47, and 20–48). The majority of work in this category involves making cuts on stock in a straight line. This is often done with the aid of the standard fence mounted on the shaper table. The procedure is as follows:

1. Mark the profile of the cutter with a pencil on the end of the work where the cut is to be made.

2. Set the stock on the table with this layout against one blade of the cutter as shown in Figure 20–45a.

3. Raise or lower the spindle until the cutter is set for the correct vertical depth of cut.

4. Adjust the fence for the horizontal depth of cut. With adjustable fences, align both halves of the fence for work in which only a portion of the edge is to be removed as shown in Figures 20–42a, 20–44a, 20–44b, 20–44c, 20–44d, and 20–44e.

5. For work in which the entire edge of the stock is to be removed (as shown in Figure 20–42b), adjust the out-feed half of the fence tangent to the smallest cutting circle so it will support the stock as it leaves the cutter. With some fences, this adjustment may be made by starting the cut and then *stopping the machine* when an inch or two of the work has passed the cutter. By holding the stock against the infeed fence, the outfeed fence may be moved out to support the work. With some fences, only the infeed half is adjustable. In this case, the whole fence is moved horizontally until the outfeed half is tangent with some portion of the cutting circle; then,

Fig. 20–43. Checking the setup for a cupboard door lip cutter with a scrap piece of stock. (Guard has been removed for illustrative purposes only.)

FENCE

FEED

CUTTER ROTATION

Fig. 20–44. Shaping with the guide fence. Both halves of the fence are in line for (*a) rabbet, (*b) tongue and groove, (*c) glue joint, (*d) drop leaf, and (*e) straight fluting.

* Illustrations identified with an asterisk (*) indicate that the guard has been removed for illustrative purposes only.

the infeed part of the fence is adjusted for the depth of cut.

6. If the stock is of narrow width, as in cutting moldings (Figs. 20–45a and 20–45b), use a hold-down and hold-in when making the set-up (Fig. 20–46).

7. Turn on the machine and advance the work at a steady rate of feed.

8. Use a push stick or another piece of wood against the trailing end of narrow stock to push it safely past the cutters.

9. *Edge or face shaping of large panels* is often handled more easily with the work in a vertical position. For this type of work, make a wooden fence (often called a *high fence*) and clamp it to the table (Fig. 20–47a). For special jobs that require feeding the work supported at an angle, construct a guide as shown in Figure 20–47b.

10. To shape the outside edges of disks,

make a guide as shown in Figure 20–48.

Shaping with collars (Figs. 20–40, 20–41, 20–49 and 20–50). This method of shaping should only be performed on work of substantial size. A minimum of $\frac{1}{8}$ in. must be left to bear against the collar. The edge of the work to be shaped must have been previously smoothed to finished size. Any irregularities in the edge that rides against the collar will be duplicated on the cut surface.

Use *antifriction collars* when possible. These rotate on ball bearings and eliminate scoring, discoloring, or burning of the work that bears against the collar. Whenever standard collars are used, be sure they are clean and free from gum and pitch. If necessary, *remove* and clean the collars with gasoline or benzine and a stiff bristle brush.

For shaping curved or irregular edges of stock against collars (Figs. 20–40 and 20–41) or for shaping with patterns

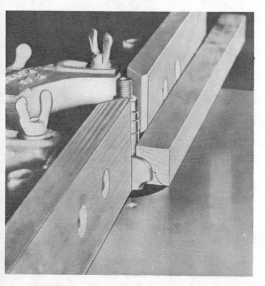

Fig. 20–45. * The cutter height is adjusted while holding the stock against one knife of the cutter.

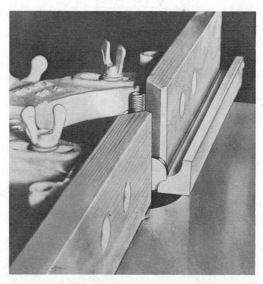

Fig. 20–45. * A second cut may produce various molded shapes.

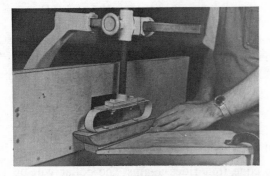

Fig. 20-46. Shaper setup to provide maximum protection to operator. Fence guides stock past cutter; hold-down serves as a guard, keeps stock in place on table. Feather board holds work against the fence.

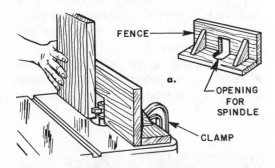

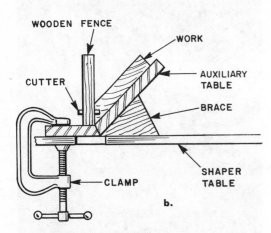

Fig. 20-47. (a) Wooden high fence is used to aid face shaping of larger panels. (b) A homemade bevel guide shown making a spline cut.

(Fig 20–50), the same general procedures are followed:

1. Remove the fence from the table.
2. Select a cutter(s) with the desired profile and collars of the proper diameter to control the horizontal depth of cut.
3. Mount the cutter(s) and collars on the spindle as usual.
4. Adjust the spindle for the vertical depth of cut.
5. Important! Be sure that an adequate edge allowance is left (not cut away) to bear against the collar.
6. Insert the starting pin into one of the holes in the table near the spindle. Locate the pin to the right of the spindle for a counterclockwise rotation (Fig. 20–41a). Locate it to the left for a clockwise cutter rotation (Fig. 20–41b).
7. Start the machine. *Place the work against the pin first.* While pivoting the work on the pin, ease the work into the cutter and against the collar. *Caution!* When the edge of the work first comes in contact with the cutters, it may have a tendency to kick back. The work cannot bear against the collar until the cut has reached its full horizontal depth. Hold the work firmly.
8. After the cut is started and the edge is bearing against the collar, the work may safely be moved away from the starting pin. *Keep the work against the collar throughout the cut.*
9. Slow down the feed rate when cutting across or against the grain.
10. Avoid excessive pressure against collars that are not of the anti-fricton type. Friction causes scoring or burning of the work edge.

Shaping with patterns (Figs. 20–50, 20–51, 20–52, 20–53a, and 20–53b). This method is employed when the en-

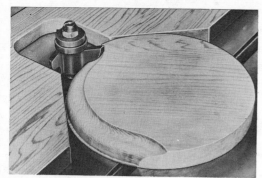

Fig. 20–48. * This guide board with a V-cut opening, clamped to the table, provides two points of contact for shaping edges of disks.

Fig. 20–51. *Using a straight cutter in combination with a collar and pattern to shape stock.

tire edge is to be shaped or when a number of duplicate pieces are to be shaped. With a straight knife cutter, the pattern shaping processes are especially useful for shaping irregular edges (Fig. 20–51).

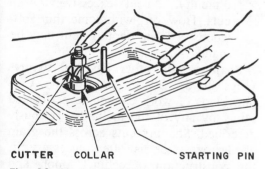

CUTTER   COLLAR   STARTING PIN

Fig. 20–49. * Shaping an inside edge with the work guided against a collar and pin.

Fig. 20–50. * Shaping with a pattern.

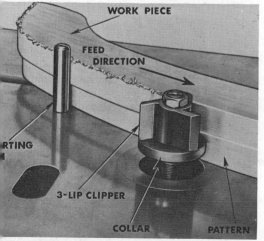

The same procedure is followed in shaping with patterns as in shaping against collars. A suitable pattern must first be constructed. Some points to consider when preparing and using patterns are the following:

1. Use hardwood, hardboard, or plywood materials for constructing the patterns. Allowable thicknesses are from 3/8 to 1 in.
2. Cut the outline of the pattern and carefully smooth it to the contour desired for the workpiece. NOTE: depending upon the diameter of the collars at hand, it may be necessary to make the pattern slightly smaller

* Illustrations identified with an asterisk (*) indicate that the guard has been removed for illustrative purposes only.

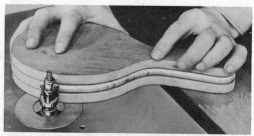

Fig. 20–52. Two patterns, one on top and one on the bottom of the workpiece, permit turning the work over to favor the grain.

or larger than the desired work-piece.

3. Devise a dependable method of fastening the work blank to the pattern so it will not slip during the operation. Acceptable methods include using nails (Figs. 20–51 and 20–52), screws, clamps (Fig. 20–53), and anchor points (nails or pointed screws that project through the pattern and into the blanks).

4. To shape work of smaller sizes, it is a good idea to attach handles to the pattern. This keeps the hands a safe distance away from the cutters.

5. In some cases, it may be advisable to make two patterns of the same outline and thickness and attach one above and one below the workpiece (Fig. 20–52). This procedure permits the work to be turned over when necessary to cut with the grain.

6. For edge shaping a number of long narrow pieces (chair rockers or legs), make a *double-edge pattern* as shown in Figure 55. This holds two workpieces. One edge of each piece is shaped and then the pieces are interchanged on the pattern so the opposite edges may be shaped.

7. To prepare the blanks (or work-

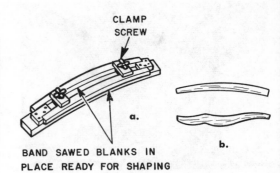

CLAMP SCREW

a.

b.

BAND SAWED BLANKS IN PLACE READY FOR SHAPING

Fig. 20–53. (a) The construction of a double edge pattern; (b) some typical shapes that may be produced.

pieces) for pattern shaping, bandsaw them to approximate size. As a general rule, this is about $\frac{1}{16}$ to $\frac{1}{8}$ in. larger than the pattern. This amount may be removed without difficulty. Avoid excessively deep cuts. However, with some thin softwoods, a $\frac{1}{2}$-in. depth of cut may be made.

Shaping with other jigs and fixtures (Figs. 20–54, 20–55, and 20–56). Certain kinds of work cannot be performed safely by any of the methods previously described. Shaping cuts across the grain of narrow stock is often necessary in the construction of cabinet, door, and

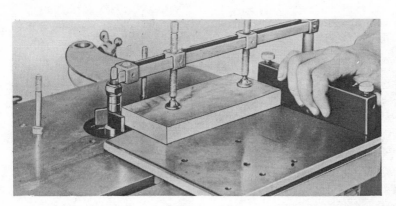

Fig. 20–54. The sliding table jig is used to hold a small workpiece safely. In this picture, the supporting arm has been removed to show the cut more clearly.

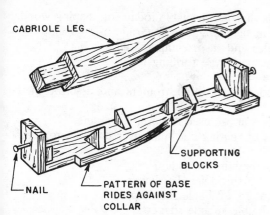

CABRIOLE LEG

SUPPORTING BLOCKS

NAIL

PATTERN OF BASE RIDES AGAINST COLLAR

Fig. 20–55. A jig to hold a cabriole leg for rounding the outside corner on the shaper.

window frames. For cuts of this type and for other small work, use the *sliding table jig* as shown in Figure 20–54.

1. With the power disconnected, place the work in the jig.
2. Set the miter gauge head to the desired angle and lock it.
3. Hold the workpiece on the table jig and adjust the depth of cut by raising the spindle until the work and the cutter line up as desired.

4. Clamp the work to the table jig and proceed to shape as usual.

On some machines, the tenoning jig shown on page 377 may also be used on the shaper. It is particularly useful for face shaping narrow stock.

For work with compound contours or odd shapes, a special fixture must be made. It should be constructed to support the work well enough to ensure safe operation. Figure 20–55 shows a typical example of a shaping problem and the suggested work-holding fixture.

The *fluting fixture* shown in Figure 20–56 is another example of a special work-holding device. Basically, this fixture holds the work between centers much like a lathe. The headstock has a spur center and indexing disk. A pin is engaged in one of several holes of the disk to hold the work steady during the fluting (shaping) operation. The base of the fixture is designed to ride against a collar, thus providing a uniform depth of cut along the tapered leg. Figure 20–56 also shows how stops are provided to limit the length of cut.

Fig. 20–56. Shaping table leg with a jig.

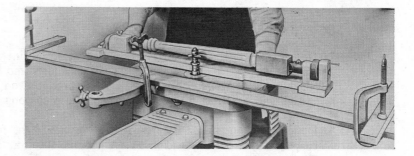

REVIEW QUESTIONS

1. Name and describe the early hand tools used for shaping wood.
2. Who developed the first portable router? The first shaper?
3. Describe some of the features of the early routers and shapers used in the 1850's.
4. Distinguish the difference between tang and socket chisels.

5. List and describe other hand tools that are available today for shaping wood.
6. What does the term "cut" mean in file terminology? Grade of coarseness?
7. How does the cutting action of files and rasps compare?
8. Describe the cutting action of the mesh-type forming tools.
9. What types of portable routers are in use today?
10. Name the basic parts and accessories of portable routers and describe their adjustment for use.
11. Describe the different types of bits that are used in portable routers.
12. What are the principle advantages of routing machines over portable routers? Disadvantages?
13. What are the principle kinds of shapers in use today?
14. Name the parts and adjustments of a single spindle shaper.
15. Identify the three basic types of cutters available for shapers.
16. What is the primary function of double spindle shapers?
17. List the methods used in industry for guiding and feeding stock into shapers.
18. What is a pattern milling machine?
19. Describe the mechanical functioning of multiple-spindle carvers.
20. Explain how a chisel is used to cut concave and convex curves.
21. What safety precautions should be observed in the operation of the portable electric router?
22. Explain the importance of the rate of feed and the direction of feed in router operations.
23. Describe the procedures involved in templet and pattern routing operations.
24. What four methods may be employed in the school shop for guiding or supporting work on the shaper?
25. List the safety rules that apply to shaper operation.
26. Explain the relationship that should exist between spindle rotation and the direction of feed in shaper work. In routing.
27. What shaping jobs require the use of an adjustable fence?
28. Describe the procedure for starting a cut against a shaper collar.
29. Describe the use of hold-downs and finger-boards in shaper operation.

SUGGESTED STUDENT ACTIVITIES

1. Design and construct a single-spindle carving machine for "flat back" work.
2. Make a display of shapes made by various router and shaper cutters.
3. Make a list of wooden household objects produced on profile shapers.
4. Design and construct a pattern for shaping a ping-pong paddle on the spindle shaper.
5. Design and construct a fixture for making one of the following items on the shaper: (1) a pool cue, (2) a round tapered furniture leg, (3) a lamp base.
6. Design and construct a fixture for relief cutting on a production router.
7. Design and construct a templet and fixture for use in duplicating a pattern with a portable electric router.

Chapter 21 Drilling and Boring

The terms drilling and boring refer to the process of making round holes in wood with a rotating cutting tool that penetrates in a direction parallel to its axis. In drilling the cutting tool is known as a *drill,* and in boring it is called a *bit*. Bits are generally used to bore holes larger than ¼ in. Drills and bits are made in a variety of styles.

Drilling and boring are essential processes in both the custom and mass-production industries. These operations are primarily related to the assembly of wood

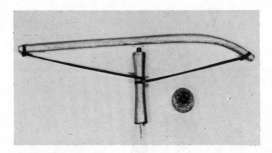

Fig. 21–2. A bow drill of the Bronze Age.

products involving various wood-to-wood joining methods or mechanical fasteners. The machines for drilling and boring have evolved from the tools of early man. They have been continually improved over the years.

Evolution of Drilling and Boring Machines

Drilling and boring implements were among the tools man first produced. Over 7000 years ago man fastened pieces of flint to a cross-like brace to drill or bore holes in wood (Fig. 21–1). At an earlier time, he had developed a grinding process to abrade (scrape away) holes in harder materials such as bone and stone so that handles and shafts could be fitted to his crude tools and weapons.

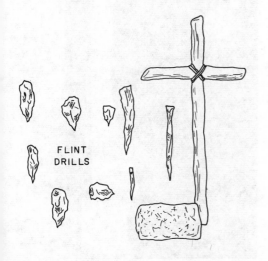

FLINT DRILLS

Fig. 21–1. Flints were used for drilling and boring holes over 7,000 years ago.

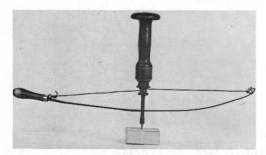

Fig. 21–3. A later version of the bow drill, typical of those used in this country around the early 1600's.

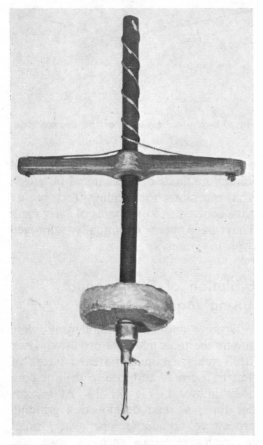

Fig. 21–4. A pump drill typical of those used by the eighteenth-century cabinet-maker.

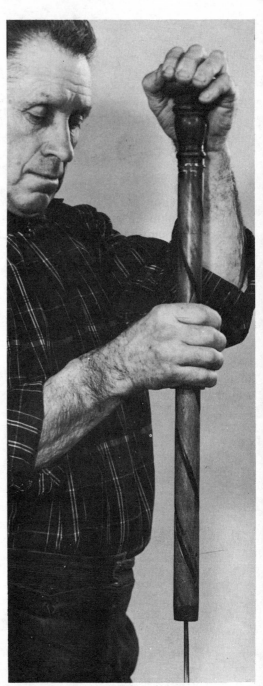

Fig. 21–5. An 1820 push drill made of walnut with a spoon bit.

The Bronze Age provided the first wood-cutting bits made of metal, and the Iron Age produced an even better metal for this purpose. With the advent of steel, tools underwent further change.

The **bow drill** (Figs. 21–2 and 21–3) was here first used for starting fires. The bow string was looped once around a vertical wooden stick. The operator placed the stick on a piece of wood and applied pressure to it with a cap which he held in the palm of his hand. The back and forth movement of the bow rotated the stick. Dry moss or shavings under the stick were ignited from the heat produced by the friction of rotation. Eventually the stick wore a hole through the wood. This led to fastening cutting bits to the rotating stick and a more efficient drilling or boring device was produced. This tool was used by the ancient Egyptians, and similar types were used in America by the early settlers.

The **pump drill** (Fig. 21–4) is another early type of bit-holding device used to supply a rotating movement for drilling holes. The rotary motion was attained by pushing down on the cross arm forcing the raw hide thong to unwind, thus turning the shaft and bit. A heavy round weight, about 10 in. in diameter, acted as a flywheel to build up momentum, winding up the leather thong again. Continuous pumping action with the correct timing produced a reasonably fast back and forth rotation of the bit. This tool dates back to the early 1700's and was popular with Colonial craftsmen.

The **push drill** (Fig. 21–5) is similar in its cutting action to the modern push drill shown in Figure 21–7. Early push drills were made of wood and were rotated by moving a driving barrel up and down.

The **hand drill** (Fig. 21–6) is used with various twist-drill bits and other round

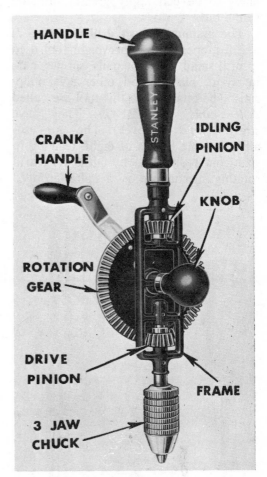

Fig. 21–6.   Hand drill.

shank tools for cutting holes. The size of the hand drill is the maximum diameter which can be held in the three-jaw chuck. There are three common sizes available: 0 in. to ¼ in., 0 in. to ⅜ in., and 0 in. to ½ in. Square shank (tang) bits must never be used in a three-jaw chuck. The *breast drill* is another hand powered drill which usually has a chuck capacity of ½ in. This drill is fitted with a metal saddle in place of the wood handle on the hand drill. In use, the saddle is placed against the operator's chest so he can apply greater pressure to the bit.

The **automatic push drill** (Fig. 21–7) is a fast-operating, light-weight tool used to drill small holes for nails, screws, etc., in wood, plaster, and other soft materials. The bits used in this tool are called *drill points* (Fig. 21–7). They have straight *flutes* (grooves). They are usually available in sets of eight, ranging in size from $\frac{1}{16}$ to $\frac{11}{64}$ by 64ths. The drill rotating mechanism is a spiral-grooved

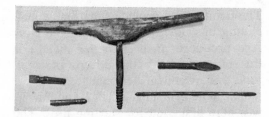

Fig. 21–8. Typical wood-cutting tools made by the village blacksmith. Shown are several sizes of boring bits and taps for cutting threads in wood.

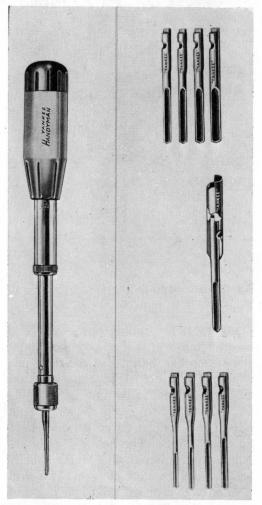

Fig. 21–7. Automatic push drill and set of drill points

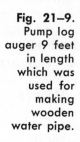

Fig. 21–9. Pump log auger 9 feet in length which was used for making wooden water pipe.

shaft which turns the bit several revolutions with each push of the handle. At the release of the downward pressure a spring returns the handle automatically to its original position, ready to be pushed again. Usually the handle is hollow and provides a handy storage compartment for the drill points.

Early boring devices, as we already know, employed a flint or crude metal bit fastened in a wooden cross bar. Two slightly improved versions of these tools that were still in use in the seventeenth and eighteenth centuries are shown in Figures 21–8 and 21–9. These boring tools enabled the craftsman to apply

Fig. 21–10. Early bit stock and bit holders made of wood.

greater feed pressure to the bit, and provided more leverage for turning the bit than could be obtained with drilling devices.

Around the 1700's the boring tools that appeared in Sweden became known as *bit stocks* (Fig. 21–10). They had square holes for the chucks and were the forerunners of our modern hand braces. The metal bits were driven into square wooden blocks which fitted into

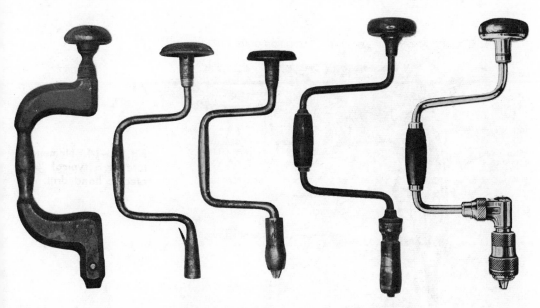

Fig. 21–11. The evolution of the modern 2-jaw hand brace.

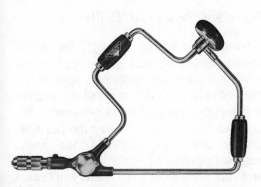

Fig. 21–12. Corner brace.

the square opening of the bit stock. The first bit stocks were made of wood, but later models were made of metal (Fig. 21–11).

The **hand brace** (Fig. 21–11) has been used for many years and it is still popular today for boring holes ranging from ¼ in. to 3 in. in diameter. The size of the brace is determined by the *sweep* or *swing,* which is the diameter of the circle made by the handle as it is revolved. Braces range in size from 6 to 16 in.; the

10-in. size is most common. Better braces are equipped with a ratchet mechanism which allows the bit to be turned in either direction with successive short strokes of the handle. There are two *jaws* inside the chuck which adjust to grip the square, tapered tang on the shank of the auger bits. Some braces feature *universal jaws* which grip round as well as square bit shanks.

Other types of hand braces include the *corner brace* (Fig. 21–12), which is use-

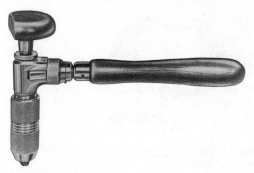

Fig. 21–13. Right angle brace.

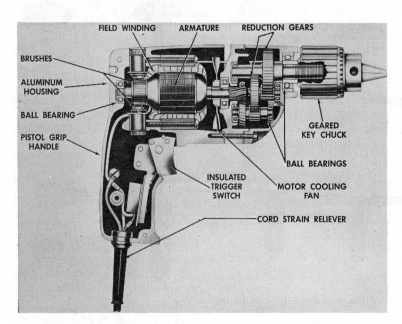

Fig. 21–14. Nomenclature of a typical ¼-in. electric hand drill.

ful for boring in corners and against walls or beams where a standard ratchet type will not work because of minimal clearance. This brace is similar to the standard type described above, but it is equipped with a movable bow, off-set at an angle to the direction of the bit travel. Another tool used in boring is the *right-angle brace* (Fig. 21–13). Sometimes it is referred to as the *short brace*. This is designed for boring holes in very close quarters.

Portable Powered Drills

Following World War II, the small electric motor became a practical source of power for many tools and appliances. Portable electric drills flooded the market and rapidly replaced hand powered drilling and boring tools. Today the portable electric drill (Fig. 21–14), the pneumatic (air-driven) drill (Fig. 21–15) and the "cordless" or battery-operated drill (Fig. 21–16) are commonplace.

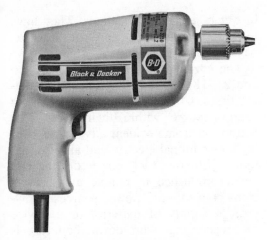

Fig. 21–15. This insulated electric drill has a nonmetallic housing that offers protection against electrical shock.

Portable power drills perform a variety of operations with greater ease and accuracy than is generally possible with hand tools.

The size of portable drills is stated as the maximum capacity of the chuck. Sizes range from the light-duty ¼-in. types (Fig. 21–14) to larger heavy-duty types with a 1-in. capacity. The popular sizes today are the ¼ in. for general light-duty

Fig. 21–16. A ½-in. "cordless drill." This tool has two speeds and contains a rechargeable power pack within.

work, and the ⅜ in. or ½ in. for medium to heavy-duty work (Fig. 21–16). The speed and horsepower ratings vary from one manufacturer to another. Generally, the smaller drills have the highest speeds. Some drills have speeds as high as 4000 rpm, while the larger sizes generally have slower speeds ranging between 400 to 800 rpm.

The **portable electric drill** (Fig. 21–14) is very popular in industry, schools, and home shops. Home craftsmen use it with an endless variety of attachments (most of doubtful value) ranging from buffers for car and shoe polishing to attachments for sawing. Some of the new electric drills feature a speed selector which is controlled by either a dial or a switch. The variable-speed drill allows the operator to match the correct speed for the operation with the cutting character of the various materials. Some drills also feature reversing switches. Reversing the direction of the chuck rotation is especially useful for backing bits out of bored holes. It is also useful to the home craftsmen for disassembly work. When fitted with a screwdriver attachment, the drill may be used to drive or back out screws. All-insulated electric drills (Fig. 21–15) have been introduced recently to provide maximum protection against electrical shock. In addition to the conventional insulation around the motor and lead wires, the housing of this tool is made of nonconducting reinforced fiber glass. This added protection reduces to a minimum the possibility of electrical shocks. Insulated drills are equipped with the usual 2-prong plug which does not require precautionary grounding as do the usual 3-prong plugs or adapters. In the near future most electric tool housings will probably be made of some nonmetallic material to provide greater safety against accidents.

Fig. 21–17. A two-hand pneumatic (air) drill used for production work. This has a ½-in. chuck, revolves at 1800 RPM and will drill holes in wood up to 1-in. diameters. The handle at the left is connected to the air hose and the squeeze lever is the control throttle.

The **pneumatic drill** (Fig. 21–17) is commonly used in industrial plants for portable drilling and boring work. Pneumatic drills rotate the bit by means of a rotary vane or piston type of motor. They are powered by air pressure supplied through ¼- or ⅜-in. hoses connected to an air compressor. A pressure of 90 lb. per square inch at the tool is required for it to operate efficiently.

Drills are available with motors ranging from ⁶⁄₁₀ to 15 hp depending upon the type of motor mechanism and hose size. Heavy-duty drills are geared to rotate at 300 to 600 rpm. Lighter drills range upward to 20,000 rpm.

Pneumatic drills have certain advantages over electric drills. They are much lighter in weight than electric drills of equal capacity. They operate at lower temperatures and may be used with safety in wet or explosive locations. They have fewer working parts and are less expensive to operate and maintain.

The **cordless power drill** (Figs. 21–16 and 21–18) is another sign of our changing times. Cordless drills carry their own energy source within themselves. This feature has some evident advantages over the conventional electric and air-powered tools. With this tool, power drilling can be accomplished in remote areas, away from conventional power sources. However, a supply of batteries or a device for recharging worn-down batteries is necessary. A charger operates on 110 to 125 volt AC and requires several hours to recharge the cells completely.

Drill chucks are designed to hold drills, bits, and other cutting tools with straight (cylindrical) shanks. Chucks usually have 3 jaws which adjust equally to grip shanks of various sizes within its capacity. The capacity of chucks range from ¼- to 1-in. diameters. There are three different chucks found on power hand drills: (1) the *friction chuck* (hand tightening); (2) the *hex-key chuck* (tightened with an allen wrench); and (3) the *geared-key chuck* (tightened

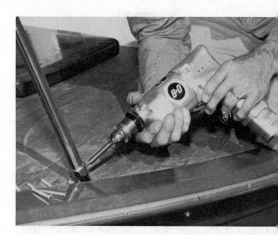

Fig. 21–18. Screwdriver attachment used with a ⅜-inch cordless electric drill.

driven by water power. Skilled craftsmen hand carved and shaped the wooden gearing necessary to transmit the power from the water wheel to the main line shaft. The line shaft ran the length of the factory and all the machines were belt-driven from this source of power. At the time of the industrial revolution in England boring machines like all other machines, were designed and constructed by individual craftsmen. Manufacturers began to produce woodworking machines in this country during the first decades of the nineteenth century. A typical vertical post boring machine used in the early woodworking factories is shown (Fig. 21–19). A double-spindle machine was developed in the early 1800's that could bore two holes at once. These early double-spindle machines were used to bore holes for drawer pulls. Sash and door manufacturers of this period substituted the mortise-dowel joints for the long standing mortise and tenon joint. This created a demand for special-purpose boring machinery, and *horizontal boring machines* were introduced. Early vertical and *horizontal* boring machines featured an adjustment for the center-to-center spacing of holes. These machines were the forerunners of our modern multi-spindle and gang boring machines used in industry. A power-fed drill press was invented in England by James Nasmyth in 1840. This permitted adjusting the rate at which the drill penetrated various materials.

Drill presses (Fig. 21–20) are made in many different sizes and styles. Some are designed as single-purpose machines while others, such as those used in school shops, are general-purpose machines. However, all types are similar in their operation and function.

The *size* of a drill press is stated as the diameter of the circle that may be drilled

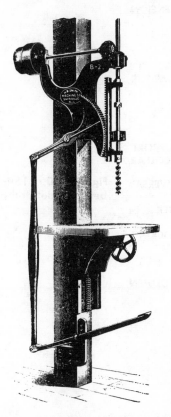

Fig. 21–19. A belt-driven vertical post borer made of cast iron and supported by a wood post. The boring bit was held in the spindle by a bolt. The bit was fed to the work by a foot-treadle-operated segment gear and rack.

with special matched key). On portable power drills, the chuck is usually screwed on to the end of the threaded spindle as shown in Figure 21–14. Threaded chucks are also used on drilling and boring machines. Some chucks have a tapered socket that fits a tapered spindle. Others have a tapered shank. This type fits into a tapered hole in the spindle of the machine.

Boring machines first appeared in the latter part of the 1700's. They were

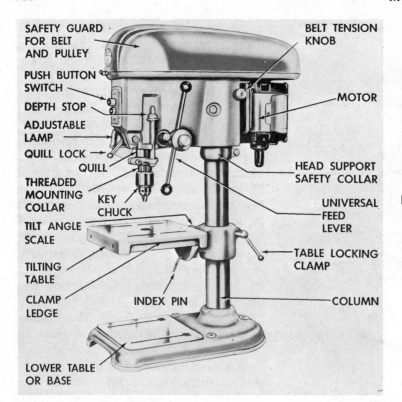

SAFETY GUARD
FOR BELT
AND PULLEY

PUSH BUTTON
SWITCH

DEPTH STOP

ADJUSTABLE
LAMP

QUILL LOCK

QUILL

THREADED
MOUNTING
COLLAR

KEY
CHUCK

TILT ANGLE
SCALE

TILTING
TABLE

CLAMP
LEDGE

INDEX PIN

LOWER TABLE
OR BASE

BELT TENSION
KNOB

MOTOR

HEAD SUPPORT
SAFETY COLLAR

UNIVERSAL
FEED
LEVER

TABLE LOCKING
CLAMP

COLUMN

Fig. 21–20. 15-in. bench model drill press.

at its center on the machine. Thus, a 15-in. drill press can drill a hole in the center of a disk that has a 7½-in. radius. This is the distance from the center of the drill chuck to the front of the column. There are four basic parts common to all drill presses: the *head, column, table,* and *base.*

The *head* is attached to the upper end of the column and is the main working mechanism of the machine. Within the head, the *spindle revolves* inside a movable sleeve called the *quill.* The hand or *foot feed lever* is geared to the quill to provide the downward movement of the quill and spindle. A flat coil spring returns them to their normal position when the feed lever is released. Interchangeable spindles are available for most drill presses in order to adapt the machine for other work. For example, a *hollow ta-*

Fig. 21–21. The belt on these four-step cone pulleys is in the position for maximum spindle speed. The spindle on this machine is made to receive taper shank drills.

Fig. 21–22. An accessory pulley provides a selection of 12 speeds to more efficiently machine wood, metal, plastic, and other materials.

pered spindle is used for fitting mortising attachments to the drill press. The *standard spindle* has a short tapered projection which fits into the tapered hole in a ½-in. geared-key chuck.

Different spindle speeds on conven-

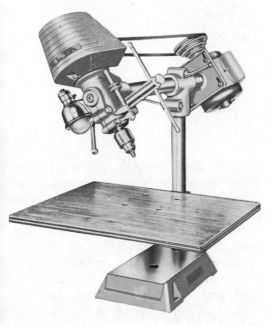

Fig. 21–23. This bench type radial drill press is for light industrial woodworking.

tional models are obtained by changing the position of the belt on the step pulleys (Fig. 21–21). Speeds range from 300 to 5000 rpm. The largest step of the cone pulley on the spindle is used with the smallest step of the pulley on the motor to obtain the slowest speed. They are powered by motors of various speeds, but 3600 rpm is most common. A ⅓-hp motor is sufficient for average drilling operations. Sometimes an accessory pulley is used which provides 12 different speeds for a variety of operations on different materials (Fig. 21–22).

The **radial drill press** (Fig. 21–23) is primarily used for angle-drilling and boring operations. The head and arm swivel in a complete circle around the column. The head also swivels up to 90 deg. to the right or left for angle and horizontal drilling. Heavy-duty radial drill presses (similar to the one illustrated) are used in industrial pattern shops, maintenance departments, and machine shops. Tilting the head instead of the stock or the table provides greater flexibility, faster setups, and requires less time and expense in making special work-holding fixtures. Radial drills generally have a greater capacity (distance from the front of the column to the center of the spindle) which allows for handling larger work than the conventional types of drill presses.

The **overhead drill press** is a special industrial machine which is used where large work is difficult or impractical to move to the drill press. It is essentially a single spindle, floor model drill press with the head inverted. The base is fastened to a carriage which is suspended from an overhead track that allows free movement over the work.

The **boring machines** found in today's modern industrial plants are of many makes, styles, and sizes which encompass

Fig. 21–24. A multiple spindle boring machine set-up to bore holes in chair bottoms. The 15 spindles are driven by flexible shafts which are in turn belt driven by 3 motors. The feed is controlled hydraulically.

a wide range of special boring operations. The particular machine used by a manufacturer might range from a hand-fed single-spindle unit to a specially designed machine with multiple heads. Often extra spindles and bit clusters are adapted to the boring requirements of a particular production item (Fig. 21–24).

Basically, industrial boring machines are classified into two groups: *vertical* or *horizontal*. The vertical types are the most common. In both groups are *single-spindle* and *multiple-spindle* borers. These are either hand-fed or automatically (hydraulically) fed machines. Generally, industrial boring operations may be grouped into two categories: (1) *face boring,* which involves boring straight or angled holes in the surface of wide boards or panels (Fig. 21–25), and (2) *edge* and *end boring,* which includes straight or angle boring in the edges or ends of stock.

Vertical boring machines (Figs. 21–26

Fig. 21–25. Face, or flat boring, on a gang boring machine. The spindle carriage is moved to and from the work table hydraulically. Note the fence and stop block for accurate positioning of the work.

and 21–27) are useful for both categories of boring operations. Vertical single-spindle boring machines are somewhat similar in mechanical functioning to a drill press. However, they are supplied with more powerful motors (2 to 5 hp) with spindle speeds of 1600 to 2000 rpm. They also have a greater throat clearance and depth of *stroke*. The stroke is the vertical travel distance of the spindle or quill.

The spindle stroke capacity of these machines varies from 9 in. on the hand-fed models up to 16 in. on the larger, heavy-duty, hydraulic-feed machines. The single- and the multiple-spindle boring machines are often fitted with *multiple*

heads or *bit clusters* (Fig. 21–28). These special attachments permit boring holes on very close centers from one drive spindle. They can be adapted to both the horizontal and the vertical machines.

Horizontal boring machines (Figs. 21–29 and 21–30) are primarily used for edge and end boring operations. Horizontal single-spindle machines are widely used to bore holes in parts of frames and core stock materials that will be assembled with dowels and glue. Some machines are equipped with a pneumatic or mechanical hold-down mechanism to

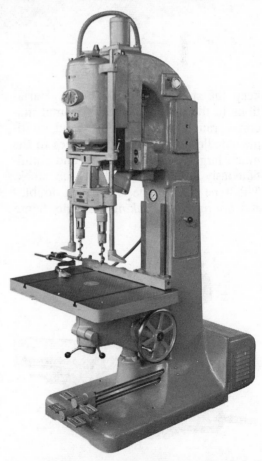

Fig. 21–26. A double spindle, vertical boring machine. It has a hydraulic spindle feed and a 5-hp, two-speed motor.

Fig. 21–27. This vertical, double column, multiple borer will bore as many as 20 holes in one feed cycle. The table on this machine is hydraulically raised and lowered to feed the work into the bits.

keep the stock flat on the table. Variations in the design of the horizontal machines range from the single- and multiple-spindle dowel-boring machines to the much larger units that chuck and simultaneously bore each end of the stock. This type of machine is called a double-end *boring and chucking* machine. Some of the boring and chucking machines are equipped to do end trimming and notching with trim saw units (Fig. 21–30).

Fig. 21–28. A boring head fitted with a bit cluster. This grouping of bits permits boring holes with close centers.

Fig. 21–29. Horizontal boring machine can also be used with multiple-spindle heads. It features a foot feed which moves the 2-speed motor horizontally into the work.

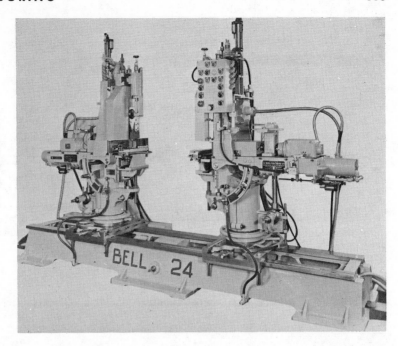

Fig. 21–30. A horizontal boring machine for high production use. It saws, chucks, and bores both ends of the work at rates up to 1500 pieces per hour. It will handle stock over 6 feet in length. It carries two 16-in. diameter saw blades.

Hopper feeding. Production boring machines are often automatically *hopper-fed* (Fig. 21–31). The *hopper* is a device which holds the pieces one on top of another. Each piece is automatically transferred to the boring area of the machine, bored, and then moved out through the rear of the machine to be dropped on a conveyor or removed by an attendant. Drilling attachments are also fitted to the hopper of automatic lathes for drilling one or more holes for dowels, lag bolts, or screw fasteners.

Fig. 21–31. This hopper-fed boring machine automatically positions the work for boring and then moves it out of the rear of the machine.

Drills and Bits

The early drills and bits were either a flat type, called "pod or spoon bits" or they had two straight grooves designed to cut whichever way the bit revolved. The first auger bits with twists and a one-direction cutting edge were handmade by village blacksmiths. These early auger bits were used to bore holes to receive the locking pins used in the framing of buildings. Another early application of the auger was for making wooden pipe. These sections of pipe known as pump logs, were originally used to bring water up from the well to the hand pump. Later, they were also used to transport

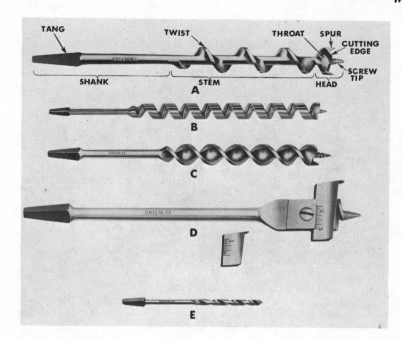

Fig. 21–32. Basic types of boring tools for use with a hand brace.

water to houses in villages. Special augers were made for boring a 1½-in. diameter hole in green logs. Some pump log augers were 9 ft. in length.*

Many of the drills and boring bits of today are not greatly changed from those of grandfather's day. The carpenter and other skilled workers in the custom trades still occasionally use a hand brace and bit. In the following paragraphs you will become acquainted with the cutting tools which are used in hand and machine drilling and boring operations in today's major areas of woodworking.

Auger bits are used for boring holes with the bit brace. The most commonly used sets of auger bits range in size from ¼ to 1 inch in diameter by 1/16 inch increments. Sizes from 3/16 to 2 inches are also available. The number stamped on the shank indicates the size in sixteenths of an inch. For example, a number 6 bit

is 6/16 or 3/8 inch in diameter. Figure 21–32 illustrates the parts of a typical auger bit. The *screw point* centers the bit and pulls it into the work. Screw points have slow, medium, or fast threads. The *spurs* outline the cut and sever the wood fibers in advance of the *cutters*. The cutters lift the chips and start them through the *throat*. The *twist* serves to elevate the wood chips from the hole, thus preventing clogging. Modern auger bits are made in three different styles.

1. The *solid center*. Shorter bits of this type (Fig. 21–32 a.) are called *dowel-auger bits*. They are primarily used to bore holes for dowels.

2. The *single twist* (Fig. 21–32 b.) is used for deep holes. The chips move freely through the center without clogging. The single-twist types are widely used by electricians, ship builders, plumbers, pipe fitters, bridge and dock workers, and other general construction workers.

* See Figures 3–5 (page 322), and 8–10 (page 324), for illustrations of early types of drills and bits.

3. The *double twist* (Fig. 21–32 c) is sometimes referred to as the cabinet-maker's bit. It provides excellent chip elevation on both sides.

The **expansive bit** (Fig. 21–32 d) is an adjustable bit used in the brace to bore holes in sizes ranging from 7/8 to 3 in. in diameter. The bit is set for the desired size by moving the adjustable cutter until the distance from the spur to the screw point equals the radius of the hole. Many carpenters have replaced this bit with hole saws used in power drills.

The **gimlet bit** is not used much today.

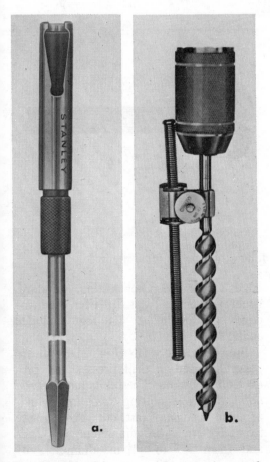

Fig. 21–33. (a) auger bit extension and (b) bit gauge.

This bit has a square tang. It cuts a shallow tapered hole suitable for wood screws. It has one short twist on the head similar to that of the early pump-log auger bit shown in Figure 21–9 on page 324. Sizes of this bit range from 1/8- to 3/8-in. diameters by steps of 1/32 in.

Brace drill. Bits of this type (Fig. 21–32 e) are also called twist bits. They are twist drills with square tangs. Sizes range from 1/16- to 1-in. diameters. Variations of this bit in longer lengths are called *bellhanger's* or *electrician's bits.* These are used for boring through walls and beams for telephone and wiring installations and for other deep boring operations.

The **bit extension and the bit gauge** (Fig. 21–33) are hand-boring accessories. Bit extensions are used to give extra length to the bit. They are available in 12-, 18-, and 24-in. lengths and follow an 11/16-in. diameter hole. The bit gauge is clamped to the shank of the auger bit and is used to indicate when a hole is of the proper depth. A home-made bit gauge may be constructed by boring a hole in a block and cutting it so that the length of bit necessary for the desired depth of hole is exposed.

Twist drills (Fig. 21–34 a) are used to drill wood, plastics, and metals. They are made of *carbon steel* or *high-speed steel.* Some are tipped with *tungsten carbide.* Generally, the carbon-steel drills are cheaper, easily dulled, and are intended for the occasional drilling of a variety of materials which are softer than steel. High-speed steel twist drills retain their cutting edge even when drilling at high temperatures. They are good for all-purpose drilling. Drill sets are available in sizes ranging from 1/64 in. to 1/2 in. by 64th-in. steps. Carbide-tipped drills retain their service life about 50 percent longer than high-speed steel drills. They

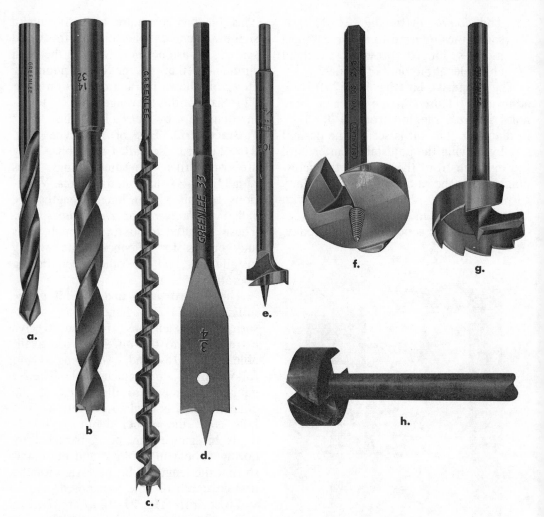

Fig. 21–34. Common cutting tools for power drilling and boring operations.

are used in industry for all types of difficult cutting jobs such as drilling in masonry and for machining of high-strength steels and alloys. Carbide-tipped drills are available in sizes from $\frac{1}{8}$ in. to $1\frac{1}{4}$ in. by $\frac{1}{32}$-in. steps. The twist drills are made with either *straight* or *tapered* round shanks. The straight shank must be used in the standard three-jaw chuck. Tapered shanks must be used in tapered spindles. Twist drills that are used exclusively for wood drilling have a 60-deg. included angle on the cutting edges to provide faster cutting. Standard, general-purpose, twist drills have cutting edges ground to a 118-deg. included angle.

Spur machine drills (Fig. 21–34b) are generally used in drill presses and production machines. These bits have a *brad point* and two cutting *spur lips* which produce a clean, fast cut. Sizes range from $\frac{3}{16}$- to $\frac{1}{2}$-in. diameters by 32nds and from $\frac{1}{2}$- to $1\frac{1}{4}$-in. diameters by 16ths.

Machine auger bits (Figs. 21–34c) are

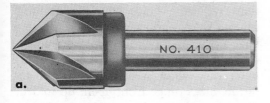

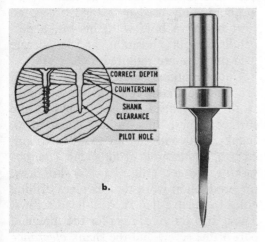

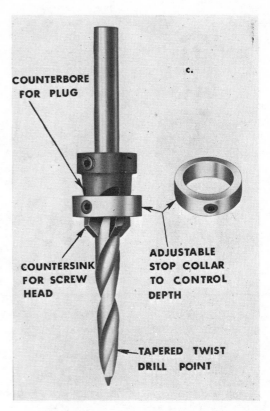

Fig. 21-35. (a) countersink bit; (b) wood drill and countersink; (c) combination drilling, countersinking, and counterboring tool with an adjustable collar.

designed for fast cutting in boring machines. They are similar to auger bits, but with round shanks. The point is either a brad point for making holes that do not go through the wood, or a threaded point designed for boring through holes with portable power drills. These bits are designed to cut wood only.

Spade-power bits (Fig. 21-34d) are relatively new in woodworking, but similar types were used for hand boring over 100 years ago. These bits usually have ¼-in. shanks to fit three-jaw drill chucks and are available in sets ranging from ¼-in. to 1-in. diameters by 16ths. They cut clean smooth holes and the brad point permits boring at an angle.

The **power bore bit** (Fig. 21-34e) has

one cutting edge, spur, and brad point. It is a fast-cutting bit, ideally suited for boring holes in softwoods and most hardwoods with small electric drills. Sizes range from ⅜ in. to 1 in. by ⅛-in. increments.

The **large hole bit** (Fig. 21-34f) is used for boring holes for cylinder lock sets in doors, etc. It is available in three sizes: 1¾-, 2-, and 2⅛-in. diameters. The shank of this bit is designed to fit three-jaw chucks and also hand braces.

The **multi-spur bit** (Fig. 21-34g) is generally made with a ½-in. round shank for use in three-jaw chucks. It has several spurs, one edge, and the brad type of center point. This bit bores large holes in hard- and softwood at any angle. It is

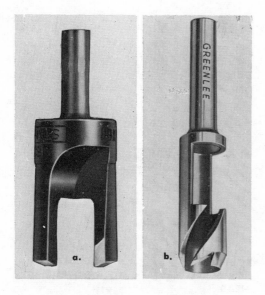

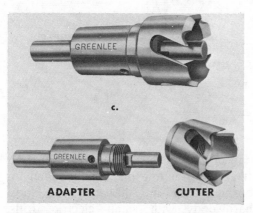

ADAPTER   CUTTER

Fig. 21–36. Plug cutters: (a) blade type; (b) spiral type plug cutters and (c) adapter type plug cutters.

ideal for boring overlapping holes on close centers. A special feature of this type of bit is that it has little tendency to split or tear veneer even when boring completely through the workpiece from one side. The sizes generally range from ½-in. to 4-in. diameters, with about 37 different sizes between.

Forstner bits (Fig. 21–34h) are used for many intricate woodworking opera-

tions requiring holes with flat bottoms, smooth sides, and sharp edges. These bits have no screw or brad point common to other bits. This bit is guided by the sharp outer rim, which is bevel ground on the inside. Sizes range from ¼-in. up to 3-in. diameters. Bits with round shanks are used in 3-jaw chucks; square tang shanks are commonly used in a hand brace. To start boring a hole with this bit, a perpendicular bit position and moderate feed pressure are required.

Countersinking cutters (Fig. 21–35) are used to make cone-shaped openings so the screw head will set flush with the surface. These bits usually have ¼-in. shanks, and will cut up to ¾-in. diameters. *Combination drilling and countersinking cutters* (Fig. 21–35) are used for production work that involves drilling holes to receive flat- or oval-head screws. These drill the *pilot hole* for the threaded part of the screw and the shank *clearance hole, countersink* for the conical head of a flat-head wood screw and *counterbore* a hole, all in one operation. The counterbore permits the screw head to set below the surface so the hole may be fitted with a plug.

Plug cutters (Fig. 21–36) are of several different types. They are used for making the round wooden plugs that fit into counterbored holes to hide screws and other types of fasteners.

The *blade type* of plug cutter produces straight plugs which are slightly beveled on one end for easy insertion and an exact fit into the counterbored hole. This type does not eject the plugs. They remain in the board, but they can be broken out with a screwdriver, or the board can be sawed to free the plugs. The two-blade cutter types are available in ⅜-, ½-, and ⅝-in. sizes with ¼-in. diameter shanks. Four-blade types are also available which make plugs up to

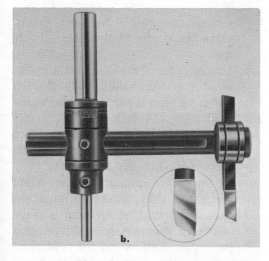

Fig. 21–37. Tools for cutting large holes and disks. (a) hole saw; (b) adjustable circle cutter.

1½ in. in diameter. These generally have a ½-in. diameter shank.

The *spiral plug cutter* (Fig. 21–36) is used to cut cross-grain plugs or end-grain dowels up to 2 in. in length. The plug is outlined with the knife edge rim, and cut with one slightly pitched cutting edge. The plug is ejected from the opening as a new cut pushes out the previously cut plug. The *adapter-type plug cutter* (Fig. 21–36) is a high-production cutting tool which is used for producing plugs of generally larger sizes. This design permits the use of one adapter with

cutters of different sizes. It has a spring-loaded ejection device which removes the plug from the cutter.

Hole saws and circle cutters (Fig. 21–37) are used to cut large holes and circles in wood, plywood, laminates, and other materials on a small production basis. Generally these tools have high-speed steel cutting edges. These two types of cutting tools are usually fitted with pilot drills. Hole saws feature removable blades of different sizes and spring ejection devices or they have knock-out holes provided to remove the cores.

The circle cutter will make holes ranging from ⅞ in. to 8 in. in diameter. The circle cutter is a dangerous tool if used carelessly. It should only be used in a drill press and the work should be firmly clamped to the table. The cutter must have a free path in which to turn.

Drilling and Boring Processes in the School Shop

The primary factors which affect the quality of drilled and bored holes are:
1. The workability of the wood being used.
2. The condition of the bit or drill and the tool or machine in which it is used.
3. The speed and feed rate of the bit or drill.
4. The skill of the operator in using the tools and equipment.

The workability of different species of wood varies. Several species may be drilled and bored effectively. Others tend to crush and tear. Holes drilled in some woods will actually be somewhat smaller than the size of the bit. This is due to the fact that the fibers of some woods recover after having

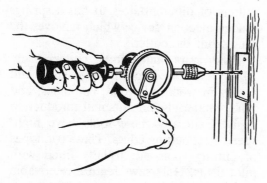

Fig. 21–38. Horizontal drilling with a hand drill.

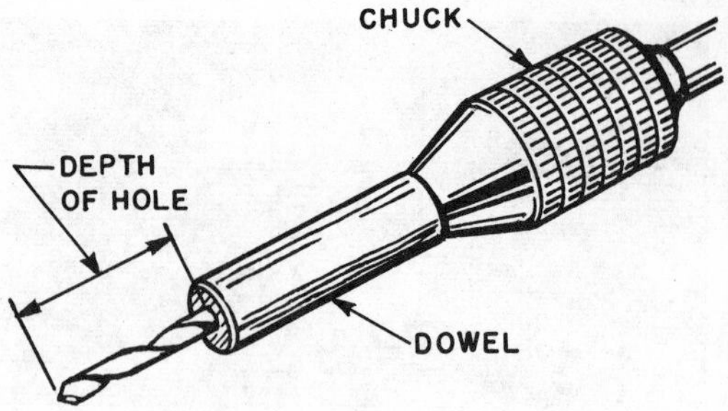

been flattened or compressed during the cut. If dowels are driven into holes that are too small, the work may split.

Using Hand Drills

1. Open the jaws of the chuck by turning the shell with one hand while holding the crank handle with the other.
2. Insert the drill into the center of the chuck. Tighten the drill by turning the crank handle with the right hand while holding the shell tightly with the other hand.

Fig. 21–39. A dowel depth gauge.

3. Clamp or support the work firmly, mark the center of the hole with an awl.
4. Set the point of the drill on the mark. Hold the drill handle with the left hand, keeping it perpendicular to the work (Fig. 21–38).
5. With moderate feed pressure, turn the drill by rotating the crank handle clockwise with the right hand.
6. To prevent splintering the wood when the drill breaks through the back side, back it up with a piece of scrap. Where some splintering is permitted, ease up on the feed pressure as the drill begins to break through.
7. Use a gauge cut from a piece of

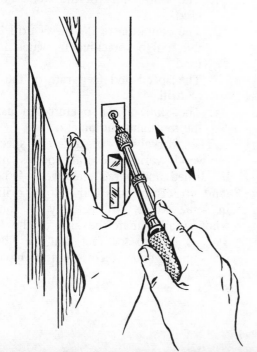

Fig. 21–40. Using an automatic push drill.

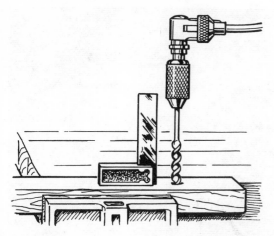

Fig. 21–41. Checking the bit direction with a square.

dowel (Fig. 21–39) to drill holes to equal depth.

8. Use the automatic push drill when making holes for screws or nails or for jobs in which one hand must be free to hold the work (Fig. 21–40).

9. An improvised drill bit may be made from a nail. Cut off the nail head with a pair of wire cutters. Chuck the nail and drill as with a twist drill.

Boring With a Bit and Brace

1. Open the jaws of the chuck by turning the handle with one hand while holding the shell of the chuck with the other hand. Insert the bit tang in the square socket in the bottom of the chuck and tighten the jaws.

2. Hold the stock securely in a vise or with a clamp.

3. To bore a vertical hole, set the screw point of the bit on the center mark and hold the brace perpendicular to the work surface. Check the angle of the bit with a square placed near the bit in two positions 90° apart (Fig. 21–41).

4. Start the bit into the stock (Fig.

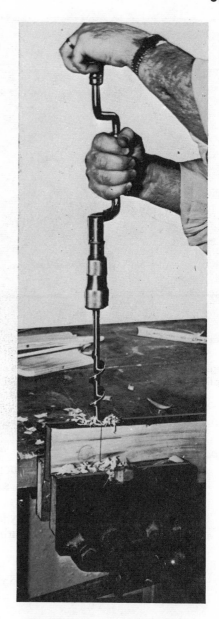

Fig. 21–42. Boring a hole vertically.

21–42). As soon as the hole is started, check again the direction of the bit with a square. Make the necessary corrections and then complete the hole.

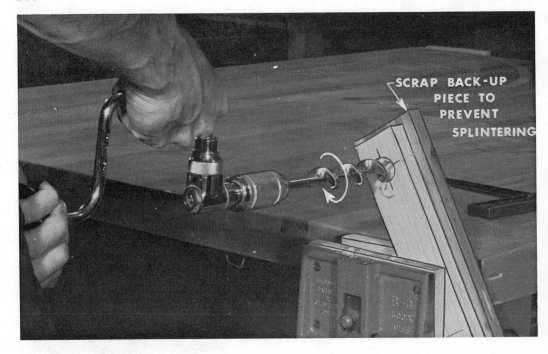

Fig. 21–43. Boring a through hole horizontally. A scrap piece of wood is used to prevent splintering the back of the work as the bit cuts through.

5. When boring at an angle, use a T-bevel to check the bit angle.

6. Clamp a bit gauge (Fig. 21–33b, page 337) to the bit when boring two or more holes to the same depth.

7. To bore a horizontal hole, apply pressure to the head of the brace with the body (Fig. 21–43).

8. To bore completely through the stock without splintering the work on the exit side, back up the work with a piece of scrap wood as shown in Figure 21–43.

9. An alternate method of boring through holes is shown in Figure 21–44. Stop boring when the screw point breaks through the work. Withdraw the bit from the hole, reverse the work, and complete the hole from the reverse side.

10. Use a Forstner bit for boring holes

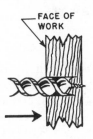

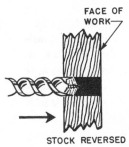

STOCK REVERSED

Fig. 21–44. Another method of boring a through hole to prevent splintering.

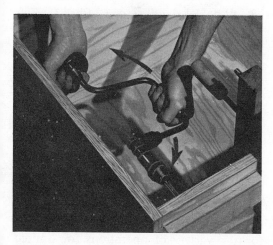

Fig. 21–45. Using the ratchet permits boring a hole in places where a full sweep of the handle can not be made.

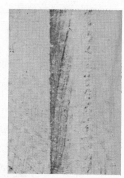

Fig. 21–46. The left hole was bored with a twist drill rotating at 200 rpm and the feed rate was 60 in. per min. The smooth hole at the right was bored with the same bit rotating at 800 rpm and the feed rate was 2 in. per min.

where the auger bit screw point would go through the work. Also, use the Forstner bit on end grain, thin stock, and near the edge of stock where the screw point might cause it to split.

11. When boring in a corner or where some object prevents making a full sweep of the handle, turn the ratchet control on the brace to the right. This activates the ratchet mechanism and permits rotating the bit with successive short strokes of the handle (Fig. 21–45).

Power Drilling and Boring

Speed and feed are important factors to be considered when power drilling and boring. Speed refers to the rpm's of the tool; feed to its penetration per revolution. Rough holes result from the use of dull bits or from improper rates of feed and speed. The proper speed and feed are determined by the size of the bit and the hardness of the work. Generally, the rate of feed should be slow enough to permit the drill to cut, rather

than tear the wood, yet fast enough that it does not burn it. Samples of holes made with correct and incorrect rates of feed are shown (Fig. 21–46). The correct feed will produce shavings rather than chips or dust. Generally, the larger the bit and the harder the material, the slower the speed. Speeds for large bits should range from 1200 to 1500 rpm. Twist drills ¼ in. and smaller should turn at speeds from 3000 to 5000 rpm. Circle cutters, large hole saws, and multi-spur bits should operate at speeds around 600 rpm and less. When using hand-fed power tools, develop a "feel" for the correct feed. Learn to recognize the sound of a properly cutting bit. Always ease up on the feed pressure as the point breaks through to prevent pinching the bit and splintering the exit side of the stock. Always use sharp bits. Refer to page 589 for information about bit sharpening, care, and maintenance.

Using portable power drills. Review the general safety precautions pertaining to portable power tools on page 152.

1. Hold the work firmly in a vise or

Fig. 21-47. Inserting a twist drill in a geared key chuck. Tighten the chuck firmly with the chuck key in each of the three holes provided.

clamp. Provide an extra board as a backup to prevent splintering the exit side when completing the hole.

2. Install the correct type and size of bit.

3. Tighten the bit in the chuck with the key (Fig. 21-47). The key should be twisted tightly in each hole in the chuck. This will prevent the bit from slipping in the chuck jaws and damaging the shank of the bit.

4. Start the hole with a scratch awl. When drilling metal, the hole center must be center-punched.

5. Set the point of the bit lightly in contact with the work.

6. Pull the trigger and allow the drill to gain its full speed before applying feed pressure.

7. Feed the bit with an even steady pressure. This produces shavings, not chips.

8. A dowel depth gauge (Fig. 21-39) may also be used for drilling several holes to a uniform depth.

9. To drill holes at an angle to the work surface, use a T-bevel to check the angle or make a special jig, similar to the one shown in Figure 21-48, to guide the drill.

Using the drill press. The drill press can be used for edge or face drilling and boring operations. It will effectively drive most of the power bits used by industry. The versatility of the drill press permits setups with various attachments to perform a variety of operations for limited production jobs. Some of the operations in addition to drilling and boring that may be performed on the drill press are: routing, shaping, grinding, buffing, polishing, carving, planing, mortising (page 362) and sanding (page 510).

The following safety rules should be observed for all drilling and boring operations on the drill press.

1. Make adjustments only while the drill press is stopped.

2. Determine the best speed for the

Fig. 21-48. Angle drilling with the aid of a jig.

size of bit. Adjust the machine accordingly.

3. Be sure the belt guard is in place.
4. Tighten the bit in the chuck firmly. *Always be sure to remove the chuck key before turning on the power.*
5. Wear approved safety goggles or a face shield for protection against flying shavings.
6. Feed the bit so that shavings are cut. Do not force the bit through the stock. Ease up on the feed pressure as the bit begins to cut through the stock.
7. Use V-blocks when drilling holes in round stock.
8. Always hold the work tightly or clamp it firmly to the table. Methods of holding small pieces and work of irregular shapes are shown in Figures 21–49 and 21–50.
9. Place a piece of scrap (base block) under the work to prevent drilling into the drill press table.

Drilling and boring holes with the drill press. The holes should be accurately laid out and the hole locations indented with a scratch awl. If a base block or table board is not used under the work, the hole must be made directly over the center hole in the drill press table. It is common practice to fasten a board or a piece of plywood to the drill press table with C-clamps, bolts, or screws. This permits boring and drilling through holes over any part of the table.

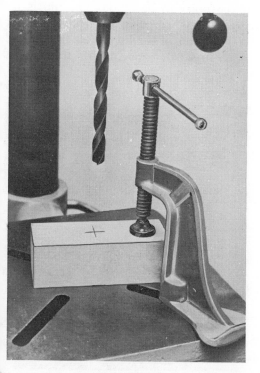

Fig. 21–49. Using a hold-down clamp for safe drilling of small work on a standard table.

Fig. 21–50. Using a hand screw clamp to hold irregular shaped work. Note the use of a square to position the work surface perpendicular to the drill.

Fig. 21-51. Drilling to a specific depth. The lock nuts are tightened on the depth stop while holding the quill assembly and bit to the depth marked on the stock.

Boring to depth is accomplished by setting the depth stop as shown in the photo (Fig. 21-51). To bore deeper holes than permitted by the limit of the spindle travel, stop the motor and slide a block of wood under the work (Fig. 21-52). As an alternate, raise the table. Back the bit out of the hole frequently to clean out the shavings and to prevent burning.

Edge boring dowel holes may also be accomplished on the drill press. A plywood auxiliary table and a straight board to serve as a fence are needed (Fig. 21-53). The fence must be at least twice as long as the pieces to be bored. It is clamped at the location dictated by the work requirements. Hand screw clamps or blocks of wood are fastened to the fence to serve as stops to position the stock for the end holes. A removable dowel pin fits into holes in the fence to locate other holes. The holes must be bored in the exact center of the edge. Adjoining pieces must be bored with the face side of one, and the back side of the other, against the fence. Unless this is done, the holes will not line up when the pieces are assembled.

Drilling holes in series. To drill several equally spaced holes, the auxiliary table and fence should be used with the addition of a location pin as shown in Figure 21-54. The pin is a length of dowel or metal rod of a diameter equal to that of the holes to be made. The pin is located so that the distance from its center to the center of the bit equals the desired center to center spacing for the row of

Fig. 21-52. Boring a hole deeper than the limit of the spindle travel is accomplished by sliding a board under the work.

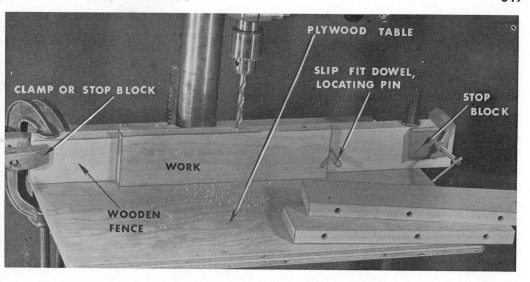

CLAMP OR STOP BLOCK

PLYWOOD TABLE

SLIP FIT DOWEL,
LOCATING PIN

STOP
BLOCK

WORK

WOODEN
FENCE

Fig. 21–53. Boring holes in the edges of boards for doweled edge joints.

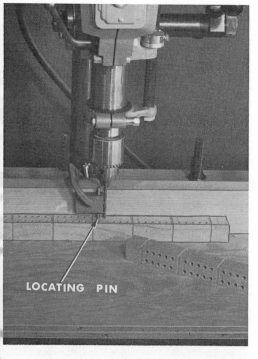

LOCATING PIN

Fig. 21–54. Drilling evenly spaced holes in a straight row with a locating pin and fence.

Fig. 21–55. Spacing holes evenly around a disk is accomplished with a locating pin.

holes. After the first hole is drilled, the
dowel is slipped into that hole. This establishes the spacing between holes.

The same principle is employed to drill
evenly spaced through-holes around a circle (Fig. 21–55). The first two holes
of the series are laid out and drilled, but
the drill is left in the second hole. A nail
is then driven through the center of the
workpiece into the wooden table to provide a pivot point. A second hole is
drilled in the worktable with a hand
drill, using the first hole as a guide. The
remaining holes are then made using a
dowel spacing pin as shown.

Boring holes in round work requires
the aid of a V-block (Figs. 21–56 and
21–57). The V-block must be held or
clamped to the table so that the hole
will be accurately centered. To bore radial
holes in round stock (Fig. 21–56) the
correct position of the V-block may be
found by lowering the bit into the apex
of the V. When the V-block is clamped
in this position, any round stock that is
placed in the V will automatically center
itself.

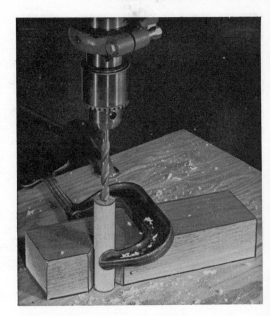

Fig. 21–57. Using a V-block support for
drilling the end of a dowel.

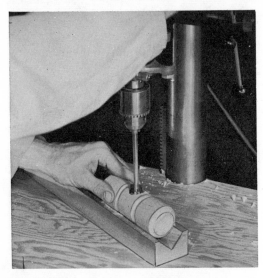

Fig. 21–56. Using a V-block to bore a
hole radially in round work.

Fig. 21–58. Using a multi-spur bit to bore
a 1⅝-in. hole.

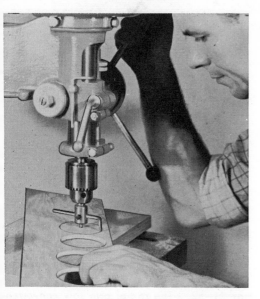

Fig. 21–59. Using a circle cutter to cut large holes. Note the base board under the work.

Holes over ½-in. diameter are generally classified as large holes. For this class of work, large hole bits, multi-spur bits (Fig. 21–58), hole saws, and fly or

Fig. 21–60. Using a fixture to drill holes at an angle.

circle cutters (Fig. 21–59) may be used. Use a speed of about 600 rpm. Fasten a base board or auxiliary table to the drill-press table for through holes. Clamp the work to the table.

Drilling or boring holes at an angle. Drill presses with tilting tables may be adjusted to the correct angle. The work must be clamped to the table to prevent it from slipping during the operation. Boring at an angle on a drill press without a tilting table requires a special work-holding fixture such as the one shown in Figure 21–60. The beveled block fixture shown in Figure 21–61 is used to support the work while drilling angled pocket holes in rails which will be fastened to table tops.

Horizontal drilling and boring processes. There are times when it is desirable to perform horizontal boring operations in the school shop. A horizontal boring machine is the best for this purpose, but most school shops are not so equipped. The radial arm saw may be quickly converted to do horizontal edge boring as follows:

1. Refer to page 189 of the sawing unit, and also refer to the manufacturer's instruction manual for information on adjusting the machine.
2. Remove the saw blade and guard.
3. Mount a threaded adapter, a chuck, and a bit to the arbor.
4. Mount a safety guard over the arbor for protection.
5. Use a flat board about 1½ in. high to raise the work and support it against the fence (Fig. 21–62).
6. Swivel and lock the motor in position.
7. Raise or lower the arm to position the bit.
8. Start the motor and slowly push the yoke (motor-holding assembly) and bit into the work.

Fig. 21–61. This setup is used to drill pocket holes for screws at 15-degree angle in a rail to be fastened to a table top.

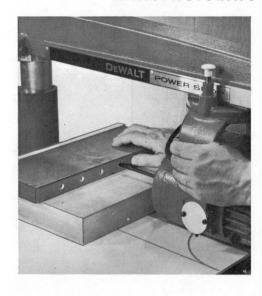

Fig. 21–62. The radial arm saw converted to do horizontal boring. Note the 1½-in. work supporting block and fence.

Multiple or gang boring processes. Several different methods may be employed to perform multiple boring operations in the school shop. Two drill presses may be connected with an auxiliary table. Bit cluster heads, driven from one spindle, are also available. Flexible shafts may be used as shown in Figure 21–63.

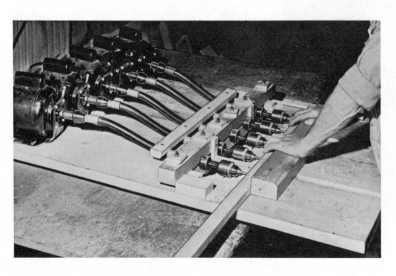

Fig. 21–63. Using 5 motors and flexible shafts to drill 5 holes at once. The work is fed into the bits with an improvised guide that tracks in grooves in the table.

REVIEW QUESTIONS

1. At what period in history were boring tools introduced? What was their use?
2. What sources of power have been incorporated in drilling and boring operations?
3. What is a post boring machine?
4. What determines the size of 3-jaw drill chucks? What are the likely consequences of chucking a square tang bit in a 3-jaw chuck?
5. What are universal drill-chuck jaws?
6. What power sources are available for portable power drills? What are the advantages and disadvantages of each?
7. What determines the size of a drill press?
8. What are the major parts of a drill press? What adjustments are involved in its use?
9. What is a radial drill press? What are its advantages over a standard drill press?
10. What are the principal types of drilling and boring machines used by industry?
11. What is a bit cluster?
12. What are the different types of bits and drills used in hand drilling and boring? How are augur bits sized? Twist drills?
13. What kinds of bits are used in portable power drills?
14. Describe the cutting action of an auger bit.
15. Name the three different kinds of materials that are used in the manufacture of twist drills. What are the characteristics of each?
16. What is the difference between a machine auger bit and a spur machine drill?
17. What are the uses of Forstner bits?
18. What are the different types of plug cutters?
19. Explain the procedure for boring a "through" hole with a bit and brace.
20. Explain the methods of drilling or boring a number of holes to uniform depths with the hand drill, bit and brace, and the drill press.
21. Explain some important steps to observe when installing a drill in a chuck.
22. What classes of work require the use of a V-block in drilling or boring jobs?
23. Describe a technique for drilling equally spaced holes in several pieces.
24. How may industrial multiple or gang boring operations be simulated or performed in the school shop?

SUGGESTED STUDENT ACTIVITIES

1. Construct working models of an early bow drill and a pump drill.
2. Design a universal, adjustable jig for guiding drills or bits for an angle hole.
3. Design a horizontal boring machine.
4. Make a list of machining operations, other than drilling and boring, that may be performed on a drill press.
5. Prepare a display of the different kinds of tools used for drilling and boring. Also display pictures of the various kinds of drilling and boring machines.
6. Devise a method for determining the power requirements for drilling holes of various sizes in different woods.
7. Prepare a report on the evolution of drilling and boring processes.
8. Design and construct a useful object to be made principally on a drill press.

Chapter 22 Mortising

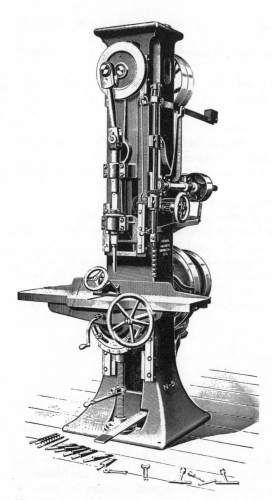

Fig. 22-1. This reciprocating solid chisel mortising machine was used in the middle 1800's.

Mortising is the process of cutting openings or cavities of either square, rectangular, round, or oblong shape into which tenons are fitted. The tenoning operations involve entirely different processes and are discussed in Chapter 23. Refer to the chart of joints on page 420, which illustrates the many type of mortise and tenon joints.

Evolution of Mortising Processes and Machinery

Mortise and tenon joints have been used for centuries because they are a rigid and permanent means of joining wood members. They were used in the construction of early wooden spoke wheels, frame assemblies for wagons, implements, furniture, ships, and buildings. In fact, the wooden frame buildings erected in this country by the early colonists and pioneers were held together with this joint, and reinforced or locked with wooden pins. Nails were hard to get and expensive during those early days. This, plus the fact that labor was cheap, justified the long and laborious task of hand cutting and fitting mortise and tenon joints to frame a house. Many of these early structures are still standing and serve as monuments to the enduring strength of this joint and the craftsmanship of the builders. Until about the nineteenth century, the mortise and tenon continued to be the principal joint used in constructing products ranging from small furniture to large churches.

Before the first mortising machines were introduced in the early 1800's, mortises were usually made by boring a row of holes and then squaring the corners and removing the waste by hand with ordinary chisels. The early mortising machines performed the operations in the same order. First holes were bored and then a solid chisel was forced into the wood to shape the mortise. The cutting tools of these machines were moved into the work by either hand- or foot-operated feed levers (Fig. 22–1).

In 1874, identical twin brothers, Ralph and Robert Greenlee, invented a revolutionary new machine called the hollow-chisel mortiser. Unlike the previous solid chisel machines, this new machine cut square mortises in a single operation. This was accomplished with a special wood boring bit which revolved inside of a hollow chisel with a square cross-sectional shape. The bit bored a hole slightly in advance of the cutting edges of the chisel which cut the corners square as they followed. The original machine mounted the chisel horizontally. A later model, manufactured and sold by the two inventors in the 1890's, is shown in Figure 22–2. Today, hollow-chisels are used on both horizontal and vertical machines.

Industrial Mortising Machines and Processes

There are three different types of mortising machines used in industrial plants. These are: the *hollow-chisel* (Fig. 22–3), the *chain-cutting* (Fig. 22–4), and the

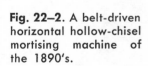

Fig. 22–2. A belt-driven horizontal hollow-chisel mortising machine of the 1890's.

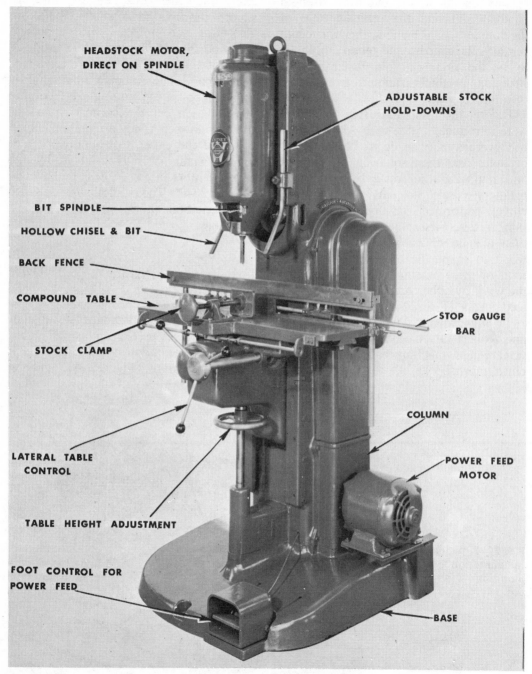

HEADSTOCK MOTOR, DIRECT ON SPINDLE

ADJUSTABLE STOCK HOLD-DOWNS

BIT SPINDLE

HOLLOW CHISEL & BIT

BACK FENCE

COMPOUND TABLE

STOP GAUGE BAR

STOCK CLAMP

COLUMN

LATERAL TABLE CONTROL

POWER FEED MOTOR

TABLE HEIGHT ADJUSTMENT

FOOT CONTROL FOR POWER FEED

BASE

Fig. 22–3. A vertical, single spindle hollow-chisel type mortiser. The power feed moves the head up and down as long as the foot control is depressed.

oscillating bit (Fig. 22–5). Each machine has certain advantages and limitations.

Hollow-chisel, single-spindle mortisers (Fig. 22–3) are widely used in pattern shops and cabinet and mill-work plants. The basic parts of this type of machine are the base, column, table, and the headstock assembly. The *spindle* is directly driven by the headstock motor. The motor sizes range from 1 hp on light hand-fed machines up to 5 hp on larger power-fed machines. The motor speed is usually 3600 rpm. The headstock assembly (sometimes referred to as the ram) moves up and down on the accurately

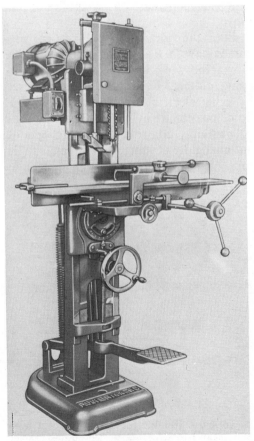

Fig. 22–4. A chain mortiser.

machined column. The spindle and the chisel are fed downward into the work by a mechanical linkage, activated by a hand- or foot-operated lever or by motor power. The feed motor is generally 2 hp with a slower rpm. On manual-feed machines the headstock assembly is returned to the top position on the column by a heavy coil spring when the feed lever is released.

Power-fed machines also feature a mechanism which will automatically move the head up and down as long as the foot control is depressed. The rate of automatic feed strokes on these machines range from 15 to 70 spm.

The *table* supports the work. It has a *back fence,* clamp, adjustable stops, and generally tilts to 45 deg. The table may be raised or lowered and moved toward or away from the column. Most machines feature a *compound table.* A compound table will move to the left and right, thus permitting oblong mortises to be cut by successive feed strokes without unclamping the work from the table.

Chisels and bits range in size from ¼ to ½ by ¹⁄₁₆-in. increments. Others are available for heavy-duty mortisers which will cut mortises up to 2 in. wide by 7 in. deep. The cutting edges of the chisel are beveled on the inside, and the chips they produce are lifted out along with the chips from the rotating bit. A hole in the side of the chisel (Fig. 22–6c) permits the chips to escape.

Chain-cutting mortisers (Fig. 22–4) are also referred to as *chain-saw mortisers* because their cutting action is similar to that of a portable chain saw. Chain-cutting mortisers are primarily used in cutting mortises in doors, windows, sashes, and frames. This type of mortiser is faster cutting than the hollow-chisel machines. The chain-cutting capacity generally ranges from ¼ to 1 in. wide, and cuts

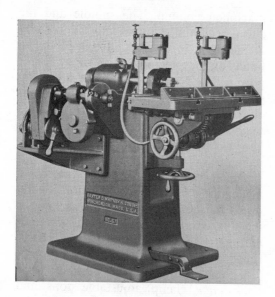

Fig. 22–5. Oscillating bit mortiser with air-clamps and power feed table.

mortises up to 2¾ in. long by 4 to 6 in. deep with each feed stroke.

This type of cutting head makes a mortise with a rounded bottom. The head assembly is basically made up of a chain, motor with a drive sprocket, guide bar, oiler, chip blower, adjustable chip breaker, and front guard. The chain is made of hardened-steel saw teeth in the form of links. They are loosely riveted together. The flexible chain is driven around the guide bar by the sprocket which is coupled directly to the motor shaft. The motor ranges from 1 to 10 hp with a sprocket speed of 3600 rpm. An oiler automatically provides the necessary lubrication to the bearing parts of the sprocket, chain, and guide bar. A built-in blower removes the chips and shavings. A chip breaker is located on one side of the chain to prevent splintering of the work as the chain moves out of the mortise.

The chain on the mortising head of the machine shown in Figure 22–4 is fed into the work when pressure is applied to the foot treadle. Similar machines may be fed by an hydraulic or pneumatic feed mechanism. The table and the other mechanical parts of the chain-cutting mortising machine are similar to the hollow-chisel mortisers.

Gang-mortising machines (Fig. 22–7) are large vertical or horizontal machines used in industrial plants to produce several mortises simultaneously. They utilize both the chain-cutting and the hollow-chisel types of mortising heads. The chain-cutting heads are found on the vertical type of machine only. The machines function as the single-spindle models do except that the headstock assemblies do not move.

Both the horizontal and vertical machines have a *feed table*. The feed table moves the work into the stationary mortising cutters. Feed tables are powered by either electric-drive motors or hydraulic or pneumatic cylinders. The feed may be manually controlled or set to operate automatically at any rate between 7 to 21 spm.

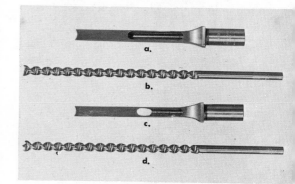

Fig. 22–6. (a) hollow-chisel for softwoods, (b) hollow-chisel bit for softwoods, (c) hollow-chisel for hardwoods, (d) hollow-chisel bit with diamond point for hardwoods.

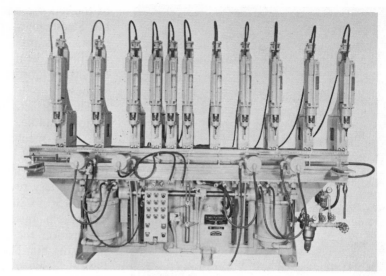

Fig. 22–7. Vertical multiple head mortiser. This machine may be fitted with either hollow-chisel or chain type mortising heads.

The tables also have powered holddown clamps. The clamp mechanisms automatically grip the stock during the mortising stroke, hold the work until it is withdrawn from the mortising chisel, and then release the work. The operator may move the work endwise between stops when making oblong mortises.

Some of the vertical machines may be adapted to a combination of operations. Chain and hollow-chisel mortising heads may also be adapted for use with single or multiple boring bit spindles and clusters. Horizontal mortising machines may be fitted with end-boring attachments to mortise and bore work simultaneously. This attachment is used to bore holes for casters in the ends of table legs or bed posts while they are being mortised.

Oscillating bit mortisers (Fig. 22–5) cut mortises at very high speeds with a router bit. As the bit (Fig. 22–8) rotates, it moves longitudinally (oscillates) the length of the mortise. The stock is fed into the bit to the designed depth. The mortise produced has rounded ends equal to the cutting arc of the bit. The width

Fig. 22–8. Double flute carbide router.

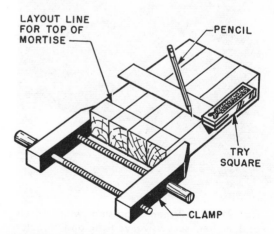

Fig. 22–9. Marking the lengths of the mortises as shown insures that all pieces will be identical.

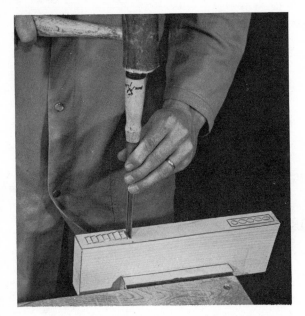

Fig. 22–10. Two methods of hand mortising. Left, starting a mortise with a chisel and mallet. Right, series of bored holes remove much of the stock prior to chiseling.

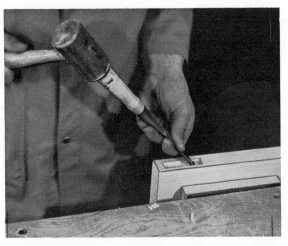

Fig. 22–11. When mortising with chisels and mallet, successive vertical and angular cuts are made until the desired depth is attained. The mortise is then pared to size with a chisel.

of the mortise equals the diameter of the bit. Sizes range from ¾₁₆- to ¾-in. diameters. This process is limited to a 2-in. maximum depth of cut. It is well suited to cutting mortises in curved or irregular shapes.

The mortising head consists of a drive motor, spindle, and bit chuck. The entire head mechanism oscillates horizontally. It travels on ways a distance equal to the desired length of the mortise. The bit generally revolves at 7200 rpm, with about 150 to 200 oscillations per minute. The table raises and lowers vertically to position the stock in relation to the mortising bit. The work is clamped to the table which carries it into the oscillating bit.

Mortising Processes in the School Shop

In the school shop you may cut mortises by one or more of the following methods: (1) with a chisel and mallet (Figs. 22–10 and 22–11); (2) by boring several holes with a brace and bit and chiseling to size (Fig. 22–10); (3) with a portable electric router (Fig. 22–12); (4) with a mortising attachment on a drill press (Fig. 22–13), or (5) on a mortising machine.

Hand Mortising Procedures

1. Lay out the mortise on the stock with a knife or sharp pencil. If several pieces are to be identically mortised, clamp them together and lay out the length of the mortise on all the pieces at the same time (Fig. 22–9). Lay out the width of the mortises with a marking gauge. Mark each width line on all pieces before changing the gauge to a new setting. The width of the mortise should equal about half the thickness of the stock

on which the tenon is to be cut.

2. Clamp the stock firmly in a vise.

3. Bore a row of holes with a bit slightly smaller than the width of the mortise as shown in Figure 22–10.

4. Score the outline of the mortise with a chisel and mallet. Keep the bevel of the chisel on the waste side. Remove the waste stock with a chisel (Fig. 22–10).

5. With a chisel, make paring cuts to finish the mortise to size.

6. If a bit and brace are not used, an alternate method is to cut the entire mortise with chisels. Score the outline of the mortise first. Select a chisel slightly narrower than the width of the mortise and remove the waste as shown in Figure 22–11.

Procedure for Cutting Mortises With Portable Electric Routers

Review Chapter 20, page 299, for basic operations of the router.

1. Mark the outline of the mortise in the center of the stock with a sharp pencil or knife. Also prepare a trial piece from scrap with the same cross-sectional dimensions.

2. Position the trial piece in a vise.

3. Attach the router guide. Insert a straight bit $\frac{1}{16}$ or $\frac{1}{8}$ in. smaller in diameter than the total width of the finished mortise. Adjust the guide so the bit will cut on the line. Set the bit to the desired depth and tighten all adjustments securely.

4. Start the router, and slowly lower the bit into the wood until the base of the router rests on the stock. Move the router to cut the desired length of the mortise (Fig. 22–12). Check the trial cut for accuracy. Then proceed with the prepared stock. (Hardwoods may require several shallow passes to reach full depth).

5. After the first cut is completed, position the router guide against the opposite side of the stock and make the second cut to finished width of the mortise. This technique places the mortise in the exact center of the work.

NOTE:

1. When a mortise is to be cut on the edge of narrow stock, clamp a piece of scrap to each side of the stock to give it sufficient width to support the router base.

2. Some mortises must be located off the center of the edge. Select a bit of proper size and proceed to cut as above, but reset the guide and make the second cut along the same side of the stock.

3. For identical mortises, make a jig (templet) that will clamp to the stock. A templet guide installed on the router will then guide the cuts. This eliminates the need for several layouts and ensures that all mortises will be alike.

Fig. 22–12. Completing the first cut for a routed center mortise.

Fig. 22-13. Mortising with a drill press attachment.

Hollow-Chisel Mortising

Either a drill press attachment (Fig. 22-13) or a mortising machine (Fig. 22-14) may be used. If several identical mortises are to be made, only one need be laid out. Once the machine is set up, layout marks are unnecessary if stops are

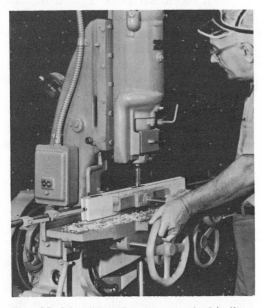

Fig. 22-14. Mortising on a vertical hollow-chisel mortiser. Note the use of the stop rod to locate the work.

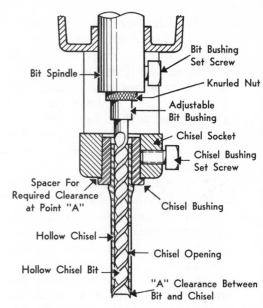

Bit Spindle
Bit Bushing Set Screw
Knurled Nut
Adjustable Bit Bushing
Chisel Socket
Chisel Bushing Set Screw
Spacer For Required Clearance at Point "A"
Chisel Bushing
Hollow Chisel
Chisel Opening
Hollow Chisel Bit
"A" Clearance Between Bit and Chisel

Fig. 22-15. Hollow-chisel and bit assembly. First, install the chisel bushing and a $\frac{1}{32}$-inch spacer. Insert the chisel and bit and tighten the bit bushing set screw. Remove the spacer, seat the chisel and chisel bushing against the socket, and tighten the chisel bushing set screw.

used to regulate the length of the cut. If stops are not used, the length of each mortise must be marked.

Many school shops utilize a mortising attachment on the drill press. The installation and operation directions supplied by the manufacturer should be carefully followed.

The **assembly of the hollow-chisel and bit** is shown in the section drawing (Fig. 22-15). The cutting end of the bit should extend $\frac{1}{32}$ in. beyond the end of the chisel to provide clearance. On large ($\frac{3}{4}$-in. and above) chisels the bit extension should be increased to approximately $\frac{1}{16}$ in. This clearance is most important. Too little clearance results in friction between the chisel and bit. Friction causes heat and this will destroy any cutting tool.

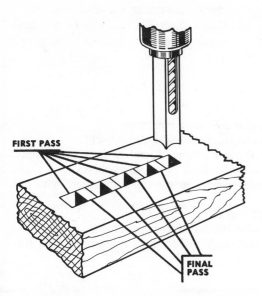

FIRST PASS

FINAL PASS

Fig. 22–16. Procedure for making hollow chisel mortising cuts. Note that full cuts are made at intervals on the first pass. This procedure insures even distribution of pressure on the bit and chisel.

Setting up or changing mortising bits and chisels requires some care. Alignment is usually a built-in feature of the machine. Correct bit and chisel clearance is obtained by adjusting the chisel, bushing, or bit after they are positioned in the mortiser. The back side of the chisel should be parallel with the back fence. The sides of the chisel should be perpendicular to the fence.

Using hollow-chisel mortisers. The mortiser (Fig. 22–14) is a relatively safe machine to use. It does not present any great hazards to the operator unless he is careless. More often this machine is misused, causing permanent damage to the bit and hollow-chisel.

Safety Precautions for Hollow-Chisel Mortising

1. Insure that proper clearance exists between the bit and the chisel.
2. Make successive cuts as shown in Figure 22–16. This procedure will prevent bending and breaking of the cutting tools caused by unequal pressures that result when the chisel cuts on three sides.
3. Insure that the work is firmly clamped in place.
4. Insure that the hold-downs are adjusted so that the stock remains in position on the table while the chisel is being withdrawn from the cut.

Cutting a Mortise

1. Lay out the length of the desired mortise on the proper surface(s) of the stock. Mark the depth of the cut on the side of the stock.
2. Set up the machine.
3. Clamp the stock in position on the table and make the necessary adjustments for the depth of cut. This adjustment is made on either the table or the head. Move the head to the bottom of its stroke and adjust the depth control so that the end of the chisel lines up with the depth layout line on the side of the stock.
4. Adjust the table so that the bit is positioned above the mortise layout.
5. If several identical mortises are to be made in pieces of stock having the same dimensions, set the stops to control the length of cuts (Fig. 22–14).
6. Adjust the hold-down with sufficient clearance for the stock to move freely under them. (Most machines have a movable table to which the stock is clamped and thereby moved into position for the various cuts).
7. Make trial cuts on scrap stock of the same thickness, and check all measurements for accuracy.

8. Cut the mortise. Be sure to make passes as shown in Figure 22–16.
9. Make the final pass, being certain that the bit is centered over the stock remaining for each cut.
10. Clean the table of chips before positioning the next piece to be mortised.

REVIEW QUESTIONS

1. Describe the cutting action of the first mortising machines.
2. Who is credited with the invention of the hollow-chisel mortiser?
3. What are the three types of mortising machines found in industrial plants? What characterizes the mortise made by each of these machines?
4. Name the principle parts of a single-spindle hollow-chisel mortiser. What are their functions and adjustments?
5. How are mortises made with hand tools?
6. Explain the use of a portable router for mortising operations.
7. What is the procedure for laying out stock to cut identical mortises on a hollow-chisel mortiser?

SUGGESTED STUDENT ACTIVITIES

1. Make sketches of the various kinds of mortise joints.
2. Inspect the furniture in your home and make a list of the different kinds of mortise and tenon joints and where they are used.
3. Prepare samples of the various kinds of mortise and tenon joints.

Chapter 23   Tenoning

Tenoning is the process of making *shoulder* and *cheek* cuts (Fig. 23–1a, 23–1b, and 23–1c) on a piece of wood so that a portion of it will fit into a mortised opening in another workpiece. The assembled components comprise a mortise and tenon joint. Some applications of this joint were discussed previously on page 354. Mortise and tenon joints are also illustrated on page 366. Tenons may be of many different kinds (shapes) as shown in Figures 23–1a, 23–1b, and 23–1c.

In large-scale production, tenons (other than round ones) are cut automatically on huge machines known as *double-end tenoners*. These machines cut tenons simultaneously on both ends of the stock. The stock is also cut to length as it is carried through the machine. In addition to tenoning, double-end tenoners are capable of performing a number of other operations. Some of these operations are illustrated and discussed briefly in this unit so that you may understand the potential and unusual versatility of these large industrial machines.

In smaller factories or cabinet shops, where small to medium production runs of tenoned parts are needed, a hand-fed machine known as a *single-end tenoner* is often used. As implied by its name, this machine tenons only one end of the stock at a time.

Tenoning in custom manufacturing and school shops is usually done on radial arm or table saws or spindle shapers. Special work-holding devices may be used with these machines to simplify the job and make it safer. Tenoning is seldom done with hand or portable power tools.

Evolution of Tenoning Processes and Machinery

Before the development of power saws, all tenoning was done with hand tools. A special hand tool was developed for tenoning operations in colonial times and was used by wheelwrights. This tool, known as a *spoke rounder,* fit into a bit brace. It was used to cut the ends of wheel spokes round (Fig. 23–1c) so they would fit into holes bored in the wooden "felloe" or the rim of the wheel. Flat, tenons, however, were cut with hand saws and then pared to size with wood chisels.

The invention of Miller's circular table saw in 1777 and the first tenoning cut-

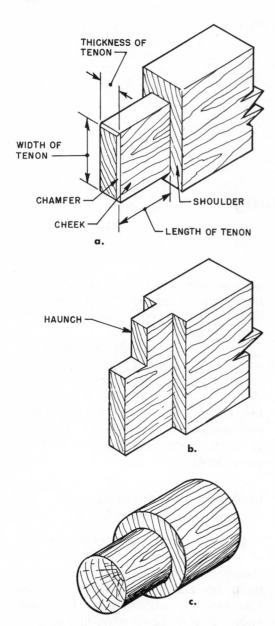

Fig. 23–1. Tenons: (a) most common type and its basic terminology, (b) a haunched tenon, and (c) a round tenon.

offered by double-end tenoners soon became well known and today they are commonly used in wood manufacturing plants.

ters developed by Samuel Bentham in the 1790's provided the basis for the development of tenoning machines.

The first *single-end tenoner* was invented by J. A. Fay in 1834 (the same year a foot-powered chiseling machine was invented for mortising). The first models of the single-end tenoners (Fig. 23–2a) were constructed with wooden frames. The arbor bearings were held in cast iron yokes which in turn were bolted to the framework. The ways for the table wheels and some of the other brackets were also made of cast iron. The single-end tenoner soon became recognized as an accurate, time-saving production machine. In a relatively short time, they became standard equipment in most of the early wood manufacturing factories. The wooden frame models of the 1850's were replaced by machines constructed of fully metal frames by the 1860's (Figs. 23–2b and 23–2c).

The first *double-end tenoner* (Fig. 23–3) was patented by the H. B. Smith Machine Co. in 1866. At first it was believed that these machines were too large for general use, but eventually they were accepted by the furniture industry. Before the turn of the century, Greenlee Bros. and Co. was building very large double-end tenoners to handle timbers (12 in. by 12 in. by 12 ft.) that were used in the construction of railroad cars. These were the largest tenoners ever built. They were removed from the market in the early 1900's when the railroad car industry converted to all metal construction.

The overall value of the double-end tenoner in large scale mass production work was actually established in the 1920's, the era of wood frame automobile bodies. The cross bars in the lower bodies of the 1924 Packards were all machined with double-end tenoners. The advantage

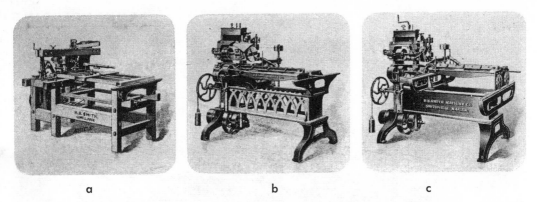

Fig. 23–2. Evolution of single end tenoners: (a) wood frame type marketed in 1850, (b) first iron frame tenoner built about 1860, and (c) improved metal frame tenoner.

Tenoners and Industrial Tenoning Processes

Tenoners today are still available as single-end or double-end machines. They are vastly improved over their earlier counterparts.

Single-end tenoners (Figs. 23–4 and 23–5) have two cutterheads (Fig. 23–6), known as the *upper tenoning head* and the *lower tenoning head*. Each completes a cheek and a shoulder of a flat tenon as the work is passed between them. The cutterheads are driven directly by individual 2-hp motors rotating at a speed of 3600 rpm. On light-duty machines they are belt-driven from a single 1-hp motor at a speed of 3450 rpm. The tenoning heads are adjustable, both vertically and horizontally, The adjustment mechanisms are arranged to provide individual adjustment for each head or to

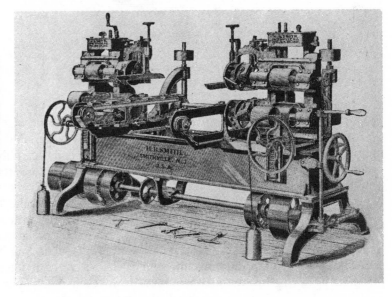

Fig. 23–3. Original double-end tenoner patented in 1876 by the H. B. Smith Machine Co. This machine had 4 rates of feed from 6 to 20 feet per minute. All spindles ran in Babbit bearings. Cope spindles were individually adjustable.

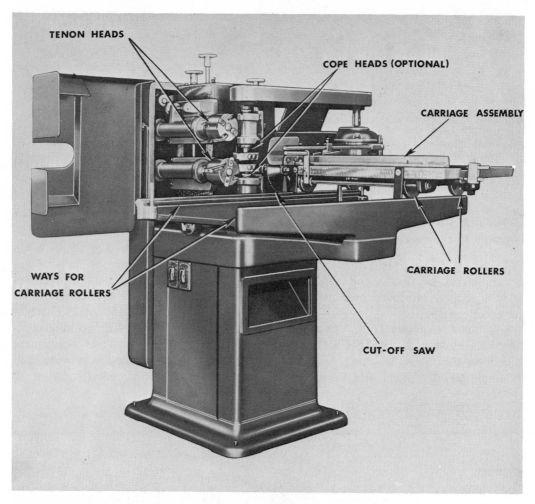

TENON HEADS

COPE HEADS (OPTIONAL)

CARRIAGE ASSEMBLY

CARRIAGE ROLLERS

WAYS FOR
CARRIAGE ROLLERS

CUT-OFF SAW

Fig. 23–4. The feed end of a single-end tenoner showing the relation of the principal operating parts.

permit both heads to be moved simultaneously so that a specific tenon thickness is maintained.

Cope heads (Fig. 23–4) are two in number, rotate vertically, and are located behind the tenoning heads. They are used to make the cope (shaped) shoulder cuts such as those on window moldings and door rails (see also Fig. 23–10). The cope heads on medium-duty machines are powered by a one-hp belt-driven motor.

On heavy-duty machines, each head operates by a direct-drive 2-hp motor. The cope heads are also adjustable independently in both vertical and horizontal directions. On the heavy-duty machine (Fig. 23–5), the top and bottom cope heads are mounted on the top and bottom tenoning carriages respectively. This permits changing the position of these heads without altering their relationship to each other. The *cut-off saw* is 7 to 9

**WORK CLAMP
MECHANISM**

Fig. 23–5. A single-end tenoner with the cutting heads mounted on the arbors of 3600 rpm motors. Note the push button control panel. A master switch stops all motors simultaneously.

in. in diameter and it is mounted on a horizontal arbor behind the cope heads. It is either powered by a direct motor or by belted drive. The cut-off unit is also adjustable, both vertically and horizontally by means of a hand crank. The *table* or *carriage* assembly moves horizontally past the tenoning and coping heads and the saw. It rides on rollers along accurately machined ways or tracks. The work piece is positioned with the aid of stops and a fence. It is held to the table with a rubber-faced work clamp. The clamp is operated manually by squeezing a pivoted handle. This holds the stock securely in position while advancing the table past the cutters and the saw.

Double-end tenoners (Figs. 23–7 and 23–8) basically consist of a massive one-piece bed (weighing close to 2 tons) and 2 large columns. Tenoning and cut-off

Fig. 23–6. A typical tenoning head for single- or double-end tenoners. The knives are placed at an angle for shearing cheek cut. The spurs cut ahead of the knives to produce a clean shoulder cut.

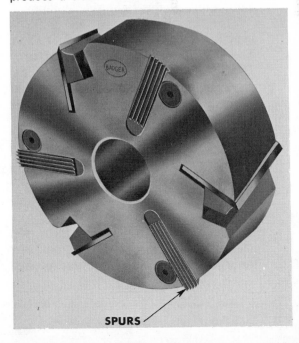

SPURS

Fig. 23–7. A double-end tenoner equipped with an exhaust system.

units similar to those of a single-end tenoner are mounted to each column. The right column is stationary. The left column is adjustable to accommodate different lengths of work. It is moved on machined ways on the bed casting by means of a screw mechanism which is operated with a 1-hp motor. Both columns are equipped with mountings for beams and chain-feed mechanisms. Figure 23–9 illustrates the feed mechanism and beams of the right side column.

Tenoners of this type are built to handle stock lengths from 48 to 192 in. The chain beams will handle stock from 28 to 92 in. in width. The feed mechanisms are driven by a 3-hp, 1200 rpm motor. They also have variable feed rates from 15 to 60 fpm; higher speeds are found on some machines. The tenoning and cope units are generally driven directly by 5- or 7½-hp motors turning at 3600 rpm.

Double-end tenoning processes include a wide variety of operations. These are typified by the examples of work shown in Figure 23–10, which point out why the double-end tenoner is often referred

to as "a woodworking plant in itself." With the appropriate attachments, these machines are capable of doing almost every operation that is possible on single

Fig. 23–8. The double-end tenoner in operation. Here panels are cut to size and tenoned on both edges.

purpose machines. In addition to standard tenoning and sawing operations, tenoners will do dovetailing (Fig. 23–11a), straight and irregular edge sanding (Fig. 23–11b), multiple boring (Fig. 23–11c), jump dadoing and routing (Fig. 23–11d), and serpentine shaping (Fig. 23–11e). A novel procedure is employed for setting up the machines to do irregular edge shaping operations (Figs. 23–12a, 23–12b, and 23–12c). This requires no complicated layout work, but utilizes an easily prepared hardwood disc cam (Fig. 23–12a), which is made on the machine itself (Fig. 23–12b). In this way, practically any contour can be duplicated automatically without previous handsawing or the usual hand operations required of conventional spindle shapers (Fig. 23–12c).

Many of the machining processes described above are incorporated in a newly developed machine concept known as the "Abrat." The name is derived from the abbreviation of automatic boring, routing, and tenoning machine. This complex machine is actually three double-end tenoners (with special attachments) that are linked by material transferring units (Figs. 23–13 and 23–14).

The Abrat was developed by the Greenlee Bros. and Co. in cooperation with the Hamilton Manufacturing Co., a producer of institutional cabinets. This machine has 18 work stations which automatically perform all of the operations required to complete a product part in one pass. The machine maintains an accuracy within .015 in. on all cuts. Over thirty different cabinet parts (with about 200 modifications) undergo machining at an output of over 1400 pieces every 8 hours. Some parts require thirteen or more different machining operations.

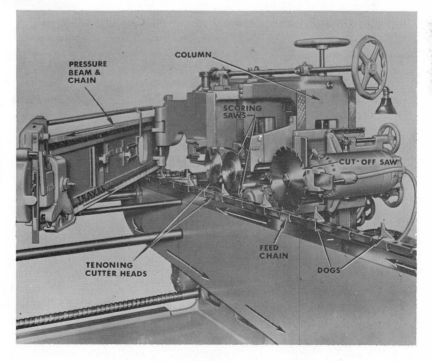

Fig. 23–9. View showing major functioning parts from the infeed end of the tenoner. This shows the pressure beam swung away from the cutting units.

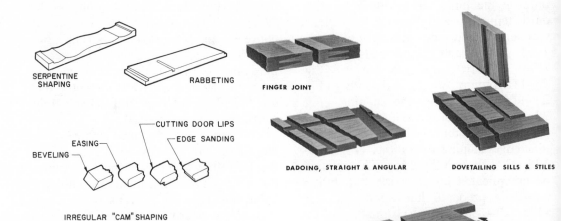

SERPENTINE SHAPING RABBETING FINGER JOINT

BEVELING EASING CUTTING DOOR LIPS EDGE SANDING

IRREGULAR "CAM" SHAPING

DADOING, STRAIGHT & ANGULAR DOVETAILING SILLS & STILES

SILL HORNING

Fig. 23–10. Examples of work produced on double-end tenoners.

Operated by 3 men, this machine does the same amount of work as 10 men using single-purpose machines.

Tenoning Processes in the School Shop

Most school shops are not equipped with tenoning machines like those just described. However, conventional flat tenons may be produced in the school in a number of ways. Generally, these are cut with hand, table, or radial-arm saws. Spindle shapers may be employed to perform the same class of work that is done on single-end tenoners with coping cutterheads.

Hand-tenoning procedures. Refer to Chapter 6 and 11 for basic information concerning laying out and hand sawing processes.

1. Lay out the length of the tenon(s) and mark a line all around the work piece to indicate the location of the shoulder. (The length of the tenon

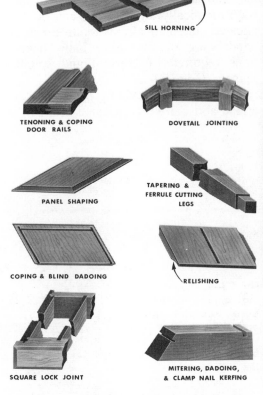

TENONING & COPING DOOR RAILS DOVETAIL JOINTING

PANEL SHAPING TAPERING & FERRULE CUTTING LEGS

COPING & BLIND DADOING RELISHING

SQUARE LOCK JOINT MITERING, DADOING, & CLAMP NAIL KERFING

should be approximately ⅛ in. less than the depth of the mortise).
2. Lay out the required thickness of the tenon with a marking gauge.
3. Make the cheek cuts with a back (or rip) saw as shown in Figure 23–15.

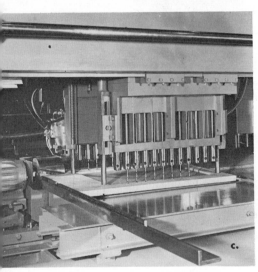

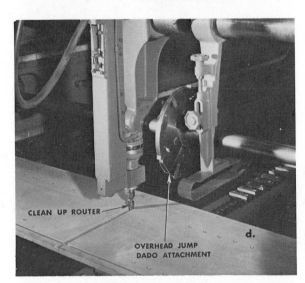

CLEAN UP ROUTER

OVERHEAD JUMP
DADO ATTACHMENT

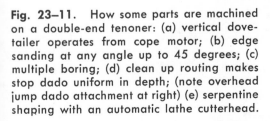

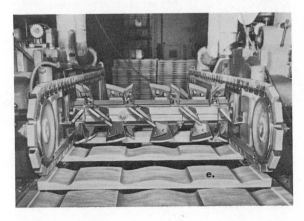

Fig. 23–11. How some parts are machined on a double-end tenoner: (a) vertical dovetailer operates from cope motor; (b) edge sanding at any angle up to 45 degrees; (c) multiple boring; (d) clean up routing makes stop dado uniform in depth; (note overhead jump dado attachment at right) (e) serpentine shaping with an automatic lathe cutterhead.

MASTER PATTERN

CAM

FINISHED WORK PIECE

a.

Fig. 23–12. Steps involved in irregular edge shaping on the tenoner: (a) a pattern, cam, and completed piece; (b) a cam being made on the machine. As the master pattern moves through the machine, the roller transfers the outline to cutters and shapes the wooden cam. (c) After the cam is made, the cutters and rollers are interchanged. In operation, the cam roller and lever transmit the cam pattern to the shaping spindle, thus shaping the edge of the workpiece.

ROLLER ON SHAPER SPINDLE RIDES AGAINST PATTERN

CUTTER

CAM

MASTER PATTERN

b.

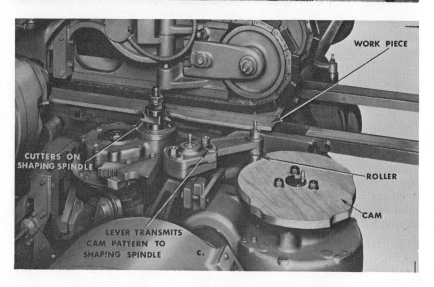

WORK PIECE

CUTTERS ON SHAPING SPINDLE

ROLLER

CAM

LEVER TRANSMITS CAM PATTERN TO SHAPING SPINDLE

c.

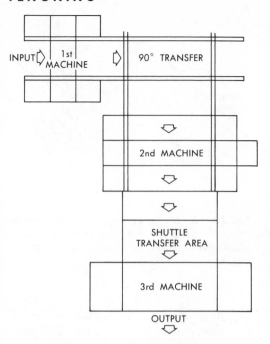

INPUT ▷ | 1st MACHINE ▷ | 90° TRANSFER

2nd MACHINE

SHUTTLE TRANSFER AREA

3rd MACHINE

OUTPUT

Fig. 23–13. A schematic illustration of the Abrat.

4. Make the shoulder cuts with a miter box or with the aid of a guide strip clamped to the stock, as shown

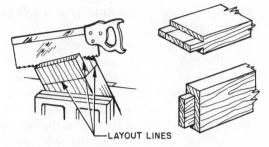

LAYOUT LINES

Fig. 23–15. Basic steps in making a tenon with hand tools.

in Chapter 11, page 151, Figure 11–17.

5. Make a test fit into the mortise.

6. Pare the tenon to size with a chisel.

7. Chamfer the ends of the tenon and make a trial assembly.

Table saw tenoning processes. Refer to Chapter 13, "Table Sawing Processes in the School Shop," for background information concerning safety and machine operation. Tenons may be cut on the table saw in many different ways, but the most common methods employ dado

Fig. 23–14. An automatic, 90-degree transfer unit of the Abrat which moves workpieces from the first machine to the second.

heads, a tenoning attachment, or a home-made tenoning jig.

1. *Dado tenoning* (Fig. 23–16). Assure that all the workpieces are of uniform thickness and squared to finished length. Usually the full complement of cutters is used to provide the widest possible cut. Adjust the depth of cut so that the desired tenon thickness will be left after each face of the stock has been passed over the dado head. Adjust the fence so it will serve as a stop. Locate it so that the shoulder will be cut by the points of the teeth farthest from the fence. If the length of the tenon is greater than the width of the dado head, the inside cut should be made first, cutting the shoulder and a portion of the cheek. Then, the work is moved away from the fence for additional passes (Fig. 23–16) until the cheek cut is completed. Turn the stock over and complete the remaining shoulder and cheek cuts in the same manner.

2. *Radial-arm dado tenoning* is accomplished in much the same manner as dado tenoning on the table saw. Refer to page 192 for dadoing on the radial-arm saw. Clamp a stop block to the guide strip to locate the first cut and to prevent "creeping."

3. *Table saw tenoning with an attachment* (Fig. 23–17). First saw the shoulder cuts with the stock flat on the table. Use the fence as a stop. This is done in essentially the same way as making the first cut in dado tenoning. Remove the saw guard. Adjust the tenoning attachment so the cheek cut will be made on the waste side of the line. After cutting one cheek, unclamp the work, turn it around so the opposite face is against the tenoning attachment, and complete the second cheek. When a large

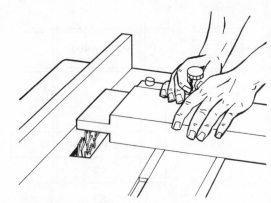

Fig. 23–16. Dado tenoning. Cut the shoulder first with stock against the fence. Move the work away from the fence for additional passes.

quantity of identical tenons are to be made, it is advisable to use two saw blades (of the same diameter) on the arbor. They should be separated by a spacer so that both cheek cuts may be made in one pass. NOTE: If a tenoning attachment similar to the one shown in Figure 23–17 is not available, construct a device that will support the work in the same way as the tenoning attachment. Attempting to saw tenons on stock "freehand"

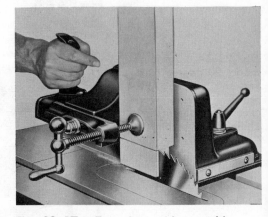

Fig. 23–17. Tenoning with a table saw attachment.

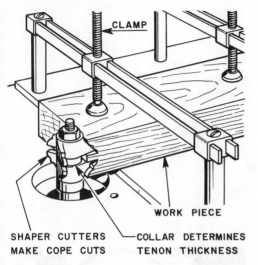

CLAMP

WORK PIECE

SHAPER CUTTERS COLLAR DETERMINES
MAKE COPE CUTS TENON THICKNESS

Fig. 23–18. Tenoning and cope shoulder cutting on the spindle shaper with the work held in the sliding jig.

(without a jig) is a hazardous practice since the work is not adequately supported and will very likely kick back.

4. *Shaper-tenoning processes* (Fig. 23–18). Refer to page 309, Chapter 20, "Shaping Processes in the School Shop." The advantage of tenoning on the shaper lies in the fact that when needed, cope cuts may be made simultaneously with the tenon by using the appropriate cove cutters. All tenoning and coping operations must be done with the work clamped in the sliding jig attachment for the shaper. Figure 23–18 shows the tenon and a coped shoulder cut being made with the work clamped in the jig so the end of the stock will just ride against the collar. The thickness of the tenon may be increased by placing a paper shim between the cutter and collar.

REVIEW QUESTIONS

1. Outline the significant steps leading to the development of modern tenoning processes and equipment.
2. What are the principal types of cutters embodied in conventional single- and double-end tenoners?
3. What is the significance of this phrase: "a double-end tenoner is a woodworking plant in itself?
4. Describe some of the major machining operations that may be performed on production tenoners.
5. What different methods of tenoning may be performed in the school shop?
6. Describe the operation of dado tenoning.
7. How may the miter box be employed to make tenons?

SUGGESTED STUDENT ACTIVITIES

1. Design and construct a wooden tenoning jig for the table saw.
2. Illustrate (sketches) how tenon and cope cuts in sash work may be made simultaneously in one pass on the shaper.
3. Design and illustrate suitable methods of cutting round tenons on the ends of dowels with these machines: (1) jointer, (2) drill press, (3) portable router, (4) shaper, (5) table saw, and (6) radial-arm saw.
4. Develop a strength test for the various mortise and tenon and dowel joints.

Chapter 24 Turning

Turning is the process of cutting or scraping wood to a cylindrical form in a lathe. The *lathe* is a machine which revolves the wood on a horizontal axis as it is shaped to the desired profile with cutting tools that are controlled either by hand or automatically.

Evolution of Turning Processes and Lathes

The **bow lathe** (Fig. 24–1) is the first woodworking machine recorded in history. It is believed to have been invented about 740 B.C. in Egypt. The bow lathe supported the work between two pointed pieces of wood. The bow string made one loop around the workpiece. While the wood turner moved the bow forward and backward with one hand the work rotated alternately in opposite

Fig. 24–2. The pole lathe was used until the 18th century. It is still used today in some remote parts of the world.

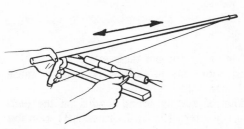

Fig. 24–1. The bow lathe was in use in Egypt by 740 B.C.

directions. The cutting tool was applied to the work only while it turned toward the operator.

The **spring-pole lathe** (Fig. 24–2) was also used by the ancient Egyptians. This type of lathe operated on the same principle as the bow lathe except that the operator was free to use both hands to control the cutting tool. A rope was fastened to the end of either a tree

Fig. 24–3. A treadle lathe converted to high speed drive with the aid of the "great wheel" at the left. The crank handle fastened to the wheel was turned by an apprentice.

branch, a young sapling, or if indoors, a spring pole fastened to the ceiling. The rope extended downward, made one turn around the work piece, and the lower end was tied into a loop to serve as a "foot treadle." When the wood turner pressed down on the treadle the rope rotated the work and sprung the tree branch. When the operator released his foot pressure, the tree branch or spring pole pulled the rope up again and reversed the rotation of the workpiece. Like the operation of the bow lathe, the cutting tool was applied to the work only when the rotation was toward the operator, i.e., against the cutting tool.

The pole lathe was used for many centuries without much improvement. In some parts of the world, it was used until the eighteenth century. The early lathes were made of wood except for the two centers which supported the ends of the work. These were made of iron, as were the cutting tools themselves. Around A.D. 1200, man conceived the crankshaft and the idea of transmitting rotary power through belts looped over wheels. This power source was adapted to the lathe. The drive wheel was powered by a foot treadle connected to a crankshaft. A belt connected the drive wheel to a spindle pulley. This drive mechanism produced a continuous rotary movement of the workpiece. Figure 24–3 shows a lathe, originally powered by this means, which has been converted to a more efficient power source.

The **great-wheel lathe** (Fig. 24–3) was used by turners who employed an apprentice. The "great" wheel was about 6 ft. or more in diameter and it was linked by a belt or rope to the spindle pulley. This type of lathe delivered a continuous rotary movement at high speeds because of the mechanical advantage obtained by the large drive wheel. In time, the "great"

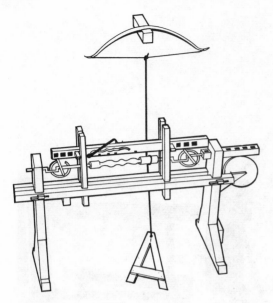

Fig. 24–4. This lathe of 1569 had a templet tracing device.

Today, hand wood turning is almost extinct except where wood turning is practiced in custom manufacturing shops and in the home. Automatic and production turning lathes not only eliminated the slower hand processes, but made possible the production of identical parts in unlimited quantities.

The **first successful production lathe** was invented by Thomas Blanchard of Philadelphia in 1819. The original model (Fig. 24–5), known as *Blanchard's Profile Lathe,* was designed to shape gunstocks. This machine was the forerunner of the modern industrial lathe. Some of the basic principles incorporated in Blanchard's lathe are still used in present-day production lathes. Blanchard's lathe incorporated these fundamental devices: (1) a guide mechanism that followed a pattern to control the cutterhead and thus shape any number of identical pieces, and (2) a rotating-knife cutterhead. The first device is employed in modern copy lathes and the latter in the automatic shaping lathe. Both of these types of lathes are discussed later in this unit.

Following Blanchard's lathe, many improvements were made in all lathes. Around the middle 1800's, iron parts began to replace wood frames and bases.

wheel was rotated by a water wheel, then a steam engine, and finally an electric motor.

The products produced on the lathe by the early wood turners were always in great demand. The major items included wooden table ware such as ladles, trays, bowls, and plates. Also, furniture parts, handles, spokes, parts for spinning wheels, and many other products were made on these lathes. The majority of the skilled wood turners in this country were located in the New England states. They were men of extraordinary skill. The business and "art" of wood turning was passed on from generation to generation until the early 1800's. At this time the growth of factories and the substitution of machines for skilled craftsmen resulted in a steady decline of the art. In fact, as early as 1569 duplicate part production was attempted on a crude wooden lathe that incorporated a templet tracing device (Fig. 24–4).

Fig. 24–5. Blanchard's profile lathe of 1819.

After the 1850's, other lathes appeared that were designed to do specialized types of work.

The great westward movement stirred by the discovery of gold in California in 1849 created a demand for carriage and wagon wheels. Special hub-turning lathes and automatic spoke-turning machines were developed and manufactured by the Defiance Machine Works of Ohio. The growth of the furniture industry and the need for wooden handles on tools and implements led to the development of other kinds of lathes which were capable of turning out a number of different products rather than just one specialized item. An example of one of these multi-purpose lathes which is still in use today is the back-knife gauge lathe.

One of the first *back-knife lathes* (Fig. 24–6) was developed about 1866 by Mr. G. N. Goodspeed of Winchendon, Massachusetts. In 1880, the Baxter D. Whitney Company designed and introduced a back-knife lathe for the wooden-chair industry. These early machines had many characteristics which have been retained in their modern counterpart.

The early back-knife lathe incorporated a carriage mechanism which moved along the bed. The workpiece was rotated between centers in the same manner as on other kinds of lathes. Knives attached to a bar on the carriage made one or more roughing cuts as the carriage moved toward the drive (spindle) end of the machine. The bar holding the knives was pivoted at one end. As the carriage moved, the knife bar rode on top of a metal templet and the knives roughed out its contour in the work. The final shape was cut into the work by a back knife with a cutting edge ground to the shape desired for the finished turning. It moved downward in a vertical frame and produced a smooth shearing cut. Essentially this is the same way in which present-day back knives function. Refer to Figure 24–23 and page 393 for more information.

The *automatic turning lathe* originated in 1897 when Christian Mattison of Beloit, Wisconsin, obtained a patent on a shear-cutting, multiple-knife cutterhead. The development of these machines is largely credited to his company, the C. Mattison Machine Works, now located in Rockford, Illinois. Automatic turning lathes shape the work with a high speed rotating cutterhead. The *cutterhead* on an automatic lathe of today is still much like the cutterhead used in earlier lathes. The cutterhead is the heart of this kind of lathe. The knives in Mattison's cutterhead were made in sections, each with their cutting edges ground to cut the desired profile. The knives were fastened to a slotted cylinder in such a way that they made a shearing cut. The work was supported between centers on a carriage which moved it into the rotating cutterhead. The workpiece rotated from one to four turns during the complete cutting operation.

The forerunner of the automatic turning lathe constructed by Mattison was made on the order of a saw table with

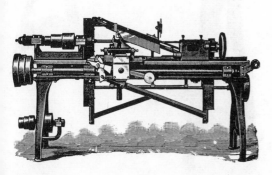

Fig. 24–6. An early belt-driven back-knife lathe manufactured between 1866 and 1912.

Fig. 24-7. One of the forerunners of the modern, automatic shaping lathe. The flat belt pulley spindle drive on the left of the machine rotated the cutterhead at 2400 rpm. One handle at the right was used to move the carriage (holding the stock) against the rotating knives. The other handle was used to revolve the stock during the cut.

an opening large enough to accommodate cutterheads 10 to 24 in. in length. The table was hinged at the rear like the early saw tables. A hand wheel at the front of the machine regulated the depth of cut by raising or lowering the table. The work to be turned was supported in a slide mechanism which moved in grooves in the table. In operation, the slide was pushed forward, moving the stock into the revolving cutterhead. The stock was then revolved by a crank until it was cut to shape.

The *baluster* machine (Fig. 24-7) was another step in the development of the modern automatic turning lathe. This floor-model machine had a swinging carriage to hold the work and advance it into the rotating cutterhead. It was used to turn balusters (vertical spindles of stair and balcony railings), table legs, and the like. The stock was held in square hollow chucks and revolved by hand during the cutting operation. These machines did not carry head- or tail-stocks, but they were later added to the carriage. Eventually a power-drive system was added to rotate the stock while cut-

Fig. 24-8. A light duty speed lathe mounted to a bench.

ting. The rotation stopped automatically when the carriage was in the loading position to receive the next workpiece.

Industrial Lathes and Turning Processes Today

The major kinds of wood-turning lathes today may be grouped as follows: (1) speed and pattern lathes, (2) back-knife lathes, (3) variety lathes, (4) copy lathes, and (5) automatic shaping lathes. There are also other special-purpose lathes which are primarily limited to one particular product such as wooden spools, bobbins, and veneer. The following pages of this unit discuss the most common types of lathes which are being used to produce the majority of our turned-wood products.

On a *speed lathe* (Fig. 24–8 and 24–9) the operator applies the cutting tool to the wood by hand. These lathes are often referred to as *bench lathes,* al-though they may actually be a floor model (Fig. 24–8) as well as a bench or stand model (Fig. 24–9). The speed lathe is most widely used in pattern or model shops, schools, and home workshops. The major parts (Fig. 24–9) of a speed lathe are the bed, the headstock (and drive motor), the tailstock, and the tool rest.

The *size* of all kinds of wood lathes is designated as the maximum diameter of work that may be swung over the bed and the maximum length that may be held between the two centers. Generally, the most common sizes of speed lathes are the 8- and 9-in. light-duty models and the 11-, 12-, and 14-in. models which include the medium- and heavy-duty kinds used in schools and for custom work. The length of stock handled on different-size lathes varies from 24 to 62 in.

The *bed* of larger-model lathes is made of heavy cast iron. The upper surfaces

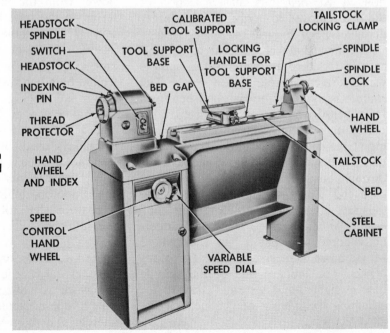

Fig. 24–9. A 12 inch variable speed gap bed lathe.

HEADSTOCK SPINDLE
SWITCH
HEADSTOCK
INDEXING PIN
THREAD PROTECTOR
HAND WHEEL AND INDEX
SPEED CONTROL HAND WHEEL
TOOL SUPPORT BASE
BED GAP
CALIBRATED TOOL SUPPORT
LOCKING HANDLE FOR TOOL SUPPORT BASE
VARIABLE SPEED DIAL
TAILSTOCK LOCKING CLAMP
SPINDLE
SPINDLE LOCK
HAND WHEEL
TAILSTOCK
BED
STEEL CABINET

Fig. 24–10. The indexing mechanism holds the work for reeding and fluting operations.

are machined smooth and are referred to as the "ways." Some light-duty machines are made of tubular steel construction. The bed supports the headstock in a fixed position, as well as the tool rest and the tailstock, both of which may be moved along the bed and clamped at any position. A *gap-bed* lathe has a section of the bed removed to permit turning larger diameters. See Figure 24–9.

The *headstock* is fastened to the left end of the bed. It contains the spindle which drives or rotates the work. The *spindle* is mounted on two ball bearings. It is belt-driven by either a step cone pulley or a variable-speed drive operating from a split V-pulley. On most lathes the spindle is hollow and extends through the headstock. It is threaded at each end. The end extending toward the tailstock is called either the "front end" or the *"inboard end."* This end is internally bored to either a No. 1 or No. 2 Morse taper to receive the live (or spur) center. The inboard end of the spindle has a right hand external thread for attaching faceplates and chucks (Fig. 24–12b).

The *outboard* end of the spindle has external lefthand threads to which is normally fastened a combination hand wheel and faceplate (Fig. 24–12a). On many machines the spindle may be locked by depressing a plunger on the headstock. This feature facilitates changing faceplates. Also, many lathes have an "indexing mechanism" as shown in Figure 24–10. This consists of two rows of holes spaced evenly around the rim of the drive pulley on the spindle. The outer row has 8 holes spaced 45 deg. apart; the inner row has 60 holes spaced 6 deg. apart. The holes may be engaged by a pin to hold the work in one position. The indexing mechanism is used for such jobs as fluting table legs.

The *motor* driving the spindle may be $\frac{1}{3}$, $\frac{1}{2}$, $\frac{3}{4}$, or 1 horsepower depending on the size of the lathe. The motor is located either below the bed (Fig. 24–8 and 24–9) or built into the headstock (Fig. 24–11). The latter type of lathe is often called a *motor-in-head lathe*. The power from the motor is usually transferred to the spindle by V-belts and pulleys. The variable speed lathes (Figs. 24–9 and 24–11) range between 300 and 4000 rpm in speed and are controlled by a hand wheel or lever. The step pulley lathes (Fig. 24–8) generally provide a choice of four different speeds. The actual speed depends upon the size of pulleys used, but as a rule this type does not exceed a spindle speed of 4000 rpm. Some types of lathes have four speed motors built into the headstock. The rotor shaft of the motor serves as the lathe spindle.

The *tailstock* is a heavy casting machined to slide on the bed ways. The tailstock carries the dead center on which the work rotates. The dead center fits into a tapered spindle (Fig. 24–9). The spindle may be adjusted by means of a

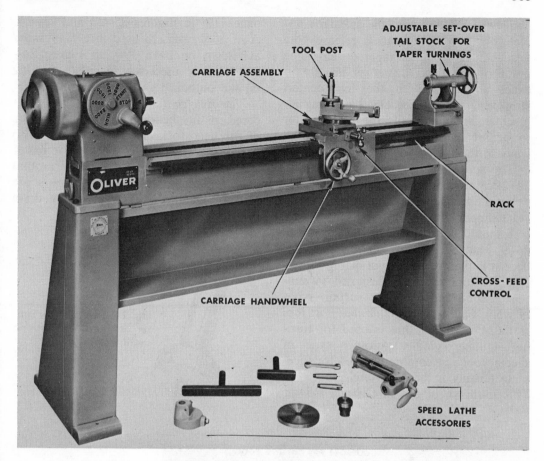

Fig. 24–11. A 12-in. motor-in-head pattern lathe. A motor-driven split pulley is belted to the splindle to produce speeds of 800 to 2750 rpm.

Fig. 24–12. Common lathe accessories: (a) outboard hand wheel; (b) inboard faceplate; (c and d) tool supports; (e) screw chuck; (f) knockout rod; (g) tool support base; (h) spur (live) center; (i) cup (dead) center; and (j) faceplate and hand wheel wrench.

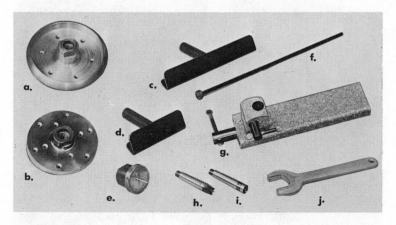

hand wheel. Retracting the spindle completely into the headstock releases the dead center from its tapered seat. The point of the dead center is usually in exact alignment with the live center. However, some tailstocks have an adjustment which permits the dead center to be set over (at right angles to the ways of the lathe) for taper turning.

The *tool rest* (or tool support, Fig. 24–12c and d) is clamped to the bed between the headstock and tailstock. It provides support for the cutting tools. It may be adjusted vertically, swiveled, or (Fig. 24–9) moved to any point along the bed. It is then secured by a clamp. Other types of tool rests are designed to support the cutting tools for certain types of work. One type is the *double post tool rest* (24 in. long) that is used for turning a long spindle. Another type of special tool rest commonly used for faceplate turning is the *right-angle tool rest*. This is shown in use in Chapter 25 on

page 412, in Figures 25–23 and 25–24. Also, tool rests are used in a *floor stand* as shown on page 390, in Figure 24–20. This is used for faceplate turning on the outboard side of the lathe.

The *live center* (Fig. 24–12h) is tapered to fit the opening in the spindle of the headstock. The live center is also called the *spur center* because it has 4 sharpened spurs spaced equally around a conical center. In use, the spurs are forced into the work. Thus they drive the stock to be turned.

Fig. 24–13. A screw center is used for turning small parts.

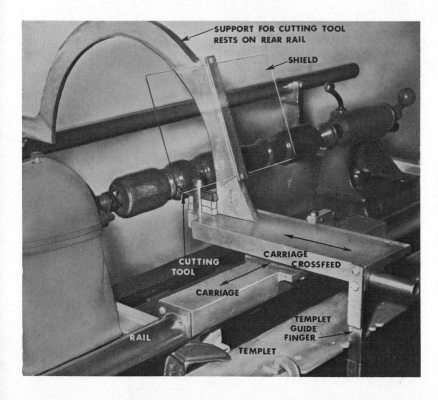

Fig. 24–14. A duplicate parts turning attachment. Note the cutting tool, flat templet, and guide fingers.

Fig. 24–15. The steady rest prevents the work from vibrating during the cut.

The *dead center* (Fig. 24–12i) is tapered and fits into the tailstock spindle. The usual *cup* type has a small center point encircled by a sharp rim. The rim reduces the possibility of splitting the work when the dead center is forced into it. Neither the live center nor the dead center rotates within its respective tapered spindles. They fit so well that the friction between the mating surfaces keeps them from spinning. The dead center serves only as a pivot point. Since it tends to wear its way into the work while in use, it must be kept lubricated.

Ball bearing dead centers are available for wood turning lathes. The center point rotates in a thrust ball bearing. It turns with the work and consequently does not wear its way into it.

The *faceplate* (Fig. 24–12b) is a circular steel disk that is threaded internally to fit on to the inboard end of the drive spindle. Holes are provided in the faceplate so that stock may be fastened to it with wood screws. Faceplates range from 3 to 8 in. in diameter. The *screw chuck* (Fig. 24–12e) is a very small faceplate with a screw center. It is used for turning small workpieces. The stock is normally mounted by turning it onto the screw.

Another device that is often used for the same purpose is the *screw center* (Fig. 24–13). This is tapered to fit into the spindle.

Copy or **duplicating attachments** (Figs. 24–14 and 24–15) are now available to fit most speed lathes. This attachment is used to turn duplicate parts. The cutting tool follows the outline of either a flat templet (Fig. 24–14) or the profile of a previously turned pattern which is mounted in the attachment.

The duplicator has a *carriage* which slides on *rails* parallel to the bed of the lathe. It also moves in and out perpendicularly to the axis of the work. A general-purpose cutting tool is mounted in the tool post of the carriage. The cutting tool is similar in appearance to a cutting bit used in metalworking lathes. A "finger" guides the tool as it follows a templet or the pattern of a workpiece. In use, the operator focuses his attention on the pattern rather than on the workpiece. He moves the carriage manually so that the finger follows the contour of the pattern being duplicated.

The *steady rest* is used when turning long spindles of small diameters between centers. It is fastened to the bed of the

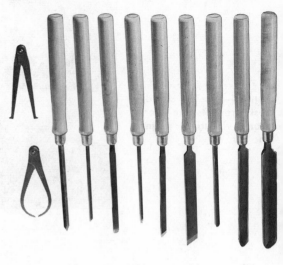

Fig. 24–16. Two common lathe attachments which fit into the tapered opening of either the spindle or tailstock: (a) drill chuck, and (b) sanding drum.

Fig. 24–17. A complete set of turning chisels and an inside and outside calipers.

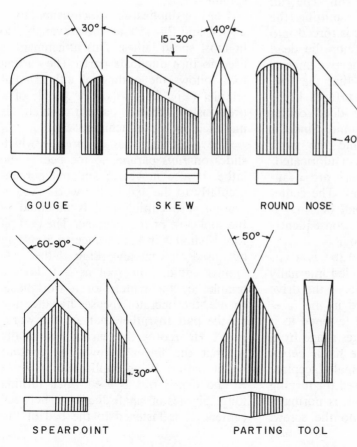

GOUGE   SKEW   ROUND NOSE

SPEARPOINT   PARTING TOOL

Fig. 24–18. This shows the cross-sectional shape, the profile, and the bevel angles of the five basic turning chisels.

lathe and its function is to support the stock opposite the cutter to reduce vibration. Steady rests are made in several different sizes and designs. One example is illustrated in use in Figure 24–15.

Other attachments often used on the lathe include drill chucks (Fig. 24–16a), sanding disks, and sanding drums (Fig. 24–16b). *Drill chucks* have tapered shanks that fit into either the tailstock or the headstock spindle. They are used for such purposes as drilling holes into the ends of turned spindles or in the centers of faceplate work. When mounted in the tailstock they are advanced into the work with the hand wheel. When mounted in the headstock spindle the work is held against and advanced with the tailstock spindle. Sanding drums also have tapered shanks. These fit into the headstock spindle. Sanding disks are threaded and attached to the spindle like faceplates. Grinding wheels, wire brushes, and buffing wheels may also be driven from the headstock spindle, but these as a rule are not widely used.

The *turning chisels* (Figs. 24–17 and 24–18) are used to cut or scrape the rotating stock to shape. They are made of high-grade steel. A tang is fitted into a long hardwood handle. Some are available with tungsten-alloy tips. These have a longer life and may be used for cutting almost any kind of material which can be turned freehand and within the speed range of the wood lathe.

Turning chisels are applied to the wood in such a way that the stock is either cut (Fig. 24–19a) or scraped (Fig. 24–19b) away. These two techniques of using turning tools are commonly referred to as the *cutting* and *scraping* methods of wood turning. As you will experience later, each method has certain advantages and disadvantages. The cutting method is employed on most industrial lathes, but

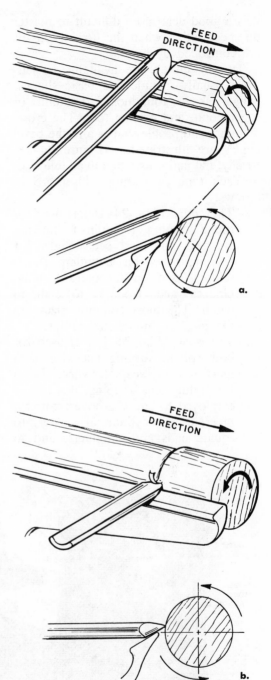

Fig. 24–19. The two methods in which turning chisels are used to give shape to the wood: (a) the cutting method; (b) the scrapping method.

it is a good deal more difficult to master on speed lathes when the turning chisels are controlled by hand.

Turning chisels are available in sets. They usually include five basic shapes: gouge, skew, roundnose, diamond or spear point, and parting tool. The cross-sectional and profile shapes and the bevel angles are illustrated in Figure 24–18. Briefly, the major uses and available sizes of each type of turning chisel are as follows:

1. The *gouge* (Fig. 24–18) is used for rough turning (scraping), making concave cuts, and occasionally for shearing cuts on cylinders. It is seldom used on faceplate turning. Gouges range from ⅛ to 2 in. in width. The most common sizes are the ¼-, ½-, and ¾-in. widths.

2. The *skew* (Fig. 24–18) is used for both spindle turning (between centers) and for faceplate work. Useful for cutting and scraping, this tool is employed to cut V-grooves, convex, tapered, and cylindrical shapes, to square ends and shoulders, and to scrape flat surfaces. In some cases, skews are bevel-ground only on one side. Such chisels are designated either right or left skews, as appropriate. Skew chisels range from ⅛ to 1½ in. in width. The ½- and 1-in. sizes are most widely used.

3. The *round nose* (Fig. 24–18) is a scraping tool. It is widely used for scraping convex forms in faceplate and spindle turnings. They range from ⅛ to ¾ in. in width.

4. The *spear point* (Fig. 24–18) is essentially a combination of a right- and left-hand skew. It is used as a scraping tool to shape small convex beads, V-grooves, and flat surfaces. The most common size is ½ in. in width.

5. The *parting tool* (Fig. 24–18) is also referred to as the cut-off tool. As these names indicate, the tool is used for cutting off, turning to a diameter and for making small grooves. The parting tool may be used to cut shoulders, but it does not make a smooth cut because it is

TOOL REST

PORTABLE FLOOR STAND

Fig. 24–20. This large pattern lathe has a 96-inch inboard swing and a 104-inch outboard swing. Note the stand and tool rest at the outboard end. Also notice that the headstock, ways and carriage, and the tailstock are on independent columns.

primarily a scraping tool. The cutting edge is about ⅛ or ³⁄₁₆ in. in width.

Pattern lathes (Figs. 24–11 and 24–20) are basically the same as speed lathes in that single-point cutting tools are controlled by hand. The essential differences are: (1) they are much larger in size, (2) they employ special cutting tools (Fig. 24–21), which are mounted in a tool post, and (3) they have a movable carriage mechanism on which the tool post is mounted. Pattern lathes are used in shops that specialize in turning wooden patterns to be used in making metal castings in foundries. Smaller sizes of pattern lathes like the one shown in Figure 24–11 are found in some school shops. With the carriage removed and with the appropriate attachments, the pattern lathe may serve as a speed lathe.

In general, the swing on pattern lathes ranges from 12 to 104 in. These lathes are capable of handling stock from 4 to 62 ft. in length. The larger pattern lathes have faceplate attachments up to 38 in. in diameter. Pattern lathes are driven by ¾ to 5-hp motors. Spindle speeds range from 600 to 2750 rpm.

The *carriage* of the pattern lathe is similar in operation and function to that of the engine lathe used in metalworking. They do not have power-driven carriages as do metalworking lathes. However, this feature is available on some models. The carriage moves along the upper ways of the bed. It is activated by a hand wheel on the front (apron) of the carriage. This turns a pinion gear that meshes in a rack (a straight gear) which extends the length of the bed. The carriage also has a *cross slide*. This operates by means of a screw mechanism that is also controlled by hand. The cross slide moves the cutting tool into the work.

The large pattern lathe shown in Fig-

Fig. 24–21. Special turning tools used in the tool post of pattern lathes.

ure 24–20 is called a *universal turning lathe*. The headstock, tailstock, and bed and carriage are individual units which may be mounted at any location on the heavy cast-iron *sole* plate. The sole plate has "T" slots running both crosswise and lengthwise. The movable bed and carriage column may be positioned so that it may be used for faceplate turning on the inboard side of the headstock. In this position, the bed is perpendicular to its normal position.

Back-knife lathes (Figs. 24–22 and 24–23) are production machines which are used to turn spindles of any predetermined shape in large quantities. Modern lathes of this type are greatly improved over the earlier models shown in Figure 24–6, on page 381. However, the basic principle of operation is essentially the same. The major functioning parts of a back-knife lathe are shown in Figure 24–23.

In general, the size of back-knife lathes range in turning capacities from 3 to 20 in. to 3 by 50 in. They are V-belt driven by 10-hp motors and have 12 different spindle speeds, from 1600 to 7200 rpm.

Back-knife lathes are capable of turning up to ten pieces per minute. This

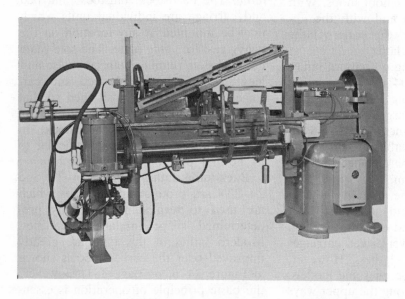

Fig. 24–22. Modern air hydraulic back-knife lathe: (a) front view with hopper feed attachments. (b) Rear view of machine showing the knife bar and sash.

rate is based on turnings of 8- to 10-in. lengths. It is proportionately less with longer pieces. Automatic hopper feeding devices (Fig. 24–22a) coupled with a combination of electric and pneumatic controls have been incorporated in the construction of these lathes since 1955. These new features are responsible for the increased output and overall efficiency of the modern back-knife lathe.

The steps involved in completing a turned article on these machines are performed automatically. They include the following:

1. The blank drops from a hopper onto a centering mechanism. The stock is carried in this device (by an air cylinder) to a position that is in line with the head and tailstock spindle centers.

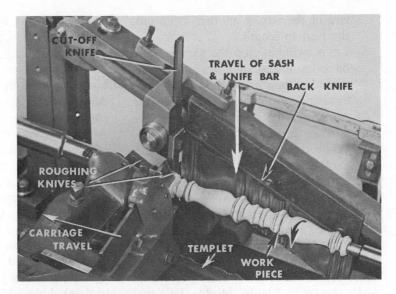

Fig. 24–23. Functioning parts of a modern back-knife lathe.

Fig. 24–24. A circular back-knife lathe with air-hydraulic controls.

2. The headstock is moved in by another cylinder and instantly "dogs" the blank as the centering device is retracted.

3. As the blank turns between the lathe centers, a hydraulic cylinder (Fig. 24–22b) feeds the carriage at a rate between 0 and 40 fpm. The carriage knives (Fig. 24–23) make a rough-ing cut as they follow the contours of the steel templet (Fig. 24–23).

4. Immediately after the knives have made the roughing cut, the back knife moves into the work to produce the finished shape. This back knife is so shaped and attached to the sash knife bar (at a 20-deg. angle) that it makes a shearing cut. At the

end of the stroke another knife cuts the part to length.

5. Limit switches stop the carriage and back knife and they are quickly returned to their original positions. The headstock automatically releases the work and the operator removes the finished turning.

6. While this turning was being made, another blank had moved onto the centering device ready for the next cycle.

To produce different shaped turnings with back-knife lathes, different templets and back knives are required.

A variation of the back-knife lathe described above is the *circular back-knife lathe* shown in Figure 24–24. This machine incorporates a pneumatically fed carriage and templet-controlled knives similar to those of the standard back-knife lathe. The major differences in this machine are the method used to center the stock and the circular knives used

to cut the blank to shape.

The operator places one end of the blank into a ring die opening and aligns the other end with a screw chuck. The blank is held by the operator until he depresses the starting button which engages the stock with the screw chuck. As the carriage moves forward a roughing knife cuts off the corners of the blank and sizes it to fit the hole of the die. A gouge or a circular back knife (controlled by the templet) cuts the stock to its final shape. At the end of the feed stroke of the carriage, another knife (activated by an air cylinder) cuts the stock to finished length.

Variety lathes (Fig. 24–25) are industrial machines that are used to produce items of small sizes, such as golf tees, wooden checkers, small balls or beads, chair plugs, and many other fancy or decorative items. Variety lathes can produce turnings up to 1½ in. in diameter by 3 in. in length. Production rates vary

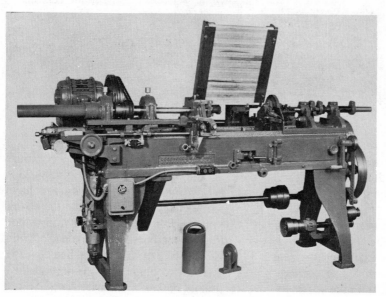

Fig. 24–25. Air operated hopper-fed variety lathe is used to produce small turnings such as golf tees. Production rates from 30 to 100 pieces per minute are possible.

from 1800 to 6000 pieces per hour depending upon the size, species of wood, and shape of the turning to be made.

Lathes of this type are fully automatic. The stock is transferred from a hopper. One end fits into a screw chuck (on the revolving spindle) and the other end fits into the bell shaped opening of a ring die. The sliding headstock advances the blank horizontally into the ring die. The drive pulley shaft is hollow. The spindle slides through the shaft. A key fastened to the shaft rides in a keyway in the spindle and transmits the rotary motion to it. The maximum speed of the spindle is 6000 rpm. It is driven by a 5-hp motor.

The cutting tools, called forming knives, are milled to the desired shape of the turning. The turnings are cut to exact lengths by small saws or other types of special cut-off attachments. These special cut-off devices produce rounded ends on the work, cut cupped ends on golf tees, or cut tenons on handles and similar items.

An air operated sliding head feeds the rotating blank a certain distance horizontally. The part is turned, cut off, and the blank is advanced again for another cycle. A special attachment is used to bore holes in the turnings when necessary. This device will bore up to a 2¾-in. maximum depth. After the last piece has been turned from a blank, the sliding head retracts and a new blank is taken from the hopper and the cycle is started again. One operator may feed up to 6 of these machines.

Copy lathes (not illustrated) are high production machines that are used to produce turned items in large quantities. They are made in a wide variety of sizes and types. Most of the copy lathes used in this country are foreign imports. Copy lathes generally have larger turning capacities than variety lathes. Typical work produced by these machines includes ta-

pered furniture legs and brush handles. These lathes are also capable of turning and boring simultaneously to produce articles with a hole at one end.

Copy lathes are either semiautomatic or fully automatic in operation. With semiautomatic machines, the operator positions each workpiece in a centering device and then it is clamped between the centers by a hydraulic system. Fully automatic copy lathes take piece after piece from a hopper. In both types of machines, the work is shaped by two knives (one roughing and one smoothing) attached to a templet-controlled carriage. The templet, made of metal, is previously cut to the profile shape desired for the turnings. The speed of the carriage travel is variable between 0 and 40 fpm. With the completion of the turning operation, the carriage returns at a much faster rate. As the carriage returns, both knives disengage and the workpiece is unclamped automatically. On semiautomatic machines, the operator must remove the completed turning; with fully automatic machines, the lathe ejects the workpieces. The output rate ranges up to 1800 pieces per hour depending upon the length, diameter, etc., of the work.

Automatic turning lathes (Figs. 24–26 and 24–27) are high production machines used to produce almost any conceivable shape that may be turned between two centers. Today's automatic lathes, for example, turn out an average of three baseball bats or furniture legs every minute, about 150 bowling pins per hour. Automatic turning lathes are also referred to as automatic *shaping lathes*, because they embody a high speed rotating cutterhead which carries knives shaped to cut the desired pattern.

The *capacity* of automatic lathes is generally stock from ¾ to 5 in. in diameter by 42 to 46 in. in length. Modern automatic lathes have either hydraulic, pneumatic, or electrically operated carriages and tailstocks. They also feature automatic stock centering devices and steady rests. Attachments are available for hopper feeding, automatic drilling, and special-purpose chucking. In production setups, the operator merely loads the hopper with blanks (Fig. 24–27) and the automatic cycling system of the machine does the rest. It centers the workpiece, engages it with the rotating knives, and ejects the finished turning.

The *cutterhead* is either square (Fig. 24–28), hexagonal, octagonal, or round (Fig. 24–29). It has slots machined into it to which the knives or special knife holders are mounted. The knives are placed in the cutterhead so that they shape the work with a shearing cutting action. For example, knives in a cutterhead set to turn a taper will shear the stock from the highest point (the largest diameter of the taper) toward the lowest point (the smallest diameter).

Although the cutterhead appears relatively complicated, it is designed to make only three basic kinds of cuts. These are: (1) the bead or convex cut, (2) the cove

Fig. 24–26. An operator removing a turned bowling pin from an automatic turning lathe. Note the horizontal rods and vertical stops below the operator's hand. These are used to locate the blank workpiece in line with the lathe centers.

or concave cut, and (3) the straight cut. All wood turnings are made up of these three principal cuts in different combinations. Therefore, the manner in which

Fig. 24–27. Here one operator attends two automatic hopper-fed shaping lathes with a production output of 700 turned table legs per hour. Note the air exhaust system attached to each machine to remove shavings.

Fig. 24–28. This Early American pattern requires ground-to-pattern knives, (attached to the knife carriers) for each differently shaped part of the turning.

the knives are placed in the cutterhead is determined by the shape of the pattern. The more intricate the pattern, the greater the number of knives that must be used to minimize any tearing and chipping of the workpiece. An example of a cut-

terhead of this type is shown in Figure 24–28. Compare this to the cutterhead in Figure 24–29 designed for a bowling pin. It is a relatively simple pattern made up of a concave and convex cut. It should be noted that the cutterhead must be

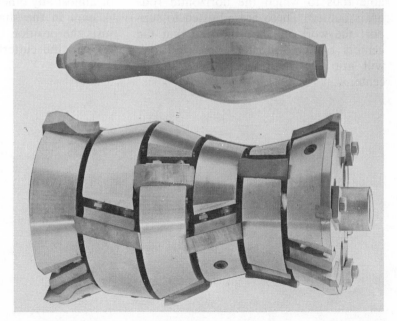

Fig. 24–29. A closeup of a round cutterhead for an automatic turning lathe. This particular cutterhead has three (corrugated back) knives to cut each differently shaped part of the bowling pin.

perfectly balanced to eliminate vibration. A change in pattern is made quickly by slipping the cutterhead off the arbor and sliding on a different one.

The *base* of the machine is of very heavy cast-iron construction to make it rigid. The *cutterhead arbor* is constructed of high-quality steel and rotates at 2700 to 3600 rpm. It is normally $2\frac{5}{8}$ in. in diameter, and varies in length depending upon the size of the machine. The arbor is belt-driven by either 10-, 15-, or 20-hp motors.

The *carriage* contains the headstock and tailstock. The *headstock* and *tailstock* are both power-driven by one $1\frac{1}{2}$-hp, two-speed, reversible motor. It has a system of gearing or belt-driven shafts that revolve the stock at any one of 8 preset speeds between 2 and 30 rpm. The rate at which the stock revolves is actually the feed rate of the machine. Normally, the headstock and tailstock both have live spur centers. The stock centering device consists of two horizontal rods with adjustable stops and two vertically adjustable rods to which the horizontal rods are mounted. These are adjusted to support the work in a position so that the centers of the headstock and tailstock will grip the workpiece exactly in the center.

The tailstock is equipped with a hydraulic or air-operated cylinder with about a 1-in. stroke. The tailstock is clamped in position, according to the length of the stock, so that the stroke is sufficient to grip the work. The spur center of the tailstock spindle is advanced by the cylinder. This also engages the spur center of the headstock in the workpiece.

The carriage moves the work into the cutterhead by means of another cylinder. The stroke length of the carriage is preset with adjustable stops to provide the desired depth of cut. The carriage and tailstock operate automatically.

The tailstock retracts its center and releases the turning. The carriage returns to the loading position and engages another blank from the hopper. A toothed clutch mechanism on the headstock and tailstock operates a cam trip lever to stop and start the stock rotation as the carriage moves in and out. With cam attachments, automatic turning lathes can produce turnings with square, octagon, or almost any other cross-sectional shape. A cam in the shape of the pattern adjusts the position of the work with reference to the cutterhead.

Chapter 25   Wood Turning Processes
in the School Shop

The speed lathe and a standard set of hand turning chisels are used for most wood turning operations in the school shop. The two basic types of work produced on the lathe are spindle- and faceplate turnings. In *spindle turning,* the stock is rotated between centers and the chisels are applied to shape the work by either the *scraping or the cutting* method. Typical spindle turnings include table or chair legs, baseball bats, and similar, long, slender, cylindrical shapes. In *faceplate turning,* the stock is held to the faceplate (by screws) and the chisels are applied to shape the work by the *scraping method exclusively.* Examples of faceplate work include bowls, lamp bases, and similar disk-shaped objects.

The **selection of turning woods** is definitely related to successful lathe performance because, by nature, some wood species have better turning characteristics than others. For example, softwoods are not always the easiest to turn. They are less dense than hardwoods and when turned by the scraping method, the shaped surfaces will be rough and splintered and will require considerable sanding to make them smooth. Softwoods should be turned by the cutting method.

Hardwoods generally turn much better than softwoods by either method. Walnut is one of the best species for turning. Beech, mahogany, cherry, and maple are other good choices. Refer to pages 24–25 for a table showing the various qualities of most wood species.

Safety Precautions for Lathe Work

1. Assure that loose clothing such as shirts and aprons are tight or tucked in, ties are removed, and dangling sleeve ends are either buttoned down or rolled up. It would be hazardous if clothing should catch in the revolving work.
2. *Always* wear approved safety goggles or a face shield for protection against flying chips and shavings.
3. Check the condition of the stock. Be sure that it is free from knots, checked ends, improperly cured glue joints or other conditions which may cause parts of it to fly out of the lathe.
4. In mounting the work, be sure that it is well centered and balanced in the lathe. For faceplate work first

TABLE 25–1
WOOD TURNING LATHE SPEEDS

Dia. of Work.	Roughing	General Cutting	Finishing
Under 2″ dia.	900 to 1300 R.P.M.	2400 to 2800	3000 to 4000
2″ to 4″ dia.	800 to 1000 R.P.M.	1800 to 2400	2400 to 3000
4″ to 6″ dia.	600 to 800 R.P.M.	1200 to 1800	1800 to 2400
6″ to 8″ dia.	400 to 600 R.P.M.	800 to 1200	1200 to 1800
8″ to 10″ dia.	300 to 400 R.P.M.	600 to 800	900 to 1200
Over 10″ dia.	300	300 to 600	600 to 900

band-saw the stock to a round shape before mounting it. This avoids excessive vibration and the hazards presented by the rotating corners. With a plane or saw, remove the corners of spindles which are larger than 2 in. square.

5. Lubricate the end of spindle stock which spins on the dead center. This minimizes frictional heat and burning. This is not necessary if ball-bearing dead centers are used.

6. Keep the tool rest adjusted as close as possible (⅛ in.) to the stock. This supports the chisel near its cutting edge and reduces vibration, chattering, and the possibility of the chisel being wrenched from your hand.

7. Always rotate the stock by hand before starting the lathe to ensure that the stock will not jam against the tool rest.

8. Keep your attention focused on the turning operation. One unintentional shift of the turning chisel may cause it to be caught in the stock and thrown from your grip. It may also ruin the workpiece.

9. Keep the turning chisels sharp. Turning necessitates frequent conditioning of the cutting edges. Refer to p. 584 for the procedures pertaining to grinding and whetting lathe chisels.

10. Start all lathe jobs at a slow-spindle speed until the stock has been turned to its rough shape. Then change to higher speeds. As a rule: the larger the diameter of the stock, the slower the spindle speed. See Table 25–1

11. Periodically during the turning operation, stop the machine and readjust the tool rest. Also check the dead center. If you are faceplate-turning, check the screws holding the work for tightness.

12. When stopping the lathe, let the work coast to a standstill. *Never* grab the stock with your hand to slow it down. This may cause slivers, or burns or it may tear flesh from your hand.

13. Use a steady rest for long thin turnings. Otherwise the stock may chatter or break from the pressure of the cutting tool.

14. Remove the tool rest for sanding or finishing on the lathe. *Do not* hold sandpaper or rags wrapped around the work. If they should grab, your fingers might be torn off. It is safer to fold abrasives or rags into a pad and hold them against the surface at one point.

15. *Caution!* The speed on some variable speed lathes can only be adjusted when they are in operation. Therefore, when turning off the power on

this type of lathe, at the completion of the job, be sure to adjust the lathe to its slowest speed. Thus, when the next person uses the machine it will be at a safe speed for any kind of work.

16. Always use the scraping method when faceplate-turning. Never use a gouge for internal turning.

Work speeds primarily depend upon the diameter of the workpiece being turned. In general, the higher speeds produce the best results for finish turning. Slow speeds should be used to work the stock down to cylindrical or rough shape. The recommended lathe speeds for spindle and faceplate turning are given in Table 25–1.

When using lathes with belted drives, the spindle speed must be set by shifting the belt to pulleys of the correct size. Remember that the combination of a large motor pulley and a small spindle pulley produces a fast speed; a small motor pulley and a large spindle pulley results in slower speeds. To determine the actual spindle speed of belt-driven lathes, use the following formula:

$$\text{Spindle Speed} = \frac{\text{Motor rpm} \times \text{Dia. of Motor Pulley}}{\text{Dia. of Spindle Pulley}}$$

Spindle Turning Processes

All turned spindles consist of any one or a combination of three basic profile shapes: (1) *straight* (or tapered), (2) *convex* (or beads), and (3) *concave* or coves). Therefore, any specified profile may be turned by applying the knowledge and skills necessary to turn these three profile shapes. For the beginning wood turner, it is recommended that these shapes be turned on a practice piece (Fig. 25–1) and that both the scraping and cutting methods be employed to turn each shape.

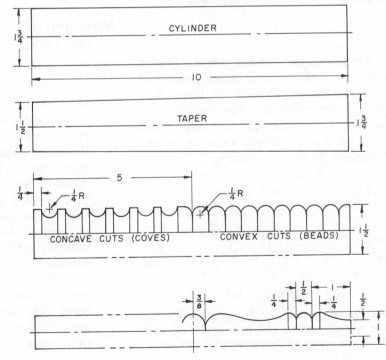

Fig. 25–1. A turning exercise. Shape all the profiles shown from one piece of stock. Use the scraping and cutting method on half of each exercise.

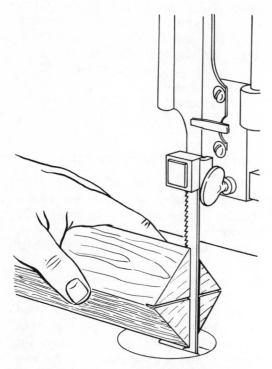

Fig. 25–2. Band sawing diagonals in hardwood for the spurs of the live center.

Preparing the turning blank. Ensure that the stock is approximately square in cross section and about ¼ in. larger than the greatest diameter specified for the turning. Square the ends and allow about 1 in. extra in the length for squaring and trimming the finished turning in the lathe.

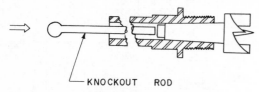

KNOCKOUT   ROD

Fig. 25–3. Removing the spur center from the spindle with a soft iron knock out rod. Hold the center so that it will not fall out.

Locate the centers by marking diagonals on each end. For hardwoods, drill a ⅛ in. hole ¼ in. deep at the intersections (softwood may be merely punched with a scratch awl or nail). Make saw kerfs on the diagonal lines ⅛ in. deep on the headstock end of the workpiece. This may be done with either a backsaw, or with the band saw as shown in Figure 25–2.

If the turning block is over 2 in. square, remove the corners (with a plane or saw), transforming it to an octagonal shape. Remove the spur center from the headstock spindle as shown in Figure 25–3. Set the stock on end and drive the spur center into the stock (on the diagonal lines or saw cuts) with a mallet as shown in Figure 25–4. Do not use a hammer for this job, as this will eventually "mushroom" the tapered end of the spur center and cause a poor fit inside the spindle.

Mounting the Stock in the Lathe

1. Loosen the clamps at the bases of the tailstock and the tool rest.
2. Hold the turning blank and the spur center together and insert the tapered end of the center into the headstock spindle.
3. Hold the stock so the spur center remains "seated." Slide the tailstock into position until the point of the dead center enters the hole made in the end of the workpiece. Lock the tailstock to the bed at this position.
4. Advance the dead center into the workpiece with the tailstock hand wheel while rotating the stock by hand. The rim of the dead center need only be forced into the wood to a depth of about ¹⁄₁₆ in. to seat it

adequately. Avoid forcing it in too deeply.

*5. Retract the dead center and apply some soap, wax or a few drops of oil (too much stains the wood) to lubricate it. This is essential in order to minimize friction and burning of the stock.

6. Advance the tailstock spindle (as before) until the dead center is pressed firmly against the wood. Lock the tailstock spindle.

7. Move the tool rest into position so the first cuts may be made on the workpiece at the tailstock end. Adjust the tool rest so it is parallel to and ⅛ in. from the work and about the same height as the lathe centers (or ⅛ in. above). Rotate the stock by hand to assure that the corners will not strike the tool rest. See Figure 25–5.

8. Check the lathe speed. If necessary, adjust it for the appropriate roughing speed as given in Table 25–1 on page 400.

9. Check all clamping devices. Be sure that the cutting edges of the chisels are sharpened for the work at hand.

Rough turning (Fig. 25–6) is the process of transforming the workpiece from a square (or octagon) to a round cross-sectional shape. Use a large gouge and employ the *cutting method* as described below:

1. Stand to one side and turn on the lathe.

2. Grasp the handle of the gouge firmly in the right hand with the palm down. Hold the blade on the tool rest with the left hand as shown in Figure 25–6. Note that this illustration shows the left wrist bent so that the outside of the little finger slides

---
* Omit this step if a ball-bearing dead center is used.

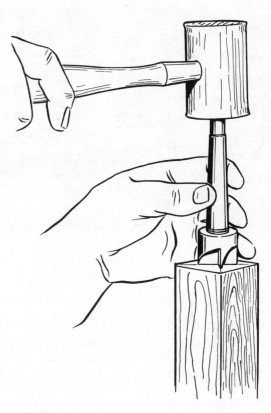

Fig. 25–4. Seating the spur center in the stock with a mallet.

along the front of the tool rest. The gouge is rolled (on its convex surface) to the right. The handle should

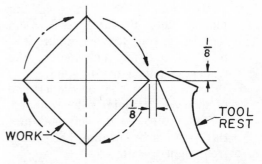

Fig. 25–5. End view showing the adjustment of the tool rest in relation to the work.

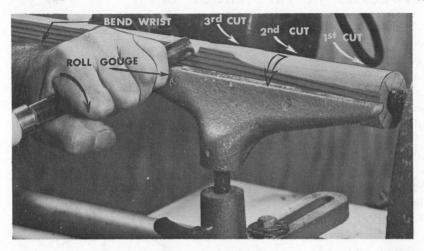

Fig. 25-6. Rough cutting with a gouge. Note the position of hand with wrist bent and little finger against tool rest.

be lower than the cutting edge. The depth of cut is controlled by raising or lowering the handle, using the tool rest as the fulcrum point.

3. Start the first cut 2 or 3 in. from the end of the work near the dead center. Slowly raise the handle to bring the cutting edge of the chisel into the rotating work. The cutting edge should be tangent to the rotating surface.

4. Take a light cut by sliding the gouge along the tool rest parallel to the center axis of the work. Complete the stroke, cutting off the end of the work with a follow through motion.

5. Start the second cut above 2 or 3 in. to the left of the first cut. Feed from left to right as before. Progressively remove the corners in this manner until all but 2 to 3 in. of the work is rounded. See Figure 25-6. Short roughing cuts reduce the tendency of the stock to splinter.

6. When only 2 or 3 in. on the left end of the work remain to be rounded, roll the gouge to the left and turn this portion by feeding the gouge from right to left.

7. As the work approaches a cylindrical shape, stop the lathe and readjust the tool rest to within ⅛ in. of the work. This must be done from time to time as the diameter of the work is continually made smaller.

8. Always work toward the ends of the workpiece. Attempting to start a cut at the end of a workpiece is dangerous because the chisel will usually catch and chip it or be forced from your hands.

9. Continue rough-turning until the stock is round and within ⅛ in. of final diameter. Stop the lathe to check the diameter with an outside caliper.

Laying out spindle work (Figs. 25-7 and 25-8a) that involves a combination of different shapes may be done in sev-

Fig. 25-7. Using a half section pattern to mark the locations of cuts on a cylinder.

eral ways. First, turn the stock to cylindrical shape. Indicate where shoulders or other necessary sizing cuts should be made by transferring the dimensions from the drawing and marking them off along the length of the workpiece with a ruler and a pencil. Make the pencil marks about ½ in. in length so they will be visible when the work is rotating. Turn on the power and touch the pencil point to the rotating workpiece to mark the lines around the circumference of the stock.

For *laying out duplicate turnings* construct and use either a *half-section pattern* as shown in Figure 25–7 or a *layout board* similar to the one shown in Figure 25–8a. Both of these devices mark the work while it is rotating under power.

Turning straight or tapered cylinders to specified dimensions requires the use of the parting tool, outside calipers, and the skew chisel.

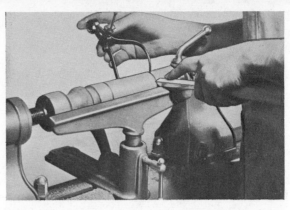

Fig. 25–9. Making sizing cuts with the parting chisel while checking the size with the outside calipers.

1. Set the lathe for the proper cutting speed. See Table 25–1, page 400.
2. Set the calipers about ⅟₁₆ in. larger than the specified diameter.
3. With the parting tool in one hand and the calipers in the other make "sizing cuts" at several locations along the length of the work (Fig. 25–9). When turning tapers, cut two grooves at the locations of the largest and smallest diameters. If deep grooves are required, make them a little wider than the cutting edge to reduce friction (See Fig. 25–11a).
4. Remove the excess stock between the sizing cuts with a gouge as in rough turning.
5. Turn cylinders or tapers to finished size with the skew chisel. Employ either the scraping or cutting method. *Scraping* (Fig. 25–10a) is the easiest, but it produces a rough surface and dulls the cutting edge quickly. *Cutting with the skew* (Fig. 25–10b) produces a smooth surface, but requires practice. Hold the tool high on the work and tilted so the handle is approximately at 60 deg. to the axis of the work. *Always* keep the blade supported on the tool rest. Hold the skew so that the cutting is done close to the heel of the

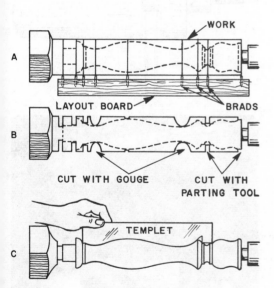

Fig. 25–8. Steps in making a turning: (a) marking the stock with a layout board, (b) sizing cuts rough out the shape, (c) checking the profile with a templet.

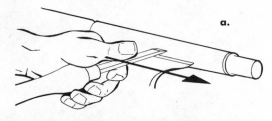

Fig. 25–10. Straight turning with the skew chisel: (a) scraping method; (b) cutting method.

chisel. When turning tapers, always feed the chisel from the large diameter toward the small diameter (Fig. 25–10a). Cut until a straightedge connects the previously made sizing cuts.

Shoulder cutting and squaring or trimming the ends of cylinders may be accomplished by either the scraping (Fig. 25–11b) or the cutting method (Fig. 25–12). The latter is more difficult for beginners; but cutting produces a smoother surface and should be employed whenever the surface will be visible on the finished product. For invisible surfaces, the *scraping method* should be utilized. Use the parting or skew chisel as shown in Figures 25–11a and 25–11b. This is easier and more accurate for jobs such as making the shoulders of turned tenons or for cutting off the ends of table legs, and other work in which

smooth shoulder cuts are not essential.

To employ the *cutting method* for turning shoulders, first work the stock to within $\frac{1}{16}$ in. of the required dimensions with the gouge and parting tool. Make the final finishing cut with the toe of the skew as shown in Figure 25–12a. Make the finishing cut on the horizontal surface with the heel of the skew by making a cut as shown in Figure 25–12b.

Cutting off stock in the lathe (Figs. 25–11a and 25–13) is an operation required for many turning jobs. First, work the diameter down to $\frac{3}{8}$ or $\frac{1}{4}$ in., cutting on the waste side of the layout line. Use either the scraping or cutting method as dictated by the nature of the job. *Adjust the lathe to its slowest speed.*

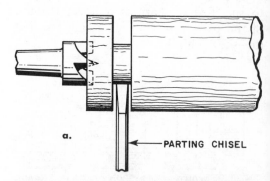

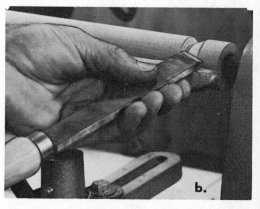

Fig. 25–11. (a) Cutting off and (b) scraping a shoulder with a skew chisel.

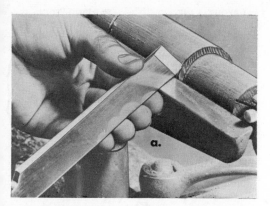

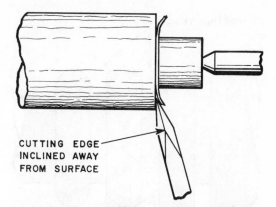

CUTTING EDGE
INCLINED AWAY
FROM SURFACE

Fig. 25–12. Making a shoulder by the cutting method with a skew: (a) squaring and trimming the shoulder. Artists sketch shows the top view of this operation. (b) smoothing the inside corner with the heel of the skew.

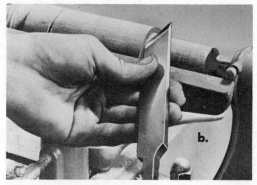

Hold the chisel in one hand and place the other hand in position (under the workpiece). Catch it as the chisel separates it from the waste stub (Fig. 25–13).

Convex profiles (beads) may be scraped with the skew or spear-point chisel as shown in Figure 25–14. They may be made with the skew by the cutting method.

When cutting convex shapes, first make grooves at each end of the bead with the parting or skew chisel as shown in Figures 25–14 and 25–15a. Several diagonal cuts will be necessary before a V-groove can be made with the skew. Shape the beads by cutting off the corners with the heel of the skew (Fig. 25–15b). Start the cut at the top of the bead. Hold the skew as when turning a cylinder by the cutting method. As the cut begins, raise the handle slowly, and simultaneously roll the chisel into a vertical

position while pushing it into the bottom of the groove. Support the skew on the tool rest throughout the cut. Each half

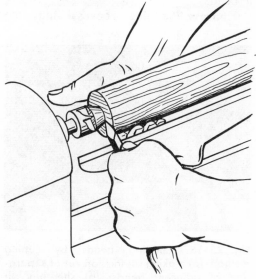

Fig. 25–13. Cutting off stock in the lathe.

PARTING TOOL CUTS

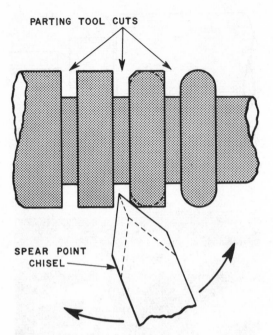

Fig. 25–14. Top view showing beads being shaped by the scraping method with the spear point chisel.

of a bead must be cut separately by this process. The skew handle should be held in the left hand to turn the right half of a bead.

Concave profiles (coves) may be

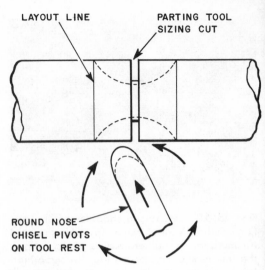

Fig. 25–16. Top view showing how a round nose chisel is applied to form a cove by the scraping method.

scraped with the roundnose chisel. For wide coves, it is often helpful to make a "sizing cut" with the parting chisel, cutting to within ⅛ in. of the required diameter at the center of the cove (Fig. 25–16). Hold the blade of the round-nose chisel flat on the tool rest. Advance it to the work, and simultaneously move the handle in a horizontal arc while

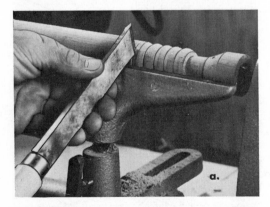

Fig. 25–15. Shaping beads by cutting method: (a) making an incision cut at separation of adjacent beads; (b) shearing cut finishes each half of bead profile.

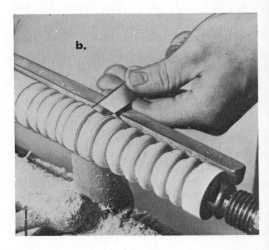

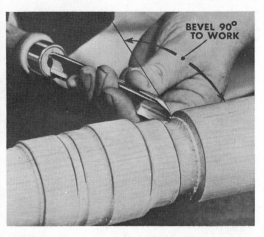

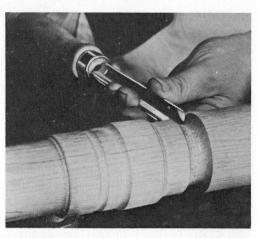

Fig. 25–17. Using the gouge to finish turn a cove by the cutting method: (a) starting the cut.

(b) Rolling the gouge to finish half of a cove.

pivoting the blade on the tool rest. The cutting edge will sweep in a small horizontal arc to shape the cove (Fig. 25–16). Finish with two light cuts, one from each side toward the center of the cove.

Concave shapes may be *cut* with the gouge after they are roughed out by scraping with the roundnose chisel. Start the cut by holding the gouge on its side as shown in Figure 25–17a. The bevel of the gouge should be at 90 deg. to the axis of the work. Make a thin shearing cut by rolling the gouge (Fig. 25–

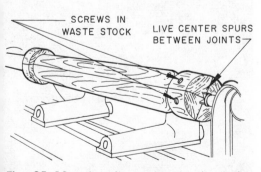

Fig. 25–18. A split turning in the lathe. Note locations of spurs in the work and screws in waste stock.

17b) so the cutting point moves in an arc toward the bottom of the cove. Cut each half of the cove separately, starting at the top and ending at the bottom.

Split turnings are half (or quarter) sections of turned spindles. They are made by splitting a cylindrical turning lengthwise after it has been turned to the desired shape. There are a number of uses for this class of lathe work such as making half round moldings, decorative parts, or sometimes split construction is advantageous for wiring long lamp stems and similar jobs.

To make a split turning, fit and glue two pieces of stock together with a piece of *heavy kraft paper* in the joint. Allow the glue to cure thoroughly. For some work, it is a good idea to make the blank long enough so that screws may be inserted near the ends for added strength and safety. Drill holes in each end of the blank for the center points. Position the spurs as shown in Figure 25–18. After the stock has been turned, remove it from the lathe and part it by tapping the edge of a butt chisel into the paper-glue joint.

Faceplate Turning

Faceplate work is done on either the inboard or outboard side of the lathe. *Inboard* turning is most common. In this class of work, stock from 4 or 5 in. in diameter up to the maximum diameter permitted by the swing of the lathe is turned on standard faceplates (Figs. 25–19a and 25–20). Smaller diameters (generally less than 4 in.) are usually turned on screw centers (Fig. 20–19b). The turning chisels are supported on the tool rest (or right-angle rest) clamped to the bed of the lathe. Since the dead center is not used to support faceplate work, move the tailstock to the far right end of the bed.

When the diameter of the work is too large to be turned on the inboard side of the lathe, it is fastened to a special faceplate or to the hand wheel and turned on the *outboard* side of the lathe. NOTE: Turning discs over 18 in. in diameter is hazardous. Centrifugal force can tear the work apart. If such large pieces must be turned, batten strips should be screwed at right angles to the grain on the back side of the piece. In turning, use the slowest speed. *Do not stand in line with the revolving piece and warn others to stand clear.* Wear a face shield. In *outboard turning,* the chisels are supported on a tool rest mounted in a portable floor stand as shown in Figure 25–25.

The basic operations for turning are essentially the same in both inboard and outboard work. Preparing the stock for faceplate work usually involves the following procedure:

1. Select stock that is at least ¼ in. larger than each dimension of the finished article.
2. True one surface.
3. Locate the center of this face and lay out a circle with a diameter ¼

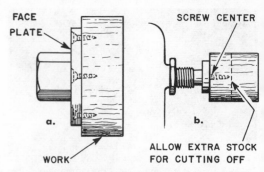

Fig. 25–19. Direct mounting: (a) on a standard faceplate; (b) on a screw center.

Fig. 25–20. Fastening the faceplate to a backing block which is in turn glued to the prepared workpiece with paper in the glue joint. The paper facilitates removing the backing block after the turning is completed.

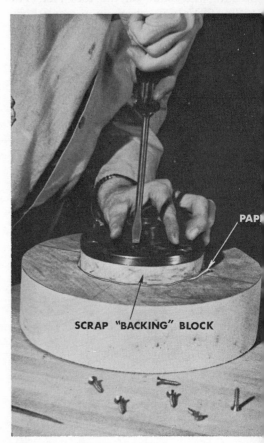

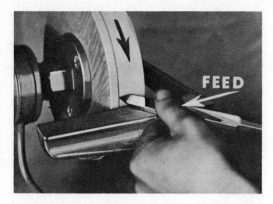

Fig. 25–21. Truing the edge with a spear point chisel. Note the right angle tool rest which facilitates turning both the edge and face of the work without adjusting the tool rest.

in. larger than required for the finished turning.

4. Select a faceplate that is smaller than the diameter of the base of the turning. Using the same center points as in 3 above, lay out a circle that is equal to the diameter of the faceplate.

5. Saw the block to circular form on the band saw, following the outer layout line.

Fig. 25–22. The shaded quadrants of solid stock are shaped against the grain by the scraping tool.

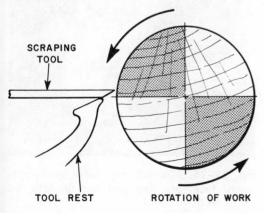

SCRAPING TOOL

TOOL REST   ROTATION OF WORK

6. Screw the faceplate to the work within the marked circle with screws of appropriate size. See Figure 25–19a.

7. If the screws will interfere with turning the work to shape, or if screw holes in the bottom are objectionable, prepare a backing block as shown in Figure 25–20. Make the backing block from ¾ in. S2S stock, saw it to the same diameter as the faceplate and glue it to the workpiece with a piece of heavy paper between. Center this carefully and allow the glue to cure thoroughly before attaching the faceplate and mounting the work on the lathe.

8. Remove the spur center from the spindle (Fig. 25–3).

9. Mount the faceplate and work on the lathe spindle. NOTE: On some lathes the faceplate has a tendency to work itself tightly against the spindle shoulder during the turning operation, thus making removal difficult. To prevent this, make a cardboard or leather washer and slip it over the lathe spindle before mounting the faceplate.

Faceplate turning is performed only by the *scraping method*. Here are some helpful suggestions for performing basic faceplate operations:

1. Adjust the height of the tool rest so that the cutting edge of the chisel will be about level with the center of the revolving workpiece. See Figure 25–22.

2. Move the tool rest in close to the work and clamp it in a position so the first cuts may be made on the edge of the work. Check to insure that the stock will not strike the tool rest, by revolving it by hand.

3. Adjust the lathe for its lowest speed.

4. True the edge (Figs. 25–21 and

25–22), using a roundnose chisel
or the spear point as shown in Figure 25–21. *Important! Sharp chisels*
and *very light cuts are essential* for
this operation. This is because you
are actually making scraping cuts
against the grain on two quadrants
of the work as shown in Figure 25–
22. Therefore, a certain amount of
roughness must be expected in these
2 areas. Obviously, sanding will be
necessary in order to smooth these
surfaces.

Fig. 25–24. Turning a concave shape with
the roundnose chisel.

5. Make templets conforming to the
   shape dictated by the plan.
6. True the face (Fig. 25–23) before
   marking layout lines on it. Use either
   the round- or square-nose chisel as
   shown in Figure 25–23. Chisels
   must be applied only to that part
   of the work which is revolving downward (toward the tool rest). See
   Figure 25–25.
7. When the work is uniformly round
   and balanced, step up the lathe speed
   in accordance with the recommendations for the diameter of the work
   given in Table 25–1 on page 400.
8. Mark the necessary layout lines on

the work to indicate the locations for
the cuts.

9. Concave openings (Fig. 25–24),
   such as in a bowl or dish, are turned
   with the roundnose chisel. Make the
   inside cuts from the outer rim toward the center of the work. Do not
   use gouges since they will catch in
   the work.
10. Make convex cuts by working from
    the center toward the outer rim of
    the work. This produces the smooth-
    est cut since the cutting edge is fed
    at an angle to the grain.

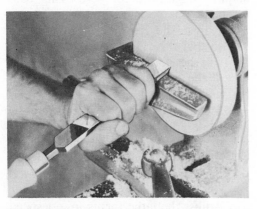

Fig. 25–23. Facing off with a square-nose
chisel.

Fig. 25–25. Turning large work on the outboard faceplate. The tool rest fits into the
portable floor stand.

BACKING
BLOCK

Fig. 25–26. Remove the completed turning from the backing block by separating the paper-glue joint with a chisel edge.

11. Figure 25–26 shows a bowl (which has been turned, sanded and finished) being separated from the backing block.

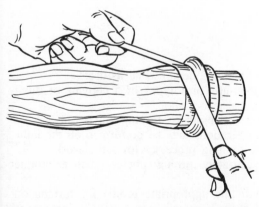

Fig. 25–27. Hold the folded abrasive on the rotating work. Sand large faceplate work with the abrasive folded into a pad.

Sanding may be performed in the lathe after the piece has been turned to the desired profile. Move the tool rest well out of the way for safety purposes. Begin sanding with the appropriate grit of paper depending upon the condition of the turned surfaces. Rough surfaces such as spindles and bowls turned by the scraping method will necessitate at least ½ grit abrasive for a starter. Refer to page 484, for information on different types and grits of abrasives. Run the lathe at one of the slowest speeds. High spindle speeds will burn the abrasive paper. Fold the sand paper into a pad of several layers, or make a strip (Fig. 25–27) of the abrasive so that it can be held between the thumb and forefinger of each hand. *Caution:* Do not hold the abrasive wrapped around the work. Hold it as shown in Figure 25–27 so that if it catches on the revolving work, it will be pulled easily from your grip. The abrasive will cut quite fast and caution should be exercised on intricate turnings so that shoulders, beads, etc., are not cut off or rounded. Keep the abrasive moving back and forth over the surfaces. Change to finer grit abrasives as necessary. Sand out the small cross-grain scratches made by the abrasive with the lathe stopped. Sand lengthwise with the grain.

Finishing, like sanding, is more easily done with the work in the lathe. Refer to Chapter 31 for information concerning various coating materials and procedures for application. *Rubbing and polishing* operations are also well adapted to lathe work since it is merely a matter of holding a pad of rubbing compound, wax, or other material against the work and letting the power of the lathe do the work.

REVIEW QUESTIONS

1. What distinction does the lathe have in the historical development of wood-working machinery? How is the potter's wheel related to the lathe?
2. Who is credited with the invention of the first lathe?
3. Outline the development of turning lathes.
4. Identify the major parts of the turning lathe.
5. How are lathes sized?
6. Define these terms: spindle turning; inboard turning; outboard turning.
7. In what ways are lathes driven?
8. Name the types of turning chisels used with speed and patternmaker's lathes.
9. Describe the difference between the "scraping" and "cutting" methods of turning.
10. Describe the cutting action involved in each of the following: carriage lathe; pattern lathe; back-knife lathe; variety lathe; automatic turning lathe.
11. List the safety rules that must be observed in school shop turning operations.
12. Why are softwoods generally considered more difficult to turn than hardwoods?
13. Describe the steps involved in preparing a 6 by 6 by 12-in. block for turning between centers.
14. What are the three profile shapes that are incorporated in most turned objects?
15. Describe the important steps involved in the rough turning of spindle work.
16. What layout and measuring methods and tools are used in lathe work?
17. Explain how spindles are cut off in the lathe.
18. What is a split turning? How is stock prepared for this operation?
19. What different methods may be used for mounting stock for faceplate turnings? What precautions must be taken when turning large diameter work on the outboard end of the lathe?
20. How is the spur center removed from the lathe? The cup or dead center?
21. Is the "scraping" method or the "cutting" method of turning recommended for faceplate work? Why?
22. Explain the relationship of the grain direction and the direction of advancing the turning chisel in faceplate work.

SUGGESTED STUDENT ACTIVITIES

1. Make a working model of the bow lathe and demonstrate its use.
2. Design and construct a wooden mock-up (prototype) of a copying or duplicating attachment for the lathe in the school shop.
3. Sketch several designs for a lathe to be used for turning bowls only.
4. Sketch three ways in which boring operations may be performed on the lathe.
5. Illustrate in sketches four different sanding processes for lathe work.
6. Design and develop a method of accurately turning spheres (such as croquet balls) on the lathe.
7. Design and grind a lathe chisel with the appropriate profile for turning out wooden drawer pulls. (Use an old file.)

Chapter 26 Wood Fastening and Hardware

Wood fastening includes a variety of processes for joining or assembling pieces of wood in the fabrication of a product. This very important segment of manufacturing requires a knowledge of the kinds and applications of wood joints and also the methods of holding (fastening) the parts or pieces together.

A **joint** is that part of a wood assembly or structure where two or more members are united or fitted together. Wood joints are usually secured with mechanical or chemical fastenings, or a combination of both.

Mechanical fastening is the process of using engineered devices such as nails, screws, bolts, and other connectors of various shapes to hold joints intact.

Chemical fastening, commonly known as gluing, is the process of applying an adhesive substance to the mating parts of a joint to make them hold fast.

Since the end of World War II many advances and radically new developments have been made in wood fastening and assembly methods. These developments are helping to increase industrial production rates and improve overall product quality. Improvements in the holding power of both mechanical and chemical fasteners and the reduction of the costs of using them have been the subjects of research by many commercial and governmental agencies. The manufacturers of millwork products, crating and packaging materials, furniture, toys, boats, homes, house components, and mobile homes are only a few of the many industries that are now benefiting from better fastening methods and materials.

One example of the economic advantages resulting from research and development may be seen in the nailing machines used in the manufactured-house industry. On-site nailing involved in the conventional construction of an average 5-room home requires approximately 600 lb. of nails, roughly 75,000 individual nails. A good carpenter can drive one nail with 4 hammer blows. Therefore, 300,000 hammer blows are required to fabricate a single house. The cost of the nails represents less than 1 percent of the total cost of the house, but the nailing time represents about one third to one half of the total carpentry labor costs. One type of automatic nailing machine now being used on factory built houses is capable of driving as many as 180 screw-nails per minute. It can drive 75,000 nails in less than 7 hours.

The **future of wood fastening processes.** Research and development will continue to bring about new fastening devices and materials. Experimental models of portable electrically powered hammers that hold and drive staples or nails are now being tested. Adhesives with accelerated cold-setting times and greater strength or bonding ability at low clamping pressures are now the subjects of research. Developments such as these are a part of the continuing effort to reduce the costs of on-site construction as well as factory construction.

Historical Development of Wood Fastening Processes

Joinery, the art of making wood joints and using fastenings, had its beginning when man emerged from savagery. Crude fiber lacings and wood pitch were used by early man in the assembly and fastening of his tools and structures. As new tools were developed for cutting, shaping, and boring, man devised more complicated joinery cuts for structures such as wheels, wagons, ships, and other implements.

Nails were originally formed by hand as a family or household industry (Fig. 26–1). These *wrought nails,* as they were known, were made from small strips of soft iron. Nail making machinery came into existence in 1786 when Ezekiel Reed pattented his first machine. The familiar round-wire nail did not come into existence until 1835.

The *penny system* for designating the size (length) of nails originated in early England. The letter "d" was adopted as

Fig. 26–2. Some early forms of hammers.

the abbreviation for penny (Latin *denarius*). The early meaning of the penny system is explained in two different ways: (1) 100 nails of a certain size, say 6 d (six penny), cost sixpence, or (2) 1000 nails of this size weigh 6 lb. Common use, however, relates the term penny to the length of a nail. For example, a 6 d nail is 2 in. long. Lengths vary by ¼ in. between 2 d (1 in.) and 10 d (3 in.) inclusive.

The **development of the hammer** began with Stone Age man. The first primitive hammer consisted of a grooved stone with a slender branch wrapped around it and bound as shown in Figure 26–2. The ancient Romans are credited with the development of the first metal claw hammer. In 1941, portable pneumatic nailing machines were introduced.

The **invention of the screw** is credited to Archimedes (287–212 B.C.), the famous Greek mathematician (Fig. 26–3).

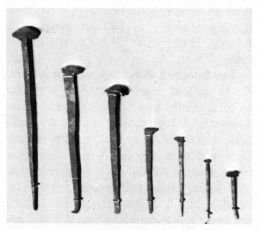

Fig. 26–1. Early hand-forged nails.

Fig. 26–3. Archimedes, the inventor of the screw.

He invented a machine used in irrigation that consisted of a flexible tube wound spirally around a solid axis. Modifications of this device are still in use today. Later, weight lifting devices and various types of gears employing this principle were developed. The screw was not generally used for fastening processes until the nineteenth century. The first wood screws were forged and cut by hand. Screw making machinery was introduced in 1836. Today, literally thousands of different kinds of fasteners are made with screw threads.

The **historical development of glue** may be traced back to the Egyptians of 3000 years ago. The craftsmen of this early culture glued veneer to mummy cases with a casein glue made from sour milk and lime. The early Romans also formulated a waterproof glue. This is evidenced by the relatively recent recovery of a Roman craft with joints still intact after having been submerged for eighteen centuries. During the Middle Ages, the craftsmen in each family prepared their own mixtures of adhesives and passed the formulas on from generation to generation.

In the late 1800's and early 1900's, *animal and starch glues* were the most popular adhesives. During World War I, the first practical water-resistant casein glues and blood glues were developed for commercial use in this country. These glues resulted from the accelerated development of wood and canvas aircraft construction for military uses. In the early 1920's, *soybean glues* were introduced for interior softwood plywood. The first *phenol-resin glues* were introduced into this country from Germany in the early 1930's. They were used to bond plywood veneers. These were soon followed by the *urea-resin glues. Melamine-resin glue* was first used in hardwood plywood in the late 1930's. The first practical *resorcinal-resin glues* were introduced in 1943. This glue played a very important part in bonding wood veneers and laminates for aircraft and ship construction so vital in World War II. The introduction of the first *polyvinyl-resin emulsion glue* in 1945 relieved a shortage of animal glue that resulted when postwar production of furniture soared. Since then, *synthetic-resin glues* have been improved and are replacing older nonresin glues.

Early clamps (Figs. 26–4a, 26–4b, 26–4c, and 26–4d) and other work holding devices also evolved from ancient times. Workpieces were held stationary for shaping and fastening by utilizing leather thongs, or fiber or hair ropes. When pressure was needed, it was obtained by the use of heavy stones or sand weights, levers, and wedges (Figs. 26–4a and 26–4b). Eventually, pressure by means of a screw thread (Figs. 26–4c and 26–4d) was developed. The screw thread was applied to a screw press (Fig. 26–4c) around A.D. 60. The large screws of these presses were hand carved of wood.

The first all metal (iron) clamps were

made in France in the early 1800's. Steel-bar clamps of the type found in most industrial-arts shops were first made in this country around 1880.

The **evolution of hardware.** The colonists of 350 years ago devised ways to make wood serve the purposes of modern metal hardware. They hand-carved hinges, pulls, latches, and other furniture mountings from wood. Later, in the seventeenth and eighteenth centuries village blacksmiths pounded out brass and wrought-iron hardware. This was of the type that is now being reproduced today on a commercial basis for furniture of Colonial or Early American design. See Figures 26–87 on page 475.

Joints and Their Use in Construction

Although the major purpose of a particular kind of joint is to link two or more pieces of wood together, it may also serve one or more of these secondary functions:

1. To increase the size (thickness, width, or length) of a wood member. This permits the use of small pieces of wood that would otherwise be discarded.
2. To increase the strength and durability of individual members or structures. Certain joinery cuts provide increased surface contact which makes for a stronger glue joint.
3. To simplify the assembly of components of structures. Certain types of joints permit easy alignment of parts in clamps or presses.
4. To reduce internal stresses of wood (caused by swelling and shrinking). This minimizes splitting, checking, warping and the like.
5. To increase the appearance and over-

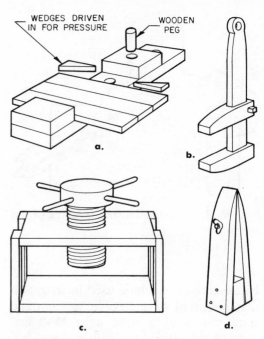

Fig. 26–4. Early clamps: (a and b) wedge acting clamps, (c and d) clamps employing screw threads for pressure.

all value of the product.
6. To provide for greater flexibility in product design. The selection and application of various joinery techniques enables the designer to utilize the physical and mechanical properties of wood to the best possible advantage.

There are literally hundreds of different kinds of joints used today. Special joints are sometimes developed by individual companies to serve the particular requirements of product design and manufacturing methods.

There are several ways in which joints may be classified. They may be grouped by various types such as butt, lap, mortise and tenon, mitered, and doweled joints. Joints may also be classified according to the relationship of grain direction in each member. For example, parallel-grain fastening includes edge-to-edge and face-to-face joints, joints with perpendicular grain direction include butt, mitered, mortise and tenon, dado, rabbet, and many others.

The joints illustrated in this chapter are divided into two groups according to the feasibility of their production in the school shop.

1. *Common joints.* These include the joints most widely used in industry and in the school shop. These are illustrated and identified in Figures 26–5a through 26–10.
2. *Special joints.* These joints are primarily used in the production of millwork to conserve material. They are seldom fabricated in the school shop because special cutters are necessary. See Figures 26–14, 26–15, and 26–16.

Joint-strength factors and reinforcements. An understanding of the nature of wood, its strength-grain direction characteristics, and other physical properties is essential to the intelligent selection and design of wood joints. Refer to pages 24–25. One of the primary factors to consider when selecting a joint is that it should have sufficient strength for its intended purpose. Furthermore, it must be able to withstand the stresses caused by changes in moisture content as these tend to separate or loosen the joint parts. If the dimensional changes in each member of the joint will be unequal, some auxiliary means must be employed to maintain a tight joint.

Generally, for joints in which the grain directions are parallel, such as edge-to-edge (Fig. 26–5a) or face-to-face (parallel laminations), auxiliary fasteners other than the glue are not required. In prac-

tice, these joints may be made as strong as the wood itself. Dimensional changes due to changing moisture content are usually about equal in the mating pieces of wood. Consequently, there is little tendency for the joints to separate for this reason. The tongue and groove joint (Fig. 26–5b), has a theoretical strength advantage in its greater area of gluing surface. In practice it *does not* provide greater strength than an edge-to-edge joint because of the difficulty in producing an accurate fit of the parts (one of the primary requirements for a good glue joint).

Joints that involve joining end grain such as the end butt joints (Fig. 26–6) and miters (Fig. 26–7) or end-to-side grain, are difficult to make sufficiently strong even when the strongest adhesives are used. This is due to the poor penetration of glue into end grain. Therefore, it is necessary to employ auxiliary fasteners (nails, screws) in the joint and/or supplementary devices such as glue blocks, dowels, splines, or tenons to reinforce the joint. These latter methods bring side grain into contact with side grain, provide larger gluing surfaces, and tend to counteract the effects of dimensional changes caused by variations in moisture content. Joints on plywood edges should always be reinforced with splines or dowels, or by means of tongues and grooves.

Glue blocks (Fig. 26–6) are small pieces of wood that are used to strengthen joints. They are usually cut with a triangular cross section. They are used in inside corners and other inconspicuous spots under shelves, drawer bottoms, table tops, and the like.

Splines (Figs. 26–6 and 26–7) are small, thin pieces of wood that are glued into a saw kerf or groove in each member of a joint. Thin plywood or hard-

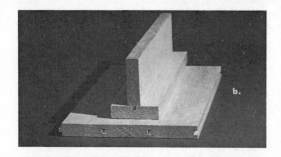

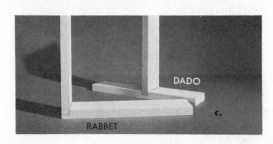

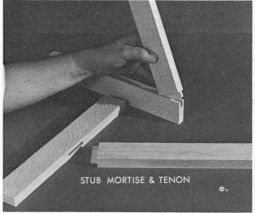

STUB MORTISE & TENON

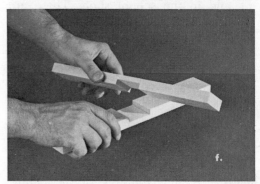

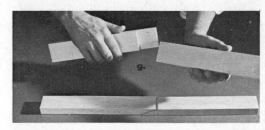

DADO

RABBET

Fig. 26–5. A few of the common joints: (a) edge butt, (b) tongue and groove, (c) dado and rabbet, (d) box, (e) stub mortise and tenon, (f) middle lap, (g) end lap, (h) mitered lap (top) and half lap (bottom).

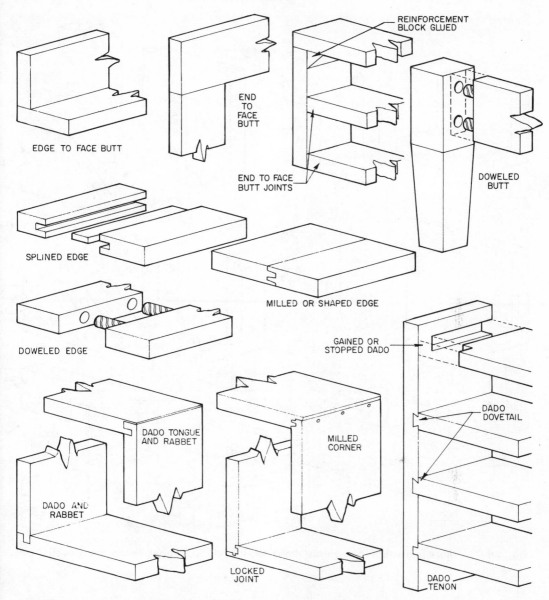

Fig. 26–6.   Other types of butt, edge-to-edge and right-angle joints.

board is often used for splines. Kerfs and grooves may be cut so that the splines are invisible when the joint is assembled. *Keys or feathers* (Fig. 26–7) serve a purpose similar to splines but they are used on miter and other oblique angle joints. If solid wood strips are used as splines or feathers, the grain should always be at right angles to the joint as shown in the illustrations.

Dowels (Figs. 26–6, 26–7, and 26–10) are round wooden pins usually made of birch. Dowel rods are commonly available in diameters varying by ⅛ in. from

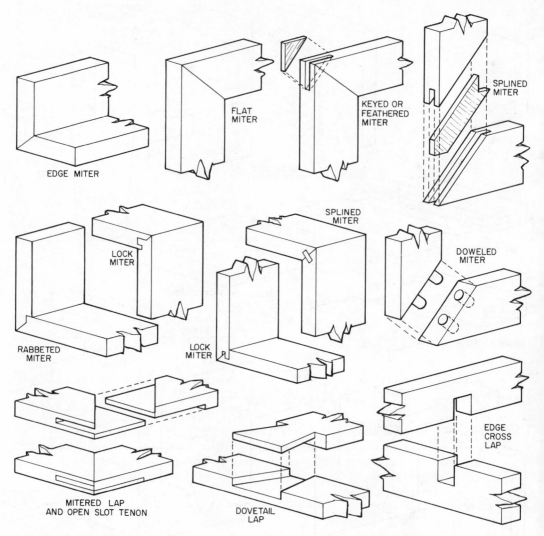

EDGE MITER

FLAT MITER

KEYED OR FEATHERED MITER

SPLINED MITER

LOCK MITER

SPLINED MITER

DOWELED MITER

RABBETED MITER

LOCK MITER

MITERED LAP AND OPEN SLOT TENON

DOVETAIL LAP

EDGE CROSS LAP

Fig. 26–7. More joints that incorporate the miter, lap, dado, rabbet, tenon and dovetail cuts.

⅛ to 1 in. and in 3-ft. lengths. They are cut to the desired lengths and the ends are chamfered on a sander or with a dowel pointer (Fig. 26–11). Commercially prepared *glue joint dowels* of various sizes are available. These are usually grooved spirally (as illustrated) or lengthwise to allow the excess glue and air to escape from the dowel hole. Forc-

ing a dowel pin without this groove into a hole full of glue may result in splitting the wood.

Dowel jigs (Figs. 26–12, 26–13a, and 26–13b) are available to ensure accurate alignment when drilling or boring the dowel holes in each joint member. Dowel jigs are of two types, adjustable and self adjusting. The adjustable type (Fig.

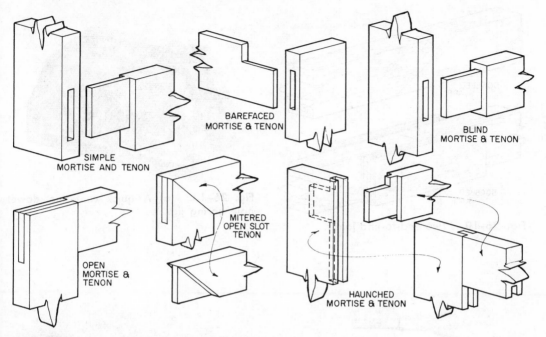

Fig. 26–8. Other applications of the mortise and tenon joint.

26–12) has replaceable guides for the various sizes of bits. The self-adjusting type (Fig. 26–13a) automatically centers the bit guide holes over the center of the work as its two jaws are closed by an adjusting screw. Both types are useful when boring holes for hand mortising in the school shop.

Gussets or **scabs** (Fig. 26–10) are used to strengthen butt joints in carpentry and timber framing. Plywood, with the aid of adhesives and metal fasteners (usually nails) makes these joints relatively strong. Special metal gussets are also available. These are illustrated with other mechanical fasteners later in this chapter.

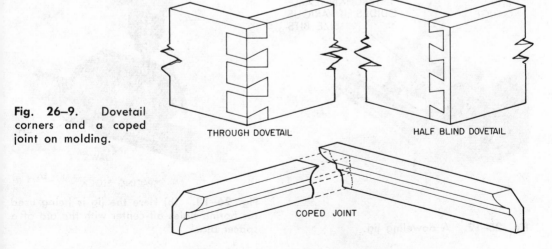

Fig. 26–9. Dovetail corners and a coped joint on molding.

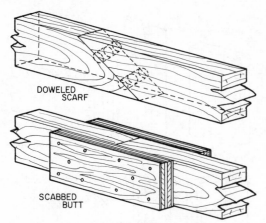

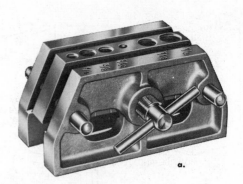

Fig. 26–10. Two end-to-end joints.

Fig. 26–13. (a) A quick centering dowel hole boring jig.

Fig. 26–11. A dowel pointer.

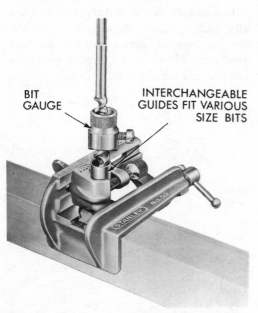

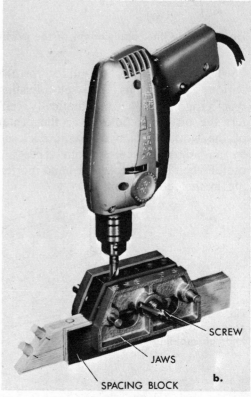

Fig. 26–12. A doweling jig.

Fig. 26–13. (b) Here the jig is being used for boring holes off-center with the aid of a spacing block.

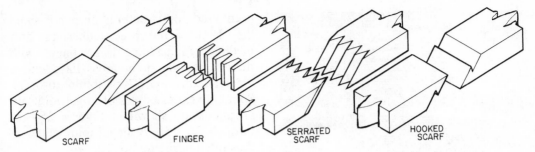

Fig. 26–14. Some joints used in millwork plants to join wood end to end.

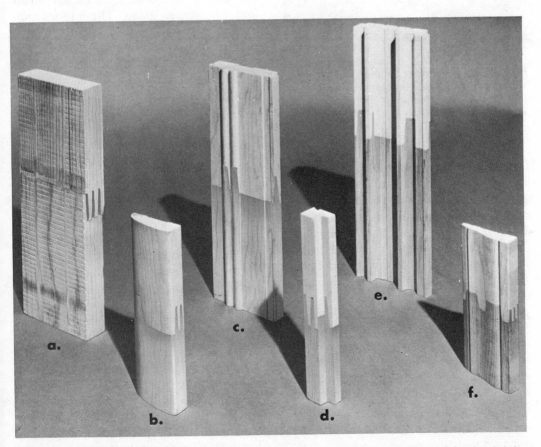

Fig. 26–15. Some applications of the finger joint on millwork products: (a) glued joint ready for machining, (b) casing, (c) window frame head jamb, (d) corner post for kitchen cabinet, (e) window side jamb, (f) molded casing.

Fig. 26–16. A finger jointing set up on a shaper. The shaper is equipped with a table mechanism for clamping and feeding the stock.

End-to-end joints made in industry (Figs. 26–14 and 26–15a through 26–15f). Several types of joints have been developed for joining wood end-to-end. Because of the cost of the cutters (Fig. 26–16) and machinery involved in this operation, this class of work* is not practical for the school shop or the small custom manufacturer. The two major types of joints used are the *scarf* and the *finger joints* (Fig. 26–14). The design of these joints is such that the surfaces tend to approach those of a face-to-face glue joint. Scarf joints are used in laminated beams and other structural members. The joints are staggered within the layers of stock. Glued finger joints have

* NOTE: Although finger-joint cutters are available for the spindle shapers used in the school shop, these cutters are very expensive.

been used for structural purposes since the 1940's. Improved adhesives and methods of machining deeper fingers with their larger glue-joint areas have led to greater utilization of this joining process. Some typical examples of finger-joint applications are shown in Figures 26–15a through 26–15f. A finger-joint cutter is illustrated in Figure 26–16.

Construction Details

Although joinery applications vary from manufacturer to manufacturer, there are some elements of construction which find widespread usage. The construction details most widely accepted in practice consist of combinations of the various joints illustrated previously in this unit. If necessary, they may be modified to meet the requirements dictated by time and machining facilities, or the skill and experience of the workman. By applying the knowledge gained from the study of the units dealing with machining processes, you should be able to design and fabricate wood products incorporating the joinery and construction details that are presented here.

Boxes and chests (Fig. 26–17) may be constructed by employing any of the many kinds of joints and fasteners. If the end grain of butt or rabbet joints (Fig. 26–17a) is objectionable, miter joints should be used. Items such as chests or wall cabinets with box lids are first made as completely closed boxes. Finally, the box lid is formed by sawing as shown in Figure 26–17b.

Cases such as those used for books or trophies may be constructed as shown in Figure 26–18. Toe boards or legs may be used to support the structure on the floor. They are omitted on wall hung units.

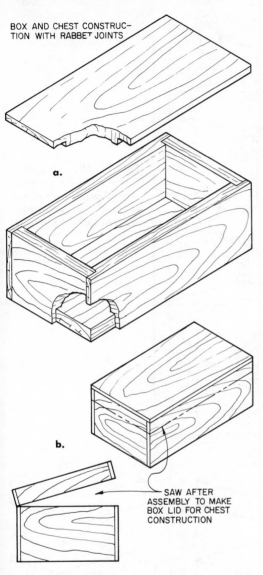

BOX AND CHEST CONSTRUCTION WITH RABBET JOINTS

a.

b.

SAW AFTER ASSEMBLY TO MAKE BOX LID FOR CHEST CONSTRUCTION

Fig. 26–17. Simple box and chest construction.

The **shelves** of cases may be permanently installed with dado or stopped dado (gain) joints, or they may be made adjustable as shown in Figure 26–19.

Various treatments for plywood and particle board that conceal unsightly

edges are suggested in Figure 26–20.

Tops that overhang the sides of cases or cabinets may be handled by any of the methods shown in Figure 26–21.

Leg and rail assemblies are generally made with mortise and tenon or doweled joints. These assemblies are generally supported by wood corner blocks (Fig. 26–22a) or special corner braces of metal (Fig. 26–22b). Refer to page 477 for other leg hardware.

Cabinets may be regarded as a type of box or case construction with the addition of drawers or doors or a combination of both. Figure 26–23 illustrates the relationship of the basic parts of a 5-drawer kitchen cabinet unit. This type of construction features *skeleton* (open) *frames* with center guides that support and guide the drawers. The frames are

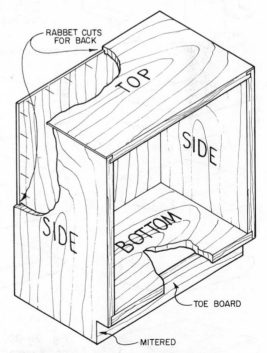

RABBET CUTS FOR BACK

TOP

SIDE

SIDE

BOTTOM

TOE BOARD

MITERED

Fig. 26–18. Basic case construction.

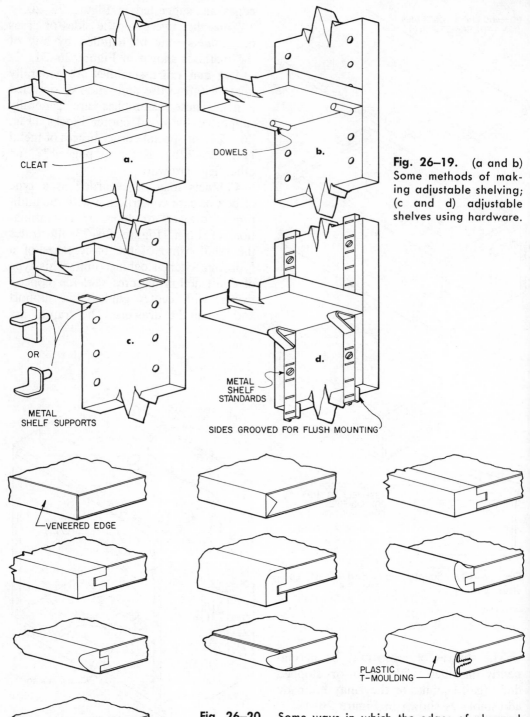

Fig. 26–19. (a and b) Some methods of making adjustable shelving; (c and d) adjustable shelves using hardware.

CLEAT

DOWELS

METAL SHELF SUPPORTS

METAL SHELF STANDARDS

SIDES GROOVED FOR FLUSH MOUNTING

VENEERED EDGE

PLASTIC T–MOULDING

PLASTIC LAMINATES

Fig. 26–20. Some ways in which the edges of plywood or veneered particle board may be hidden.

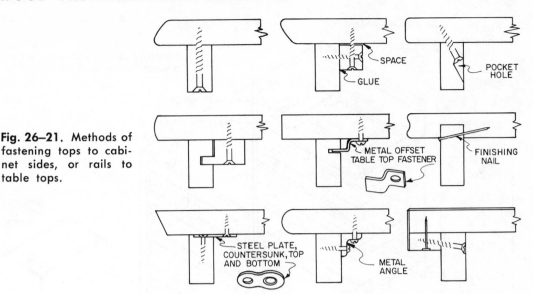

Fig. 26–21. Methods of fastening tops to cabinet sides, or rails to table tops.

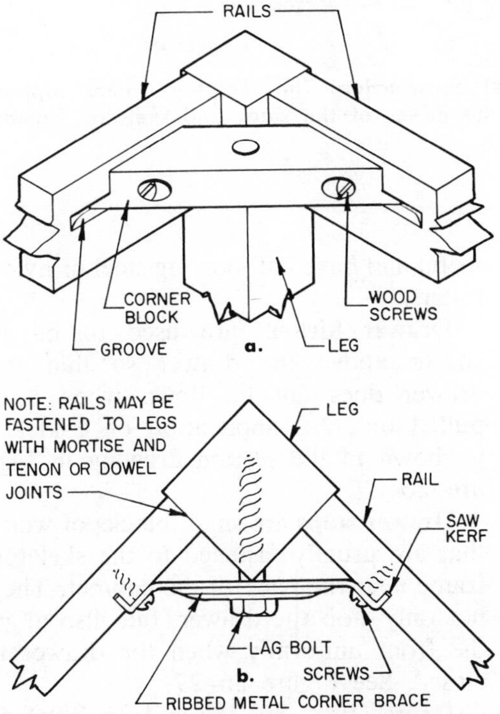

SPACE

GLUE

POCKET HOLE

METAL OFFSET TABLE TOP FASTENER

FINISHING NAIL

STEEL PLATE, COUNTERSUNK, TOP AND BOTTOM

METAL ANGLE

RAILS

CORNER BLOCK

WOOD SCREWS

GROOVE   **a.**   LEG

NOTE: RAILS MAY BE FASTENED TO LEGS WITH MORTISE AND TENON OR DOWEL JOINTS

LEG

RAIL

SAW KERF

LAG BOLT

b.   SCREWS

RIBBED METAL CORNER BRACE

Fig. 26–22. This shows two typical supports for reenforcing leg and rail joints.

made of inexpensive softwood. They fit into through dadoes cut into each of the side panels. The side panels are usually made of plywood and the edges of both the skeleton frames and the sides are covered on the front with another framed assembly of hardwood. This is known as the *cabinet facing.* The outside vertical members are known as *stiles,* and they generally extend the full height of the facing. Horizontal members are called *rails.* Vertical divisions of openings are called *muntins.* The *skeleton frames* may be made to include *dust panels* as shown in Figure 26–24b. This helps to prevent the contents of the drawer from becoming soiled by dust. Stopped dadoes and notched corners are employed as shown in Figure 26–24b for flush drawer construction.

Simple drawer construction (Fig. 26–25) employs rabbeting, dadoing, and grooving operations. More substantial drawer construction generally embodies lock joints or dovetailing at the sides, fronts, and backs. See Figures on page

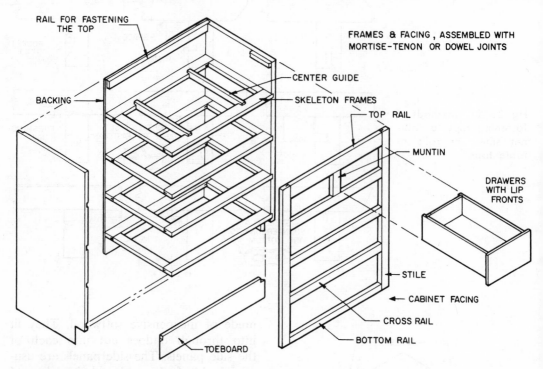

Fig. 26–23. Exploded view of simple cabinet construction. The skeleton frames support drawers (with lip fronts). The facing conceals the edges of the sides and skeleton frames. The top is not shown in this drawing.

307 of Chapter 20.

Flush drawers permit somewhat greater flexibility in overall design. Figure 26–26 illustrates some details of fine cabinet work that are often used in desks and chests of drawers.

Drawer slides and guides allow for easy movement of the drawer. When designing a drawer, consideration must be given to its size, probable weight of contents when in use, and clearance for expansion in humid weather. The recommended guide for large drawers is the center type, similar to the one shown in Figure 26–26. Other guides that may be used are shown in Figure 26–27. The most substantial guides are made of

metal and have ball-bearing steel or nylon rollers.

Drawer kickers are used to fill in spaces above the drawer so that the drawer does not tip down when it is pulled out. An application of a kicker is shown in the section drawing in Figure 26–27.

Drawer stops are small blocks of wood that are usually fastened to the skeleton frame near the back of the cabinet. They not only stop the drawer, but also align the front uniformly when the drawer is closed. See Figure 26–27.

Doors (Figs. 26–28a and 26–28b) of cabinets may be of either flush or lip design. They may be constructed of solid

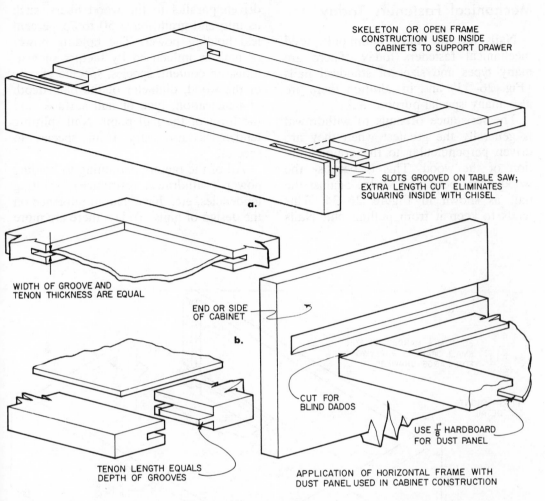

SKELETON OR OPEN FRAME
CONSTRUCTION USED INSIDE
CABINETS TO SUPPORT DRAWER

SLOTS GROOVED ON TABLE SAW;
EXTRA LENGTH CUT ELIMINATES
SQUARING INSIDE WITH CHISEL

a.

WIDTH OF GROOVE AND
TENON THICKNESS ARE EQUAL

END OR SIDE
OF CABINET

b.

CUT FOR
BLIND DADOS

USE $\frac{1}{8}$" HARDBOARD
FOR DUST PANEL

TENON LENGTH EQUALS
DEPTH OF GROOVES

APPLICATION OF HORIZONTAL FRAME WITH
DUST PANEL USED IN CABINET CONSTRUCTION

Fig. 26–24. Details of horizontal framing of cabinets: (a) open framing, (b) framed dust panel (note the cut made on the frame when stopped dadoes are cut into the side or end of the cabinet).

wood, plywood, veneered particle board (Fig. 26–28a), or framed panels (Fig. 26–28b). *Hollow core doors* used in house interiors are constructed as shown in Figure 26–29.

Framed glass doors (Fig. 26–30) require an inside rabbet for the glass. This facilitates replacement should the glass become broken. This would be impossible if the glass were put into a grooved frame like that used to enclose wood panels.

Sliding doors (Figs. 26–31 and 26–32) may be solid, framed, or of glass construction. There are several types of tracks that may be used with them. Figures 32a, b, c, d, and e show types that are suitable for small doors. However, they are not too efficient for doors larger than $1\frac{1}{2}$ to 2 ft. square or for those where the height is greater than the width. Special hardware should be used for glass doors to achieve free movement.

Mechanical Fasteners Today

Nails are the most commonly used mechanical fasteners today. There are many types and sizes of standard nails (Fig. 26–33) and in addition there are also many special-purpose nails.

The resistance of nails to withdrawal is generally the greatest when they are driven perpendicular to the grain direction of the wood. This is because the wood fibers bend and wedge against the nail as shown in Figure 26–34. This tends to keep it from pulling out. Nails

driven parallel to the wood fibers, such as into end grain, have 50 to 75 percent less holding power. The holding power of nails is influenced by factors such as moisture content, species, specific gravity of the wood, diameter of the nail, depth of penetration, type of nail surface, and the form of the nail point. Nail splitting tendencies also vary from species to species.

All of the factors pertaining to holding power (withdrawal resistance), splitting tendencies, etc., have had an influence on the design of nails. Today, there are more

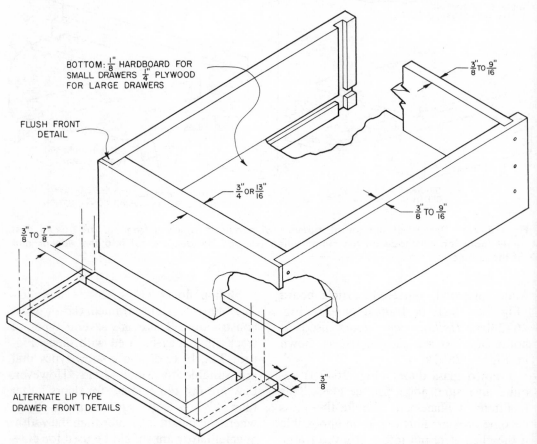

BOTTOM: $\frac{1}{8}$" HARDBOARD FOR SMALL DRAWERS $\frac{1}{4}$" PLYWOOD FOR LARGE DRAWERS

FLUSH FRONT DETAIL

$\frac{3}{8}$" TO $\frac{9}{16}$"

$\frac{3}{4}$" OR $\frac{13}{16}$"

$\frac{3}{8}$" TO $\frac{9}{16}$"

$\frac{3}{8}$" TO $\frac{7}{8}$"

$\frac{3}{8}$"

ALTERNATE LIP TYPE DRAWER FRONT DETAILS

Fig. 26–25. Basic drawer construction. Note that either lip or flush type fronts may be made.

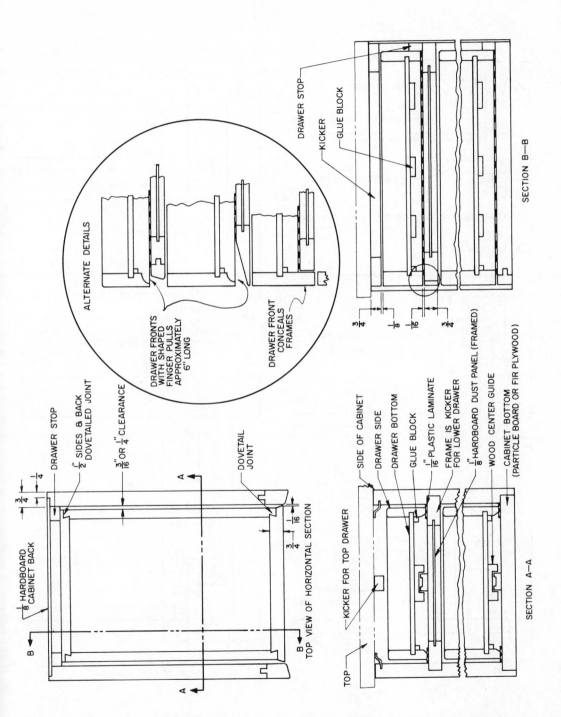

Fig. 26–26. Details of flush drawers and related parts found in fine cabinetwork.

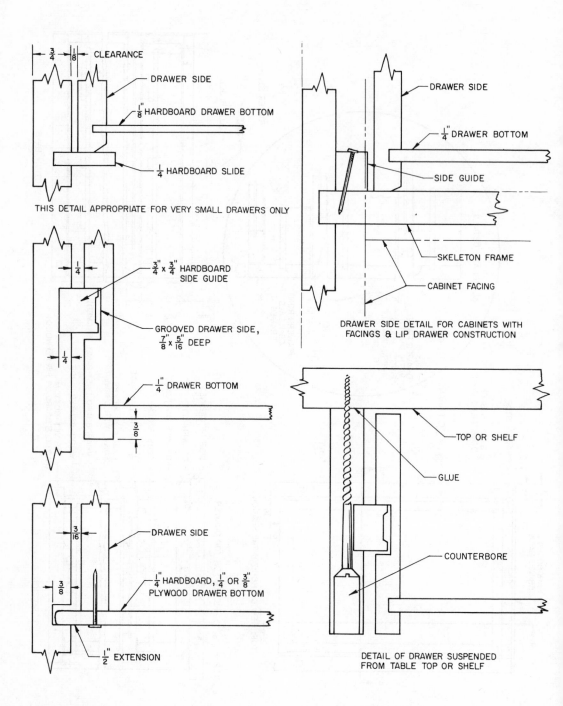

Fig. 26–27. Some other methods of making drawer slides or guides.

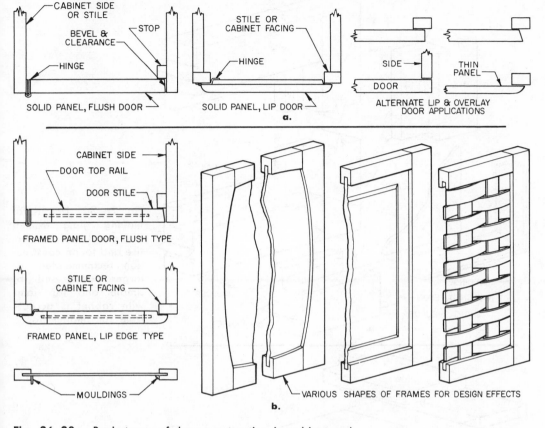

Fig. 26–28. Basic types of door construction in cabinetwork.

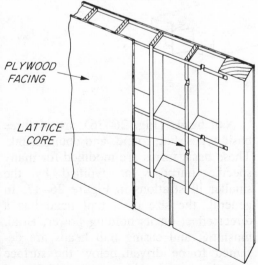

Fig. 26–29. Hollow construction of large interior doors.

than 10,000 different sizes and types of nails to serve a wide variety of purposes.

Nail points (Fig. 26–35) are designed for definite purposes. The diamond point is the most common. Sharply pointed nails accentuate the splitting tendencies of certain species of wood. Blunt or flat points reduce the splitting tendencies. They have lower holding powers than other point forms because they cut their way through the wood and thereby preclude any wedging action of the wood fibers. Special forms of nail points include the *duck bill* which is designed for clinching (bending over of the nail on the exit side).

Nail shanks are made in many shapes

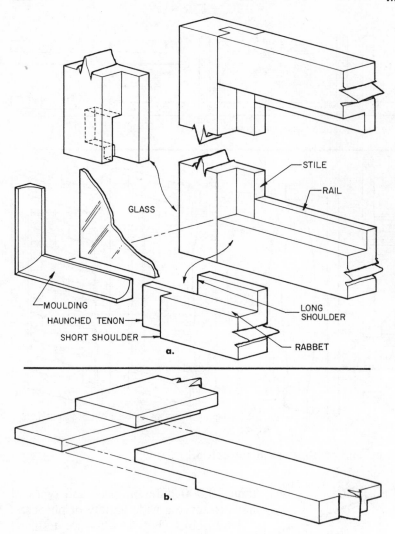

Fig. 26–30. Details for making glass framed doors: (a) typical mortise and tenon construction recommended for larger doors, and (b) simple end lap joint with rabbet is acceptable for smaller doors.

(Fig. 26–33a through 26–33g, p. 439). Annular-grooved (Fig. 26–33e) shanks hold best in soft and medium hardwoods. The annular grooves fill with wood fibers and help to wedge the nail in place. Spiral-grooved shanks (Figs. 26–33f and 26–33g) rotate as they are driven and enter the wood with a minimum of disturbance to the wood fibers. Nails of this type are best suited to nailing into hardwoods and into end grain.

Nail heads (Fig. 26–36) are of three basic types; flat, round, and countersunk. These basic forms are modified for many specific purposes as typified by the smaller illustrations in Figure 26–37. In general, the size of a nail head has a direct effect on its holding power. Brad, finishing, and casing nail heads are designed to be driven below the surface and do not provide great withdrawal resistance.

Fig. 26–31. Sliding doors in metal track.

Nail composition. Nails are made of carbon steel, stainless steel, brass, bronze, aluminum alloys, and other metal alloys. Nails for exterior use should be corrosion resistant and should not discolor the wood. When a plain steel nail rusts, it expands, enlarges the hole in the wood, causes unsightly stains, and loses much of its holding power.

Nail coatings. Nails are sold as "bright" (uncoated) or with treatments for imparting characteristics such as color (baked lacquers) or increasing withdrawal resistance. *Cement-coated* steel nails have galvanized coatings plus a cement coating. The cement serves to glue the nail to the wood fibers after the nail is driven. Nails may also be purchased *blued* (sterilized), annealed, tinned, and electroplated with different materials.

Basic kinds of nails (Fig. 26–38 and Table 26–1). The following are the most

TABLE 26–1
COMMON NAILS

Size	Length	Gauge	Diameter Head Inches	Approx. No. to Pound
2d	1 inch	No. 15	$\frac{11}{64}$	870
3d	1¼ inch	No. 14	$\frac{13}{64}$	550
4d	1½ inch	No. 12½	¼	300
5d	1¾ inch	No. 12½	¼	260
6d	2 inch	No. 11½	$\frac{17}{64}$	175
7d	2¼ inch	No. 11½	$\frac{17}{64}$	158
8d	2½ inch	No. 10¼	$\frac{9}{32}$	105
9d	2¾ inch	No. 10¼	$\frac{9}{32}$	95
10d	3 inch	No. 9	$\frac{5}{16}$	68
12d	3¼ inch	No. 9	$\frac{5}{16}$	63
16d	3½ inch	No. 8	$\frac{11}{32}$	47
20d	4 inch	No. 6	$\frac{13}{32}$	30
30d	4½ inch	No. 5	$\frac{7}{16}$	23
40d	5 inch	No. 4	$\frac{15}{32}$	18
50d	5½ inch	No. 3	½	15
60d	6 inch	No. 2	$\frac{17}{32}$	11

BOX NAILS

Size	Length	Gauge	Diameter Head Inches	Approx. No. to Pound
3d	1¼ inch	No. 14½	$\frac{7}{32}$	590
4d	1½ inch	No. 14	$\frac{7}{32}$	455
5d	1¾ inch	No. 14	$\frac{7}{32}$	390
6d	2 inch	No. 12½	$\frac{17}{64}$	225
7d	2¼ inch	No. 12½	$\frac{17}{64}$	200
8d	2½ inch	No. 11½	$\frac{19}{64}$	135
10d	3 inch	No. 10½	$\frac{5}{16}$	90
16d	3½ inch	No. 10	$\frac{11}{32}$	70
20d	4 inch	No. 9	$\frac{3}{8}$	50

FINISHING NAILS

Size	Length	Gauge	Diameter Head Gauge	Approx. No. to Pound
3d	1¼ inch	No. 15½	12½	850
4d	1½ inch	No. 15	12	575
6d	2 inch	No. 13	10	300
8d	2½ inch	No. 12½	9½	192
10d	3 inch	No. 11½	8½	122

CASING NAILS

Size	Length	Gauge	Diameter Head Gauge	Approx. No. to Pound
4d	1½ inch	No. 14	11	450
6d	2 inch	No. 12½	9½	240
8d	2½ inch	No. 11½	8½	145
10d	3 inch	No. 10½	7½	94
16d	3½ inch	No. 10	7	71

Table 26–1. Sizes and approximate number of nails per pound of the four kinds of most widely used nails.

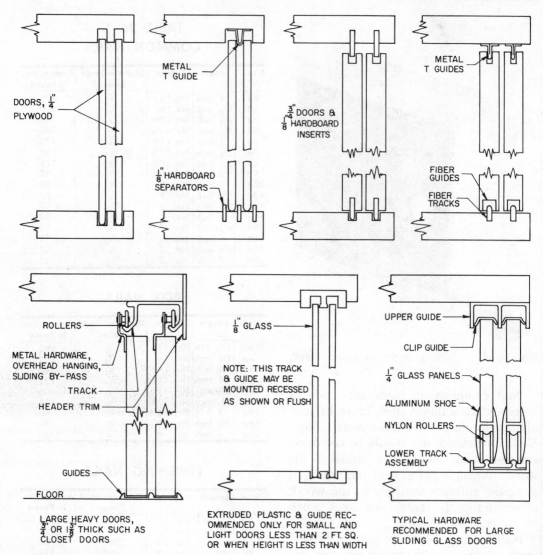

Fig. 26–32. Sliding door details showing shop made and other kinds of commercial guides and special hardware.

widely used kinds of nails. They are available in various sizes, configurations of heads, shanks, and points as discussed above.

Common nails are round, carbon steel wire nails with flat heads. They have been used for more than a century in construction (structural and rough carpentry) in which appearance is a minor consideration. *Spikes* are large common nails, from 20d (4 in.) to 60d (6 in.) in size. Spikes are used for fastening heavy planks to beams and framed members.

Box nails (Fig. 26–38) are similar in appearance to common nails. They have thinner shanks and heads than common nails of the same size. See the chart,

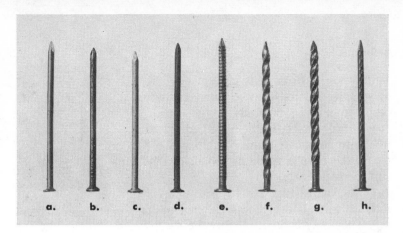

Fig. 26–33. Nails with various surface treatments: (a) bright, smooth wire nail, (b) cement coated, (c) zinc-coated, (d) chemically etched, (e) annular grooved, (f) spirally grooved, (g) spirally grooved and barbed, and (h) barbed nail.

a.   b.   c.   d.   e.   f.   g.   h.

Fig. 26–34. Nails hold because the wood fibers bend and wedge the nail in place.

Fig. 26–35. Kinds of nail points.

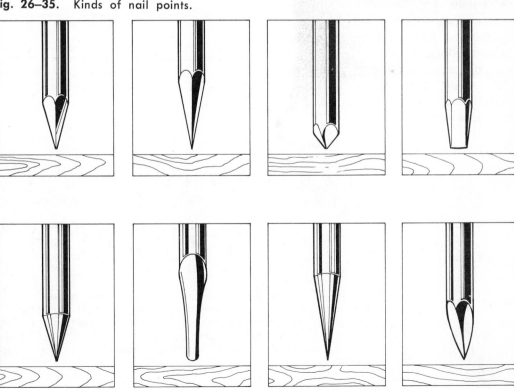

Table 26–1. Box nails are less likely to split wood, and they are driven more easily than common nails.

Finishing nails (Fig. 26–38) are used in finish carpentry and cabinet work where the head is to be driven below the surface of the wood.

Casing nails (Fig. 26–38) are used for interior trim, flooring, and cabinet making. They may be identified by their small cone-shaped heads which are usually cupped for setting with a nail set.

Scaffold or double-headed nails (Fig. 26–38) are used for temporary jobs such as cement forms, scaffolding, crating, and anchoring freight to wood floors. The length is measured from the lower head.

Masonry nails (Fig. 26–38) are hardened carbon-steel nails used for fastening wood to cinder and concrete blocks, brick, concrete, and other masonry materials. Sizes range from ½ to 4 in. in length.

Cut nails (Fig. 26–38) are similar to the hand-forged nails of early times. Today, they find limited use for nailing flooring and siding. They are also used for fastening wood to masonry materials. Their major advantage is that they do not split wood as readily as round wire nails. Cut nails range from 1 to 4 in. in length.

FLAT   ROUND   COUNTERSUNK

Fig. 26–36. Three basic nail heads from which all other nail heads evolved.

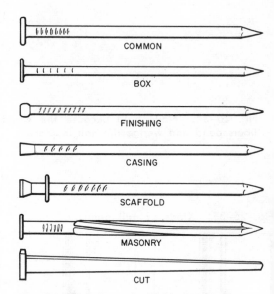

COMMON

BOX

FINISHING

CASING

SCAFFOLD

MASONRY

CUT

Fig. 26–38. Some basic kinds of nails.

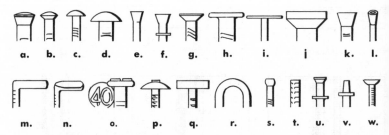

a. b. c. d. e. f. g. h. i. j. k. l.

m. n. o. p. q. r. s. t. u. v. w.

Fig. 26–37. (a and b) oval countersunk, (c) oval, (d) round, (e) flooring brad, (f) double head countersunk, (g, j, k) flat countersunk, (h, i) flat, (l) cupped, (m) metal lath, (n) hoop fastener, (o) tie and pole-dating, (p) umbrella, (q) lead head, (r) staple, (s) brad, (t) headless-pin, (u) scaffold or double-headed, (v) shade roller pin, (w) curved.

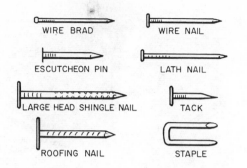

Fig. 26-39. Other kinds of nail fasteners.

Wire brads (Fig. 26–39) look like small finishing nails. They are made of thin gauges of wire and range from ¼ to ‿ in. in length. They are sold in ¼- to 1-lb. packages.

Wire nails (Fig. 26–39) look like small box nails. They are available in the same sizes as brads.

Escutcheon pins (Fig. 26–39) are made of brass or lacquered steel. They are used for decorative purposes as well as for fastening hardware and metal trim. Sizes range from ¼-in. to 1¼-in. lengths.

Lath nails (Fig. 26–39) are blued (sterilized) because lathers hold the nails in their mouth while working. Lath nails are made of thin gauges of wire and are 1 or 1⅛ in. in length.

Shingle nails (Fig. 26–39) are made with heads about ⅜ in. in diameter for holding asbestos shingles. They are generally zinc coated and range from 1 to 2 in. in length. Nails for wood shingles are similar to box nails.

Roofing nails (Fig. 26–39) have larger heads than other nails, ½ in. in diameter. These range from ¾ to 2 in. in length.

Tacks (Fig. 26–39) are short blued nails. They range from ⅛ to ¾ in. in length and range from 16 to 13 wire gauge sizes. Tacks are usually identified

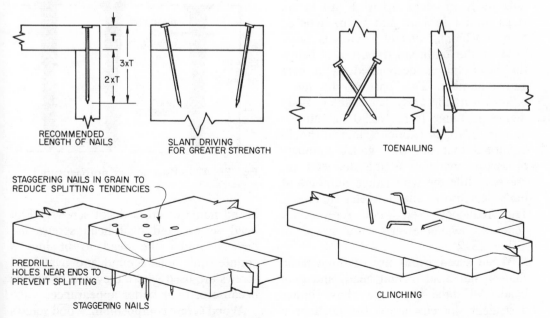

Fig. 26-40. Some basic principles of nailing.

for specific purposes such as upholstery, carpet, canvas, and poster tacks.

Staples (Fig. 26–39) are used for wire fencing, screening, tile, and other fiber materials. They are made in several different shapes and sizes. Staples are usually driven with special tools.

The basic techniques involved in *custom nailing* processes are illustrated in Figure 26–40.

Wood screws (Fig. 26–41) are among the most important fasteners used in the wood manufacturing industries. It is estimated that about 10,000 different screws are used in the construction of the furniture, cabinets, and millwork of the average home. Wood screws are made in many different sizes, with three types of heads; they are made of various metals and with different kinds of surface finishes.

Wood screw sizes (Fig. 26–42) are specified according to both length and diameter. Wood screws range from ⅛ to 6 in. in length. Standard lengths are available in ⅛ in. steps up to 1 in., ¼ in. steps from 1 to 3 in. and ½ in. steps up to 6 in. The *diameter* of a screw is measured at the unthreaded part just below the head and is designated by a wire gauge number. This part of the screw is known as the *body* (or shank). Body diameters range from No. 0 (about ¹⁄₁₆ in.) up to No. 24 (about ⅜ in.). It should be noted that the wire gauge numbers of screws increase as the diameter increases while the wire gauge numbers of nails decrease as the diameter increases. The frequency used wood screw sizes generally available are summarized in Table 26–2.

Wood screw heads are of three basic shapes: flat head, round head, and oval head. All three types may have either a straight slot cut across the head or a crossed slot. (Phillips head screws are a

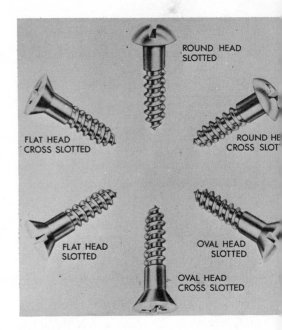

Fig. 26–41. Basic kinds of wood screws.

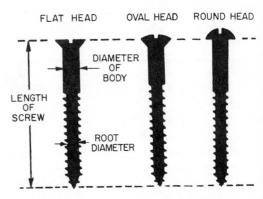

Fig. 26–42. How screws are measured.

brand name of crossed-slot screws.) Flat head screws and oval head screws are beveled under the head to fit into a countersunk hole. Round and oval head screws are used where they will be visible because of their better appearance.

Wood screw composition. Wood screws are made of steel, brass, aluminum,

TABLE 26–2

Length	\multicolumn{18}{c}{Shank Numbers}																	
	0	1	2	3	4	5	6	7	8	9	10	11	12	14	16	18	20	24
¼ inch	0	1	2	3														
⅜ inch			2	3	4	5	6	7										
½ inch			2	3	4	5	6	7	8									
⅝ inch				3	4	5	6	7	8	9	10							
¾ inch					4	5	6	7	8	9	10	11						
⅞ inch							6	7	8	9	10	11	12					
1 inch							6	7	8	9	10	11	12	14				
1¼ inch								7	8	9	10	11	12	14	16			
1½ inch							6	7	8	9	10	11	12	14	16	18		
1¾ inch									8	9	10	11	12	14	16	18	20	
2 inch									8	9	10	11	12	14	16	18	20	
2¼ inch										9	10	11	12	14	16	18	20	
2½ inch													12	14	16	18	20	
2¾ inch														14	16	18	20	
3 inch															16	18	20	
3½ inch																18	20	24
4 inch																18	20	24

Table 26–2. The most commonly used lengths and wire gauge shank sizes of wood screws.

stainless steel, and silicon bronze. Each has certain advantages in strength, corrosion resistance, and appearance. Brass and stainless screws are more expensive.

Finishes of screws include: plain (or bright) and blued; nickel, chrome, and cadmium plated; and galvanized.

Installation of wood screws. Screws should always be turned into place. They should not be driven with a hammer. This practice tears the wood fibers and injures the screw threads, seriously reducing the holding capacity of the screw.

Certain drilling, boring, and countersinking operations prevent splitting the wood, making driving the screw easier, and permit hiding the screw head below the surface of the wood.

A *shank clearance hole* should be drilled through the piece of work on which the screwhead will rest. A smaller hole, known as a *pilot hole* (sometimes called an anchor hole), should be drilled in the other piece to receive the threaded part of the screw. The pilot-hole size should be equal to the root diameter of the screw to obtain maximum holding power. It should permit the full thread to penetrate the walls of the hole. See Figure 26–44. The recommended hole sizes for installing wood screws is given in Table 26–3. The depth of the pilot hole should be slightly less than the length of the screw.

Flat-head screws should be countersunk so they are flush with the surface or they may be installed below the surface in counterbored holes. When screws are set below the surface, they may be covered with plugs, filler, or screw hole buttons as shown in Figure 26–43.

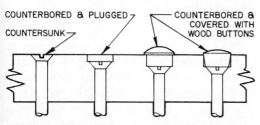

COUNTERBORED & PLUGGED
COUNTERSUNK
COUNTERBORED & COVERED WITH WOOD BUTTONS

Fig. 26–43. Examples of countersinking, counterboring, and covering of flat-head screws.

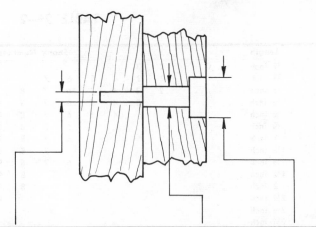

| No. of Screw | Basic Decimal Size | PILOT HOLES | | | | SHANK CLEARANCE HOLES | | COUNTERBORE |
| | | HARDWOODS | | SOFTWOODS | | | | |
		Twist Bit (Nearest size in fractions of an inch)	Drill Gauge No. To be used for maximum holding power	Twist Bit (Nearest size in fractions of an inch)	Drill Gauge No. To be used for maximum holding power	Twist Bit (Nearest size in fractions of an inch)	Drill Gauge No. or Letter To be used for maximum holding power	No. of Auger Bit To Counterbore for sinking head (by 16ths)
0	.060	1/32	66	1/64	75	1/16	52	—
1	.073	—	57	1/32	71	5/64	47	—
2	.086	—	54	1/32	65	3/32	42	3
3	.099	1/16	53	3/64	58	7/64	37	4
4	.112	1/16	51	3/64	55	7/64	32	4
5	.125	5/64	47	1/16	53	1/8	30	4
6	.138	—	44	1/16	52	9/64	27	5
7	.151	—	39	1/16	51	5/32	22	5
8	.164	7/64	35	5/64	48	11/64	18	6
9	.177	7/64	33	5/64	45	3/16	14	6
10	.190	1/8	31	3/32	43	3/16	10	6
11	.203	—	29	3/32	40	13/64	4	7
12	.216	—	25	7/64	38	7/32	2	7
14	.242	3/16	14	7/64	32	1/4	D	8
16	.268	—	10	9/64	29	17/64	I	9
18	.294	13/64	6	9/64	26	19/64	N	10
20	.320	7/32	3	11/64	19	21/64	P	11
24	.372	1/4	D	3/16	15	3/8	V	12

Table 26–3. The recommended hole sizes for screw installation.

Lubricating screws makes for easier insertion. Applying soap or paraffin to the screw prior to driving, especially in hardwoods, prevents breaking the screw off in the hole. The lubricant has little adverse effect on the holding power of the screw.

Drive screws (Fig. 26–45a) are mechanical fasteners which combine some of the features of both screws and nails. They have sharp spiral threads which provide about four times the holding power of nails. Drive screws are available in various sizes. They are often sub-

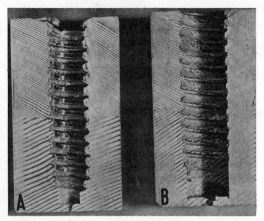

Fig. 26–44. (a) The correct size pilot hole provides deep thread penetration, (b) shallow penetration of thread as a result of an oversized pilot hole.

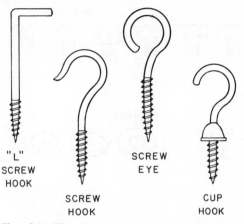

"L" SCREW HOOK

SCREW HOOK

SCREW EYE

CUP HOOK

Fig. 26–47. Screw hooks and screw eyes.

Fig. 26–45. (a) Drive screw, (b) self pilot-hole-drilling screw.

a.

b.

stituted for wood screws. Their slotted heads permit their being backed out with a screw driver.

Self pilot-drilling wood screws (Fig. 26–45b) have a part of the thread ground away to form a cutting edge. As it is driven the chips collect in the groove. This type of fastener is similar to self-tapping metal screws. Self pilot-drilling wood screws are available in standard sizes, with flat, round, hexagon or decorative heads. They are also available with crossed slots.

Lag screws (Fig. 26–46) are used in heavy construction work. They are usually made with a square head for driving

TABLE 26–4

Length inches	Diameter in Inches								
	¼	5⁄16	3⁄8	7⁄16	½	5⁄8	¾	7⁄8	1
1	s	s	s	s	s				
1¼	s	s	s	s	s				
1½	s	s	s	s	s	s	s		
1¾	s	s	s	s	s	s	s		
2	2″ to 8″ Lengths advance in ½″ Steps								
	8″ to 10″ Lengths advance in 1″ Steps								
10	These Lengths Made in All Diameters								
11		s	s	s	s	s	s	s	
12		s	s	s	s	s	s	s	
13					s	s	s	s	
14					s	s	s	s	
15	s = steel				s	s	s	s	
16					s	s	s	s	

Fig. 26–46. Lag screw and common sizes.

BOLT HEADS

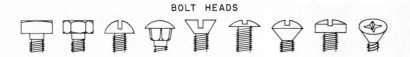

WASHERS   COMMON NUTS

Fig. 26–48. Bolt, nut, and washer types.

BOLTS

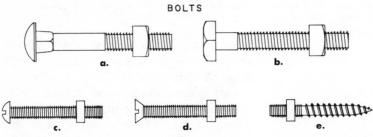

with a wrench. Lag screws (Fig. 26–46) are sized according to diameter (in fractions of an inch) and by length as given in the Table 26–4.

Screw hooks and screw eyes (Fig. 26–47) are not considered fasteners in the usual sense. They are primarily used for holding or supporting various items. They are available in a variety of sizes and many finishes such as bright, brass, and plated.

Bolts and machine screws (Fig. 26–48) are widely used in wood manufacturing processes. They are used for such heavy construction jobs as timber fastening and the construction of forms, for fixtures and jigs, and in the maintenance of equipment. Bolts differ from screws in that they are installed completely through the parts to be fastened and a nut is screwed on the end to hold the work. Most bolts are made of steel, but they are also available in other materials and finishes. There are also various nut and washer styles as shown in Figure 26–48. The most commonly used bolts are:

1. *Carriage bolts* (Fig. 26–48a). They are made with oval heads and square nuts. A portion of the shank just below the head is square to prevent the bolt from turning in the hole. Sizes range from $\frac{3}{16}$- to $\frac{3}{4}$-in. diameters and $\frac{1}{2}$ to 24 in. in length.

2. *Machine bolts* (Fig. 26–48b). Made with square heads and square nuts, they may be obtained in diameters from $\frac{1}{4}$ to 1 in. and from $\frac{1}{2}$ to 30 in. in length.

3. *Machine screws* (Fig. 26–48c). Available in slotted, fillister, or oval head styles, they are made with either coarse or fine threads and may be obtained with either square, hexagon, or wing nuts. Machine screws are sized by gauge numbers from 0 to 12 and by fractions from $\frac{1}{4}$- to $\frac{1}{2}$-in. diameters. They range from $\frac{1}{8}$ to 3 in. in length.

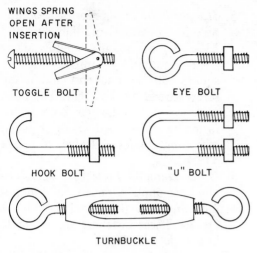

TOGGLE BOLT

WINGS SPRING
OPEN AFTER
INSERTION

EYE BOLT

HOOK BOLT

"U" BOLT

TURNBUCKLE

Fig. 26–49. Five common bolts.

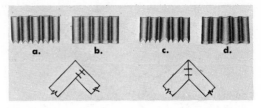

Fig. 26–50. Plain and saw-edge corrugated fasteners.

4. *Stove bolts* (Fig. 26–48d). Available in flat, round, or truss head styles, they are coarse threaded, sold with square nuts, and range from $\frac{1}{8}$ to $\frac{1}{2}$ in. in diameter and $\frac{3}{8}$ to 6 in. in length.

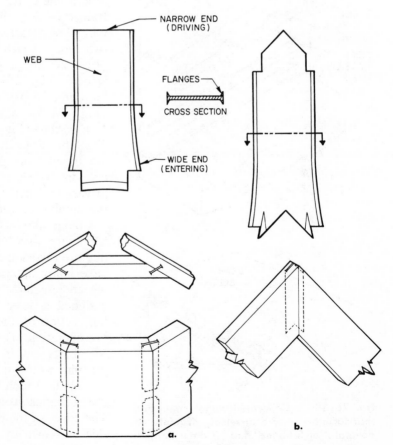

NARROW END
(DRIVING)

WEB

FLANGES

CROSS SECTION

WIDE END
(ENTERING)

Fig. 26–51. Clamp nails: (a) standard type, (b) special miter joint type.

a.

b.

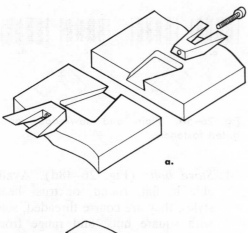

a.

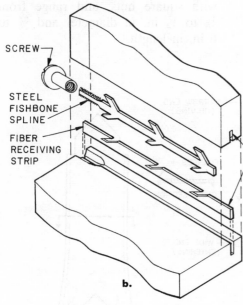

SCREW

STEEL
FISHBONE
SPLINE

FIBER
RECEIVING
STRIP

b.

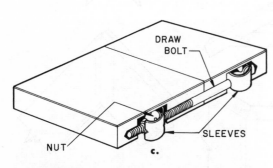

DRAW
BOLT

SLEEVES

NUT

c.

Fig. 26–52. Concealed panel connectors that facilitate easy disassembly of joints: (a) dovetail, (b) fishbone, and (c) draw bolt.

5. *Hanger bolts* (Fig. 26–48e), obtainable in ⁵⁄₁₆- and ³⁄₈-in. diameters and 2½-, 3-, or 3½-in. lengths. They have standard V threads and a square nut on one end and a lag screw thread on the other. The most common use of hanger bolts is for fastening table and chair legs to mounting plates. (Refer to page 477.)

6. *Other common bolts* that occasionally have applications in wood manufacturing are illustrated in Figure 26–49. These fasteners are available in a variety of sizes.

Corrugated fasteners (Fig. 26–50), also known as *"wiggle nails,"* are used to fasten boards at the edges. They are used in the construction of crating, boxes, framed items such as screens, and similar jobs. These fasteners are available with two types of edges; plain for hardwoods (Fig. 26–50b), or saw edge for softwoods (Fig. 26–50a). They may also be obtained with *parallel corrugations* (Figs. 26–50a and 26–50b) or *divergent corrugations* (Figs. 26–50c and 26–50d). The latter draw the wood together as they are driven. Corrugated fasteners are available in ³⁄₈-, ½-, and ⅝-in. widths and in various lengths which are specified by the number of corrugations.

Clamp nails (Figs. 26–51a and 26–51b) are thin tapered metal fasteners that are used somewhat like splines. They have many applications in wood fastening and manufacturing. Clamp nails are designed to exert a drawing or "clamping" action on the joint during the driving operation. They are driven into narrow kerfs cut in the abutting parts of the joint with a special 22-gauge circular saw blade. (Such blades are available for use in shapers, routers, and drill presses.) The edges of the nail are flanged on each side as shown by the section drawing in

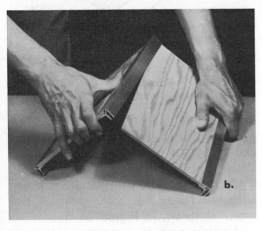

Fig. 26–53. Vertical panel connectors: (a) "H" type, and (b) corner post.

Figures 26–51a and 26–51b. These flanges have sharp edges which cut into the wood fibers as they are driven into the joint. Joints fastened with clamp nails are less likely to separate as a result of expansion and contraction than is the conventional wood spline joint. Clamp nails for flat miter joints are shown in Figure 26–51b. Clamp nails may be obtained in sizes from ⅜ to 3½ in. in length and ⅜ to ⅞ in. in width.

Concealed panel connectors (Figs. 26–52a, 26–52b, and 26–52c) are fasteners that are partially hidden. They are par-

ticularly important in the manufacture of knock down furniture and prefabricated panel units. The *dovetail panel fastener* (Fig. 26–52a) is based on the principle of the screw and nut. The dovetail cuts in the panels are made with a portable router, equipped with a guide to follow a templet. *Fishbone connectors* (Fig. 26–52b) fit into fiber strips glued in saw kerfs cut in the abutting members of the joint. A short cove cut in each piece provides clearance for the locking screw. *Draw-bolt connectors* (Fig. 26–52c) consist of two round sleeves, a bolt, and a round threaded nut. Installation involves boring holes part way into the back surfaces of each member to receive the metal sleeves. Holes for the bolt are bored into the edges to intersect the other holes. The sleeves and bolt are inserted and the round nut is tightened. The nut is turned with a nail set which fits into small holes in it.

Decorative panel connectors are used to join panels in a vertical position as shown in Figures 26–53a and 26–53b. They are generally made of aluminum and are available in sizes to fit ¼-, ½-, and ¾-in. panels. These connectors are either cemented or screwed to the panels.

Corner braces, corner irons, and mending plates (Figs. 26–54a through 26–54d) are used to reinforce joints in light construction. They are made of mild steel and may be unfinished for interior use, or zinc plated for exterior applications. *Corner braces* (Fig. 26–54a) are used to reinforce joints on tables, chairs, church pews, and the like.

Structural fasteners and connectors (Figs. 26–55 and 26–56) are used in joining members of engineered structures, particularly roof trusses. *Truss plates* (Fig. 26–55) are used in the assembly of light roof trusses for residential constructions. They are made of galvanized

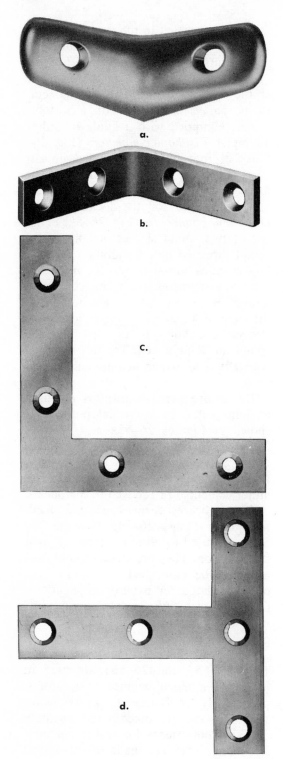

a.

b.

c.

d.

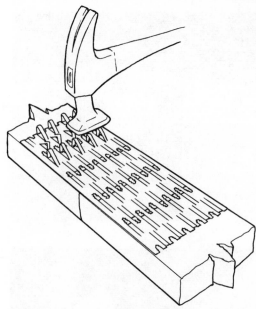

Fig. 26–55. A truss plate being used to connect members end to end.

sheet steel in 18- or 20-gauge thicknesses and in lengths and widths for specified loads. Truss plates are of two general types, namely those with *prepunched nail holes,* or those that have *stamped nail forms* as shown in Figure 26–55.

Another type of a structural fastener is known as the *split ring connector* (Fig. 26–56a). It is a split steel ring, the cross section of which is slightly tapered from the center to the edges. A circular groove is cut $\frac{3}{8}$ in. deep into each member with a special tool (Fig. 26–56b). When installed, one half of the ring is in each of the two overlapping members. A $\frac{1}{2}$-in. bolt and nut hold the assembly together. The rings are made in $2\frac{1}{2}$- or 4-in. diameters.

Fig. 26–54. Braces and mending plates: (a) iron corner brace, (b) bent corner iron, (c) flat corner iron, and (d) T-mending plate.

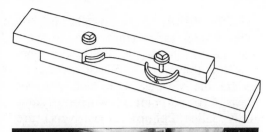

Fig. 26–56. (a) Split ring connectors (artist's sketch), (b) the grooving operation.

Hand Tools for Fastening and Assembly

The principal hand tools used with mechanical fasteners include hammers, nail sets, ripping bars, screwdrivers, and staplers.

Hammers (Figs. 26–57a and 26–58b) are used to drive and draw nails. They are available in several sizes and in several head and handle styles. Claw hammers are sized by weight: 5, 7, 13, 16, and 20 oz. The 13- and 16-oz. weights are most widely used. Heads are made

with either a bell face (Fig. 26–57a) or a plain face (Fig. 26–57b). Carpenters usually prefer the bell face for it allows them to drive nails flush to the surfaces with less chance of denting the surrounding area. Curved claws facilitate nail pulling. Straight claws do not pull nails as well, but they are more useful for prying boards loose.

Nail sets (Figs. 26–58a and 26–58b) are hit with a hammer to "set" or drive finishing nails, casing nails, and brads below the surface of the wood. They are about 4 in. in length and come with hardened cupped tips of various sizes. The

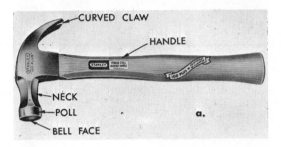

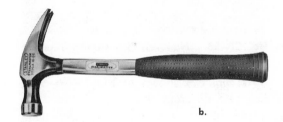

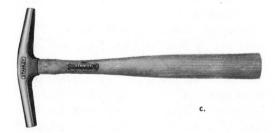

Fig. 26–57. Hammers: (a) bell face curved claw; (b) plain face, straight claw, tubular steel rubber grip handle; (c) a 7-oz. upholsterer's tack hammer with magnetic head.

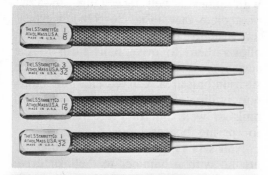

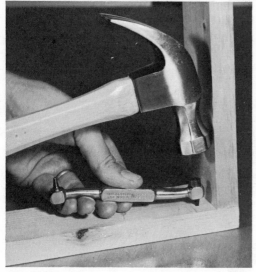

Fig. 26–58. Nail sets: (a) standard set of 4, (b) offset type.

offset nail set shown in Figure 26–58b, has two different diameter points. It is useful in confined places as shown in the illustration. Special *clamp nail sets* are available for setting clamp nails.

Ripping bars and nail claws (Figs. 26–59a, 26–59b, and 26–59c) are used to tear down scaffolding and other work; remove moldings, nails, and tacks; and in general, to provide leverage where it is needed. Three types of tools for this class of work are illustrated in Figures 26–59a, 26–59b, and 26–59c.

Screwdrivers (Figs. 26–60a through 26–61b) are used for driving and withdrawing screws. They are obtainable in a variety of sizes (Figs. 26–60a and 26–60b). Blades range from 1 in. to more than 12 in. in length. Blade tips vary in width, thickness, and style to accommodate the various styles and sizes of screws. Crossed point screwdrivers (commonly called Phillips screwdrivers) are made in No. 1, 2, 3 and 4 sizes to fit the different sizes of cross-slot screws (Fig. 26–62c). Screwdriver *bits* (Fig. 26–61a) are made in sets of three to be interchanged in spiral ratchet screwdrivers (Fig. 26–60e). Large screws are often driven with screw-driver bits (Fig. 26–61b) that are held in auger bit braces.

Hand staplers are of two types — the one-hand and the strike (Fig. 26–62). Both are loaded with a strip of staples. *One-hand* staplers are sometimes called *hammer tackers*. Heavy duty *one-hand* staplers will drive staples up to ½ in. in length. They are used for fastening crat-

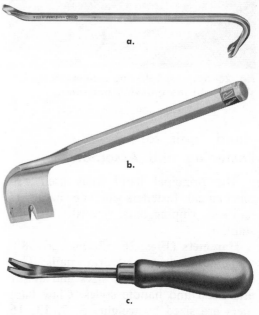

Fig. 26–59. Tools for prying, and withdrawing nails: (a) goose neck ripping bar, (b) molding chisel, and (c) tack claw.

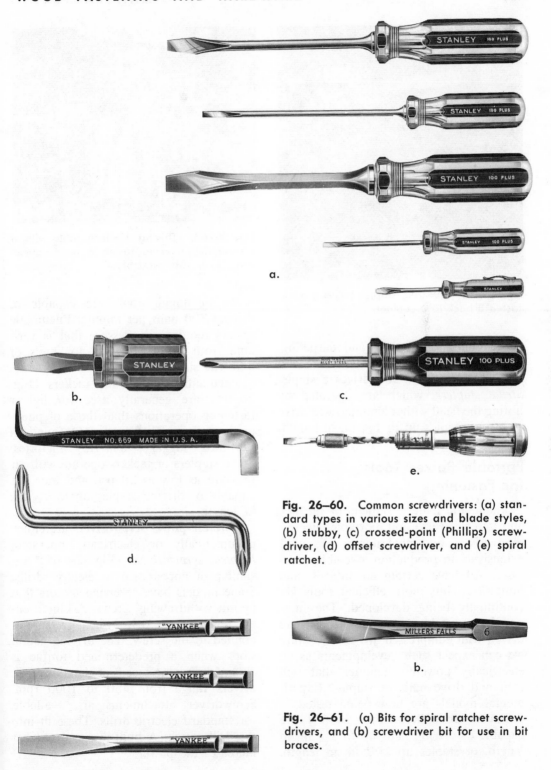

Fig. 26–60. Common screwdrivers: (a) standard types in various sizes and blade styles, (b) stubby, (c) crossed-point (Phillips) screwdriver, (d) offset screwdriver, and (e) spiral ratchet.

Fig. 26–61. (a) Bits for spiral ratchet screwdrivers, and (b) screwdriver bit for use in bit braces.

Fig. 26–62. A strike stapler being used to fasten a back to a cabinet.

Fig. 26–63. Driving 1½-inch nails with a pneumatic nailer to fasten a metal gusset plate to a truss assembly.

ings, roofing, insulation, and carpeting. The stapler operates like a hammer; with every blow it feeds and drives a staple. *Strike staplers,* which are operated by hitting the head with a hammer, will drive 18-gauge staples up to 1⅛ in. in length.

Portable Power Tools for Fastening

Pneumatic nailers, staplers or tackers, and screwdrivers, and portable electric screwdrivers and nut runners are used extensively in production assembly processes. All have certain advantages, and limitations, but more efficient tools are continually being developed. The most popular portable fastening tools are driven with compressed air. In the future we can expect such developments as an electrically powered hammer that will feed and drive nails or staples. Experimental models are now being tested.

Pneumatic nailers (Fig. 26–63) are capable of driving nails up to 2½ in. in length, or staples up to 2 in. in length.

Some pneumatic tools are capable of driving 300 nails per minute. Pneumatic nailers require air pressure that is variable from 40 to 110 psi for nails of different sizes.

Pneumatic staplers and tackers (Fig. 26–64) are generally used for lighter fastening operations than those of pneumatic nailers. They are often found in furniture, luggage, and toy factories. Some staplers or tackers operate with air pressure as low as 20 psi, and they are capable of driving staples up to 9/16 in. in length.

Portable power screwdrivers are either pneumatically or electrically operated. *Electric screwdrivers* (Fig. 26–65) are similar in appearance to electric drills. Some models have reversing motors that permit withdrawing screws. A clutch engages the power drive when pressure is applied to the screw. The driving action stops when a predetermined torque is obtained. Driving speeds of electric screwdrivers range from 450 to 1000 rpm. Screwdriver attachments are available for standard electric drills. These fit into the drill chuck. A built-in speed reducer increases the power.

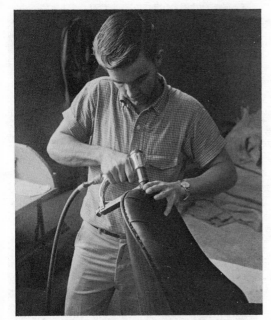

Fig. 26-64. Using a pneumatic stapling gun for tacking upholstery in place.

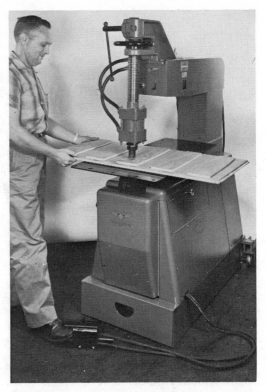

Fig. 26-66. Wire feed automatic nailer being used to fasten overlays to furniture panels. The nails are driven upward from the bottom.

Pneumatic screwdrivers are of many styles, including the conventional pistol grip, angle head, and lever designs. They are also made in a variety of speeds, torque ranges, clutch types, weights, and chuck designs. Some have magnetic holders or screw finders.

Nut runners are similar to electric and pneumatic screwdrivers except that sockets (usually magnetic) are used for driving nuts, bolts, and lag screws.

Automatic nailing machines are of three basic types — (1) the *multiple tack,* (2) *wire feed,* and (3) *bulk feed* with remote gun. *Multiple tack machines* are large machines that feed and drive up to 40 nails with one stroke. High nailing rates are attained by virtue of a multiple bulk feeding system that delivers threaded or smooth shank nails to the nailing heads. Machines of this type are used in the assembly of prefabricated structures. In some plants, they are incorporated into automated production lines and electronically programed for continuous operation.

Fig. 26-65. An electric screwdriver.

Fig. 26–67. This automatic bulk feed nailer is operated by compressed air. It is capable of driving 8d nails in one blow at the remote gun as fast as it can be applied to the work.

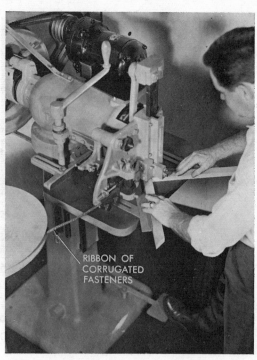

RIBBON OF CORRUGATED FASTENERS

Fig. 26–68. Corrugated fasteners, in ribbon form, are cut to length and driven by this machine.

Wire feed machines (Fig. 26–66) are pneumatically powered. They make their own nails from a coil of threaded wire. As the operator activates the foot treadle, the wire is fed into the machine, cut, headed, and driven. With the treadle continuously depressed, a steady stream of nails is driven at a rate up to 3 per second. Simple adjustments are provided for changing nail length, setting, and clinching. Nailing machines of this type are used to supplement gluing operations in furniture and millwork factories and in the assembly of laminated girders. The nails act as clamps to sustain pressure until the glue cures.

Bulk feed machines with remote guns (Fig. 26–67) offer the advantage of portability. The fasteners are fed to the gun through a delivery hose from a bulk feeder unit. The nails pass through a wheel hopper mechanism in the feeder unit which arranges them so they enter the hose point first. Nails, in sizes up to

8d, are driven in one blow as fast as the operator can activate the trigger.

Corrugated fastener driving machines (Fig. 26–68) first appeared in the early 1900's. They are still effectively employed in industry to assemble many products, particularly those involving framing or butt jointing operations. The fasteners are cut to predetermined lengths of ¾ to 1½ in. from a long corrugated steel ribbon that is fed into the machine. Ribbon widths range from ¼ to ¾ in. As many as eighty to ninety corrugated fasteners per minute may be driven with some models. The power requirements vary from ¾ to 5 hp for the different machines.

Automatic screwdriving machines operate in much the same manner as automatic nailers with remote guns. Automatic feeding devices carry screws, one at a time, through a tube from the hopper to a pneumatic screwdriver gun. The screws are driven as fast as the operator can pull the trigger. The only time he touches a screw is when he loads the large hopper.

Wood Glues and Adhesives Today

Since wood is a porous material, it is relatively easy to glue pieces of it together. However, some woods, because of their oily nature, are quite difficult to glue. Furthermore, the conditions to which some wood products are subjected make it necessary that special glues be used. Many types of glue are formulated for specific gluing jobs while others are intended for more general usage. A "foolproof" glue, serviceable under all conditions, has not yet been developed. Thus, one must have a knowledge of the kinds available and an understanding of their applications.

At one time scientists thought that wood pieces were glued solely together by the mechanical interlocking of the glue with the pores or cellular cavities of the wood. Today, this process is believed to be a combination of this mechanical action coupled with a chemical bonding of the adhesive film and the wood substances.

The *glue line* between two pieces of bonded wood consists of a thin layer of cured adhesive that ranges from .002 to .005 in. in thickness. Tentacles of glue extending from this layer into the open wood pores provide the mechanical holding action in the glue joint.

The various *types of wood adhesives* may be divided into two major groups: (1) glues formulated from materials of natural origin, and (2) synthetic resin glues, a product of modern chemistry.

Glues of natural origin include animal, vegetable, casein, soybean, and a group known as liquid glues.

1. *Animal glues,* also called hide glues, are probably the oldest known type of wood glue. They are prepared from the hides, bones, sinews, and hide fleshings of cattle. Animal glues are available in liquid or in dry form. The dry glue is soaked in water for several hours, heated to about 145 degrees, and applied while hot. Liquid animal glues are ready to use at room temperature. Animal glues are available in different grades. The higher grades are preferred for joint work; the lower grades are suitable for veneering. Hot animal glues develop strength first by cooling and gelling and later by drying. They are often preferred for hand spreading on joints used in furniture assemblies. The chief disadvantages of animal glues are their relatively high cost, their need for careful temperature control when being used, and the low water and moisture resistance of the joints.

2. *Vegetable (starch) glues* are usually made from cassava starch. They are sold in powder form and may be mixed cold with water and alkali, but heat is commonly used in their preparation. These glues are relatively cheap, can be used cold, and remain in good working condition, free from decomposition, for many days. Vegetable glues prepared from powder are too viscous (sticky) to be spread by hand. Special liquid starch glues, although easier to spread, are more expensive. Vegetable glues set relatively slowly, mainly by loss of water to the wood. In the past, vegetable glues were widely used, particularly for veneer-

TABLE 26–5 CHARACTERISTIC OF COMMON GLUES

Adhesive Type	Form	Mixing Procedure	Color Glue Line	Chief Application and Use	Advantages
Animal Glue (Dry)	Granular	Mix with water, soak, heat to 145°F.	Tan-brown	Assembly, edge gluing and laminating	Very durable for inte use, quick setting
Animal Glue (Liquid)	Liquid	None	Off white brown	Assembly, edge gluing and laminating	Very durable for inte use, quick setting
Blood	Powder	Mix with water, alkali, etc.	Dark red	Fir plywood	Fast curing, tolerant rough veneers
Casein	Powder	Mix with water	Cream	Laminated timbers, doors, etc.	True cold setting (down freezing point) tough, silient excellent bond wood, not critical of fit
Contact Cement	Liquid	None	Yellow-tan	Plastic & similar laminating	Quick bond, pressure necessary; shock resiste moisture proof, very c venienet
Epoxy Resin	Liquid	Mix with liquid catalyst	Varies	Special applications	Capable of wide modifi tion, outstanding in g filling, poly-functional
Melamine Resin	Powder	Mix with water and shell flour	Colorless-tan	Hardwood plywood, laminated timbers	Permanent except for m severe uses
Melamine Urea Resin	Powder or Liquid	If powdered type, mix with water cat- lyst optional	White-tan	Tapeless splicing, hard- wood plywood, edge and end-glued lumber, laminated timbers	Moderate cost, excell durability for severe terior use
Phenol Resin	Liquid or Powder	Usually mixed with shell flour filler	Dark red	Fir plywood	Durable bond, waterpr
Phenol-Resorcinol Resin	Liquid	Mix with powdered catalyst	Dark red	Laminated timbers, sandwich panels, general bonding	Moderate cost with no in durability, increa craze resistance, perr nent even for exte uses, including marine
Polyvinyl (Aliphatic Resins)	Liquid	None	Yellowish or whitish transparent	Assembly gluing laminating, edge gluing	Colorless, odorless, qu green strength, no fire h ard, economical, sets do to chalk point circa 50 wide variety of adhere except metal
Resorcinol Resin	Liquid	Mix with powdered catalyst	Dark red	Laminated timbers, trusses, marine structure, highpressure laminates	Permanent including r rine, sets down to 70
Soybean	Powder	Mix with water, alkali, etc.	Light	Fir plywood	Poor substitute for blc albumin, tolerant of rou ness, cheap
Urea Powder	Powder	Mix with water	Tan	Lumber & hardwood plywood	Economical, ideal col sets down to 70°F., r able for indoor use
Urea Liquid	Liquid	Mix with powered catalyst—fillers, ex- tenders optional	White-tan	Hardwood plywood, particleboard	Economical, ideal col sets down to 70°F., r able for indoor use

TABLE 26–5 (Cont.)

...advantages	Service Durability	Clamping or Processing Conditions	Approx. Shelf & Working Life — Normal Conditions	Normal Spread wet wt./M sq. ft. Single Glue Line	Comparative Cost	Tendency To Stain
...or water resistance	Interior use	Clamp at room temperature	Indefinite dry one day mixed	60-80 lbs.	Moderate	No
...or water resistance	Interior use	Clamp at room temperature	3-6 mos.	35-45 lbs.	Moderate	No
...stroyed by fungus and ...teria under certain con-...ions, very dark color, ...quires special handling	Water resistant	Hot press 230-280°F.	Indefinite dry 4-12 hours mixed	35-50 lbs.	Low	Yes
...uld susceptible, slow ...ing, may stain, hard on ...ls, expensive	Water resistant	Clamp at room temperature	1 yr. dry, 4-12 hrs. mixed	60-80 lbs.	Low	Yes
...ensive, fire hazard, sol-...t odor, poor creep re-...ant, special technique ...cessary	Water resistant	Use contact pressure only	9-12 months	60-95 (double)	Moderate	No
...or water resistance on ...od, toxic catalysts, very ...ensive	Waterproof	Varies, heat accelerates cure	Indefinite unmixed 5 min. to several hrs.	Varies, usually heavy	High	No
...ll not bond to metal, ...ensive	Waterproof	Hot press 240-260°F.	Approx. 1 yr. unmixed 10-16 hrs. mixed	35-45 lbs.	High	No
...rability and cost in di-...t proportion to Melo-...e content	Highly water resistant	Hot press 250-300°F.	6-12 mo. unmixed 3-10 hrs. mixed	30-50 lbs.	Moderate	No
...quires high temp. & ...ssure, cost more than ...stitute formulations	waterproof		Approx. 3 months	20-40 lbs	Moderate	No
...rder to cure, does not ...ve indefinite shelf cure, ...ins under some condi-...ns, will not bond metal	waterproof	Cure at room temp. or slightly above	1 yr. unmixed 3 hrs. mixed	50-70 lbs.	Moderate High	No
...t good under high stress ...low rates of loading ...ited water resistance ...r good for exterior use	Interior use	Clamp at room temp. 5 min. to 1 hr.	6 months plus	35-50 lbs.	Moderate	No
...eds and stains, high ...t, will not bond metal	Waterproof	Cure at room temp. or slightly above	1 yr. unmixed 3 hrs. mixed	50-70 lbs.	High	No
...ry sensitive to fungus ...en when phenolic modi-...d, structurally weak	Interior use	Usually cold press	1 yr. unmixed 3 hrs. mixed	50-75 lbs.	Low	Yes
...remely rigid and brittle ...e line, satisfactory for ...y wood to wood, re-...res machine fit of fray-...services	Water resistant	Hot or cold press	1 yr. unmixed 4-6 hrs. mixed	35-45 lbs.	Low	No
...remely rigid and brittle ...e line, satisfactory for ...y wood to wood, re-...res machine fit of fray-...services	Water resistant	Usually hot press	Approx. 3 months unmixed 1¼-24 hrs. mixed—depending on catalyst	30-40 lbs.	Low	No

TABLE 26–5 (Cont.)

Adhesive Type	Form	Mixing Procedure	Color Glue-Line	Chief Application and Use	Advantages
Urea — Furtural Modified	Liquid	Mix with powdered catalyst	Brown	Miscellaneous assembly, high pressure laminates	Less gap sensitive th urea, especially suited bonding high press plastic to plywood
Vegetable Starch	Liquid or Powder	Mix with water (powder) or use liquid as received	Tan-brown	Hardwood plywood, assembly gluing	New ones may have u usual properties, ol ones for veneering w delicate or fragile high figured wood
Vinly Polymer Thermosetting	Liquid	Catalyst, 5% by weight	Transluscent straw	Plastic foams, board products, general wood bending	Cold setting, weather sistant, with some mod cation will bond to met easy hot water clean-up

ing because the time between spreading and pressing (assembly time) could be varied without affecting the quality of the joint. The use of vegetable glues is limited today because they lack water and moisture resistance, like the animal glues, and because they cause staining in thin veneer. These glues have not been used extensively for joint work.

3. *Casein glues* are made from casein curd (protein) precipitated from milk either by natural souring or by the addition of acids or enzymes. Lime and other chemical ingredients are added to the casein to prepare the glue for use. Formulas are available for the user to compound his own glue from raw casein, but it is generally more convenient to use prepared glues supplied in powder form, which require only the addition of water before use. The prepared glues are available in small retail packages. The many casein glues available include glues with long pot life, but relatively low moisture resistance and glues with good moisture resistance but a definitely limited pot life. Casein glues have sufficient strength for either veneer or joint work. They are used cold (although they may be hot pressed), and, when properly mixed, can be spread with a brush. The moisture-resistant casein glues are intermediate in moisture resistance between vegetable and animal glues and synthetic resin glues. Disadvantages of casein glues are their tendency to stain veneers, the relatively short working life of some types, and the dulling effect of the glue lines on tools. Each of these limitations may be minimized separately by special formulations, but generally at the sacrifice of some other property.

4. *Soybean (vegetable protein) glues,* which are similar in general composition, properties, and use characteristics to casein glues, are formulated from dried protein of soybeans.

TABLE 26-5 (Cont.)

	Service Durability	Clamping or Processing Conditions	Approx. Shelf & Working Life — Normal Conditions	Normal Spread wet wt./M sq. ft Single Glue Line	Comparative Cost	Tendency to Stain
out the same limited rability as urea, slightly re expensive	water resistant	Hot or cold press	3 mos. unmixed 3 hrs. mixed	Usually heavy	Moderate	No
ry poor water resist- ce, mold susceptible	Interior use	Cold press	Varies depending on type	35-80 lbs.	Low	Yes
st be evaluated for pro- ction and service condi- ns, mix proportions must measured precisely, uld be stored below °F.	Boiling water re- sistance after 24 hour room tem- perature, com- plete cure in 3 minutes at 300°F.	Clamp at room temperature or slightly above	24 hrs. at 72°F. 2½ hrs. at 100°F., viscosity will in- crease but adhesive is satisfactory if it can be stirred. Maximum life at 40° to 60°F.	25-55 lbs.	Moderately- high	Some species

Soybean glues are cheaper and generally produce lower-strength joints than casein glues and are therefore mainly used for veneer gluing, primarily of the softwood species. Soybean glues are not normally suitable for hand work or small-scale operations. Their moisture resistance is similar to that of casein glues.

5. *Liquid glues* include those glues of natural origin offered in ready-to-use form. Originally they were made from heads, skins, bones, and swimming bladders of fish, but more recently they are also prepared from animal-glue bases by special treatments. These liquid glues tend to vary considerably in quality from sample to sample, but the better glues produce joints comparable to those of hot animal glue. Liquid glues are more expensive than other nonresin glues and find their greatest use for small-scale operations, such as assembly or hobby work. They are also used in place of hot

animal glue if convenience of use is important. Liquid animal and starch glues were previously mentioned. Certain synthetic resin glues are also supplied in ready-to-use liquid form. The most common type is the polyvinyl-resin emulsion glues.

6. *Blood albumin glues* were formerly used for veneering but are now entirely replaced in the United States by the synthetic-resin glues. The characteristics of woodworking glues of natural origin are summarized in Table 26-5.

Synthetic resin glues are products of the modern chemical industry and originate from raw materials derived from coal, air, petroleum or natural gas, and water. Although the intermediate raw materials are available, the complex production methods required for the resins and the fact that some are covered by current patents severely limits the small-scale manufacture of resin glues in the shop.

All of the resin glues included in this

group, except the polyvinyl-resin emulsion glues, are thermosetting types, that is, they undergo irreversible chemical curing reactions to produce insoluble, infusible glue films in the joint. The polyvinyl-resin emulsion glues are thermoplastic resins, that is, they do not undergo any chemical curing during the gluing process, but remain in a reversible state and soften on subsequent heating. The chemical curing or hardening reactions of the thermosetting resin glues, by which their joint strength is developed, are accelerated by adding catalysts to certain glues or by increasing the glue-line temperature by various methods. In addition to catalysts, any resin glue may also be modified with fillers, such as walnut-shell flour, to improve spreading properties and control penetration, or with extenders, such as wheat or other cereal flours, to reduce glue-line costs.

Some resin glues are sold in a single package ready to use or as a powder to be mixed only with water. Many others, however, must be prepared for use by mixing resin, catalyst, fillers, extenders, and water or other solvent at the time of use. In any case, the manufacturer's instructions should be followed closely.

1. *Urea-resin glues* are available in powder and liquid forms to be used with or without added catalysts, fillers, and extenders. Glues may be formulated for curing at room temperature (usually considered as about 70 deg. F) or at hot-press temperatures of 240 to 260 deg. F. Special formulations are available for tapeless splicers, high-frequency curing, and other specific applications. The glue lines are colorless to light tan in color and have only a moderate dulling effect on tools. Unextended urea-resin glues have high water and

moisture resistance, but are sensitive to temperatures of 150 deg. F or higher, particularly at high-humidity conditions. These glues are generally not recommended for exterior service. Extension with cereal flours reduces their moisture and water resistance. Resistance to elevated temperatures and exterior conditions can be somewhat improved, however, by modification with special fortifiers. When properly formulated, the unmodified urea-resin glues give high initial strength and are suitable for both veneering and joint work. Several room-temperature-setting urea-resin glues are available in small retail packages for small-scale shopwork, and require only addition of water to prepare them for use. Special liquid resins have been developed for economical tank-car or truck shipment for large-scale users, but these resins require addition of catalysts and usually extenders before use.

2. *Phenol-resin glues* are normally dark-reddish liquids and require hot pressing at 280 deg. F or higher. Some, however, are supplied in powder form to be mixed with water or other solvent. At least one phenol-resin glue comes in the form of film. This factor eliminates mixing and spreading operations, and facilitates gluing thin figured, fragile veneers. Special formulations are available for curing at intermediate temperatures, and certain acid-catalyzed resins may be cured at temperatures as low as 75 deg. F. The nonacid phenol-resin glues are one of the most durable types of wood glues, and, when properly used, give joints that are as durable as untreated wood under severe exposures. There are indications that

the acid-catalyzed phenol-resin glues produce joints that are not as durable at elevated temperatures as joints made with conventional phenol-resin and glues of natural origin. Because they require high curing temperatures, phenol-resin glues are mainly suitable for plywood production, although intermediate-temperature-setting formulations for laminating heavy timbers for severe service are cured in heated chambers. The phenol-resin glues are not ordinarily suitable for small-scale or hobby work.

3. *Resorcinol-resin glues* are dark-reddish glues and are generally supplied as liquids to which a liquid or powdered catalyst is added before use. These glues have much the same performance characteristics, including high durability, as the phenol-resin glues with the added advantage that they cure, sufficiently for many applications, at temperatures as low as 70 deg. F. They are, however, the most expensive of the current woodworking glues. Recent formulations of phenol-resorcinol resin glues are appreciably cheaper than straight resorcinol-resin glues and appear to retain most of the desirable characteristics of the resorcinol resins. Both types are used for laminating or for assembling articles where a high degree of durability is required. Their high cost prevents their use as a veneering glue except for special applications. At least one brand of resorcinol-resin glue is available in small retail packages for small-scale shop work and is of particular interest to the boatbuilder.

4. *Melamine-resin glues* are available as colorless hot-press glues at a price between that of urea-resin and phenol-resin glues and that of straight resorcinol-resin glues. Although the melamine-resin glues are as durable as the phenol- and resorcinol-resin glues, their high cost and high curing-temperature requirement limit use of the straight melamine resins to a few special applications. These resins, however, are often used to fortify and thus improve the durability of urea-resin glues.

5. *Polyvinyl-resin emulsion glues* set at room temperature to a colorless glue line. Unlike the other resin glues described, these glues do not cure by a chemical reaction but set by losing water to the wood. They remain somewhat elastic and thermoplastic in the glue line, which makes their use in highly stressed joints inadvisable. They appear promising, however, for certain types of assembly joints where their greater elasticity is an advantage over the conventional rigid woodworking glues. Characteristics of the major types of resin glues are summarized in Table 26–5.

The selection of a glue. The wide variety of types and trade-name brands of glues available today often makes the selection of the appropriate glue appear difficult. This choice may be simplified by determining some of the basic requirements dictated by the particular gluing job. The final choice is usually determined by a compromise of these four basic factors:

1. *The type of joint* to be fabricated and the particular mechanical or engineering properties, such as initial strength required of the joint design. Consideration must be given to the dimensions and sometimes to the species of wood involved. Certain plywood and flat grain-to-flat grain laminated joints are relatively easy

to glue with a variety of glues; other types of joints, such as a butt joint of two end-grain surfaces, may be very difficult or almost impossible to glue satisfactorily with any glue. Some glues, such as soybean glues, are particularly suitable for gluing softwood veneers, some for assembly work with dowels or dovetail joints, and some for heavy laminated constructions. Certain glues may be used in a variety of constructions and types of joints.

2. *The working properties of the glue.* Nearly all glues are suitable for industrial use if plants are provided with the necessary equipment, but equipment requirements vary considerably for the different types of glues. The choice of glues for small-scale operations or school shop work is likely to be more restricted than for large scale operations because of the limited equipment available. For some glues, equipment is required for heating the joints at elevated temperatures in order to develop proper strength, although others may be pressed at normal room temperatures. Consideration must also be given to the equipment needs for measuring out ingredients, mixing glues, spreading glue, and applying and maintaining pressure on the joint. Temperature requirements for the shop, wood, and glue, the length of time required between spreading and application of pressure (assembly period), and the length of time that the joint must be under pressure are important in choosing a glue. The user will also wish to consider the length of time that any glue remains usable (the working life or pot life) once it is prepared for use, as well as the length of time that the glue components may be safely stored before being prepared for use (the shelf life or storage life). Glues also differ in the ease with which they can be cleaned from equipment after use.

3. *The permanence required of the joint in service.* When properly used, most currently available glues are capable of giving high original dry-joint strength and of remaining durable under dry, normal temperature conditions. However, the resistance of the joints to deterioration in service varies widely with different glues. In fact, the improved resistance to deterioration of the newer resin glues is a principal reason for their development and increasing use. Generally, different brands of the same chemical type of glue will have similar durability characteristics. Durability of glues thus varies from the relatively low moisture resistance of animal and vegetable glues to the high all-around durability of the phenol-, resorcinol-, and melamine-resin glues, which when properly used give joints that are as durable as untreated wood itself under severe exposure.

4. *The cost.* Since prices of glues are continually changing and often depend largely on the quantities ordered, it is impractical to list exact figures. Costs increase, however, from the relatively low-cost soybean and vegetable glues to the animal, casein, urea-resin, and phenol-resin glues, to the melamine-resin glues, and finally to the resorcinol-resin glues, which are the most expensive per pound. Cost must be considered, however, in terms of the *actual cost per pound* of *mixed glue,* rather than the cost of ingredients as received, and of the amount of glue spread required;

that is, the cost to spread a certain area of surface must be considered. Wastage because of short pot life, costs of rejected material because of lack of control of the gluing process, and costs of the equipment and man-power needed for commercial processes must also be weighed in comparing glue costs.

Basic considerations involved in gluing processes. The overall quality of any glue joint not only depends upon the proper selection and application or general use of the glue itself, but the conditions related to gluing are also highly important. Although different types of currently used glues may require radically different gluing conditions, the basic gluing processes are quite similar.

To achieve strong enduring glue joints, attention must be given to these six primary considerations for all gluing processes:

1. *The moisture content of the wood* at the time of gluing has much to do with the final strength of joints, the development of checks in the wood, and warping of the glued members. In general, glues will adhere to wood with any moisture content up to 15 percent; water-resistant glues will adhere to wood with even higher moisture content. Large changes in the moisture content of the wood after gluing will cause shrinking or swelling stresses that may seriously weaken both the wood and the joints, thus, resulting in delamination. The most satisfactory moisture content at the time of gluing is that which, when increased by the moisture of the glue approximately equals the average moisture content that the glued member will have in service. Stock with 5 to 6 percent moisture is generally satisfactory for gluing

furniture, interior millwork, and similar items. Lumber for exterior use should generally contain 10 to 12 percent moisture before gluing.

2. *Surface conditions.* Wood surfaces to be glued should be smooth, true, and free from machine marks, chipped or loosened grain, torn fibers, and other surface irregularities. Surfaces should be well fitted. Preferably, machining should be done just before gluing, so that surfaces do not become distorted from subsequent changes in moisture content or atmospheric humidity. Cutting tools for machinery must be adequately sharpened to produce desirable surfaces for gluing. Dull jointer knives, for example, will burnish or polish wood surfaces which thus resist penetration of the glue into the pores of the wood. Conversely, tests have proved that intentionally roughening wood surfaces by tooth planing, scratching, or sanding does not benefit gluing processes. Sanding generally removes more wood at the edges and soft areas than at dense areas. This causes the thickness of a sanded board to be less uniform than that of a well planed board.

3. *Spreading the glue.* The glue should cover the *entire* joining surfaces evenly. Usually it does not need to be applied to both surfaces of the joining members.

4. *Assembly period.* This is the time lapse between spreading and pressing. The permissible range of assembly time differs widely for individual glues. It is also usually dependent on the temperature of the glue, wood, and atmosphere. See Figures 26–69a and 26–69b.

5. *Temperature.* Poor joints result from too low temperatures. Correct tem-

Fig. 26–69. Poor and good wood glue joints made under different gluing conditions: (a) excessively thick glue line caused by too long an assembly period, (b) too short an assembly period; the joint was pressed before the glue had reached the desired viscosity, (c) glue not adequately cured and (d) a well-made joint that developed a high percentage of wood failure when broken.

perature and pressures must be maintained until the glue is set. The recommended temperatures for different kinds of glue are given in Table 26–5.

6. *Pressure* on a glue joint should squeeze the glue out into a thin continuous film between the wood layers, force the air from the joint, bring the wood surfaces into direct contact with the glue, and hold them in this position during the setting or curing of the glue. See Figures 26–69a through 26–69d. A light pressure should be used with a thin glue.

Heavy pressures should be used with thick glues and corresponding variations in pressures should be used with glues of intermediate consistency. The strongest joints (Fig. 26–69d) generally result when the consistency of glue permits the use of moderately high pressures. This is about 100 to 250 psi. The hand clamps used in the school shop seldom produce pressures that exceed these recommendations.

Starved glue joints. Many failures in glued wood products are caused by "starved" joints, or joints in which the film of glue between the wood surfaces is not continuous. Starved joints are readily identified by broken joints showing little or no wood failure or with little or no glue visible. Such joints, according to the Forest Products Laboratory, are not necessarily the result of a lack of glue spread on the wood; heavy spreads are as likely to produce them under ordinary commercial conditions as light spreads. They are caused rather by the application of pressure to the joint while the glue is too fluid.

Starved joints are more likely to occur with glues of low viscosity, such as warm animal glue, than with casein, vegetable, and other thick glues. Starved joints have also been observed with some of the thermosetting synthetic resin glues when short assembly periods and heavy pressures are combined with thin glue mixtures. Such thin mixtures may result from use of the glue too soon after mixing.

Some woods are more susceptible to the production of starved joints than others. Birch, maple, red oak, and ash, which have open pores, absorb glue from the spread in such considerable amounts that they often leave the joints starved. Basswood and yellow poplar also take up a great deal of glue, but weak joints are not very noticeable in these woods because the woods themselves are weak. Other woods with smaller cells open to the gluing surface do not seem to be so subject to starved joints.

In some cases starved joints may result from the use of wood containing too much moisture at the time of gluing. This has been observed frequently in the use of phenol-resin glues and is likely to occur whenever wet wood is glued.

To avoid starved joints it is necessary to mix a glue solution thick or to allow it to thicken in the pot or on the wood before pressure is applied. When it is necessary to glue under conditions that might produce starved joints, the use of light pressure is advantageous.

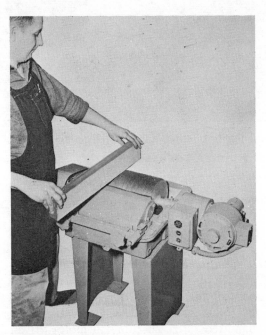

Fig. 26–70. Glue spreaders: (a) portable hand spreader for small jobs and where the spreader must be taken to the work; (b) a bench machine spreader with motor drive.

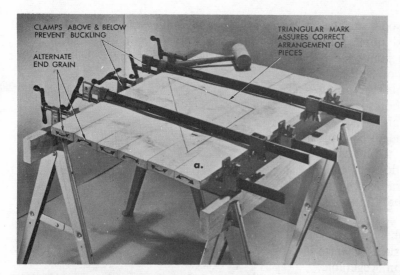

CLAMPS ABOVE & BELOW
PREVENT BUCKLING

ALTERNATE
END GRAIN

TRIANGULAR MARK
ASSURES CORRECT
ARRANGEMENT OF
PIECES

a.

Fig. 26–71. Bar clamps in use: (a) standard type for edge-to-edge gluing, (b) hinged type swings under bench when not in use, (c) clamping a framed assembly.

b.

c.

Clamps and Equipment for Gluing Processes

The tools and equipment employed in industrial and custom manufacturing include hand clamps, glue spreaders, presses, and many other types of special equipment.

Glue spreaders are used for the application of glue to wood surfaces. They control the amount of glue spread and its thickness. Spreaders are available in hand-fed (Fig. 26–70a), a motor-driven (Fig. 26–70b), and floor or bench types. Large heavy-production machines are generally power-driven. They may also incorporate a variety of optional construction features such as glue heaters, drip-proof reservoirs, various feed rates, arrangements for single or double surface coating, and circulating pumps. These large machines are similar to the roller coating machine illustrated in Figure 35–28.

Woodworking clamps are of many styles and sizes. The three most common types of hand-operated clamps are: *bar clamps* (Figs. 26–71a through 26–72), *C-clamps* (Fig. 26–73), and *hand screw clamps* (Figs. 26–74a and 26–74b). The illustrations of these clamps also point out some of the common ways in

Fig. 26–72. Combination of bar clamps and cross clamps (at arrow) to obtain pressures in opposite directions for the assembly of a cabinet.

Fig. 26–73. "C" clamps being used for face-to-face laminating.

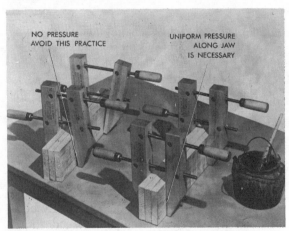

Fig. 26–74. Hand screw clamps are versatile: (a) uniform pressure along the length of the jaws is essential.

Fig. 26–75. This hand clamp consists of a canvas belt tightened by a screw mechanism. It is ideal for clamping round or irregular shapes.

Fig. 26–74. (b) Using sufficient number of clamps as shown is always advisable to ensure sufficient pressure.

Fig. 26–76. One of many types of clamps designed for applying pressure to miter joints.

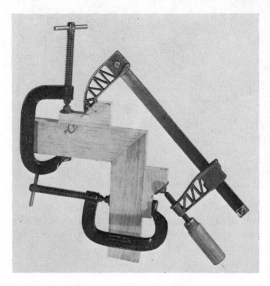

Fig. 26–77. One way of clamping miters for short run work.

which they are used to apply pressures for gluing. Other kinds of clamps for miters without special equipment is shown (Fig. 26–75) and *miter clamps* (Fig. 26–76). Another method of clamping miters without special equipment is shown in Figure 26–77.

Clamp carriers (Fig. 26–78) are large pieces of equipment which basically consist of many bar clamps fastened to an endless chain or other revolving mechanism. These machines are made in various sizes and they are usually motor driven.

Case clamps (Figs. 26–79a and 26–79b) are used in production plants for the assembly of case and cabinet units. These large clamps provide pressure by either a hand-powered screw thread mechanism or pneumatic cylinders (Fig. 26–79a). The revolving types provide vertical or horizontal pressure as desired. Case clamps are made in a wide range of sizes and with screw or stroke adjustments.

Frame and sash press clamps (Fig. 26–80) are used in industry for produc-

Fig. 26–78. A clamp carrier is used in furniture plants for clamping edge-to-edge glued joints.

tion assembly of frame and sash work. They are generally of the pneumatic pressure type. With these machines the stiles and rails are generally clamped in a horizontal position or inclined as

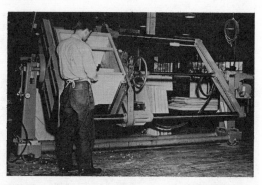

Fig. 26–79. (b) A case clamp is used for case assembly. The work may be tilted (revolved) for easier access to the work.

Fig. 26–79. (a) A revolving case clamp activated by pneumatic pressure.

Fig. 26–80. Assembled bed parts are clamped in this machine. A shield is lowered over the assembly and the glue lines are cured electronically in a few seconds.

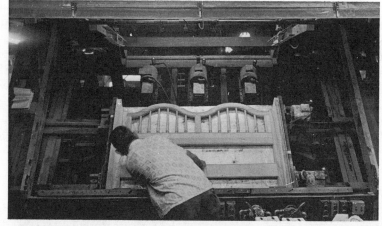

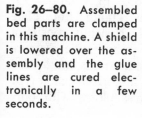

Fig. 26–81. A large laminating press before loading.

shown in Figure 26–80. Most machines have only two air cylinders which apply pressure in perpendicular directions. Machinery of this type is also available in various size capacities and with numerous optional features such as cylinders and forms for irregularly shaped work.

Laminating presses (Fig. 26–81) are of two basic types — hot press or cold press. Both types are used by industry to apply pressure for manufacturing such materials as panels with high pressure

Fig. 26–82. A hydraulic edge gluing hot plate press.

laminates, framed panels with overlays, and doors. The essential difference between hot and cold presses is that hot presses have heated platens to speed curing. In general, pressures obtained by laminating presses vary from 40 to 3000 psi. Press sizes are specified according to the vertical (daylight) opening between the top and bottom platens, and according to the size. For most wood fastening operations platen pressures greater than 250 psi are seldom required. The pressures of laminating presses are obtained by hydraulic or pneumatic pressure cylinders, or by screw thread mechanisms. Some screw type machines are driven by electric motors. Multiple opening presses that are used in the production of plywood are illustrated in Figure 35–30, page 652 of Chapter 35.

Production edge gluing hot plate presses (Fig. 26–82) basically consist of a large hot press with hydraulic pressure from the side. The material is end loaded into the press by a motorized batch-type feed table. The press closes with only

Fig. 26–83. This high frequency electronic press quickly cures all glue lines of these edge glued panels. The cured panels, 50 inches wide, are automatically ejected from the machine as shown.

enough pressure to maintain a flat register. This prevents the stock from buckling until the side pressure shoes exert full edge pressure. After a brief hesitation, the press completes its closure to maximum platen pressure for the best transfer of heat to the joints.

Electronic gluing equipment of portable "hand gun" and machine-press types (Fig. 26–83) are used for high rate production gluing processes. This process is becoming increasingly popular in many major wood industries. The advantage of the electronic process is that heat is generated within the glue line without appreciable heating of the surrounding area. An electronic generator produces and sends alternating currents at high frequencies (millions of cycles per second) through two electrodes which disturb the glue molecules. This creates instantaneous heat and almost instantly cured glue joints result. The glued assembly is immediately ready for subsequent operations or processing. Urea-resin and melamine-resin glues are used for this gluing process.

Common Furniture and Cabinet Hardware

Furniture and cabinet hardware includes a large number of different types of hinges, catches, pulls, knobs, locks, shelf supports, wood leg accessories, and many other special purpose items. The

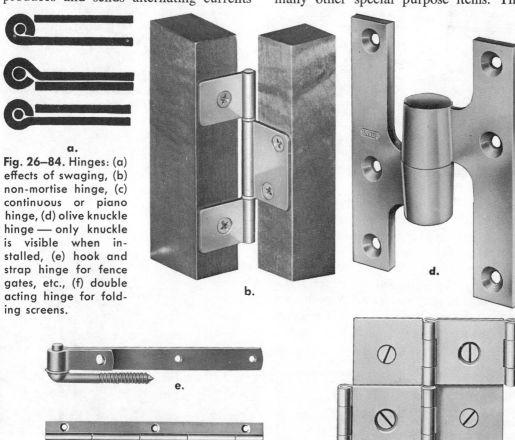

Fig. 26–84. Hinges: (a) effects of swaging, (b) non-mortise hinge, (c) continuous or piano hinge, (d) olive knuckle hinge — only knuckle is visible when installed, (e) hook and strap hinge for fence gates, etc., (f) double acting hinge for folding screens.

a.

b.

c.

d.

e.

f.

Fig. 26–85. Semiconcealed hinges: (a) reinforced door pivot hinge, (b) cabinet pivot hinge for flush overlay door to vertical frame, (c) hinge in (b) as applied to horizontal frame, (d) semiinvisible hinge mounted in saw kerf in back side of door.

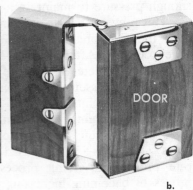

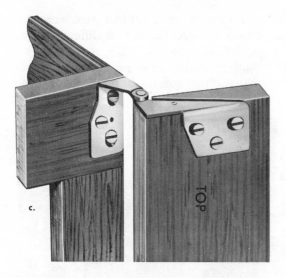

selection of the appropriate type and design of any hardware item can enhance the design, appearance, usefulness, and overall quality of a wood product.

Hinges (Figs. 26–84a through 26–87b) may be classified as either *semi-concealed* or *fully concealed*. Most hinges consist of three basic parts — two leaves that include the joint knuckles, and a

Fig. 26–86. This butt hinge for flush cabinet doors will also work for light chest lids.

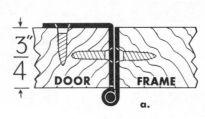

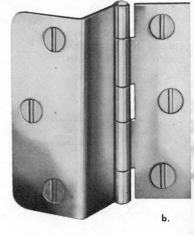

Fig. 26–87. Some typical matched cabinet hardware: (top) contemporary, and (bottom) Colonial or Early American designs in copper and black finishes.

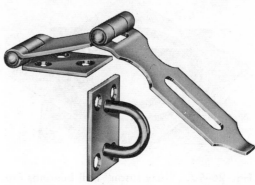

Fig. 26–89. Safety hasp and staple for padlock.

connecting pin. Hinges may have either removable or stationary pins.

Swaging (Figs. 26–84a through 26–84f) is a slight offset of the hinge leaves which permits them to fold closer together. Hinges may have nylon or ball

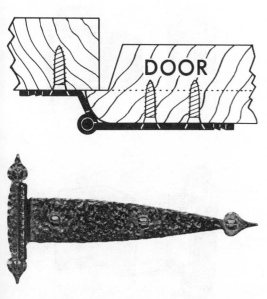

Fig. 26–88. Hinges for ⅜ inch lip type doors: (left) surface hinge with profile view of application, (right) standard semiconcealed cabinet hinge and profile of application.

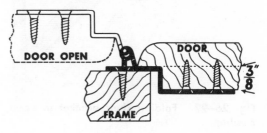

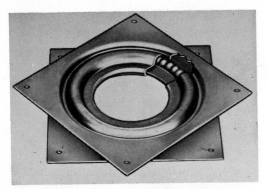

Fig. 26-90. "Lazy susan" ball bearings are available in many sizes for turntables and swivel fixtures.

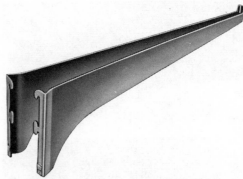

Fig. 26-93. Another kind of shelf bracket.

Fig. 26-91. Shelf bracket.

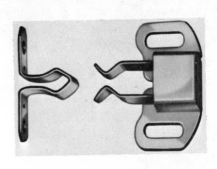

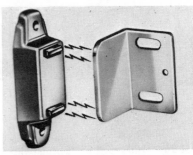

Fig. 26-92. Folding shelf bracket in open position.

Fig. 26-94. Three basic types of catches: (a) lever spring action, (b) roller, and (c) magnetic.

bearings and spring closures. Some are made to raise and lower the door as it is opened and closed. Other hardware items are illustrated in Figures 26–88a through 26–95e.

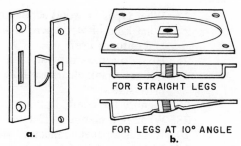

FOR STRAIGHT LEGS

FOR LEGS AT 10° ANGLE

a.

b.

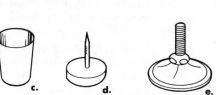

c. d. e.

Fig. 26–95. Miscellaneous hardware items used on furniture: (a) typical bedpost plate and bed rail hook, (b) leg mounting plates threaded to fit ⁵⁄₁₆ or ⅜ hanger bolts, (c) brass ferrules for bottom of turned legs, (d) leg or furniture glide, (e) adjustable leveling swivel glide.

REVIEW QUESTIONS

1. Define: joinery; penny; glue; adhesive; cement.
2. Give several examples of recent developments in wood fastening materials and processes.
3. How were early structures fastened?
4. What contribution did Archimedes make to mechanical fastening processes?
5. Outline the origin and development of glue.
6. What are some of the functions of various joints other than to hold pieces together?
7. List some of the basic joints and describe their application in common wood products.
8. What are some methods of reinforcing joints?
9. What effect does the grain have on joint design, strength, and selection?
10. Do tongue-and-groove joints provide more strength than simple edge-to-edge joints? If not, why is this type of joint used?
11. What materials are used for splines? What are the important considerations?
12. What kinds of joints are used to joint stock end to end? Which are most suitable to the school shop?
13. Describe the following: box, chest, case, toe board, skeleton frame, cabinet, center guide, stile, rail, dust panel, kicker, and stop.
14. What is the difference between flush and lip door and drawer construction?
15. Why must doors and drawers have clearance?
16. What types of joints are used in drawer construction? Which is the most durable?
17. What details must one observe when gluing stock edge to edge?
18. Name four different kinds of nails that are widely used.
19. Name four kinds of nails that are designed for a special purpose.
20. What effect does nail point sharpness have on the splitting of wood?
21. What are "blued" nails?
22. How are sizes of wood screws specified?

23. What types of wood screw heads are available?
24. What kind of wood screws should one use for interior furniture? Boats? General outdoor use?
25. How do screws provide their holding power?
26. Define: shank clearance hole; pilot hole; countersink; screw-hole button; plug; drive screw.
27. Identify the common types of bolts that are often used in wood structures.
28. What is a clamp nail? How does it work? How is it used in cabinetmaking?
29. What is a panel connector? Where are they used?
30. List three different connectors that are used in building construction.
31. How are hammers sized?
32. What is a nail set and how is it used?
33. What purpose do hand staplers serve in wood fastening processes?
34. Describe the major types of fastening power tools used in industry.
35. What makes a glue joint hold? In general, how thick is a glue line?
36. Describe the various kinds of adhesives that are used by the wood industries today. Which of these are also adaptable to the school shop?
37. Which glues are waterproof?
38. What is meant by the term "water resistant"?
39. Which glues are designed for hot press work?
40. What kind of adhesive is used in the manufacture of particle board?
41. What kinds of adhesive are suitable for bonding plastic laminates? How are they used?
42. What factors should be considered in the selection of a glue?
43. How are glue joints tested in industry?
44. Describe the basic considerations that are involved in most gluing operations.
45. What is a "starved" glue joint?
46. What effect does moisture, clamping pressure, and temperature have upon gluing processes?
47. Describe some of the clamping equipment that is used in industry.
48. What are the principal kinds of hinges that are available for cabinetmaking?
49. What kinds of catches are available for cabinet doors?
50. What type of hardware is available for furniture legs?
51. Identify some hardware devices that may be used in shelf construction. In drawer construction.

SUGGESTED STUDENT ACTIVITIES

1. Make a display of various wood joints.
2. Obtain samples of joints that are made with special machinery used by industry.
3. Measure the withdrawal resistance of several kinds of nails in a certain species of wood. In different species.
4. Compare the withdrawal resistance of nails driven perpendicular to the grain and parallel to the grain (in the end grain).
5. Visit a hardware store and obtain samples of various kinds of nails and screws. Arrange them on a display board.
6. Make tight fitting mortise and tenon joints in both green wood and kiln dried wood. Dry the green wood in an oven and compare the joints.

7. Make a starved glue joint on scrap stock.
8. Prepare a display of various glue-joint failures and list their causes.
9. Use the appropriate adhesive and make some particle board from wood shavings.
10. Devise several tests for glue joints and record the results. Use the data for a written report.
11. Design an electrically operated nail hammer.
12. Sketch six methods for making homemade clamps.
13. Design and construct a form for making laminated water skis.
14. Design and construct a scale model of a device for making laminated beams.
15. Design a clamp or press for gluing veneer stock to flat panels. To cylindrical forms.

Chapter 27 Scraping

Scraping is a process by which a blade with a specially prepared "burr edge" cuts or "scrapes" thin shavings from wood surfaces (Figs. 27–1a, 27–1b, and 27–1c). Scraping is not a production line technique, but rather a small-scale hand tool craft utilized in custom work as a supplement to planing and sanding.

Scraping tools, called scrapers, are used to smooth surfaces. Scrapers were among the earliest tools invented by man. Primitive scraping tools included flints, sea shells, sharp-edged bones, and, in time, pieces of glass. When the sharp edge became dull it was discarded and replaced by a new one. The advent of metal tools provided man with a material which could be reconditioned when the edge lost its effectiveness. Scrapers have continued in use right up to the present day reaching a peak just before the development of coated abrasives (sandpaper). At that time, scrapers were used to remove mill marks from lumber in most all cabinet and veneer work. Some factories used large *scraping machines:* a system of feed rolls which carried stock over a stationary scraper blade. Hand scrapers were also employed to smooth wood flooring before portable power sanders came into wide use. Due to the speed and overall efficiency of modern abrasives and sanding machines, scrapers find only limited small-scale use today.

Scrapers

There are four basic kinds of hand scraping tools: (1) the hand scraper; (2) the cabinet scraper; (3) the hook or hoe scraper; and (4) the swan-neck scraper. All are either filed to 90 deg. and burred on 2 edges (Fig. 27–1a), or they are filed to a bevel with one scraping edge (Figs. 27–1b and 27–1c). The cutting action of each is basically the same.

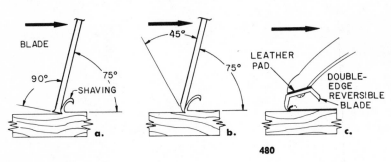

Fig. 27–1. (a) Hand and swan-neck scrapers; (b) cabinet scraper; (c) hook scraper. Heavy arrows indicate the direction of stroke.

Fig. 27–2. Hand scraper.

Fig. 27–4. A hook scraper. It has a reversible blade that provides four scraping edges.

Hand scrapers (Fig. 27–2) consist of a semi-flexible piece of alloy steel .035 in. thick by 2½ or 3 in. in width by 5 or 6 in. in length. The cutting edge is filed and whetted to 90 deg. and then burnished to a burred edge as shown in Figure 27–1a. It is used with either a push or pull cutting stroke. This type of scraper is used in school and cabinet shops to remove tool marks and smooth torn grain.

Cabinet scrapers (Fig. 27–3) contain a flat blade (2¾-in. size) which is bevel ground to 45 deg. (Fig. 27–1b). It is held in a malleable iron frame with two handles. The frame seats the blade at a 75-deg. angle to the surface of the work. Cabinet scrapers are usually applied to the surface with a push cutting stroke.

Hook scrapers (Fig. 27–4) are available in a number of sizes and types. Some are furnished with two types of blades:

(1) straight with a beveled edge (similar to a hand scraper); (2) reversible with a double-edge U shape (Figs. 27–1c and 27–4). Hook scrapers are widely used for work such as scraping paint and varnish from surfaces for refinishing. Scrapers of this type are also appropriate for removing dried glue from joints. Hook scrapers are used with a pull cutting stroke.

Swan-neck scrapers (Fig. 27–5) are hand scrapers shaped to fit a concave surface. They are useful for scraping moldings and similar surfaces.

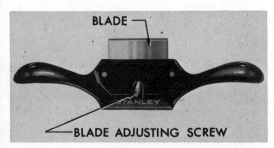

BLADE

BLADE ADJUSTING SCREW

Fig. 27–3. A cabinet scraper. The blade adjusting screw controls the depth of cut.

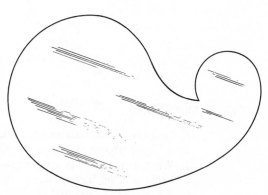

Fig. 27–5. A swan-neck scraper.

Scraping in the School Shop

Scrapers are relatively easy to use provided that their edges are correctly sharpened and burred. A sharp scraper produces very thin shavings; but when dull, nothing but dust. Refer to page 592 for the procedure of sharpening scraper blades. On hardwoods, the edge dulls quickly, so frequent sharpening is necessary.

Using hand scrapers. Grasp the blade as shown in Figure 27–6 and tilt it about 75 deg. in the direction of the stroke. Apply moderate pressure with the thumbs to spring (bow) the blade into a slight curve. This raises the corners slightly so they do not gouge the work or leave ridges. Pull or push the scraper the length of the work with the grain. Since it is difficult to start a stroke at the end of a board, begin at the center. Overlap each stroke. For difficult jobs (cross-grain), hold the scraper at an angle to the grain direction so the edge produces a shearing cut.

Adjust the cabinet scraper as follows:

1. Loosen the adjusting thumb screw (Fig. 27–3) and the two blade clamping screws.
2. Install the blade from the bottom with the bevel toward the adjusting screw.

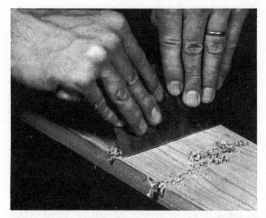

Fig. 27–6. Using the hand scraper with a pull stroke.

3. To adjust the blade so its edge is flush with the bottom of the frame first place the tool on a flat board. Then press downward on the blade lightly and tighten the clamp screws (one on each end).
4. Adjust for depth of cut by turning in the blade adjusting screw. This "bows" the blade slightly, projecting it through the bottom of the frame.
5. Make a trial cut. If necessary, change the depth adjustment until thin shavings are obtained.

NOTE: The cabinet scraper is generally used with a push stroke, although it may also be pulled.

REVIEW QUESTIONS

1. Describe the development of scrapers and scraping processes from Stone Age to Industrial Age.
2. When and for what purpose are woods scraped?
3. What are the basic types of hand scrapers?
4. What are the principal kinds and uses of scrapers?
5. How is a cabinet scraper adjusted for depth of cut?

SUGGESTED STUDENT ACTIVITIES

1. Demonstrate scraping with a piece of broken glass.
2. Design, grind, and sharpen a scraper blade for scraping concave edges.
3. Design and then fashion a scraper from an old file for removing dried glue from glued up stock.
4. Examine with a magnifying glass the scrapings produced with a dull scraper and a sharp scraper.
5. Design and construct a device to measure the energy required to scrape with a dull scraper and a properly sharpened scraper.

Chapter 28 Sanding

Sanding* is the process of employing coated abrasives (Fig. 28–1) to smooth wood surfaces by hand or machine methods. Coated abrasives are composed of paper or cloth backings to which hard, crystalline grains are bonded. The wood is smoothed by the cutting action of the sharp edges of the abrasive grains. See Figures 28–2a and 28–2b. Machines used for sanding operations are called *sanders;* they are of many types and sizes.

Sanding is one of the most important

---

* For many years, abrasive papers were coated with selected grades of sand, from which the name sandpaper evolved. However, most modern abrasives are coated with man-made substances although the term "sanding" and even "sandpaper" continue to be used to refer to the processes involved.

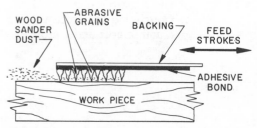

Fig. 28–1. This enlarged drawing shows the basic components of modern coated abrasives. Each abrasive grain functions as a cutting or scraping tool.

manufacturing processes. Nearly every wooden product is sanded in the course of its manufacture. Sanding operations may be classified as: (1) *"white sanding,"* which includes all of the sanding operations that are performed on wood

Fig. 28–2. (left) Sanding marks resulting from three different sizes of abrasive grits used on hard maple, (right) Sander dust of 1½ grit enlarged approximately 18 diameters.

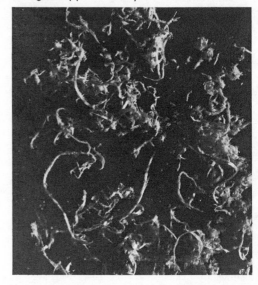

prior to the application of a finish. Such work includes sanding for the removal of mill marks, glue stains, minor machining defects, and the like; (2) *"finish sanding,"* which includes those sanding operations that occur between applications of the various finish coats. This class of work is performed to smooth the surface and to prepare it so that the next finish coat will adhere well.

A number of specialized sanding machines have been developed. They are becoming increasingly important in the mechanization of our wood using industries. Some of the newer machines are not only used for smoothing operations, but they are also used to "size" wood. That is, they serve the same basic function as planers and surfacers in that they reduce stock to thickness within close dimensional limits. This relatively new development is known as *abrasive planing*. According to experts in the field, these machines offer increased production rates, reduced operation and maintenance costs, and a surface quality equal to that obtained by any previous method.

Evolution of Coated Abrasives and Sanders

The **first abrasive material,** a dark granular stone, was referred to as "Shamir" by the Hebrews in the Old Testament. It was used to shape and sharpen the crude metal tools of those days. We know this material as *emery*. Emery has been mined in Turkey and the Grecian islands for centuries. Today, emery finds some use as a polishing agent for metals. It is of no importance to wood sanding processes.

In the thirteenth century the Chinese glued crushed sea shells to sheets of parchment with natural gums. Consequently,

they are credited with the development of coated abrasives.

Over 200 years ago, the Swiss developed a coated abrasive consisting of crushed glass glued to a paper backing. Glass did not have the strength and sharpness necessary for a satisfactory abrasive. Research led to the discovery of crushed flint quartz as a suitable abrasive. Flint paper has been used in this country about 150 years. Flint paper is still a well known coated abrasive, but it has been largely replaced in industry by more efficient and economical abrasives.

Garnet, the third of the natural minerals used in the manufacture of coated abrasives was introduced in 1877–1878. Because of its superior hardness, garnet has largely supplanted flint in most sanding operations.

Man-made abrasives, superior to natural abrasives, were introduced in the 1890's. Their manufacture followed the development of the electric furnace in which various ingredients could be fused at high temperatures. *Silicon carbide* and *aluminum oxide* are the 2 principal electric furnace abrasives that have been used since the turn of the century.

Before the development of mechanized sanding processes, all wood sanding operations were performed by hand. Good old fashioned "elbow grease" and spirited determination were essential requirements for the early woodworker who wished to transform a rough surface into a smooth one by hand-sanding. The need for greater production at reduced cost prompted the development of sanding machines.

Early sanding machines included an open-drum and a disk sander powered by line shafts. They were similar to the one shown in Figure 28–3. The first belt type machine developed was the *hand block sander* (Fig. 28–4). The *first portable*

Fig. 28–3. This combination disk and spindle sander was made in the late 1800's. The metal frame supported a wooden table. The spindle was designed to provide either a rotary (1500 rpm), or reciprocating motion, or both. The disk speed was 750 rpm.

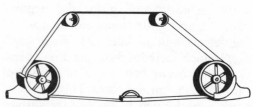

Fig. 28–4. The belt tracks on four pulleys on some hand block sanding machines.

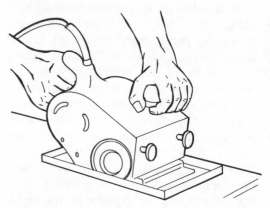

Fig. 28–5. A portable electric drum finishing sander made in 1932.

electric sanders were introduced in the 1930's. These were the drum type on which an abrasive sheet was mounted (Fig. 28–5).

Coated Abrasives Today

Coated abrasives consist of *abrasive grains,* an *adhesive,* and a *backing material* (Fig. 28–1).

The **abrasive grains** (Figs. 28–1, 28–6a, 28–6b, 28–6c, and 28–6d), used in the wood industries are of four different kinds. These are:

1. *Aluminum oxide* (Fig. 28–6a). Reddish-brown in color, these man-made crystals are the toughest and most durable of all abrasives. It is not as hard or sharp as silicon carbide, but it withstands the most severe working strains. It is ideal for sanding hardwoods.

2. *Silicon carbide* (Fig. 28–6b). Originally used for polishing diamonds, silicon carbide is man-made, blue-black in color, crystalline in shape, and close to the industrial diamond in hardness and sharpness. Because it is so hard, silicon carbide fractures readily. In use, the grains break, rather than wear, down. Consequently, new, sharp cutting points are constantly being exposed to the work. This abrasive is well suited for use in high speed sanders and for the "finish sanding" of lacquers and enamels.

3. *Garnet* (Fig. 28–6c). Red in color and a relatively hard mineral, garnet is found in nature and is a combination of silicon, oxygen, and certain metallic elements. Like silicon carbide, it fractures readily and continually presents sharp, new cutting

Fig. 28–6. The four most widely used abrasives for wood sanding: The man-made abrasives (a) aluminum oxide and (b) silicon carbide; the natural abrasives (c) garnet, and (d) flint.

points while in use. Garnet abrasives are principally used for "white sanding" of wood. They are also used between shellac coats.

4. *Flint* (Fig. 28–6d). Another form of silicon dioxide, flint is a natural substance which was the abrasive grain of the original "sandpaper." It varies in color from a dull grayish-white to a faint shade of pink. Flint abrasives are low in cost but they lack the durability of other abrasives and therefore have a short life.

The **sizes** of abrasive grains or grits range from fine to coarse. The smaller the grit size the smoother the surface on which it is used (Fig. 28–2a). Silk screens are used to separate the grits into their various mesh sizes. For example, a 220-mesh screen has 220 openings to the lineal inch (in each direction) or 48,400 openings per square inch. Grit sizes range from 12 (the coarsest) to 600. Traditionally, numbers and aughts have been used to designate the grit sizes. The newer method is to specify the mesh size. A comparison of the grit sizes of coated abrasives available today is given in Table 28–1.

Backings (Fig. 28–1) of coated abrasives are of five basic kinds: (1) paper, (2) cloth, (3) paper-cloth combination,

TABLE 28–1
SIZES OF GRITS

	Silicon Carbide	Aluminum Oxide and Garnet	Flint
Extra Fine	600	600(12/0)	
	500	500(11/0)	
	400	400(10/0)	
	360		
Very Fine	320	320(9/0)	
	280	280(8/0)	
	240	240(7/0)	5/0
	220	220(6/0)	4/0
Fine	180	180(5/0)	3/0
	150	150(4/0)	2/0
	120	120(3/0)	1/0
	100	100(2/0)	½
Medium	80	80(0)	1
	60	60(½)	1½
Coarse	50	50(1)	2
	40	40(1½)	2½
Very Coarse	36	36(2)	3
	30	30(2½)	
	24	24(3)	
Extra Coarse	20	20(3½)	
	16	16(4)	
	12		

is 40 lbs. per ream (480 sheets of 24 by 36-in. uncoated paper) and is used for finishing papers. "C" (70 lbs.) and "D" (100 lbs.) are cabinet papers; "E" weight (130 lbs.) is a heavy production paper. *Cloth* backings are used for operations that require greater strength and flexibility than provided by paper. There are two main types of cloth: Jeans (J), lightweight and flexible, but strong, and drills (X), a medium-weight cloth used for belts and disks. A *paper-cloth combination* is used when the backing must have more resistance to tearing and flexing than paper, but need not have the great flexibility of cloth. *Fiber* is stiff. It is used for rough work, such as performed by disks on portable sanders and similar jobs. *Fiber-cloth combination* provides the greatest strength and durability of the 5 kinds of backings.

Adhesives (Fig. 6) must hold the grit until it has done its work. They are of 4 general types: hide glue, synthetic resins,

(4) fiber, and (5) fiber-cloth combination. Within each group are various types and weights. Each kind has its advantages for certain jobs. *Paper* backings are made of the strongest stock available. Four weights are available. "A" weight

Fig. 28–7. Waterproof abrasives for wet sanding operations have a special adhesive bond.

modified glue, and modified resins. *Hide glue* is used for "dry" sanding operations where heat and friction are not severe. *Synthetic resins* are used for operations that generate intensive heat. Waterproof abrasives (Fig. 28–7), with which water is used as a lubricant to increase the rate of cut, are bonded with resins. *Modified glues and resins* are used where exceptional grit holding and water and heat resistance are needed.

Types of coatings (Fig. 28–8). There are two types of coatings. They are known as *closed coating* and *open coating*. Closed-coated abrasives have backings that are completely covered with grit; no adhesive is exposed. The dense coating lengthens the life of the abrasive on rugged operations. Open-coated abrasives have backings on which only 50 to 70 percent of the surface is covered with grit. The open spaces prevent "loading up" when the coated abrasive is used on soft or gummy materials.

Hand and Portable Sanding Processes in Industry

Although industry relies on mechanized sanding operations for production work, this is usually supplemented with hand (Fig. 28–9) and portable power sanding. Also, some sanding and rubbing operations are not readily adaptable to machine processing. This class of work generally includes the touch-up "white sanding" for the removal of defects that occur in the course of assembly. Delicate sanding and rubbing for fine finishes is

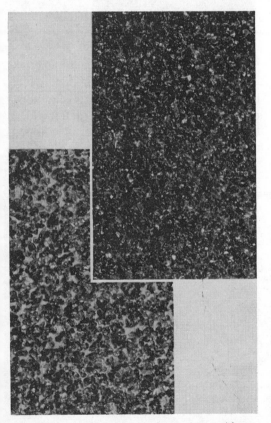

Fig. 28–8. Two types of coatings. Above shows closed coating in which the abrasive grains completely cover the surface of the backing; below, open coating, with only 50 to 70 percent of surface covered.

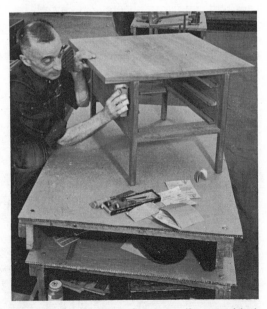

Fig. 28–9. In this factory all assembled pieces receive a final 6/0 white sanding by hand.

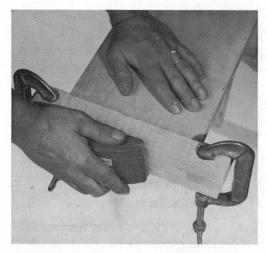

Fig. 28–10. Commercial sanding block.

often done by hand or with portable machines.

Sanding blocks (Figs. 28–9, 28–10, and 28–11) are used to back up the sandpaper. There are a number of different types of commercial sanding blocks. One made of resilient rubber (Fig. 28–11) uses cut abrasive sheets 2¾ by 9 in. Another type of block uses abrasive paper in rolls. It is loaded like a camera and handled like a block plane (Fig. 28–12). One of the most widely used sanding

Fig. 28–11. Commercial sanding block.

blocks is homemade. It consists of a block of wood with rubber, cork, or felt glued to one surface. Abrasive paper is wrapped around the block for sanding.

Portable sanders are classified as (1) orbital or reciprocating pad, (2) belt, (3) disk, or (4) drum sanders.

Orbital or reciprocating pad sanders

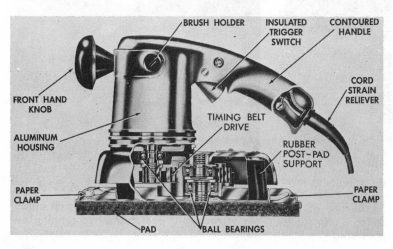

BRUSH HOLDER
INSULATED TRIGGER SWITCH
CONTOURED HANDLE
FRONT HAND KNOB
CORD STRAIN RELIEVER
ALUMINUM HOUSING
TIMING BELT DRIVE
RUBBER POST–PAD SUPPORT
PAPER CLAMP
PAPER CLAMP
PAD
BALL BEARINGS

Fig. 28–12. A portable electric orbital finishing sander.

(Figs. 28–12, 28–13a, and 28–13b) are also called finishing sanders. They are widely used for final white sanding and for finish sanding and polishing operations. Sanders of this type produce either a straight-line stroke of the pad or a small orbital stroke (about $\frac{3}{16}$- or $\frac{1}{4}$-in. circles). Some sanders in this category will produce either straight-line or orbital strokes as desired. The orbital stroke is advantageous for rapid cutting, but it produces small cross-grain scratches. Straight-line sanders produce surfaces free from cross-grain scratches. However, they generally have less power and shorter strokes than orbital sanders. Sanders in this group vary greatly in weight, number of strokes per minute, and pad and motor sizes. They are driven by air, electric, or electromagnetic vibrating motors. Straight-line sander strokes vary from $\frac{1}{8}$ to $\frac{1}{2}$ in. in length and from 3500 to 15,000 strokes per minute. The higher speeds are typical of the pneumatic sanders.

Portable belt sanders (Fig. 28–14 and 28–15) basically consist of an abrasive belt which travels over two flat pulleys (one drive and one adjustable tracking idler) powered by an electric motor. This type of sander has a continuous straight-line cutting action. It is used for fast removal of stock. The *size* of the belt sander is indicated by its belt width and length (circumference). The common sizes of belt sanders are 3 by 21 in., 3 by 24 in., 4 by 24 in., and 4 by 27 in. Belt speeds vary from 1180 to 1500 surface feet per minute (sfpm). Some models are available with a vacuum system that picks up the sanding dust and deposits it in an attached bag (Fig. 28–14). Still others have hose hook-ups that attach to vacuum cleaners or dust collection systems.

Portable disk sanders (Figs. 28–16a

and 28–16b) are used for general rough sanding. Disks for sanders of this type range from 3 to 9 in. in diameter. The abrasive disks are usually held to the pad by a flanged clamp that screws into the spindle. Disk sanders rotate at speeds between 3000 and 6000 rpm.

Portable drum floor sanders (Fig. 28–17) are used to prepare newly laid flooring for a finish or to remove an old

Fig. 28–13. Two types of pneumatic sanders: (a) single pad and (b) double pad. They are used for sanding and polishing surfaces.

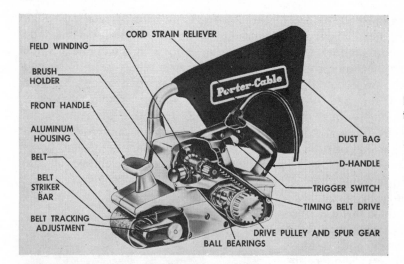

FIELD WINDING

CORD STRAIN RELIEVER

BRUSH
HOLDER

FRONT HANDLE

ALUMINUM
HOUSING

BELT

BELT
STRIKER
BAR

BELT TRACKING
ADJUSTMENT

DUST BAG

D-HANDLE

TRIGGER SWITCH

TIMING BELT DRIVE

DRIVE PULLEY AND SPUR GEAR

BALL BEARINGS

Fig. 28–14. Nomenclature of a 3 x 24-inch portable electric belt sander with a top mounted drive motor.

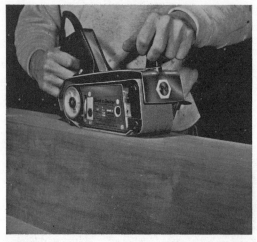

Fig. 28–15. A heavy duty two-speed 3 x 24-inch belt sander with the motor mounted between the belt pulley.

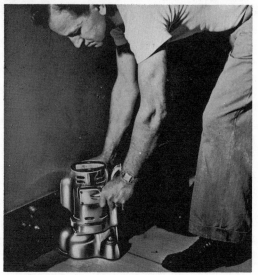

Fig. 28–16. Disk sanders. (above) light duty, all purpose type; (below) "edger" is a special disk sander used for floor sanding.

finish prior to refinishing. They weigh about 100 lb. or more and are made in several drum sizes. Abrasive paper (in 50-ft. rolls) is cut to the appropriate length and wrapped around the drum. The ends are clamped in a slot in the drum. The machine shown in Figure 28–17 has a 1½-hp motor belted to a 5¾-in. diameter by 8-in. long drum.

Sanding Machines

Some of the many kinds of sanding machines in use today are described on the following pages.

The **disk sander** (Fig. 28–18) is used in pattern shops, schools, cabinet shops, and other places where wood is custom worked. Basically, the disk sanding machine consists of a motor-driven disk faced with a coated abrasive, a stand and an adjustable worktable. Some machines have two disks and two worktables. These are known as *double-disk machines*. Sizes of disks on double-disk machines vary from 16 to 36 in. in diameter. They are driven directly by 2- to 10-hp motors. Smaller disk sanders such as the one shown in Figure 18 range from 6-in. bench types to 12-in. sizes. These are driven by ½-, ¾-, or 1-hp motors. Larger single disk machines, up to 36 in. in diameter, are also available. The worktables of all disk sanders may be tilted up to 45 deg. Some machines also have grooved tables to accommodate a miter gauge. The major operations performed on disk sanders include sanding end grain, bevels, chamfers, miters, segments, compound miters, and, to some extent, convex curves. Figure 28–19 illustrates a combination disk and belt sander.

Spindle sanders (Fig. 28–20a and 28–20b) are made in vertical and horizontal models. Vertical spindle sanders mount an abrasive cylinder (or sleeve) on steel

Fig. 28–17. Floor sander, drum type.

or rubber covered spindles. Generally, the spindles are driven directly at speeds of about 1800 rpm. Spindles on some machines also oscillate. That is, they move approximately 1 in. up and down about 60 times per minute while rotating. This helps to prevent the abrasive from becoming loaded. Vertical spindle sanders are sometimes combined with

Fig. 28–18. A disk sander.

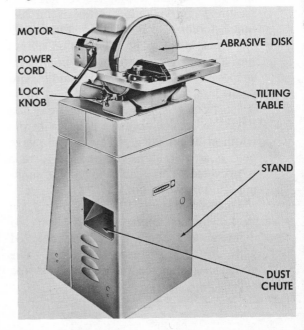

MOTOR

POWER CORD

LOCK KNOB

ABRASIVE DISK

TILTING TABLE

STAND

DUST CHUTE

Fig. 28-19. A combination disk and belt sander.

disk sanders (similar to the type shown in Figure 28–3).

Horizontal spindle sanders have either metal, rubber, wooden, or pneumatic drums on which the abrasive sleeve is mounted. A *pneumatic drum* is an air-inflated rubber roll which is fitted with an abrasive belt. The air cushion allows the abrasive to conform to contoured shapes such as found on ax handles and chair legs.

Horizontal spindle sanders may be rigged to employ abrasive belts. With the addition of an idler pulley and abrasive belt, a greater abrasive working surface is provided. This results in cooler sanding and less wood burning.

Open-drum (Fig. 28–21) sanders are steel cylinders approximately 18 in. in diameter and about 2 ft. long, covered with an abrasive paper or cloth. The abrasive is clamped in a slot across the

Fig. 28-20. Spindle sanders: (above) vertical, (below) horizontal with abrasive belt attachment.

face of the drum. The drum rotates at about 400 to 600 rpm. This machine is primarily used for utility sanding of corners, edges, ends, and the like.

Attachments (Fig. 28–22) are available to convert a drill press into a vertical drum sander. These consist of soft, rubber covered, expandable drums. They are made in diameters and lengths to fit standard-size abrasive sleeves.

Multiple drum sanders (Fig. 28–23) are large production machines that are

Fig. 28–22. Drum sanding accessories for the drill press.

Fig. 28–21. An open-drum sander being used to remove the sharp corners from the ends of a square chair leg.

primarily used in the sanding of flat work or sheet materials. They are used in millwork and structural plywood plants and furniture factories. Multiple drum sanders may have 2, 3, 4, 6, or as many as 8 drums. Single-surface sanding machines have the drums located either above or below the feed bed. Double-surface sanders have drums located both above and below so that two surfaces of the work may be sanded with one pass through the machine. Each successive drum has a finer grit abrasive. Drums are

Fig. 28–23. A three-drum sander with individual motor drive and endless bed feed.

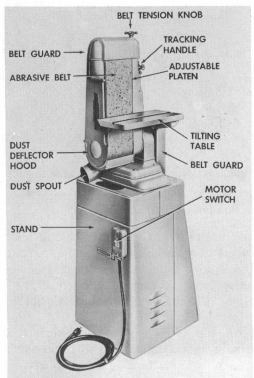

BELT TENSION KNOB

TRACKING HANDLE

BELT GUARD →

ABRASIVE BELT

ADJUSTABLE PLATEN

DUST DEFLECTOR HOOD

TILTING TABLE

BELT GUARD

DUST SPOUT

MOTOR SWITCH

STAND

Fig. 28–24. A variety belt sander.

individually adjustable. They are driven directly by individual motors of 10 to 15 hp. The drum sizes are generally about 12 in. in diameter and range from 2 ft. to over 8 ft. in length. Some machines have oscillating mechanisms which move the drums about ¼ in. horizontally about 175 times per minute.

Feed mechanisms used on drum sanders employ either smooth steel cylindrical rollers or endless traveling beds as shown in Figure 28–23. Feed rates may vary from 12 to 36 fpm.

Variety belt sanders (Fig. 28–24) are relatively small machines used in school shops and custom manufacturing plants. The platen and idler pulley may be swiveled into a horizontal position for horizontal sanding. The abrasive belt travels over two pulleys (one idler and one drive). Better machines have rubber covered drive pulleys for greater traction. Adjustments are provided to tension and track the belt. Motors are usually ½ hp.

Hand block belt sanders (Fig. 28–25a,

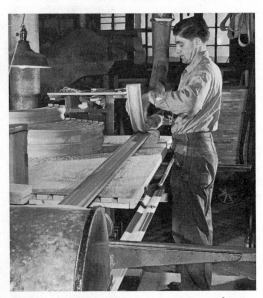

Fig. 28–25. Industrial applications of the hand belt sander. (left) on convex surfaces; and (right) on molding — a block cut in the shape of the molding is placed under the belt to make it take shape.

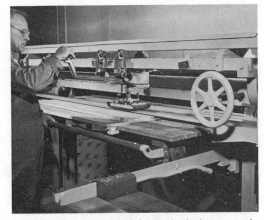

Fig. 28–26. (left) Automatic double belt stroke sander; and (right) single-belt manual stroke sander.

28–25b, and 28–25c) are machines in which the moving belt is pressed against the surface of the work. A hand block is applied to the back of the belt. A table supporting the work rides on a carriage at right angles to the belt travel. The operator may apply the belt at any point on the work. Contoured hand blocks may be used to shape the belt to contoured work.

The **automatic stroke sander** (Fig. 28–26a) provides an automatic reciprocating movement of the sanding pad over the abrasive belt. The operator controls the pad pressure on the belt while he moves the work under it. Some machines mount two belts and provide a choice of grits for the work at hand. The pad on the machine in Figure 28–26b is pressed against the belt and moved the

Fig. 28–27. An automatic edge sander.

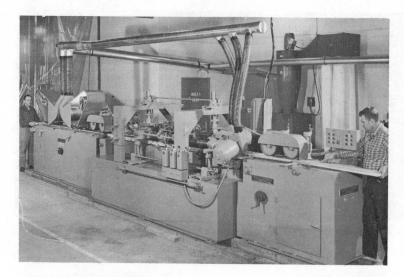

Fig. 28–28. A view of a sanding sticker showing three sanding belts at work.

length of the work manually.

The **edge belt sander** mounts a sanding belt on 2 vertical cylindrical pulleys, one a driver, the other an idler. The belt runs in a vertical plane. The workpiece is supported on a horizontal table during sanding. The belt is supported by a platen or contact roller. Machines of this type are primarily used for sanding the edges of long and narrow rectangular stock. An automatic edge sander is shown in Figure 28–27. This machine features an endless feed bed, a constant sanding pressure mechanism, and an abrasive belt that may be tilted for sanding angular edges. The belt on some of these sanders also oscillates. Platen sizes range from 6 by 18 in. to 10 by 36 in.

Sanding-sticker machines (Fig. 28–28a) will sand four surfaces of a workpiece in a single pass. Feed rates range up to 150 fpm. The machine in Figure 28–28a is approximately 17 ft. in length.

Wide-belt sanders (Figs. 28–29 and 28–30) are machines that use an abrasive belt 12 in. wide or wider and have a work-feed mechanism similar to that of a multiple-drum sander. Wide-belt sanders were first introduced to the metal-

working industries more than 30 years ago. During the early 1950's, wide-belt sanders, 50 in. wide, were introduced

Fig. 28–29. This single head, wide-belt sander carries an abrasive belt measuring 24 x 84 inches. It may be used to size assembled parts as shown here or to sand flat stock.

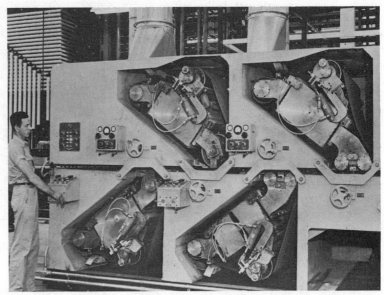

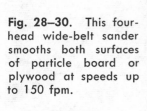

Fig. 28–30. This four-head wide-belt sander smooths both surfaces of particle board or plywood at speeds up to 150 fpm.

in the plywood industry. In the last 15 years they have become popular in many wood using industries, particularly in furniture manufacturing.

Wide-belt sanders are made in many types and sizes. Basically, they include single top (Fig. 28–29), single bottom, or any combination of single and multiple heads in top and/or bottom positions. In top or bottom sanders, the abrasive belt travels over a helically serrated (notched like a screw thread) rubber contact roll. Most wide-belt sanders transport the workpiece into the sander on an endless rubber-belt conveyor. The conveyor is supported at the contact area by a thick steel plate. Hold-down rolls keep the work against the conveyor belt as it passes under the abrasive sanding belt. On most machines, the belt is pneumatically tensioned automatically. The belt is tracked by an idler roll. Machines that are designed for final finish sanding have the belt traveling around a contact roller and under a padded platen. The platen oscillates horizontally, providing a hand-sanding action at high speed. The work is

cut to size at the contact roller and finish sanded as it passes under the platen.

Wide-belt sanders vary from 12-in. widths to those which carry belts 66 in. in width. Some machines are capable of sanding off $\frac{3}{16}$ in. per pass and to a dimensional accuracy within plus or minus .0025 in. Feed rates range up to 75, 100, or even 300 fpm on single-head machines; up to 150 fpm on the four-head sander shown in Figure 28–30. Motor sizes vary from 5 to 150 hp depending upon the width of belt used.

Belt spindle sanders (Fig. 28–31) are designed for centerless sanding of straight, tapered, or oval turnings. The machine shown incorporates two abrasive belts spaced about 54 in. apart. The workpiece is rough sanded to size by the first belt and finish sanded by the second. The work is transported from the first to the second belt by an endless belt conveyor. This machine will sand spindles up to $2\frac{1}{2}$ in. in diameter. Single belt machines of this type are also available.

Turning sanders (Fig. 28–32) are machines designed for sanding turned parts. They are almost fully automatic. The sanders are attended by the operator in much the same way as automatic turning lathes. The operator merely places the workpiece on a centering device. One of ten separate headstocks and tailstocks engages the workpiece. It is then rotated past four rows of abrasive paper of different grits and discharged from the machine. The machine uses abrasive belts that have fine, closely spaced slits in them. They pass over a set of brushes fastened to the brush bar. The location of the brushes may be adjusted to the contour of the turning. Thus, as the turning passes over the brushes, the bristles yield slightly, applying moderate pressure against the slit abrasive belts. The work is thereby sanded as it is rotated under power. Automatic turning sanders are made in various sizes. They will handle turnings up to 6 ft. in length and from $\frac{3}{8}$ to 6 in. in diameter. The spindle

Fig. 28–31. Double-belt spindle sander.

speeds vary from 1000 to 3000 rpm. Production output ranges from 6 to 18 pieces per minute on larger machines and ten to thirty pieces per minute on smaller machines.

Fig. 28–32. An automatic 2 inch Dia. x 12 inch capacity sander that smooths small turnings such as handles, spools and knobs at rates up to 30 pieces per minute.

Chapter 29 Sanding in the School Shop

The sanding processes most frequently employed in the school shop are: (1) hand sanding, (2) portable electric sanding, (3) machine sanding, and (4) sanding by means of machine attachments.

Sanding should begin after all surfaces have been smoothed as much as possible with the appropriate machine and edge tools, such as planes and scrapers. Abrasives are not generally used to remove large amounts of stock.

Hand Sanding

Select the appropriate abrasive for the job at hand. Garnet or aluminum oxide abrasives are best. Standard size sheets are 9 by 11 in. To remove tool marks, use No. 1/2 (60) abrasive grit; then follow this with No. 1/0 (80). Use grits No. 2/0 (100) to 4/0 or 5/0 (180) for the final "white sanding."

Use a small back-up block such as a wood prism or a dowel as shown in Figure 29–1. Cut the abrasive sheet to fit the back-up block. See Figure 29–2.

Sand (Figs. 29–3 and 29–4) *with the grain only.* Hold the abrasive and back-up block in one hand. Apply moderate pressure and move the abrasive back and forth over the surface (Fig. 29–3). Over-

lap preceding strokes. Let the abrasive do the work. If sanding dust tends to clog the abrasive, remove the dust by slapping the abrasive into your hand. Remember, it is best to use successively finer grit sizes until the desired surface condition is obtained.

Shallow depressions in the surface may be raised by applying a drop of water and allowing it to dry. Minor dents and scratches can be removed by using the abrasive as shown in Figure 29–4. Fold the abrasive paper and apply pressure while sanding over the defective area. Do not sand surfaces of joints. Such sanding rounds small flat surfaces and can result in a poorly fitted joint.

When sanding small flat pieces, use a 9 by 11-in. piece of abrasive paper placed face-up on a flat surface. Hold the abrasive stationary with one hand and move the piece back and forth over the abrasive with the other hand.

Curved or irregular surfaces may be sanded with the aid of a back-up block that matches the shape of the work. Wrap the abrasive over a short piece of dowel rod (Fig. 29–1), a round file, or roll it cigarette fashion when sanding concave surfaces or holes. When two or more identically curved edges need sanding,

Fig. 29–1. Simple sanding blocks are made by gluing felt to the surface for resiliency.

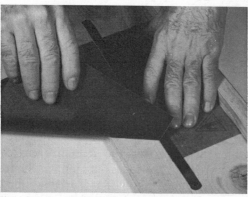

Fig. 29–2. Cutting standard 9" x 11" abrasive paper into desired sizes. Here is a simple jig made of a hacksaw blade nailed to a board.

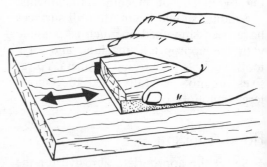

Fig. 29–3. Sanding a flat surface with the grain.

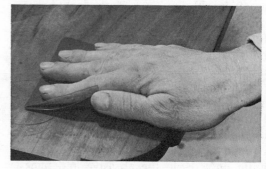

Fig. 29–4. Minor defects can often be sanded out by folding the abrasive into a pad and using finger pressure as shown here.

clamp them together to retain their uniformity. Moldings and other shaped cuts may be sanded by using the fingertips to keep the abrasive in contact with the surface (Fig. 29–5).

Sanded surfaces should be carefully examined to ensure that all scratches and defects are completely removed. Hold the surface under the light and study it carefully. End grain should be sanded until the natural grain pattern and color of the wood appear.

Sanding With Portable Electric Sanders

Portable sanders found in the school shop include the disk, belt, orbital, or straight-line type. Portable-disk and belt sanders are widely used when large amounts of stock must be removed. They may also be used with coarse, open coated abrasives to remove finishes. Disk sanders should be used sparingly because the rotary motion of the disk puts cross-grain scratches in the surface. Make certain that you know the general safety rules found on page 152 before using portable tools.

Changing abrasive disks on the portable sander is done in three steps:

1. Disconnect the plug and remove the clamp washer with a spanner wrench (Fig. 29–6a).
2. Lay the abrasive disk on the rubber backing pad and replace the clamp washer (Fig. 29–6b).
3. Tighten the assembly with the spanner wrench (Fig. 29–6a).

Using the portable disk sander (Fig. 29–7).

1. Clamp the work securely.
2. Grasp the tool with both hands, hold it away from the work surface, and then press the switch to "on."
3. Lower the tool to the work gradually. Tilt the sander slightly forward as shown in Figure 7 so that about ½ of the disk is in contact with the work. Avoid tilting it too much, for if only the outer rim of the disk is used, a rough cut will result. Conversely, if the disk is placed flat against the surface, the cutting action will be irregular and the tool will be difficult to control.

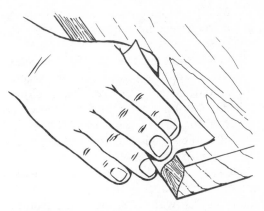

Fig. 29–5. Sanding a shaped edge.

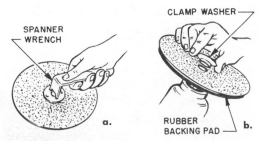

Fig. 29–6. Changing the abrasive on a portable disk sander.

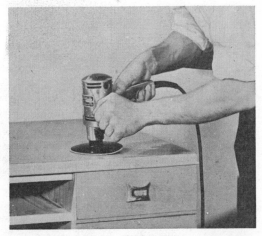

Fig. 29–7. The operation of the disk sander is shown here. Note that the tool is tipped forward with just enough pressure to bend the disk and rubber backing pad slightly.

4. Move the tool back and forth with a free sweeping motion at a uniform speed.
5. Avoid holding the tool in one spot to prevent heavy cutting in one place.
6. Avoid heavy pressure; for it slows the cutting action and reduces the working life of the abrasive. Generally, the weight of the tool supplies the correct pressure.

NOTE: The disk will leave cross-grain "swirl" marks on the work. Remove these marks with a straight-line action portable sander, working with the grain.

Replacing the Abrasive on a Portable Belt Sander

1. Disconnect the plug and place the sander on a bench with the open side up (Fig. 29–8).
2. Depress the lever which retracts the front roller and releases the belt.
3. Remove the abrasive belt from the pulleys.
4. Insert a new belt with the arrow (printed on the belt backing) point-

ing in the direction of rotation (Fig. 29–8).
5. Slide the belt down on both pulleys. Make sure it fits snugly.
6. Return the tension lever to the original position. No further tension adjustment is needed.
7. Hold the sander by the handle with one hand, turn on the power, and observe the tracking of the belt.
8. If necessary, adjust the sanding belt for proper tracking. Use the adjustment screw (Fig. 29–9).

Using the belt sander (Fig. 29–9) seldom involves any significant hazard to the operator. However, careless use can cause damage to the tool or to the work. Observe the following procedures when using belt sanders:

1. Wear goggles and a dust mask if the sander is not equipped with a dust bag or a vacuum exhaust unit.
2. Ensure that the trigger switch is in the "off" position before connecting the plug to the power source.
3. Grasp the tool firmly by the knob and handle.
4. Lift the tool off the work surface

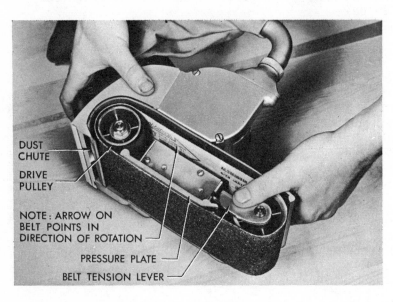

DUST CHUTE

DRIVE PULLEY

NOTE: ARROW ON BELT POINTS IN DIRECTION OF ROTATION

PRESSURE PLATE

BELT TENSION LEVER

Fig. 29–8. Changing an abrasive belt.

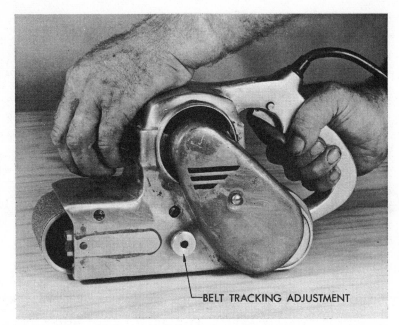

Fig. 29–9. Sanding a surface with a belt sander.

BELT TRACKING ADJUSTMENT

and press the trigger to the "on" position.

5. Allow the sander to come to full speed. Apply it to the surface by moving it down and forward.

6. The back of the pressure plate should touch the work first; then bring the pressure plate into full contact as the stroke advances.

7. Feed the sander back and forth with the grain.

8. The weight of the tool is sufficient for horizontal sanding. Added pressure only slows the cutting action. To speed up rough sanding, use a coarse belt and sand at an angle to the grain. Follow with smoother grits and stroke with the grain to get a smooth surface.

9. Move the sander back and forth over the surface in overlapping strokes. Cover the entire surface of the work.

10. Avoid tilting the sander when feeding in order not to gouge the surface with the belt.

11. To complete the sanding operation, lift the sander off the surface, turn off the switch, and allow the belt to stop before setting the tool on the bench.

12. Avoid sanding thin edges of boards and small pieces of work with the belt sander. It will cut too fast and therefore, be very difficult to control on surfaces that are narrower (or shorter) than the pressure plate.

13. Sanders may be used upside down on a bench (Fig. 29–10). Be sure to check the manufacturer's instruction manual.

14. Examine the belt tracking at frequent intervals during all sanding operations. Minor adjustments may have to be made.

Attaching abrasive to pad-type sanders is generally accomplished as follows:

1. Select the correct grade of abrasive grit and, if necessary, cut the sheet to size. Insert either end of it in the spring clamp at one end of the platen.

Fig. 29–10. Sanding small surfaces with the sander upside down. This permits the use of both hands to apply the work to the belt.

Use a screw driver or the special key (Fig. 29–11) to turn the clamp.

2. Insert the other end of the abrasive into the other clamp in the same manner. Make certain that the abrasive paper is taut. A tight fit is needed to prevent tearing of the abrasive during the sanding operation.

Using pad sanders (Fig. 29–12) is a matter of starting the machine and applying it to the work. The weight of the sander is sufficient to keep it cutting; avoid excessive pressure. Keep the tool moving continuously over the work. Use orbital sanders for rough sanding; straight-line, reciprocating or vibrating types for final white sanding — with the grain. If the abrasive paper should loosen during sanding, stop the machine and retighten it immediately.

Fig. 29–11. Attaching abrasive paper to a pad sander. This photo illustrates one of several types of abrasive holders.

Fig. 29–12. The final "white" sanding of a surface with a pad type sander.

Machine Sanding Processes

Disk, belt, spindle, and drum sanding are the machine-sanding operations most widely performed in the school shop. Belt sanding is usually done with specially designed machines. Disk and drum sanding operations are done with specially designed machines or with attachments on other machines. Sanding disks are available to fit table saws, radial-arm saws, and lathes. Drum sanding attachments can be used on drill presses, shapers, wood lathes, and radial-arm

 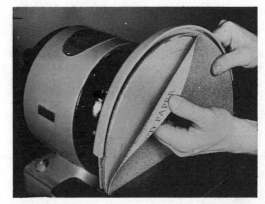

Fig. 29–13. (a) Applying adhesive to sander disk; (b) placing the new adhesive coated abrasive on to the sander disk.

saws. The basic principles of disk, belt, drum, and spindle-sanding operations are essentially the same when using either specially designed machines or attachments.

Using disk sanders. The basic operations performed with the disk sander include "freehand" sanding, and sanding with the aid of special jigs or fixtures. This machine is designed for sanding

Fig. 29–14. Rounding corners of a board on the disk sander freehand. Note the work is applied to the half of the disk which rotates in a downward direction.

small surfaces such as straight or convex edges on flat stock. It is not suited to sanding large flat surfaces as the faces of panels and large boards.

Removing and mounting abrasive disks is done as follows:

1. Remove the worn abrasive from the metal disk. Use a screw driver or blunt instrument.

2. Clean the disk to the "bare" metal.

3. Apply an adhesive to the surfaces of both the metal disk and the back of the abrasive. This adhesive is generally of a special type supplied by machine tool manufacturers. It allows the abrasive disk to be removed easily after use and has sufficient adhesiveness to hold the abrasive to the metal disk while sanding. The adhesive is sold in stick (solid) form. It is applied by holding it against the disk as it is rotated by power (Fig. 29–13a).

4. Place the abrasive sheet onto the disk (Fig. 29–13b) and press firmly. The abrasive must adhere flatly (without wrinkles) in order to do good work.

Freehand sanding (Fig. 29–14) is done by placing the work flat on the

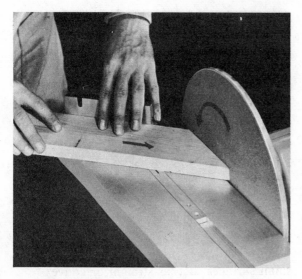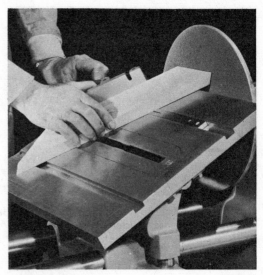

Fig. 29–15. Sanding with the aid of the miter gauge: (a) sanding a flat angle cut; (b) sanding a compound miter cut.

table and advancing it to the rotating disk. All sanding operations must be done on the part of the disk that revolves downward. If the work is applied to the other part of the disk, it will be lifted off the table and the sanding dust will be thrown into the operator's face. All work must be applied slowly and with light pressure on the disk. Heavy pressure generates frictional heat which scorches the work and ruins the abrasive. When possible, the work should be kept moving back and forth over the downward portion of the disk to distribute the wear.

Sanding with guides and jigs. One of the most widely used devices for guiding the work is the miter gauge. (The miter gauge of some circular saws will fit the groove in the table of some disk sanders.) It is particularly useful for sanding square or mitered ends (Figs. 29–15a and 29–15b). When a miter gauge is not available, the same operations may be performed by clamping a straightedge (board) to the table at the desired angle.

Pivot jigs (Fig. 29–16) may be used

to sand the edges of circular parts. The jig is clamped to the worktable of the sander. The workpiece is set on the pivot point, advanced to the disk, and rotated till the edge is sanded to a perfect circular shape.

Sanding with a pattern (Fig. 29–17a) is a good method of sanding the edges of identical parts. This method is best used by riding the pattern against a metal stop (Fig. 29–17). Sanding with a pat-

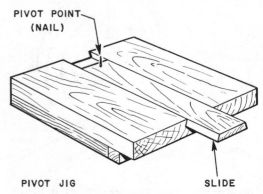

Fig. 29–16. The construction of a simple pivot jig. The slide allows the work to be advanced to the abrasive disk.

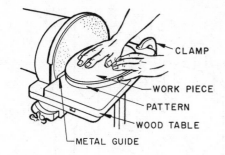

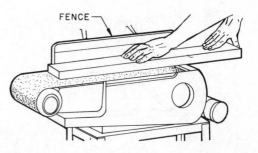

Fig. 29–18. Sanding a face surface with the belt operating in a horizontal position.

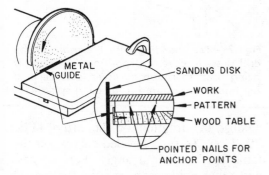

Fig. 29–17. (above) Sanding duplicate parts with a pattern; (below) construction details of a duplicate parts sanding jig.

tern is limited to work with straight or convex edges.

Using belt sanders. The operation of belt sanders first involves the changing and tracking of the abrasive belt. On most machines, the idler pulley is used to tension and track the belt. Two adjusting screws are provided for this purpose. Some belt sanders may be adjusted to run either horizontally (Fig. 29–18) or tilted to any angle up to 90 deg. vertically (Fig. 29–19).

Table attachments are available for some machines. They may be used to support or guide the work while operating in either a horizontal or vertical position. The major operations performed on the belt sander are sanding flat surfaces (Fig. 29–18), straightedges, and concave shapes (Fig. 29–20). For these operations, remove the table and belt guard to expose one roller. The roller is used as a drum sander.

Use of the table attachment with the belt rotating in the vertical position, enables this machine to perform many of the same operations as the disk sander. Among these operations are freehand, tilted table (Fig. 29–19), pivot jig, and pattern sanding.

Using drum or spindle sanders. This class of work includes sanding inside

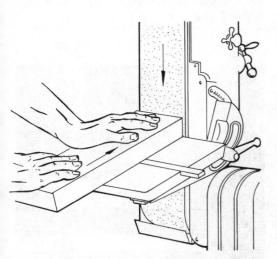

Fig. 29–19. With the table attachment and the belt set to operate in the vertical position, the machine will perform the same work operations as the disk sander.

Fig. 29–20. Concave curves being sanded on an exposed roller of a belt sander. Curves with radii smaller than the radius of the roller cannot be sanded by this method.

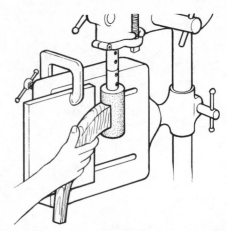

Fig. 29–22. Sanding with the table of the drill press in a vertical position. The drum is being used to shape a curved surface in a leg that is to be fitted to a round spindle.

openings or curved edges on flat stock. Spindle sanding machines or drum sanding attachments for drill presses (Figs. 29–21a and 29–21b), lathes, shapers, and radial-arm saws may be used for this work. The work should be supported on a table to keep the edge square with the face. Most of the operations call for feeding the work freehand. Feed the work against the rotation of the drum (Fig. 29–21a). To sand beveled curves, tilt the table to the desired angle. Fences, jigs, and other guides can be used for special sanding jobs. An example of this class of work is shown in Figure 29–22.

NOTE: Sanding turnings is discussed in Chapter 25, *Wood Turning in the School Shop*. Refer to page 413.

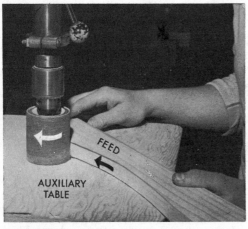

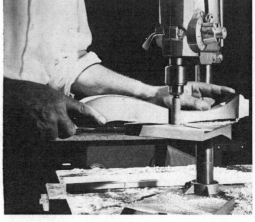

Fig. 29–21. Drum sanding on the drill press: (a) sanding an inside curve; (b) smoothing the surfaces of a cabriole leg.

REVIEW QUESTIONS

1. What are the two general classifications of industrial sanding processes?
2. What was man's first abrasive material?
3. What are the three basic components of coated abrasives?
4. Name the four kinds of abrasive grains available on woodworking abrasives today.
5. What determines the size or grading of abrasive grits?
6. What is the advantage of an open-coated abrasive?
7. What is the function of a sanding block?
8. Describe the cutting action of abrasive grains.
9. What are the various types of portable power sanders available today?
10. What is the principal disadvantage of orbital pad sanders? Portable disk sanders?
11. What kinds of sanders and abrasive materials are used in floor finishing?
12. Name the various kinds of production sanding machines. Describe the mechanical functioning of each type.
13. What are some of the advantages provided by wide-belt sanding machines?
14. Why should hand sanding always be done "with the grain"?
15. What effect does a drop of water have on wood fibers?
16. Explain some of the important techniques in using portable disk, pad, and belt sanders.
17. What are the principal operations that may be performed on disk sanders?
18. What methods are employed to hold coated abrasives on disk and drum sanders?

SUGGESTED STUDENT ACTIVITIES

1. Make a display identifying the various kinds and grades of coated abrasives.
2. Make sanding blocks for sanding round and flat surfaces.
3. Design and make a drum sander for use in the lathe or drill press.
4. Design and make a disk-sander attachment for the table saw.
5. Design and make a device for pattern drum sanding ping pong paddles on the drill press.
6. Make a jig for sanding the sawn edges of circular disks on the disk sander.
7. Prepare a report on the manufacture of coated abrasives.
8. Prepare a device to compare the effectiveness of the various kinds of abrasive papers.

Chapter 30 Finishing

Finishing is the process of coating surfaces with thin films of prepared liquids. These films dry and harden by oxidation, evaporation, or chemical change. They are selected for their protective and decorative properties. These liquid coating materials are referred to simply as *finishes*. Finishes are either transparent or opaque. *Transparent finishes* are used on wood to allow its natural beauty to show through the finish film. Familiar finishes of this type are shellac, varnish, lacquer, stain, and wax. *Opaque finishes* conceal the material, hiding imperfections and imparting color. Paint, lacquer, and enamel are popular opaque finishes. In addition to these popular finishes, there are many other kinds. For example, there are some which are used to achieve novelty effects and others are specially formulated for various atmospheric or environmental conditions.

Common methods of applying finishes are by brushing, roller coating, dipping, and spraying by hand or by machine. Later in this unit other larger scale, industrial processes will be introduced.

Basically, the reasons for applying finishes to wood are:

1. *Protection*. Properly coated woods resist mechanical wear, chemicals, stains, and spots. Coatings retard changes in moisture content which induce warping, cracking, splitting, molding, decay, and attack by bacteria or insects. A special finish for homes and dwellings provides *fire protection*. It puffs into a thick protective sponge when it reaches a certain temperature, thereby preventing the surface from igniting.

2. *Beautification*. Transparent finishes emphasize the grain, color, and natural beauty of wood. Opaque finishes add color and beauty to certain less attractive woods.

3. *Sanitation*. Well finished woods resist liquids, soaps, and detergents. Therefore, it is possible to free wood surfaces of dust, dirt, and bacteria in order to maintain adequate health standards in homes, schools, and other public facilities.

4. *Illumination*. Properly selected and applied finishes produce surfaces for a variety of lighting effects. Some finishes reflect light; others absorb it. Luminous paints provide their own special lighting effects.

5. *Insulation*. Finishes retard condensation, and resist heat radiation. Others have acoustical properties and even

can be specially mixed for electrical insulation.

6. *Stimulation.* The psychological effects of color have been recognized for centuries. Blues and greens are cool, quieting colors. Reds and yellows are warm, exciting colors. Human reactions to color are important considerations when decorating rooms or designing products for consumer appeal.

Evolution of Finishes and Finishing Processes

Paints are almost as old as man himself. They were used more than 20,000 years ago for personal decoration, religious symbolism, and ornamentation by the European cave man. As early as 3500 B.C., painting had become a dignified art in Egypt. By 1000 B.C., the Egyptians were coating mummy cases with paint and varnish applied with brushes made from reeds. In 1800 B.C., the Chinese used earth oxides mixed with oils and tree gums to produce painting materials. The ancient Chinese also made lacquer from what was known as the varnish tree. From Greece and Rome the production and use of paint and varnish followed the spread of civilization into the rest of Europe, first for artistic and later for decorative and protective effects. Many of the raw materials in common use today were familiar to the ancients: white lead, red lead, yellow ocher, iron oxide vermillion, lamp black, and others. However, progress was slow. Chemists have made more progress in the development of new finishing materials in this century than in all previous times.

Paint was scarce in the Early Colonial period. A sign of prestige among the Dutch Colonists was the red trim on their homes. This was achieved by using the oxides from iron in their paints. The production of paint ingredients became one of the early commercial products of the Colonial period. The first paint mill was set up in this country by Thomas Child in Boston in 1692. White lead was first produced in this country in 1804 and the first varnish in 1815. Until 70 years ago, most painters purchased the ingredients separately and mixed their own finishes (Fig. 30–1) on the job. Although ready mixed paints were developed in the period between 1860 and 1870, they did not come into wide use until much later. According to census records, there were only four companies engaged in the manufacture of finishes in the latter 1800's. Today, there are over 2000.

Prior to the 1920's, wood furniture finishing took weeks of tedious labor and drying time. A carelessly placed glass of water could ruin the finish in minutes. The development of nitrocellulose lac-

Fig. 30–1. Mixing white lead, linseed oil, and turpentine on the job was typical of painters 70 years ago.

quers during the 1920's provided the furniture industry with a fast drying and durable finish. In the early 1930's, the quick drying synthetic resin varnishes and resin emulsion water-thinned paints were developed. In 1937, DuPont introduced a titanium dioxide pigment to replace the traditional and poisonous white lead pigment in paints. In the late 1940's, the latex paints were introduced. Since this time, many new and improved finishes have been developed.

New finishes are being brought on the market annually through research carried on by the manufacturers of finishes. The greatest advances have been in the area of synthetic (man-made) finishes. For example, in the field of lacquers, over 40,000 patents have been granted for different mixtures or formulas. Today, there are over 2000 colors in the decorator's spectrum. Chemists have resolved some of the irritating problems traditionally associated with finishing. For example, paints are available that do not require the customary stirring to mix the ingredients which settle to the bottom of the container. They are ready for application, do not drip, and are readily thinned with water. Thus, the use of dangerous, volatile solvents is eliminated.

Modern paints dry quickly; some are ready for a second coat in 30 minutes. Colors are more readily mixed and matched. A large selection of stains and wood tones are available. New finishes wear longer than ever before. These advances are only a few of the many developments that have occurred in the field of wood finishing.

However, still to come out of the chemists laboratory are perfect, life-time finishes for exterior use. The transparent exterior finishes of today do not resist nature's abusive attacks of moisture or the sun's rays. Transparent finishes on wood siding and boats require refinishing anywhere from 6 months to a year and a half after application. Opaque finishes on exterior surfaces now hold up much longer than transparent finishes. In some cases, they last up to 10 to 15 years without recoating. Authorities predict that in the near future exterior coatings will be available that will have a service life of 30 years or more without additional recoating. This is an important goal for the wood industry if wood is to continue to compete with other building materials in the future.

Methods of applying paints changed very little until the last decade of the nineteenth century. Cave drawings were colored at first by smearing the coloring materials on with the fingers. In later times powdered colors were sometimes blown through a reed or mixed with animal fat to form a kind of crayon. The Egyptians used the frayed ends of reeds as a kind of lettering brush for use on papyrus (a form of paper). The Greeks were the first to use the tails of small fur-bearing animals for brushes. The Latin word "penicillus" (meaning "a small tail") is the origin of our word pencil. Small brushes used by artists are still called pencils. For this reason the term "lead pencil" was adopted to distinguish it from the brush. The word "brush" is of later origin. It comes from the German word for bristle — *brusta*.

During the Middle Ages, brushes were made by binding bristles to a stick. Such brushes were commonly used to whitewash the interior of castles. Eventually, brushmakers guilds were established in England and France and brushmaking became a recognized industry. Brushes were first manufactured in this country in Germantown, Pennsylvania, during the latter part of the eighteenth century. By the middle of the past century, brushes had been developed to a high level of practical design and efficiency. A short time later the influence of the industrial revolution resulted in the development of new methods of applying finishes.

The *air spray* method of applying finishes was introduced in the 1890's. With this new process, the liquid was siphoned through a spray gun, broken into a fine mist, and blown onto the surface — all by compressed air. This was the most revolutionary development in the application of coating materials since the ancient Egyptians developed reed brushes. Naturally, spraying with compressed air quickly became a standard process in industry and remained virtually unchanged until about mid-century.

Air spraying proved to be wasteful, however. A great deal of the finishing material was blown into the air rather than onto the object being coated. Special finishing booths were necessary to contain the overspray. These disadvantages of air spraying led to a search for other methods of finish application.

Certain industries devised finishing systems to suit the character of their own individual products. For small parts, dipping tanks proved satisfactory. Others initiated a flow coating process in which the liquid was flooded over the surface of the work. Also, methods were developed using rollers to finish large, flat surfaces, such as sheets and panels.

The first major change in the conventional air spray process involved heating the finishing material to lower its viscosity. In this way lower air pressure was required for spraying and heavier coats could be applied. The process is known as hot spraying. The original patent on this method was donated to the public domain by the Commercial Solvents Corporation about 1947. A *steam process* for spraying was patented by the DuPont

Company in 1950. The *airless* spray system was developed in 1955. This method, more properly called the *hydraulic spray* system, was developed by the Nordsen Corporation. It employs the same principle involved in spraying water from the nozzle of a garden hose.

Equipment for Applying Finishes Today

Brushes (Figs. 30–2, 30–3a, 30–3b, 30–4a, 30–4b, 30–4c, 30–4d, and 30–4e) are made with either synthetic filaments (nylon) or natural hair bristles (camel, sable, hog, etc.). Filaments and bristles are known as contact materials. They are generally vulcanized in rubber plugs (or cores) which in turn are attached to a wood handle by a metal ferrule. The essential difference between quality

Fig. 30–2. A quality wall brush has tapered filaments of unequal lengths.

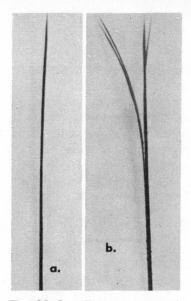

Fig. 30–3. Close-up view of filaments: (a) taper tipped, and (b) flagged.

brushes and inexpensive brushes lies in the characteristics of the contact material. Quality brushes have either nylon filaments or hog bristles of unequal lengths (Fig. 30–2). They are tapered (Fig. 30–3a) rather than straight and the ends are "flagged" (split) (Fig. 30–3b). Flagged ends provide numerous reservoirs which hold a full load of the finishing material and meter it out in a smooth, even flow. Some basic types of brushes are:

1. The *wall brush* (Fig. 30–2) is made in widths ranging from 3 to 4 in. for interior walls and ceilings and up to 6 in. for large exterior surfaces. Bristles or filaments range from

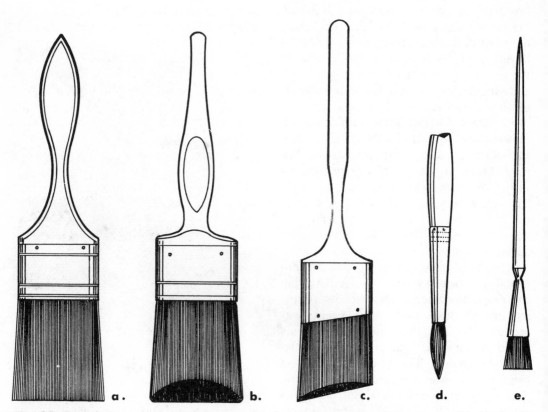

Fig. 30–4. (a) Flat, single thickness varnish brush, (b) double thickness varnish brush, (c) angled sash brush, and (d-e) marking brushes.

3 to 5 in. in length and up to 1 in. in thickness.

2. *Varnish brushes* (Figs. 30–4a and 30–4b) are flat like the wall brush. Bristles or filaments range from ½ to 3 in. in width and from 1½ to 2¾ in. in length. They are either single thickness, ¼ to $\frac{7}{16}$ in. (Fig. 30–4a), or double thickness, ½ to ⅞ in. (Fig. 4–b). Varnish brushes are used for small jobs and with any finishing material.

3. *Sash brushes* (Fig. 30–4c) are either flat or oval in cross section. Flat brushes are cut square or at an angle (Fig. 30–4c). They are made with a chisel edge to facilitate painting in close or narrow spaces on windows. They range from 1 to 2 in. in width with bristles or filaments 2¼ in. in length and $\frac{5}{16}$ to ½ in. thick. They usually have longer handles than other types of brushes.

4. *Marking and sign painters brushes* are small, round (Fig. 30–4d) or flat (Fig. 30–4e) and are used for detailed work and for touching up spots. Bristles range from $\frac{9}{64}$- to ¼- or ⅜-in. diameters and up to 1 in. in length.

Paint rollers (Fig. 30–5) are used to quickly spread coating materials on large surfaces such as walls and ceilings. They are not ordinarily used to apply the fast drying finishes (lacquer or enamels). Rollers are widely used by home owners and painters for the application of latex and other house paints. The finishing material is applied to the roller by rolling it in a special pan (Fig. 30–5). Roller coverings are detachable, and therefore can be interchanged to achieve special results or to accommodate different kinds of paint. Generally, lambskin covers are used to produce a smooth surface with oil paints. Synthetic fiber rollers are used for applying water paints.

Aerosol sprayers (Fig. 30–6) were first developed to spray insecticides during World War II. Shortly after the war, finishing materials were supplied in this convenient form. Although more expensive per-square-foot coverage than other methods, they are widely used by home-

Fig. 30–5. Staining with a hand roller. Note the special roller pan at the left.

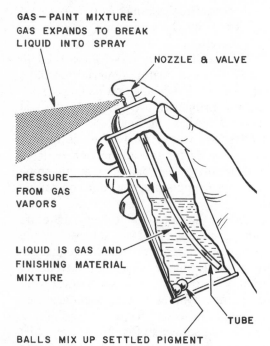

GAS — PAINT MIXTURE.
GAS EXPANDS TO BREAK
LIQUID INTO SPRAY

NOZZLE & VALVE

PRESSURE
FROM GAS
VAPORS

LIQUID IS GAS AND
FINISHING MATERIAL
MIXTURE

TUBE

BALLS MIX UP SETTLED PIGMENT

Fig. 30–6.   The aerosol sprayer.

owners and spot finishers. An estimated 100 million cans are used annually. For small jobs, aerosols are convenient because they do not need mixing and require a minimum of cleanup after the job is finished.

Aerosol sprayers use a gas (freon) in liquid form which is mixed with the finishing material inside the can. The gas provides the pressure to force the fluid through a tube and out the nozzle of the spray can. The gas also blows out of the nozzle. As the gas expands it breaks the liquid into a fine spray.

Spraying Equipment

There are five major methods (Figs. 30–7a through 30–7e) of applying finishes with spraying equipment. These are: (1) conventional *air spray;* (2) *hot spray;* (3) *cold airless;* (4) *hot airless;*

and (5) *electrostatic spraying.* In all of these processes, the coating material is *atomized.* That is, it is changed from a liquid into a misty spray by breaking it up into small particles. Each of these methods has certain advantages and limitations.

Conventional air spraying is widely used by men in industry, by students in school shops, by contract painters, and by home craftsmen. The equipment is either stationary or portable. It requires the smallest equipment investment of the spraying methods described here. The major disadvantage of air spraying is the waste due to uncontrollable overspray (Fig. 30–7a). The basic equipment consists of a compressor, connecting pipes, air regulator or transformer, hoses, material container, and the spray gun.

The *compressor* (Fig. 30–8) pumps air into a tank to develop pressures .of 80 to 175 psi to operate the spray gun. Compressors are of either the *piston* or *diaphragm* type. The piston type (Fig. 30–8) works much like a two-cycle gasoline engine. Air is drawn into a cylinder as the piston moves down. On the upward (compression) stroke, the intake valve closes and a second valve opens, permitting the air to be forced into the tank or into a second cylinder. This second cylinder further compresses the air before it is pumped into the tank. Compressors of this type are known as two-stage compressors. Piston compressors are also made in one- or two-cylinder single-stage models. Single-stage compressors will supply pressures up to 100 psi; two-stage compressors, from 140–175 psi. The better air compressors are of the piston type.

Smaller, less expensive compressors are of the diaphragm type. They compress the air by means of a flexible disk actuated by an eccentric. A flap type spring loaded

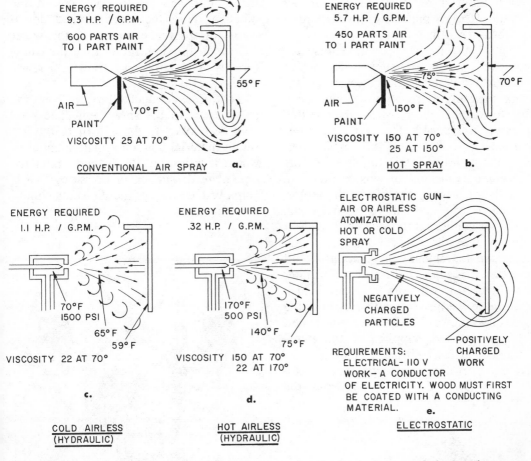

Fig. 30–7. A comparison of the five major spray methods. A, b, c, and d give the power requirements necessary to deliver one gallon of paint per minute (gpm). Note that the amount of overspray is directly proportional to the energy requirements. The electrostatic method may be incorporated with hot or cold and airless processes.

valve is located in the disk. While the disk moves in one direction the valve is open and air moves through it. When the disk reverses its direction, the valve closes and the air is forced through the compressor outlet. Because these compressors supply a pulsating stream of air, they are unsuitable where high-quality sprayed finishes are desired.

Compressors are powered by either electric motors (¼ to 15 hp) or gasoline engines (1 to 25 hp). Gasoline powered compressors are primarily used for portable spray systems in remote areas.

Compressors are rated by the number of cubic feet of air they can supply per minute. As a general rule, a piston compressor will produce 3 to 5 cu. ft. of air per minute per horsepower. Single-stage compressors will deliver approximately 30 cu. ft. of air per minute. Two-stage compressors deliver about 60 cfm. A gun operated at 50 psi to spray lacquer requires from 4 to 9 cu. ft. of air per minute. Heavier materials may require as much as 16 cfm.

Most piston type compressors are equipped with a pressure switch which automatically starts the motor when the tank pressure drops to a certain point. It stops the motor when the desired pressure is reached. The better compressors have an *unloading valve* which permits the motor to attain full speed before the compressing unit begins to function. This helps prolong the life of the motor.

The *transformer* (air regulator) (Fig. 30–9) is connected to the compressed-air pipe line at the spray booth. Its functions are to regulate the amount of air pressure that reaches the gun and to filter out dirt, rust, oil, and moisture which may be in the air. A good spray finishing system will always include a transformer. The air pressure supplied to the transformer is at least 80 psi. For most satisfactory operation, the compressor is located at least 25 ft. away from the transformer. This permits the moisture in the compressed air to condense in the pipeline. With the pipes pitched downward toward the compressor, the water collects in the tank rather than the transformer. The tank and transformer are drained daily.

The hose conducts the air from the transformer to the spray gun. The hose may be hooked to the gun or to the finishing material container. The manner in which it is hooked up depends upon the type of feed (suction or pressure) that is employed to carry the finishing liquid into the gun.

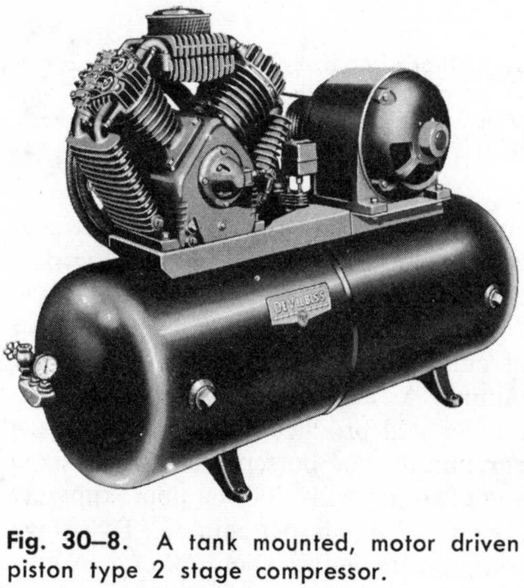

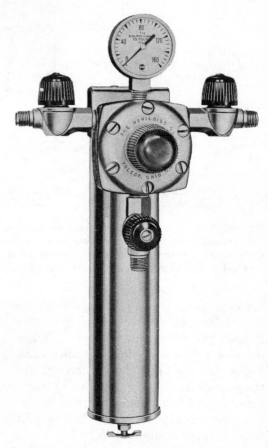

Fig. 30–8. A tank mounted, motor driven piston type 2 stage compressor.

Fig. 30–9. The air transformer cleans and regulates the air supply to the gun.

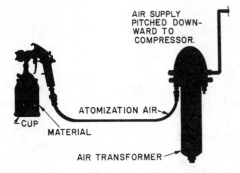

Fig. 30–10. A typical hookup with a suction feed gun.

The *suction-feed hookup* is shown in Figure 30–10. A glass or metal container (cup) is attached to the *fluid inlet* nipple of the gun (Fig. 30–11). The air atomization line is connected to the *air inlet* nipple. When the gun trigger (Fig. 30–12) is squeezed, the air valve is opened. Air flows through the passageways within the spray gun and out of the openings in the air nozzle. As the air passes over the tip of the fluid nozzle (which is connected to the siphon tube), it creates a

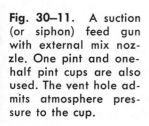

Fig. 30–11. A suction (or siphon) feed gun with external mix nozzle. One pint and one-half pint cups are also used. The vent hole admits atmosphere pressure to the cup.

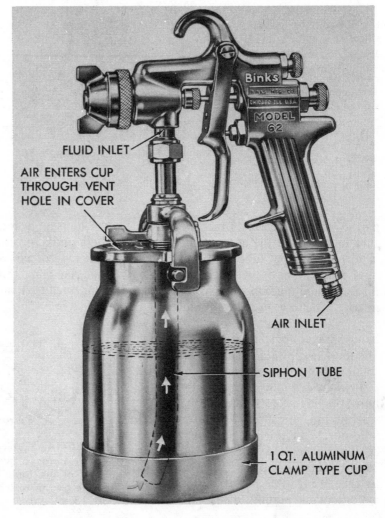

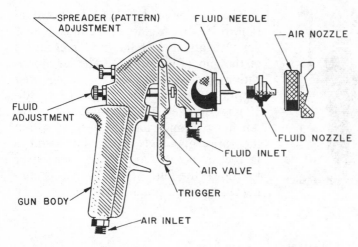

Fig. 30-12. The major parts of a spray gun. An assortment of fluid needles, fluid nozzles and air nozzles permits one gun to spray a wide variety of materials.

Fig. 30-13. Nozzle classifications. The fluid nozzle protrudes slightly beyond the air nozzle of the suction feed gun. This condition is designed to create a vacuum. Maximum fluid flow is about 12 to 14 fluid ounces per minute. Pressure feed guns will apply up to 42 fluid ounces per minute.

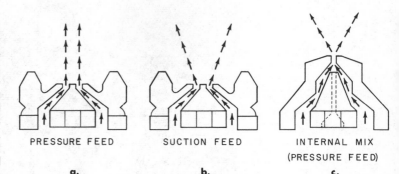

partial vacuum therein. Atmospheric pressure on the fluid in the container forces it up the siphon tube and out of the fluid nozzle. The fluid is atomized when it enters the air flowing from the air nozzle. The air pressure required will vary with the viscosity of the material being sprayed, but 35–50 psi is common. Suction-fed guns are primarily used where small amounts of finish are to be sprayed.

Pressure-fed guns are used for production spraying. The difference between a siphon and pressure-fed gun is in the fluid nozzle and air nozzle (Fig. 30–13). A typical hookup is shown in Figure 30–14. The air supply line is connected to this fitting. An air regulator on the material tank permits diverting some of

the air supply into the tank to place the fluid under pressure (Fig. 30–15). The fluid is forced through a pipe in the material tank, through the material hose connected to it, and up to the fluid nozzle.

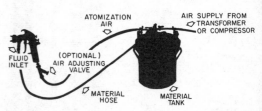

Fig. 30-14. Typical pressure feed hookup. Air pressure on fluid (1 to 10 lbs.) is regulated at the tank; atomization is regulated at the gun or at the tank as shown in Figure 30–15.

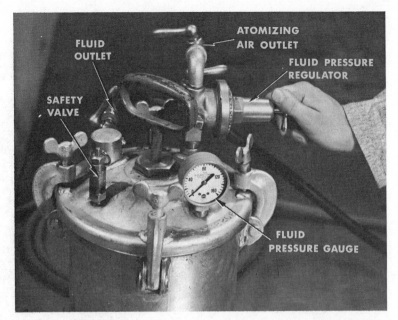

Fig. 30–15. A pressure fluid tank.

When the trigger is squeezed, the fluid squirts out of the fluid nozzle to be atomized by the air flowing out of the air nozzle. The air pressure is regulated at the gun by means of an adjusting valve.

A gauge on the tank indicates the amount of air pressure on the fluid.

The advantages of the pressure-fed system are: (1) finishes of greater viscosity can be sprayed; and (2) greater

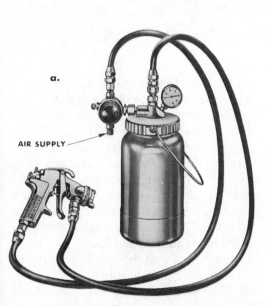

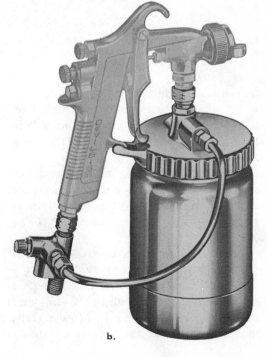

Fig. 30–16. Pressure cups: (a) portable two quart, and (b) attached one quart.

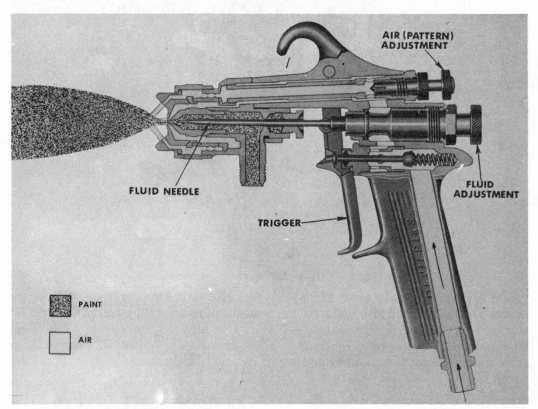

FLUID NEEDLE

AIR (PATTERN) ADJUSTMENT

FLUID ADJUSTMENT

TRIGGER

PAINT

AIR

Fig. 20–17. A nonbleeder type spray gun with an external mix nozzle showing the air and fluid passages.

quantities of finish can be sprayed in a given time. In production-line finishing, the material hose is connected to a fluid circulating system instead of the tank shown in Figure 30–14.

For short run work, as in the school shop, a pressure feed container may be used. These are of two types, the *remote* (Fig. 30–16a) or the *attached* (Fig. 30–16b).

Air spray guns (Figs. 30–11, 30–12, 30–17, and 30–18) are available in a variety of models. They may be classified as bleeder, nonbleeder (Fig. 30–17) and automatic (Fig. 30–18). In *bleeder guns,* the air flows from the gun at all times,

but the liquid flows only when the trigger is pressed. This style of gun is used where the air pressure cannot be regulated. With a *nonbleeder gun* (Fig. 30–17), the trigger controls both the flow of air and finishing liquid. The *automatic gun* (Fig. 30–18) is fixed in position and used for spraying objects as they move by on a conveyor. Several automatic guns may be set-up at different angles for gang spraying as shown in Figure 30–18b.

Spray guns may be equipped with internal mix or external mix nozzles (Fig. 30–13). With the *internal mix nozzle,* the air and fluid are mixed inside the gun. Lower air pressures are needed and less

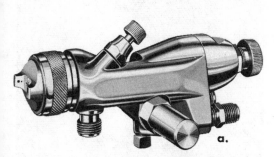

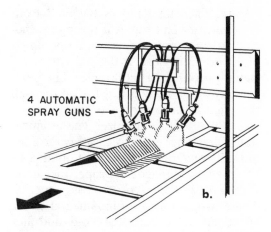

4 AUTOMATIC
SPRAY GUNS →

Fig. 30–18. (a) An automatic spray gun. (b) Gang spraying utilizing four automatic guns mounted in fixed positions.

overspray results. This type of nozzle is generally restricted to spraying the slower drying coating materials or those finishes that do not contain coarse pigments or particles. Fast drying materials usually clog this nozzle.

With *external mix* nozzles (Fig. 30–13), the fluid and air flow separately from the nozzle and mix outside of the gun. The external mix nozzle may be used for almost all finishing materials. They are the only type suitable for fast drying materials such as lacquer. Only external mix nozzles may be used on siphon-fed spray guns.

Air nozzles, fluid nozzles, and fluid needles are made for use in certain combinations only. *Air nozzles* produce different sizes and shapes of patterns. *Fluid nozzles* meter and direct the fluid into the air stream (Fig. 30–17). The *fluid needle* serves as a valve to control the flow of fluid. They are matched to fluid nozzles. The exact combination of these parts to be used is governed by the type of finishing material, the required volume of material to be applied, and the type of feed hookup used. Manufacturers' charts are available for aid in making this selection.

The **hot spray process** (Fig. 30–7b) is a modification of the conventional spray

system. A water, air, or steam heater is incorporated to raise the temperature of the finishing material (Fig. 30–19). When its temperature is raised, the fluid becomes thinner, flows more easily, and requires less air pressure for application. The reduced air pressure results in a reduction of the overspray. Reducing the fluid viscosity with heat rather than thinners results in better and quicker surface coverage. Water heaters are usually electrically operated. They consist of a thermostatically controlled *heating element*, and a *pump* to circulate hot water through a *heat exchanger* which transfers the heat to the coating material. The hot water also circulates through the fluid hose as shown in Figure 30–19. Another system superheats the compressor air, circulates it through the heat exchanger, and passes it on to the air nozzle. Hot spray equipment is used in both stationary and portable (Fig. 30–20) painting systems.

The **cold airless spraying system** (Figs. 30–7c and 30–21a) is the simplest form of airless or hydraulic spraying. The equipment basically consists of a material container, a hose, an air pump, a filter, and a gun. These components are usually hooked up as shown in Figure 30–21a. This hookup is known as a *dead-end* *system*. The pump moves the fluid from the container and forces it through a special airless spray gun at pressures up to 3000 psi. The hose is designed to withstand pressures of 6000 psi. The high velocity of the fluid as it is forced through the minute orifice of the spray nozzle forces the fluid to atomize. The atomization (breaking up into a spray) of the finishing material is dependent upon: (1) the pressure applied to propel the material; and (2) the viscosity of the material. These two factors are fundamental to the effectiveness of both the cold and hot airless spray systems. The major limitation of the cold airless system is that the liquid must be of such a viscosity that it atomizes adequately at the temperature of its environment. When thinning is necessary to reduce the viscosity, a limited film buildup per coat results. The cold airless system is therefore not employed by the furniture industries where fine finishes are required. Cold airless spraying is primarily used by painting contractors and in maintenance work where the final finish is not as important.

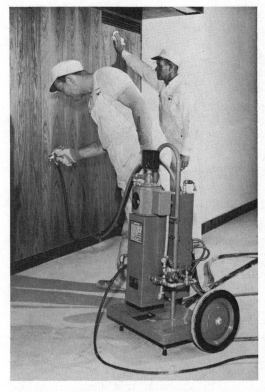

Fig. 30–20. A portable hot spray system. In the foreground is the heater and transformer on a movable cart.

Fig. 30–19. The heating unit and circulation of water in one kind of hot spray equipment.

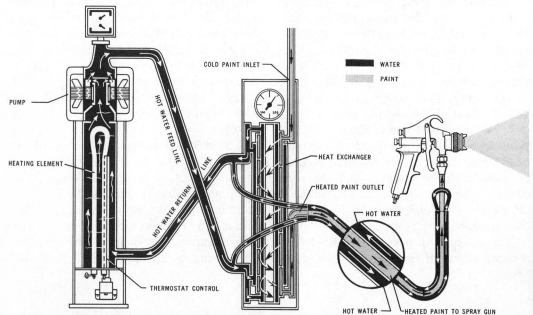

COLD PAINT INLET

WATER

PAINT

PUMP

HOT WATER FEED LINE

HEATING ELEMENT

HOT WATER RETURN LINE

HEAT EXCHANGER

HEATED PAINT OUTLET

HOT WATER

THERMOSTAT CONTROL

HOT WATER

HEATED PAINT TO SPRAY GUN

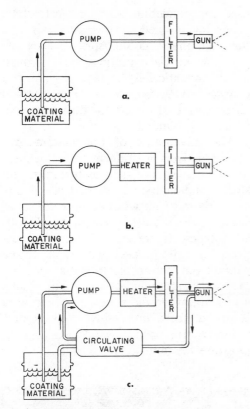

Fig. 30–21. Typical airless spray hookups:
(a) cold, (b) hot, and (c) circulating hot.

Hot airless spraying (Figs. 30–7d, 30–21b, and 30–21c) is one of the major finishing processes used in the furniture industries. The problems of the cold spray method are alleviated by the addition of a heater in the hookup. The function of the heater is to reduce the normal viscosity of the finishing liquid to make it flow better. Heating makes it possible to atomize adequately many coating materials that cannot be cold sprayed. For example, certain enamels will not atomize sufficiently when sprayed at ambient temperatures (even at 5000 psi). The same fluid, however, atomizes perfectly when it is heated to 170 deg. F. and sprayed at only 500 psi. In addition to reduced energy requirements, heating the fluid

produces a greater square foot coverage per gallon because the overspray is reduced to a minimum. Compare the methods of spraying shown in Figure 30–7.

The hot airless spray equipment is hooked up as either a dead end (Fig. 30–21b) or a circulating system (Fig. 30–21c). In the circulating system, the liquid constantly circulates through a heater. The advantage of this type of hookup over the dead-end system is that the temperature of the liquid at the gun is always the same whenever the gun is triggered. Airless spray equipment may be either stationary or portable.

Airless spray guns are essentially the same for both hot and cold spraying. They are similar in appearance to conventional air spray guns except that they have only one hose connection. (Two hose connections are used for the circulating hookup.) The most important part of the gun is the nozzle. Nozzles on these guns are generally made of brass or stainless steel. Recently, carbide nozzles have come into use. They have proved to be superior because of their greater resistance to the abrasive nature of many new coating materials. Various nozzles are used to obtain the different shapes and sizes of patterns. The orifice openings generally range from under ten thousandths of an inch (for thin consistency materials) to over forty thousandths of an inch for medium and heavier materials. Airless spray guns of the automatic type are also used for gang-spraying processes. These are used in a setup similar to that of the automatic guns used in conventional air spraying as shown in Figure 30–18b.

The *filter* catches solids too large to pass through the orifice in the spray tip.

The *heater* is electrically operated and is either of the fixed temperature or thermostatically controlled type. Heater sizes range from 2000 to 6000 watts in single units. Additional units may be incorporated into the line depending upon the number of spray guns and the application rate employed.

The *pump* is the heart of the airless principle. It provides the hydraulic pressure necessary to atomize the fluid. In the circulating hookup, it also keeps the fluid flowing through the entire system. Pumps are usually of the piston-cylinder type. The pump is normally operated by an air motor using air at 35 to 110 psi. The pump multiplies the air input pressure to deliver hydraulic spraying pressure. Pumps operate at various ratios. For example, a pump with a 10 to 1 ratio may use air at 80 psi for the motor and will deliver about 800 psi of hydraulic pressure to propel the fluid. The maximum output of these pumps is generally around 3000 psi.

Electrostatic spraying (Figs. 30–7d and 30–22). In the electrostatic process the liquid may be atomized hot or cold, with either the air or the airless system. The unusual feature of this process is its ability to apply practically all of the atomized fluid on the article being sprayed (Fig. 30–7d).

An essential requirement of this process is that the article to be sprayed must have a surface that is either permanently or temporarily an electrical conductor. As such it is capable of collecting negatively charged atomized fluids.

Although electrostatic finishing is currently being more widely used in the metal and plastics industries, it is in the developmental stages for use in wood finishing. This system utilizes a newly developed, clear solution that is applied by spraying, dipping, or hand wiping. It possesses the necessary electrical conductivity for successful electrostatic spraying.

A special spray gun (Fig. 30–22) is used in connection with an electrostatic generator as well as the usual air and fluid supplies. As the spray leaves the gun, the atomized particles pass through an electrostatic field generated by a grid charged to 90,000 volts. The charged particles are attracted to the workpiece, which is grounded.

The advantages of this system are: (1) it delivers a uniform film thickness to irregular shapes such as turnings, gun stocks, and chairs; (2) there is practically no overspray. Its wrap-around effect, as shown in Figure 30–7, has many obvious advantages. However, the technical aspects of this process will have to be worked out before electrostatic spraying of wood is more widely used. The results are erratic when the material to be coated is not uniform in quality. This is particularly true when woods varying in moisture content are finished.

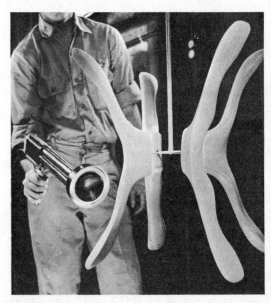

Fig. 30–22. The electrostatic spray gun emits atomized particles which are then charged and attracted to these wood table legs. The legs are first covered with an electrically conductive coating.

Spray booths (Figs. 30–23 and 30–24) are special metal enclosures in which spraying is performed. A booth collects the overspray solids and dangerous, volatile fumes from the room atmosphere and discharges them outdoors. Spray booths in modern wood finishing systems are of two basic types: the *water wash* and the *dry*. The latter type may be further classified as either baffle, "dispo," or filter. In general, booths are made of sheet-steel panels in many different sizes. All booths are equipped with an exhaust fan which carries the vapors and fumes to the outdoors.

Water wash booths (Fig. 30–23) are primarily used in industrial plants where finishing equipment is in continuous use. The overspray, fumes, and exhaust air are drawn through a curtain of water at the rear wall of the booth. As the air stream moves through the water, the particles of finishing material are washed into a collecting pan where they are periodically skimmed off. The water is recirculated by means of a pump. A strainer prevents the sludge and solids from entering the recirculating water system. The air passing out of the exhaust stack is virtually free from pigments. Therefore, water wash booths are often required to meet fire, health, and building codes.

In *dry booths,* the overspray is trapped in filters or a cloth curtain, or they pass directly into the outside atmosphere with the exhaust air. The latter is characteristic of the *baffle-type booth.* This type has either a double or single row of baffle plates at the rear of the booth as in Figure 30–24. The function of the baffles is to equalize the flow of air and provide uniform draft throughout the entire spray booth. Dry booths in which the overspray is trapped in large disposable filters at the rear of the booth are known as *filter*

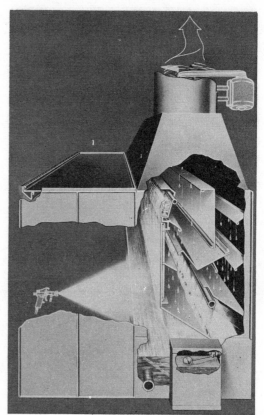

Fig. 30–23. Waterwash spray booth.

Fig. 30–24. Dry baffel spray booth.

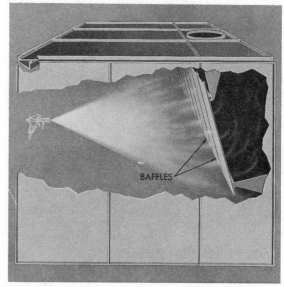

BAFFLES

Fig. 30–25. A rollercoating machine.

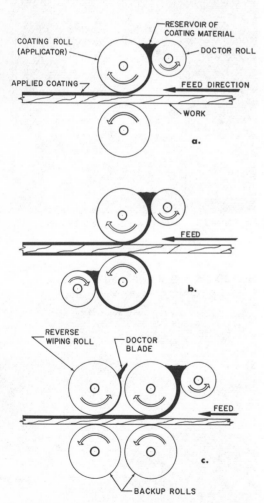

Fig. 30–26. Basic rollercoating processes: (a) single top coater, (b) double surface coater and (c) reverse roller coating.

booths. Another type of dry booth, called a *dispo booth,* traps the pigments in a large cloth filtering curtain that hangs on two rollers. When the cloth becomes filled with overspray solids, it is wound onto a manually or automatically controlled takeup roller. The used cloth is disposed of in the same manner as any paint impregnated waste material.

Rollercoating Processes

Rollercoating (Fig. 30–25) is a machine finishing process in which power-driven rollers are used to apply a finishing material to the work as it is fed through the machine. This method of application is limited to finishing stock that is flat and of uniform thickness. However, within these limitations, rollercoaters are very versatile machines. They are used to apply virtually every type of finishing material, such as, paints, lacquers, varnishes, stains, fillers, and waxes. Some machines are designed to apply melted lignin and other plastics to wood surfaces.

Rollercoating machines are of three basic types. These are the *single-surface coater* (Fig. 30–26a), the *double-surface coater* (Fig. 30–26b), and the reverse rollercoaters (Fig. 30–26c). The work to be coated is carried through the machines between two or more rollers. The crotch between the *doctor roll* and the *application roll* serves as a *reservoir* for the liquid. The coating liquid is contained in the reservoir by end plates. A pump connected to the supply line keeps the reservoir full.

The doctor and applicator rolls rotate in opposite directions. In operation, the finishing liquid is metered by the doctor roll from the reservoir onto the applicator roll which transfers it to the workpiece.

The doctor roll is made of metal with a highly polished, mirrorlike surface. The applicator roll has a special synthetic rubber covering that is not affected by the solvents of the coating materials.

The spacing between these two rollers is adjustable for regulating the thickness of the film to be applied to the work surface. The *single* and *double surface* rollercoaters operate on the same basic principle. See Figures 30–26a and 30–26b. Note that the applicator rolls rotate with the feed direction of the work.

The *reverse rollercoaters* (Fig. 30–26c) are somewhat different in principle. The doctor roll and applicator roll operate in the same way as on other types. However, as the work moves through the machine, it encounters another roller which rotates against the feed. This roller is referred to as a *reverse wiping roll*. This operation makes the reverse rollercoaters especially suitable for grain-filling operations. The reverse wiping roller has a polished surface similar to the doctor roll. Its rotation is such that it forces the filler into the pores, cracks, or depressions of the work surface. The excess coating or filler is carried upward by the reverse wiping roll to a point where it encounters a scraper, called the *doctor blade*. The doctor blade removes the surplus filler from the reverse wiping roll. It eventually transfers the filler to the applicator roll, which in turn carries it back into the reservoir again.

The rollercoating process is often used for automatic finishing. Conveyors are used in this system to transfer the work from one machine to another. Plywood, hardboard, and particle-board panels that are factory-finished are often coated by rollercoating machines. Refer to page 517 of Chapter 30 which illustrates rollercoating of plywood panels.

In general, rollercoating machines are either the floor or bench type. Capacities range from 8 to 122 in. in width. The doctor rolls are approximately 8½ in. in diameter and the applicator rolls are usually about 12 in. in diameter. Rollercoaters operate at rates of feed between 30 to 200 fpm.

Curtain-Coating Processes

Curtain coating (Fig. 30–27) involves passing the workpiece horizontally through a continuously falling stream (curtain) of coating material. This process has a distinct advantage over rollercoating. In addition to finishing flat surfaces, some irregular or contoured workpieces may also be coated. The essential components of a curtain-coating machine are the reservoir head, conveyor, trough, and pump.

The *reservoir head* is located above the trough and provides the source of fluid for the flowing curtain. The reservoirs on different kinds of machines are of two types, the gravity feed or the pressure feed. In the *gravity feed* type, the liquid flows over a weir (dam) and then drops by gravity onto the surface of the moving workpiece. The *pressure-feed reservoir head* (Fig. 30–27) is enclosed except for an adjustable slot or orifice at its bottom. The fluid is forced through the orifice under pressure. Thus, the volume and velocity of the fluid may be adjusted to fit the needs of each job. The fluid that is not intercepted by the workpiece is caught in a trough from which it flows into a storage tank. A variable speed pump returns it to the reservoir head.

The *conveyor* is generally of the endless belt type. It travels (dips) under the trough as shown in Figure 30–27 to insure equal speeds for both infeed and outfeed conveyors. The conveyor deposits

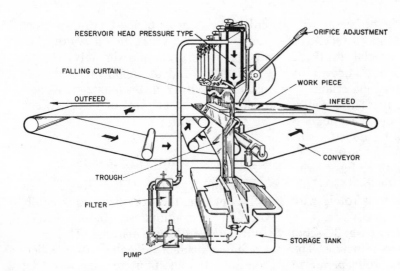

Fig. 30–27. A diagram of a curtain coating machine. This is the pressure head type.

a uniform layer of fluid on the work. Some machines also feature two pivoting reservoir heads and a tilted conveyor. The *pivoting heads* (Fig. 30–28) facilitate a quick change from one coating application to another. Each reservoir has its own trough, container, and pump. The operator merely swings one head aside and moves the other into position. Machines that do not have pivoting heads (Fig. 30–27) are referred to as *fixed-head* machines.

The *tilt-conveyor feed* machines are generally of narrower widths. They are capable of carrying the work through the curtain at angles of 0 to 45 deg. Another small belt is incorporated with the main feed belt to provide a supporting edge which keeps the work from falling off the main conveyor. This type of machine is used to expose areas of work with irregular surfaces to the curtain of coating material. For example, picture frames, moldings, siding, and other sharply contoured products can often be tilted so that their surfaces may be finished by the curtain.

Generally speaking, the conveyor speeds of curtain-coating machines range from about 80 to 840 fpm. Some special machines such as those used to apply heated coatings, have speeds up to 1500 fpm. Curtain coating machines are driven by explosion proof, electric motors ranging up to 5 hp. The various sizes of machines will coat surfaces that range in width from 12 to 100 in.

Dipping and Flow Coating Processes

Dipping (Fig. 30–29) is the method by which parts or entire products are finished by submerging them in a tank containing the coating material. After the pieces are withdrawn from the tank, the surplus finishing material drains off. This process is usually conveyorized. The articles to be dipped are attached to hangers which carry them through the dip tank. As the dipped items move along the conveyor toward a baking oven, the surplus finishing material drips into a trough and flows back to the dip tank.

Although this process would seem to be a simple and effective method of applying finishes, a number of problems arise which require the continuous atten-

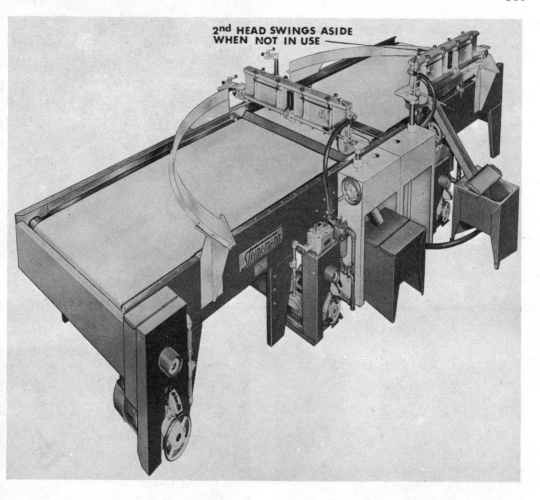

2nd HEAD SWINGS ASIDE WHEN NOT IN USE

Fig. 30–28. A curtain coating machine with pivoting heads.

tion of an attendant. For example, the buoyancy of wooden pieces poses a problem. Lightweight and hollow objects often become dislodged from the hangers. Large products require a considerable quantity of coating material in order to cover the product. Consequently, larger tanks are needed. This in turn presents other problems. The coating liquids in the tank must be agitated continuously to keep the ingredients from separating. Difficulty arises in controlling the viscosity of the liquid because of the rapid evap-

oration of the solvents from the surface of larger tanks. To combat this, enclosed dip tanks are often used (Fig. 30–29). Uneven films, sags, and runs are expected to some degree in the dip coating process. Because of these limitations, dipping processes are not used where high quality finishes are desired. Generally, dipping is employed to finish less expensive products such as brush and tool handles and toys.

There are not too many advantages offered by dipping processes. The major reason why some industries employ them is that the nature or shape of the products does not lend itself to finishing by any other process. Also, when the article may be completely submerged, this process insures that all of its surfaces will be coated.

Flow coating (Fig. 30–30) is the process of applying finishing materials by flowing them over the products. The excess material drains off the product and runs into a sump (tank) from which it is recirculated.

Flow coating is similar to dipping; but

Fig. 30–29. These commode seat covers are moving into an enclosed dip tank.

Fig. 30–30. Flow coating: (left) The workpiece travels into the flow coating chamber on a conveyor and the surfaces are flooded by the non-atomized spray as shown. (right) Sleds receive a varnish flow coat in this tunnel.

because of the manner in which the coating material is introduced to the work, many of the problems associated with the dipping process are eliminated. The items to be flow coated are carried to the finishing area by conveyors (Fig. 30–30b). The coating material is applied in a specially designed chamber through which the conveyor travels. The fluid is pumped through low-pressure nozzles. They are either of the fixed type, set to strike the work from all angles (Fig. 30–30a), or they are of the oscillating type. The latter type directs a stream of fluid with a reciprocating motion, and generally involves fewer nozzles than the fixed type. The nozzles flood the work under about 5 to 10 lb. of fluid pressure. As the streams hit the work, they splash onto all surfaces and penetrate into the hidden areas and crevices.

A drain off area is usually provided in both the dipping and flow coating systems. This is usually an enclosed chamber equipped with an exhaust fan to remove the solvents that have evaporated from the coating material. Various devices are used at the end of the drain off area to remove the beads or drops of paint clinging to the bottom edge of the work. In some cases, this excess paint is wiped off by hand.

Mass-Production Finishing

Mass-production finishing is a systematic method of moving the products through a predetermined sequence of

Fig. 30–31. A closed loop finishing line in this factory consists of a spray booth and a small infrared oven. The pieces are spray finished on pallets. Then they are moved onto the powered part of the conveyor line to be moved through the infrared oven for drying.

Fig. 30–32. Automatic buffing operation, after filling and finishing, being used in the factory finishing of flooring.

operations to produce a specified finish. Refer to the flow chart shown at the beginning of Chapter 5 (page 67). This illustration shows some typical operations commonly performed in the finishing department of a large industrial plant. The actual number or kind of operations performed is dictated by the particular products to be finished and the results desired. For example, small utility items such as tool handles and so on may require only 1 or 2 operations. Fine furniture may require 25 or 30 different operations as it goes through the complete finishing schedule.

Before the product enters the finishing room, all surfaces are carefully sanded and inspected. The pieces are passed through the final finishing sanders (see page 537) and all dust particles are removed. The workpieces move through the finishing room by power-driven conveyors or on roller tracks (Fig. 30–31). Small items are moved in boxes by forklift trucks or on carts. Power-driven conveyors are used in most industries where products are produced in volume.

Conveyorized finishing is the term used when the workpieces are carried at a uniform rate by powered conveyors

Fig. 30–33. As the case goods slowly move through this spraying booth, the operator applies a coat of clear lacquer.

through each station in the finishing department. The conveyors travel at speeds of 3 to 10 fpm. Floor mounted conveyors handle the larger products such as case goods and panels.

Smaller items and components of the larger products (legs, drawers, etc.) are often transported overhead by suspended conveyors (Figs. 30–29 and 30–30).

Automatic or powered conveyors have the work stations for different operations

Fig. 30–34. As the case goods wind back and forth through the finishing department, supplemental hand operations are performed to maintain the desired quality. Here a second coat of an oil finish is being applied ½ hour after the initial spray coat to give deeper penetration.

located at specific distances along the finishing line. This spacing allows time for drying, inspection, and supplementary hand work as the pieces move from one station to the next.

Most mass-production finishing lines loop back and forth through the finishing

Fig. 30–36. The finishing department of a large furniture factory. Here a slat bed conveyor moves the case goods through a drying oven at a rate of 3 fpm.

Fig. 30–35. Here a finisher on the production line brushes a gold stripe decoration on painted French provincial furniture.

department as shown in Figure 30–31. Some finishing lines because of the nature of the product are operated in a straight line.

Any of the various methods of applying finishes may be incorporated into the finishing line. Drying ovens (Figs. 30–31 and 30–36), wiping brushes (Fig. 30–32), buffers (Fig. 30–38), and other types of equipment may be integrated

Fig. 30–37. Filling, rubbing, and polishing are vital operations performed with pneumatic machines on the finishing line. Here a workman uses a pneumatic padding machine to fill the grain in a table top.

into the sequence of finishing operations. In addition, areas are located along the finishing line for supplemental hand operations such as hand decorating (Fig. 30–35), filling, toning, applying decals or trade marks, patching, repairing, rubbing, and polishing (Figs. 30–34 and 30–37). Each worker on the finishing line has responsibility for quality control.

Fig. 30–38. Prefinished flooring is coated with wax (under heat) and polished in the final operation before packaging.

Chapter 31   Coating Materials

The field of manufactured finishing materials is enlarging and changing perhaps more rapidly than any other area associated with woodworking. This is largely due to the continuous development and use of synthetic ingredients to formulate improved coating materials. Because of these advances many of the conventional finishes have been modified, and many entirely new coating materials are now available. Because it is impossible to discuss all the varieties of coating materials, this chapter will restrict itself to the principal kinds of coating materials available today. Their advantages, limitations, and significant characteristics will be discussed. After a study of this chapter, the reader should be able to select the appropriate type of coating material for school shop and home use and display familiarity with the finishes that are used in industry.

House Paints

Paint is composed of a finely ground powder called *pigment* and a liquid known as a *vehicle*. Pigments are obtained from natural sources or they are prepared by chemical processes. Vehicles are combinations of oils, resins, volatile thinners (or solvents), and driers. The commonly used oils in paints are linseed, tung, soybean, and chinawood. The *resins* in paints are either natural or synthetic. Many different kinds of resins are used to give the paint certain characteristics for special applications. The chief purpose of a resin is to impart hardness, wear-resistance, and other mechanical or chemical properties.

Paints are classified in many different ways. They may be grouped according to the kind of pigment, the type of resin, or the kind of solvent in the vehicle. There are six basic classifications of house paints by pigment: (1) white lead, (2) titanium-lead-zinc, (3) titanium-zinc (4) titanium-lead, (5) titanium, and (6) dark-color.

White lead paint is the oldest in terms of years of use. It has been used since colonial times. Today, however, it accounts for only a small part of the total volume of house paint used in this country. It is a durable finish. It resists staining caused by rusting metal. It is insensitive to water and consequently does not tend to blister. Its disadvantages lie in its low hiding power (opacity), its unfavorable off-white color, and its tendency to collect and retain dirt more than other types of paint. White lead wears away faster and is slightly more expensive than other types of paint.

Titanium-lead-zinc paints are very popular for exterior painting. Generally, paints of this type have brilliant and highly reflective colors, remain uniformly clean, and are durable (hard and slow wearing). Paints containing zinc, however, must be classified as moisture sensitive because they swell more than the wood when wet. Thus, they blister more readily on contact with water than do other types of paint. Another objectionable characteristic is that T-L-Z paints are also likely to become stained by nail rust and by the corrosion of iron and copper screens. Furthermore, paints that contain lead tend to discolor upon exposure to sulphides in the air.

Titanium-zinc paints have characteristics similar to those of the titanium-lead-zinc classification. The most important difference between them is that titanium-zinc paints contain no lead and do not discolor upon exposure to sulphide fumes.

Titanium-lead pigment paints are often referred to as the "breather type." They contain, in addition to titanium and lead, a high proportion of *transparent extending pigment*. Paints of this type are characterized by their lack of gloss. Titanium-lead paints are nonsensitive to moisture and highly blister resistant. They have high opacity, wear well, resist stains from rust, and have moderate color qualities. They provide a surface which is easy to repaint. They will, however, become discolored by sulfides.

Titanium paint is a combination of titanium pigment and one of several special vehicles. The most popular vehicle contains an *alkyd* resin. This paint has little or no gloss, is blister, fume, and stain resistant, and has good opacity and color qualities. It also resists sulfide discoloration.

Dark-color paints are often called trim paints. They consist chiefly of very dark colored pigments with little, if any, titanium dioxide, white lead, or zinc oxide. The major part of the vehicle is varnish, usually an alkyd-resin varnish. The iron-oxide paints (the familiar red paint seen on many barns) are often classified as dark-color paints. In general, quality dark-color paints are more durable, and less sensitive to water than any white or light-colored paint.

Emulsion paints are made by combining the pigment with resin particles which have been dispersed or emulsified in water. These are the newest exterior wood paints in general use. Paints of this type are often called *latex, rubber-base, water-thinned,* or *water-base paints*. The major types of latex are polyvinylacetate (PVA) and acrylic. Prior to the development of emulsion paints, only oil base paints with volatile solvents were available. These were predominately turpentine or mineral spirits. The solvents were necessary to thin the paints in order to make them more workable. However, with emulsion paints, the solvent is water. Recently, paints have become available in which the linseed oil vehicle is in true water solution. The oil had to be altered to accomplish this, but such paints have the properties of both oil and emulsion paints. Emulsion paints are now being used to paint not only flat (nongloss) interior walls, but they are also being used on exterior surfaces. The most promising emulsion paints for exterior use on wood are of the acrylic-resin or vinyl-resin type.

Some of the advantages of the emulsion paints are: (1) they are safer to use than paints using organic or mineral solvents which have dangerous fumes and are highly combustible; (2) they provide easy clean-up; (3) they have high resistance to moisture, blistering, fading, and dirt holding; (4) they are easy to apply; (5) they can be applied to damp surfaces; and (6) they dry to a "flat" finish, which does not emphasize defects on the surface.

For exterior painting, emulsion paints have some disadvantages. These are: (1) they generally require three coats (one oil-base primer and two top coats) for repainting weathered oil-base paints; (2) they require an oil-base primer for painting new wood; (3) they must be formulated with a fungicide to resist mildew; (4) they may not adhere well to chalky, old paint; (5) a hot dry surface must be sprinkled with water before painting; and (6) they should not be applied at temperatures below 50 deg. F.

Common exterior-paint failures (Figs. 31–1a, 31–1b, 31–1c, and 31–1d). Deterioration of paint is often caused by natural wear or weathering. This involves the chemical or physical changes which result from the action of sunlight, air, and water. Until the "perfect" exterior paint is developed for a one-coat, life-time job, a certain amount of deterioration must be expected. However, there are situations that promote the failure of paint. These should be recognized by the painter and corrected in order to obtain the maximum life or service from the paint. In general, there are four basic painting problems.

1. *Mildew* (Fig. 31–1a), which shows up as a splotchy gray or black coating, is caused by conditions of combined warmth and humidity on protected or shaded surfaces. Mildew may be corrected by cleaning with a washing soda solution and then recoated with a zinc paint or one containing a fungicide.

2. *Chalking* (Fig. 31–1b), or powdering, is the deterioration of paint as a result of exposure to the elements. Most paints oxidize or chalk to some

extent. However, paints especially resistant to chalking are available. They are used for repainting where chalk stains on brick, stone, or masonry may prove unsightly. Chalked surfaces should be washed or brushed before repainting to avoid adhesion problems.

3. and 4. *Peeling* (Fig. 31–1c) and *blistering* (Fig. 31–1d) generally result when moisture gets under the paint. Water used inside a house evaporates and passes through the walls creating a moisture vapor pressure behind the outside paint. Cracks in the siding or defective flashing around windows and doors, will also admit moisture to the walls. Peeling caused by such defects can be prevented by making suitable repairs. Venting exterior walls may also be helpful. The installation of vapor barriers and the painting of both sides of house siding is recommended for new construction.

Interior Paints

Interior paints normally last much longer than exterior coating materials because of the less harsh environment. Finishes for inside use need not be designed to withstand the rigors of outdoor exposure. In general, *enamels* are used for an opaque finish on interior surfaces where a smoother surface, better color, and a more lasting sheen are desired. Enamels dry hard and smooth. They are available in either flat, gloss, or semigloss finishes. The essential difference between an enamel and a paint is that enamels have finer (smaller) pigment particles and the vehicle consists of varnish or lacquer rather than oil or water. *Oil base paints* usually have raw or treated oils as a vehicle and coarser pigments.

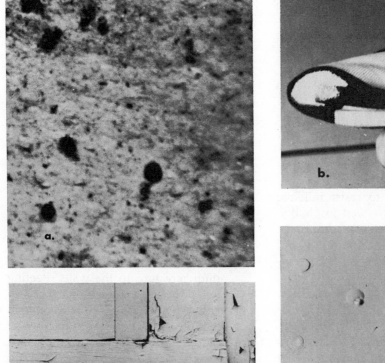

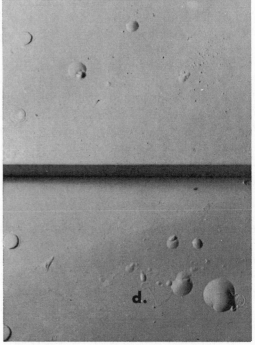

Fig. 31–1. Common exterior-paint failures: (a) mildewing, (b) chalking or powdering, (c) peeling, (d) blistering.

Enamels are less opaque than paints of the same color because they cannot be made with the same proportion of pigment.

Water base paints or latex paints offer some degree of washability for interior surfaces. They are quick drying. They are not ordinarily used in bathrooms or kitchens or for cabinets. Either a gloss or semi-gloss enamel (usually of a washable alkyd resin base) is used to finish these surfaces.

Finishes for Furniture and Allied Products

The many kinds of coating materials applied to furniture and similar work may be divided into three broad groups. Namely: *undercoats, topcoats,* and *penetrating* finishes. Included in the undercoating group are such materials as bleaches, wash coats, sealers, stains, and fillers. They are used primarily to condition the surfaces prior to the application of the topcoating material. Topcoat finishes are durable and hard wearing. They include shellac, lacquers, varnishes, and a very important group of synthetic resin-coating materials. Penetrating finishes, such as the modern oil finish, are generally regarded as a topcoating material. They normally require several coats. The first coat may or may not be of the same material.

Bleaches are used to remove the natural color in wood to produce the conventional "blond" finishes. They are also widely employed to produce such finishes as wheat, sandstone, tweed, amber, harvest, and other light-color finishes. Surfaces containing both sapwood and heartwood are bleached and then stained to produce a uniform coloration. Bleaches are watery, grain raising solutions which contain strong oxidizing ingredients. Some of the chemicals in bleaches are sodium hydroxide, hydrogen peroxide, oxalic acid, and sodium hypochlorite (laundry bleach). Following application, some bleaches require neutralizing by washing with acetic acid solutions and/or water. They are supplied in either one or two solution preparations. Commercial bleaches available to home craftsmen are generally 2 solutions. Prior to application they are mixed together to make a one solution application. This type, however, has a short working life. In industry, two-solution bleaches are applied with a double-headed spray gun.

Stains are composed either of finely ground pigments or chemical dyes suspended or dissolved in a vehicle. They are used to impart color to the surface of wood. For example, stains are applied to sapwood prior to an overall staining to produce a uniformly colored surface. Stains are often used on inexpensive woods in an attempt to imitate more costly ones. Stains are also utilized to produce special finishing effects such as antique pine, dark cherry, weathered oak, etc. There are four basic kinds of stains: (1) oil, (2) spirit, (3) water, and (4) non-grain-rising (NGR).

Oil stains are of two types, *penetrating* and *pigmented* (wood toning or *wiping*). Penetrating stains consist of oil soluble dyes dissolved in turpentine, benzol, toluol, or naphtha. Pigmented stains consist of several colors ground in oil and suspended in linseed oil or a varnish vehicle. Generally, oil stains do not raise the grain, they are easy to apply, and they provide good color effects. However, penetrating stains are not used for high-quality finishes because they fade on exposure to sunlight and have a tendency to bleed into subsequent topcoats. This means that the color is dissolved by succeeding coats of the finish. Pigmented stains, while not as clear as dye stains, are used extensively to unify and blend colors in furniture finishing. Oil stains may be applied by brushing, wiping, spraying, or dipping. After drying for several minutes, the surplus is removed by wiping.

Water stains consist of water soluble dyes dissolved in water. They are widely used in fine furniture finishing because they are inexpensive, do not bleed, have good color fastness and penetrate deeply. The major disadvantages are that they raise the grain fibers thereby necessitating light sanding. They also require a longer drying period and are not suitable for dipping operations because the water tends to weaken glue joints.

Spirit stains consist of aniline dyes dissolved in alcohol. Stains of this type provide brilliant colors and they retain their color as long as other stains. They are, however, difficult to apply uniformly. Shellac is often used as a binder. Spirit stains are not used in mass-production finishing work, but are widely used in touchup or spot-finishing work.

Non-grain-raising stains (NGR) are generally more expensive than other stains. Their high quality and many advantages offset the initial cost. NGR stains consist of acid-dyes dissolved in alcohol, glycol, acetone, toluol, or other ketones. NGR stains resist fading (have good light fastness), have limited bleeding characteristics, do not raise the grain, dry fast, and provide moderately uniform color coverage. NGR stains may be applied by most common methods. Brushing is difficult, however, because of the rapid drying.

Washcoats and sealers are thin solutions of shellac or lacquer which are usually applied to keep one finishing material from combining with another. When applied over a filler, it is referred to as a *sealer*. When applied over a stain, the coating is referred to as a *wash coat*. Sometimes a sealer is applied to the bare wood prior to sanding. In this case, it is often referred to as a *sizing coat*. Sizing is often used on very absorbant woods so the stain will color more uniformly. Washcoats and sealers also serve other purposes, such as: (1) stiffening the fibers of the wood to facilitate sanding, (2) enhancing the color of stains, (3) reducing bleeding, and (4) preventing fillers from changing the color of stained surfaces.

Fillers are finishing materials composed of pigments, a vehicle, binders, and solvents. The primary function of fillers is to fill in the pores of wood to provide smooth surfaces for later topcoats. Fillers also emphasize the grain and give depth and color to the finished wood. Fillers are either the paste or liquid type. *Liquid fillers,* such as shellac, are usually transparent. They are primarily used on close-grained woods. *Paste fillers* are either opaque or transparent, and they are used on the open grain woods. Table 31–1 lists the type of fillers normally used on different species of wood.

The oldest types of paste fillers contain linseed oil, a drier, turpentine, and silex (crushed quartz). The main disadvantages of fillers of this type include slow drying and the tendency for insufficiently dried filler to "gray" with age. This type of filler is easy to apply and to remove. The oil serves as a lubricant. Linseed oil expands on drying and helps to hold the filler in the wood pores.

A synthetic resin vehicle has been substituted for the linseed oil in a newer "fast dry" filler. Drying time is almost 30 minutes to 1 hour. These fillers are more difficult to remove and to rub in due to the lack of a lubricant. Slow dry-

TABLE 31–1

Woods not usually filled	Woods primarily filled with liquid fillers or thin semi-paste types	Woods filled with fillers of semi-paste consistency
Basswood	Beech	Ash
Cedar	Birch	Butternut
Cypress	Cherry	Chestnut
Ebony	Gum	Elm
Fir	Maple	Hickory
Hemlock	Sycamore	Locust
Hollywood	Redwood	Mahogany
Larch		Oak
Pine		Rosewood
Poplar		Walnut
Spruce		
Willow		

ing thinners may be added, but drying time is then increased. Failure to allow sufficient drying time may cause the sealer to blush (appear milky).

Shellac is the product of an insect, the *trachardia lacca* bug of India, which converts the sap of the tree into a secretion. This secretion is collected by men and purified to make shellac flakes. Pure white shellac is made by bleaching orange shellac gum flakes. Shellac flakes are dissolved or "cut" in denatured (poisoned) alcohol to make liquid shellac. The *cut* of shellac refers to the ratio between the shellac gum (in pounds) and the alcohol solvent (in gallons). A 4-lb. cut is common. That is, 4 lb. of shellac gum are dissolved in 1 gallon of alcohol. The mixture makes about 1.4 gallons of liquid shellac. Consequently, a gallon contains slightly less than 3 lb. of dry shellac. Four-pound cut shellac is usually diluted with alcohol — half and half — for a topcoating; wash coats, 1 part 4-lb. cut shellac to 7 parts alcohol. Shellac has limited use as a topcoating material today. It is sometimes used on interior woodwork, floors, toys, and musical instruments. The major disadvantage of a shellac finish is its tendency to turn white and become soft if water containing an alkali contacts it. Liquid shellac has a shelf life of about one year. Shellac has good working and wearing characteristics. It serves well as an undercoating for varnish and lacquer.

Varnish is a broad term used to describe many clear, transparent (nonpigmented) coating materials. In general, varnish consists of natural or synthetic resins, vehicles (oils), solvents, and driers. The resins are the solid portion of the finish. They provide the luster, hardness, and other desirable properties. Varnishes made with a large portion of oil are called long-oil varnishes; varnishes with a small portion of oil are called short-oil varnishes. Long-oil varnishes are slow drying, but produce a very tough, wear-resistant surface. Most exterior varnishes are of the long oil type. The short-oil varnishes dry quickly, are hard and brittle, and have a high luster. They are generally used for furniture finishes. The synthetic resins used in the manufacture of other coating materials are also used in modern varnishes. In general, the new resin components of modern varnishes provide excellent flexibility as well as hardness. They resist abrasion, chemicals, harsh cleaners, oils, and moisture. The alkyd, vinyl, and polyurethane resins have good toughness and fairly good weathering properties.

Lacquer is a coating material which dries very rapidly to form a hard film. Originally, the term "lacquer" referred to shellac and other resinous solutions in which the vehicle dried by evaporation. Presently, the word "lacquer" is applied almost exclusively to coating materials containing various cellulose resins and plasticizers dispersed in a complex volatile solvent. Lacquers made from nitrocellulose resins are one of the major topcoating materials for furniture. Thin-bodied solutions of lacquer incorporated with other resins and sanding agents are used for sealers and washcloths. Lacquer thinners are toluene, benzine, or xylene — all hydrocarbons.

Pigmented lacquers are used as toning materials. Some pigmented lacquers are formulated for exterior use. Clear lacquers generally are not suitable for exterior use. Moisture and the sun's rays tend to discolor the wood. Experiments with ultraviolet absorbing agents incorporated in the lacquer solutions have shown that discoloration may be measurably reduced. As with varnishes, many of the new synthetic resins are now found in lacquers of many different formulations.

Modern synthetic finishes consist of modified natural resins or synthetic resins and complex formulations of other chemical materials. New synthetic resins are playing an important role in the improvement of the conventional opaque and transparent coating materials discussed in the preceding paragraphs. Other new coating materials are being developed at a rapid pace. Some of the relatively new synthetic resin finishes include:

1. The *polyurethanes* are beginning to replace the oleoresinous (oil and resin) varnishes. They outperform conventional varnishes in toughness, wear and abrasion resistance, and chemical resistance. Polyurethanes are recommended for floors, and exterior uses. They do have some tendency to discolor (yellow) and they are somewhat difficult to apply as fine furniture finishes.

2. The *vinyl resin* group is now generally incorporated into varnish and lacquer formulations. They are derived from the polymerization (a chemical reaction of molecules) of vinyl compounds which are of the thermoplastic type. Their major advantages are resistance to water, oils, abrasion, and discoloration.

3. *Polyesters* are coating materials characterized by their exceptional hardness, heavy build per coat, and resistance to staining and marring. Polyesters are of the two component or catalyst reaction type. The catalyst (peroxide or cobalt) and the coating are usually applied by spraying from twin headed guns. The atomized liquids mix as they travel to the work surface. Polyester coatings are made in two basic types of formulations: wax and wax free. *Wax types* are currently in wider use for furniture finishes. Wax is incorporated to protect the coating from the air and to retard the drying rate. As the finish hardens, the wax rises to the surface. The wax film is then rubbed to a polished finish, or it is removed from the coating film.

The highly polished finish produced by the polyester types are currently being used for the glossy finishes on some wood products such as pianos. However, furniture with glossy, polished surfaces is not very popular. Therefore, a flattening agent is added to reduce the gloss. In general, a polyester finish provides a suitable thick film with a one coat application. However, on vertical surfaces, there is a tendency for this heavy film to "sag" or "run." Polyester finishes of the wax type set up in about 20 minutes and cure overnight at ambient temperature. The curing can be accelerated to a 2-hour complete cure by the use of heat.

The *wax-free* polyesters are undergoing continuous research and development. Presently they have limited application because of their higher cost. They are worth further investigation because they cure at a much faster rate than the wax type. With the application of heat, the finish will cure in about 10 minutes. This feature makes them desirable for production finishing schedules.

4. *Epoxy resin coatings* are also two component coating materials which cure by the reaction of a catalyst additive. Unlike the polyesters, epoxy coatings are not widely used as a coating material for wood. They have poor color retention and cure slowly. Atmospheric conditions must

be suitable for application (curing is best at 50 deg. F). Uneven surfaces develop when epoxies are applied in humid weather. This necessitates removing the defects by rubbing. With further refinements, it is expected that epoxy coatings will be more widely used in the future because of their superior durability. In general, epoxy coatings resist gas, fuel oils, salt water, acids, and steam. Presently, they are primarily used for exterior finishes.

5. *Butyrate coatings* are replacing the nitrocellulose lacquers. They possess similar characteristics, such as fast drying, durability, and high impact and abrasive resistance. Butyrate coatings also resist staining by rubber when used in telephone feet, wires, ash tray bases, etc. One major advantage of clear butyrate lacquers is that they are fire resistant. Because butyrate compounds are compatible with many other materials, butyrate esters are being added to improve several other kinds of coating materials.

Penetrating or oil finishes. Currently, one of the more popular furniture finishes is the simulated hand-rubbed oil finish. This is a finish which looks like the old hand-rubbed, linseed oil finish. Commercially manufactured coating materials are now available which produce the same effect with a minimum of hand rubbing. They have low viscosity and therefore penetrate deeply into the pores of the wood. These new coating materials are commonly referred to as *Danish oil finishes*. Modern oil finishes are a combination of oil and resins. They harden by polymerization. Oil finishes are ideal for all interior uses but they are susceptible to marking from water and chemicals. The Danish oil finishes are often applied in just one saturating coat by spraying, brushing, or dipping methods. Sometimes an additional coat is required; the excess must be wiped off. A protective coating of wax or a lacquer formulation may be used to provide added protection.

Other finishing supplies include hundreds of different novelty finishes, solvents, abrasives, waxing polishes and other materials. Some of the more common materials are:

1. *Flock* is used as a novelty finish and on the bases of lamps, statues, etc., for protective purposes. Flock is finely shredded fibers of nylon or rayon. They are applied (generally by spraying) over a like-colored adhesive to produce a clothlike surface.

2. *Rubbing oils* are specially formulated mineral oils that are used as lubricants with pumice stone when rubbing varnish or lacquer.

3. *Pumice stone* is volcanic ash in pulverized form, used for rubbing finish coats. The following grades are most common: 1/2, 0, F, 2-F, 3-F, and 4-F. The last is the finest.

4. *Rubbing compounds* are abrasive mixtures in paste form that are widely used in rubbing down lacquer finishes. These are available in various grades and in different types.

5. *Rottenstone* is a limestone powder generally used for polishing finish coats to a high luster.

6. *Steel wool*, which consists of fine strands of steel (usually in pad form), is used for rubbing finished surfaces. Its use between coats is not recommended because steel-wool particles are left on the surface. Steel wool is more appropriately used with a paste wax for rubbing the final coat of varnish or lacquer to produce a semi-gloss finish. Steel wool is avail-

Fig. 31–2.   Impregnated abrasive fabrics used in rubbing operations.

able in various grades (from coarse to fine): No. 3, 2, 1, 0, 2-0, 3-0, and 4-0.

7. *Impregnated abrasive fabrics* (Fig. 30–2) are used for rubbing operations. This new abrasive material consists of grit (in various grades) held by an adhesive bonding material within unwoven strands of fabric. It may be purchased in roll or pad form. It is especially good for rubbing between coats because it leaves no slivers on the surface as steel wool does.

8. *Wet or dry abrasive papers* are waterproof backed sandpapers used with water or oil lubricants in rub-

bing finishes and for sanding wash-coats. Grades generally range from 280 to 600 (coarse to fine, respectively).

9. *Burning in sticks* are solid sticklike forms of shellac or lacquer which are heated before applying. They are available in many colors and are used to repair dents and other defects in wood surfaces. Usually they are applied with a heated knife.

10. *Felt pad* is a thick block of felt used for rubbing operations.

11. *Waxes* are used for protection over topcoating materials. They are available in paste or liquid form, and generally, they are insoluble in water.

Some common types of waxes are: carnauba, paraffin, and beeswax.

12. *Masking tape* is a pressure-sensitive tape useful in finishing operations. It is used for sharp color separation by protecting the adjoining areas from drips, spatters, overspray, or overlapping brush marks.

13. *Water putty* is a dry wood powder which is mixed with water to form a paste. It sets quickly, is moderately adhesive, and makes a suitable crack filler under opaque finishes.

14. *Paint and varnish removers* are used for taking off finishes. They are chemical solvents which soften the finish and break it loose from the wood surface. The better types are nonflammable. Some require neutralizing the surface by washing with water or other specially prepared solvents.

Chapter 32 *Finishing in the School Shop*

Coating materials are usually applied in the school shop by one or more of the following methods: (1) brushing, (2) wiping with rags, (3) air spraying, or (4) aerosol spraying. In certain situations, dipping or hand-rollercoating processes may be adapted to school shop work, but as a rule, these methods have limited use.

This unit provides helpful information concerning the use and care of brushes, spray equipment and aerosols. Also provided, is a study of safety and the application techniques often associated with the common coating materials. This includes removing finishes, preparing surfaces, bleaching, the application of undercoats and topcoats, rubbing and polishing, and other operations.

Safety Precautions for Finishing Processes

1. Whenever possible use nonflammable and nontoxic coating materials and solvents.
2. Always *read the instructions* on the container before opening or using the contents.
3. Be sure that adequate ventilation and good lighting (from nonexplosive fixtures) are provided.

4. Keep a suitable fire extinguisher* readily available and be sure that you know how to use it.
5. Keep all finishing materials covered, and store them in metal cabinets. Exercise caution when working in areas where fumes and vapors exist. A special type of can, recommended by safety officials for the storage of volatile liquids, is shown in Figure 32–1. This can has a spring con-

---

* A foam or dry chemical type extinguisher is recommended for handling fires caused by inflammable liquids and electricity.

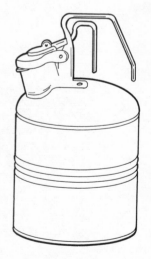

Fig. 32–1. A safety can of this type is recommended for the storage of volatile liquids in the finishing room.

trolled spout cover which prevents the escape of fumes.

6. Dispose of used rags, papers, and towels in an approved metal covered container (Fig. 32–2).

7. Wear an apron to protect your clothing. Use a respirator for protection against the inhalation of dust particles or overspray.

8. Wear rubber (or plastic) gloves as recommended by the manufacturer when handling materials that may irritate the skin.

9. Keep the finishing room and the working areas clean. Remember to clean spray booths and to dispose of filters regularly.

10. Always clean the lip of a paint can before closing the cover.

11. *Never* leave a container of finishing material uncovered (or partially closed).

12. *Caution!* Do not dispose of empty aerosol spray cans along with other waste materials that are to be burned. If this is done, they will explode because of the gas vapors remaining inside the can.

Brushing

Some general preparations. Lay down newspapers or a drop cloth to protect other surfaces from spatters or dripping, and to facilitate easy cleanup afterwards. Open the cans containing the coating material with a screw driver. Stir the contents with a paint paddle or a smooth stick until it is uniformly blended. (NOTE: varnishes should not be stirred.)

If the can has been opened before, a scum or "skin" on the surface may be present. In this case, use a strainer to remove the lumps and bits of skin. Commercially made strainers are available; a nylon stocking or a section of window screening may be substituted for the job. If stirring of the settled solids is necessary, pour most of the top liquid into another container. Stir what is left in the original container until it is thoroughly mixed with the remaining liquid. Return the liquid from the second container, a little at a time, stirring constantly. This technique will insure a uniform mixture of the solids and liquid.

Be sure that the surface of the work is smooth, free from dust particles, oil, glue, etc. Refer to page 565. As you plan and prepare to apply a finish, keep in mind that uneven coatings on opposite surfaces of wood cause warping. Surface coatings, regardless of the type or com-

Fig. 32–2. Paint filled rags and other waste materials should be placed in closed metal containers.

Fig. 32–3.   Revolve the brush rapidly to dislodge loose bristles.

Fig. 32–4.   Tap the loaded brush against the side of the can to remove excess liquid.

position, merely retard the rate at which the changes in wood moisture content occur. Thus, to minimize twisting or cupping, be sure to finish the backs and bottoms of wooden articles. Often a less expensive finish can be applied to these areas.

Using brushes. Select a brush of the appropriate type and size for the work at hand. When possible, use a narrow brush because it is more easily controlled and easier to clean. To some extent, all brushes contain short bristles which are not caught in the setting (especially new brushes). These loose bristles should be removed by revolving the brush rapidly between your hands as shown in Figure 32–3.

It is a good idea to break in a brush before using it. This is accomplished by dipping it into the thinner recommended for the coating material that is to be used. This procedure removes foreign matter from the brush and helps to prevent the coating material from hardening on the surface of the bristles. Consequently, the brush is easier to clean. Shake out the excess thinner before dipping the brush into the finishing material.

To load a brush, dip it into the fluid about ⅓ of the bristle length. Tap out the excess against the *inside* of the can as shown in Figure 32–4. If there is not enough room in the can to do this, transfer the liquid to a larger container. This is preferred to scraping the bristles against the inside rim of the container — for this usually causes air bubbles to form in the liquid.

Whenever possible, position the work so you can work on a horizontal surface. This will help to prevent runs and sags from developing. Hold the brush at approximately the same angle as shown in Figure 32–5. Start in the center area of the surface and brush toward the ends, working with the grain. Meter the coating material onto the surface with long sweeping strokes. Maintain a light to moderate pressure on the brush, and keep approxi-

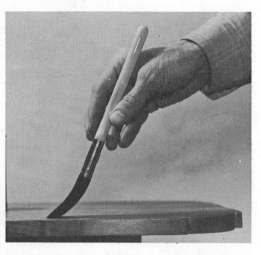

Fig. 32–5. The correct way of holding a brush. Note the angle and moderate bend of the bristles. Brush from the center toward the edge of the surface.

mately the same angle throughout the stroke. Use both sides of each brushful and end each stroke with a light lifting motion.

Start each new brushful on an un-

coated area of the surface and work into the wet edge of the previously coated portion. When applying topcoat materials, several thin coats instead of one heavy film will produce the best results. When a section has been covered, the final step is to go over the area with light, quick strokes to smooth out all brush marks and laps and to recoat any thin spots. Remove the excess finish from the brush by brushing it on a newspaper.

Keep a brush soft between coats by suspending it in the proper thinner. Standing a brush on the bottom of the can will produce an undesirable bend in the bristles. Figure 6 shows how a brush may be stored for a *short period of time.* A brush should not be left suspended in thinner (as shown in Figure 32–6) any longer than absolutely necessary. It is better to clean the brush immediately after use and prepare it for "dry" storage.

Replace the cover on the can of finish tightly. Then, for paint and enamels, shake the can vigorously. Shaking dis-

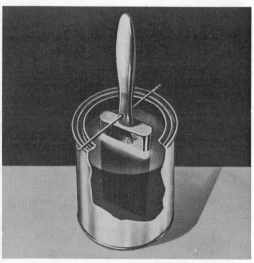

Fig. 32–6. A brush may be kept temporarily by suspending it in the proper solvent without touching the bottom of the can.

Fig. 32–7. Removing congealed paint from the heel of a brush with a steel comb.

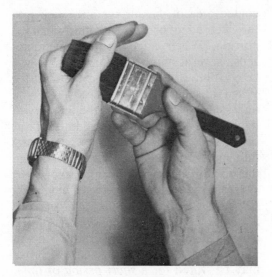

Fig. 32–8. Squeeze out solvents or water when cleaning a brush and shape the bristles.

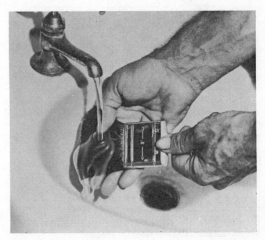

Fig. 32–9. Before storing a brush, wash it thoroughly with soap or a detergent and water.

solves the enclosed air in the finish and prevents a skin from forming.

Cleaning and Storing Brushes

1. Brush off the excess finish in the brush onto a newspaper.
2. Rinse it in the proper solvent. The solvents usually recommended for coating materials are: (a) for oil-based paints, enamels, and varnishes use turpentine; (b) for shellac use alcohol; (c) for lacquer use lacquer thinner; (d) for latex and emulsion paints use water; (e) for other materials refer to the manufacturers instructions.
3. If you are cleaning a brush that has become hard, it may be necessary to remove tough paint from the heel of the brush with a steel comb (Fig. 32–7) or a wire brush.
4. Work out the excess solvent on a rag or squeeze it out with your fingers as shown in Figure 32–8.

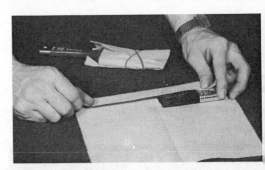

Fig. 32–10. Wrap the brush in a paper towel. One brush is wrapped and ready for storage.

5. Wash the brush with lukewarm water and a mild bar soap or detergent. Work up a good lather and rinse it thoroughly (Fig. 32–9).
6. Remove the excess water and shape the brush by squeezing the bristle between your thumb and forefinger as shown in Figure 9. Carefully wrap the bristles in a paper towel and attach a rubber band. See Figure 32–10.
7. Lay the brush flat and allow it to dry in storage.

Fig. 32–11. Checking the temperature with a thermometer.

Using Air Spray Equipment

The use of spray equipment generally involves the following operations: (1) preparing the fluids, (2) setting the air pressure and adjusting the gun, (3) spraying various types of surfaces, and (4) cleaning and maintaining the equipment.

Preparing the liquid is an important step for successful spraying. This is the general procedure.

1. Read the manufacturer's instructions on the container of finishing material.
2. Turn on the exhaust fan.
3. Check the temperature of the finishing material (Fig. 32–11). Most finishes spray well at normal room temperatures unless otherwise specified by the manufacturer.
4. Check the viscosity of the fluid. Usually it is ready to use at can consistency. As a rule, good brushing consistency is good spraying consistency (no thinner). However, when using sealers or wash coats, thinners often must be added to obtain a specific viscosity. For an accurate check of viscosity, pour a cupful of the liquid through a viscosity cup. The right mixture of thinner and liquid will flow out completely in the time (number of seconds) specified. See Figure 32–12. Avoid excessive thinning.
5. Strain the fluid through a 60- to 90-

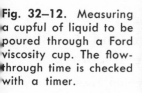

Fig. 32–12. Measuring a cupful of liquid to be poured through a Ford viscosity cup. The flow-through time is checked with a timer.

mesh screening material (Fig. 32–13). This helps to prevent clogging the spray gun. A nylon stocking, cheese cloth, or a piece of window screening may also be used for this operation.

Fig. 32–13. Straining the coating material into a suction feed cup.

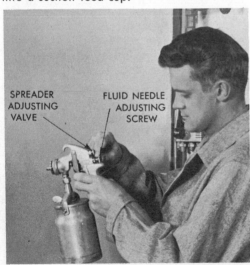

SPREADER ADJUSTING VALVE

FLUID NEEDLE ADJUSTING SCREW

Fig. 32–14. Adjusting the fluid flow on a suction feed gun. Turn it clockwise to reduce the amount of fluid flow.

6. Fill the cup or material tank with the fluid.

Setting Pressure and Adjusting for Suction Feed Operation

1. Turn on the compressor motor and drain the water from the air tank and lines.
2. Hook up the hose and spray gun.
3. Set the atomizing air pressure to approximately 35 psi. This can be adjusted higher for heavier materials or lower for thinner materials if necessary.
4. Turn the spreader adjustment valve on the gun outward (counterclockwise).
5. Turn the fluid adjusting screw (Fig. 32–14) in (clockwise).
6. Spray a test pattern with the gun held at about 6 or 8 in. from the surface.
7. If the finish looks too dry or sandy, too little liquid is flowing for the amount of atomizing air pressure being used. Turn the fluid-adjusting screw counterclockwise until a full wet coat is obtained.
8. Adjust for the type of pattern desired with the spreader adjusting valve. Turn it in to reduce the pattern width; turn it out to increase the pattern width. See the basic patterns illustrated in Figure 32–16.

Setting Pressure and Adjusting the Pressure Feed Sprayer

1. Turn on the compressor motor.
2. Turn the fluid needle adjusting screw wide open (counterclockwise).
3. Set the fluid pressure at the tank to about 15 psi.
4. Set the air-atomizing pressure to about 65 lb. (Fig. 32–15).

AIR REGULATOR
CONTROL

MAIN LINE
GAUGE

VALVES

REGULATED
AIR SUPPLY

Fig. 32–15. Air pressure set at 65 pounds per square inch for test spray.

5. Open the spreader adjustment valve (clockwise) to its limit. Finger tight only.
6. Test spray a small area (Fig. 32–16a and 32–16b).
7. If the particles are too dry (too fine a mist) reduce the atomizing air pressure 5 to 10 lb. Increase the pressure if the particles are too coarse or the sprayed film is too heavy.
8. To increase or decrease the spraying

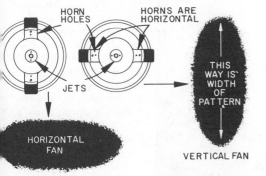

HORN
HOLES

HORNS ARE
HORIZONTAL

JETS

THIS
WAY IS
WIDTH
OF
PATTERN

HORIZONTAL
FAN

VERTICAL FAN

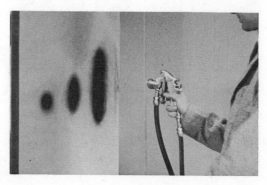

Fig. 32–16. (a) The spray patterns shown are obtained by means of the spreader adjustment on both suction and pressure feed (illustrated) guns. The pattern on the right is used most. (b) Horizontal or vertical fan patterns are controlled by the position of the air nozzle.

speed, increase or decrease the fluid pressure and correspondingly adjust the air pressure as in the previous step.

9. Set a desired pattern size and shape (Figs. 32–16a and 32–16b) by turning the spreader adjustment valve. Further adjustment of the fluid pressure may be required. If necessary, reduce the fluid flow by turning in the needle adjusting screw. However, the optimum operation is with the fluid adjusting needle in a wide open position. This reduces wear of the fluid needle.

NOTE: Generally speaking, the most efficient atomizing pressure is the lowest possible air pressure that will produce the desired effect.

Spraying flat and vertical surfaces (Figs. 32–17 and 32–18). The recommended techniques are:

1. Hold the gun perpendicular to the work and approximately 6 to 8 in. from it (Fig. 32–17). Holding the gun too close or in a tilted position will cause an uneven deposit of the coating material on the surface.

2. Make the spraying strokes by moving the gun parallel to the work surface (Fig. 32–18). Arcing the strokes produces uneven coatings.

3. The speed of the spraying stroke should be uniform and slow enough to provide full coverage without developing runs or sags. The actual stroking speed largely depends upon

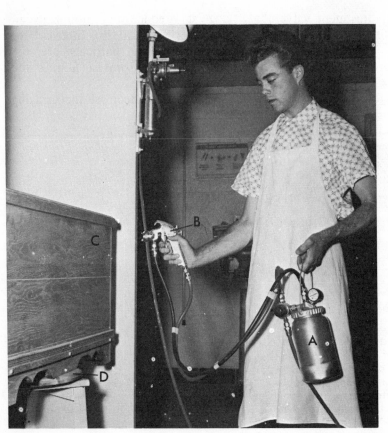

Fig. 32–17. Student spraying a flat vertical surface. Observe (a) the remote pressure feed cup, (b) the gun held perpendicular to the surface, (c) the distance to the surface is about 6 to 8 inches, and (d) the project supported on a turntable in the spray booth.

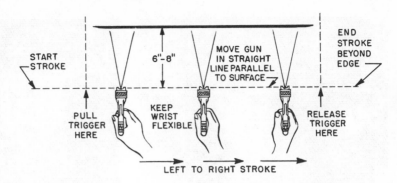

Fig. 32–18. This diagram illustrates the techniques of triggering and stroking the gun when spraying a surface.

START STROKE

6"–8"

MOVE GUN IN STRAIGHT LINE PARALLEL TO SURFACE

END STROKE BEYOND EDGE

PULL TRIGGER HERE

KEEP WRIST FLEXIBLE

RELEASE TRIGGER HERE

LEFT TO RIGHT STROKE

the rate of the fluid flow from the nozzle.

4. Stroke backward and forward across the surface holding the gun so the spray pattern overlaps about half of the previous stroke. This will produce a smooth coverage without streaks.

5. Develop the technique of "triggering" the gun with each stroke. To do this, start the stroke off the work surface before pulling the trigger. Then, pull the trigger just before the stroke reaches the edge of the work.

Fig. 32–19. Spraying a level surface on a large object. Start the strokes on the nearest edge so that the overspray from a slightly tilted gun falls on the uncoated portion of the work.

Hold the trigger while the stroke parallels the surface. Release the trigger at the other edge of the surface, but continue the stroke for a few inches before reversing for the second stroke. Study Figure 32–18.

Spraying horizontal surfaces (Fig. 32–19). Stroke in the same manner as above, but start on the near side and work toward the far side. The reason for this is that a slight tilt of the gun is often necessary; for if the overspray lands on the wet portion of the work, it will dry sandy. When a suction feed cup is used, caution must be exercised to prevent the liquid from clogging the air vent in the cup lid. This will stop the flow of material. Whenever possible, tilt the work rather than the gun.

Spraying outside edges and corners (Figs. 32–20 and 32–21). Aim the gun directly toward the edge of the adjoining surfaces. Hold it about 5 to 7 in. from the corner and direct the stroke so that 50 percent of the spray is deposited on each side of the corner (Fig. 32–20). When an object is to be coated on all surfaces, spray a "band" around all of the corners first, as shown in Figures 32–20 and 32–21. Then spray the remaining surface as usual.

Spraying inside corners (Figs. 32–22a and 32–22b) with one pass will produce

Fig. 32–20. Spray the edges first by the "banding" technique.

Fig. 32–21. A modified banding stroke is made with the gun tilted to ensure good coverage of the lower molding on this cabinet.

an uneven coating as shown in Figure 32–22a. For some classes of work this is acceptable, but for better results, use two vertical strokes. Spray each side separately as shown in Figure 32–22b.

Spraying curved surfaces. Basically, this type of work may be done by applying the spraying techniques used for other surfaces; but to keep the gun at the proper distance, the stroke should follow the curve of the surface. It may be nec-

essary to adjust the size of the spray pattern to reduce the overspray waste. Cylinders of small diameters, such as table legs or turnings, are handled better with several vertical or lengthwise, overlapping strokes (Fig. 32–23a). For this class of work, a small round pattern generally is the most practical. If a vertical fan pattern is used, the stroke speed must be increased to prevent sags or runs.

The surface on a larger cylindrical

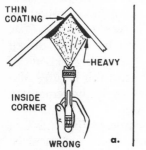
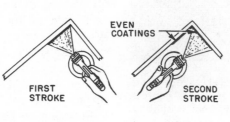

Fig. 32–22. Two methods of spraying inside corners are shown in these views: (a) one vertical stroke, (b) using two strokes, one on each side gives an even coating.

shape is sprayed better with a horizontal stroke (Fig. 32–23b) that is arced parallel to the surface. Work of this type may also be sprayed by holding the gun steady while rotating the work on a turn-table.

Cleaning a Suction-Feed Gun

1. Loosen the air cap two or three turns and remove the material cup. Hold the siphon tube over the cup.

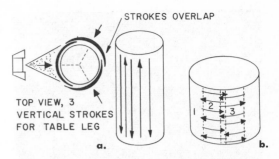

STROKES OVERLAP

TOP VIEW, 3
VERTICAL STROKES
FOR TABLE LEG

a.   b.

Fig. 32–23. Spraying curved surfaces: (a) use vertical strokes for small diameters. Adjust the pattern to avoid excessive overspray. (b) use horizontal strokes for larger surfaces.

Fig. 32–24. With the cup detached, hold a cloth over the loosened air nozzle and engage the trigger to force the liquid remaining in the gun back into the cup.

2. Hold a cloth over the air cap and pull the trigger (Fig. 32–24). This forces the fluid remaining in the gun back into the cup.
3. Empty the fluid from the cup and clean it thoroughly.
4. Fill the cup about half full with the appropriate thinner.
5. Attach the cup and spray the thinner to clean out the inside passageways of the gun (Fig. 32–25). Pour any unused thinner into a container designated for this purpose.
6. Remove the air cap and dip it in clean thinner. If it has buildup of dried finish on it, let it soak and then brush it clean later (Fig. 32–26). *Important!* Never submerge the entire gun in the thinner. This destroys the lubrication in the packing around the air valve and the fluid needle.
7. Open clogged nozzle holes with a toothpick or wooden point only (Fig. 32–27). Never use wire or twist drills for this purpose as they will enlarge the holes and destroy the spray pattern.
8. Wipe the gun with a solvent soaked cloth (Fig. 32–28).

Fig. 32–25. Spray thinner through the gun to clean the inside.

Fig. 32–26. Remove the hardened finishing material from the outside of the air nozzle with a stiff brush after soaking in solvent.

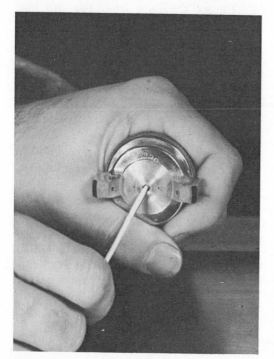

Fig. 32–27. Clean the holes in the air nozzle with a wooden probe, such as a toothpick.

Fig. 32–28. The final step in cleaning — wiping the outside of the gun and cup with a solvent soaked cloth.

Cleaning Pressure-Feed Equipment

1. Release the air pressure from the fluid tank or pressure cup.
2. Loosen the lid on the fluid container slightly.
3. Loosen the air cap and trigger the gun with a cloth held over the nozzle as in steps 1 and 2 above.
4. Empty the material container and add a suitable solvent.
5. Reassemble. Spray until the solvent appears, and then repeat the blow-back procedure as in step 3 above to wash the fluid hose and the gun thoroughly.
6. Wipe the gun as in step 8 above.
7. Disconnect the air hose from the gun.
8. Blow out the fluid hose with air to dry it.
9. Coil the hoses and hang them up.
10. Wipe the tank clean with a rag.

Fig. 32–29. Peeling a strippable coating from the inside of a spray booth.

Maintenance and Care of Spray Equipment

1. After cleaning the gun, put a drop of oil on the air-valve stem and on the trigger-bearing screw. Oil the packings of the fluid needle and the air-adjusting valve to keep them soft and pliable.
2. Store the gun on the hook provided.
3. Clean the filter on the compressor air intake; clean the filters in the transformer, as necessary.
4. Drain the air receiver tank on the compressor, and drain the transformer to remove any moisture.
5. Clean the walls, baffles, exhaust-fan blades, and all easily reached areas of the exhaust stack. Coat the surfaces of the spraybooth with a strippable coating material that is available from manufacturers of finishing supplies. This material is applied by brush or spray gun. It peels easily as shown in Figure 32–29. This makes spray-booth cleanup almost effortless. One coating should last a semester or two in the average school.
6. Where dry booth filters are used, be sure filtering materials are replaced periodically.

Spraying with aerosol cans has limited use in the school shop because it is such an expensive method. As a rule, they should only be used if other methods of application are not practical. Observe these tips when using aerosol sprayers:

1. Always read the instructions on the can.
2. Use at room temperature, about 70 deg. F.
3. Shake the can prior to use as recommended by the manufacturer. This usually takes about 1 minute.
4. The distance the nozzle should be

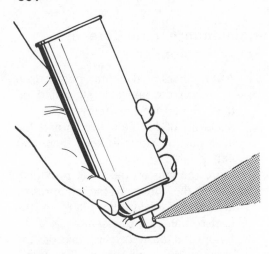

Fig. 32–30. Clean the nozzle of an aerosol can by inverting the can and depressing the nozzle for a few seconds.

held from the work varies with different-size containers. Check the manufacturer's recommendations.

5. Apply the same principles of stroking as in air spraying.
6. If the nozzle clogs, pull vertically to remove it. Soak it in lacquer thinner (or solvent recommended) and clean the orifice with a pin.
7. *Caution!* Do not attempt to probe into the valve of the can; if this is activated, the paint under pressure will be released.
8. When finished spraying, turn the can upside down and depress the nozzle (Fig. 32–30). This allows the gas vapors to escape and clean out the supply tube, valve, and nozzle.
9. Do not store aerosol cans at temperatures above 120 deg. F.

Dipping operations are sometimes adaptable to the school shop. This method of application is particularly useful when using fast drying coating materials and when a quantity of small pieces is to be finished. Dipping large objects

such as furniture or cabinets is not practical in the school shop because of the great amount of liquid and the very large tank or vat that would be required.

To dip small articles such as drawer knobs, buttons, turnings, dowels, or shafts (Fig. 32–31), fill a container (of the

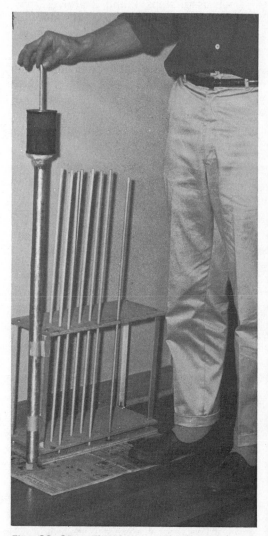

Fig. 32–31. This homemade material container is designed for dipping dowels, arrow shafts, etc. It is plugged at one end with a cork.

Fig. 32–32. Removing an old finish; using a putty knife on a flat surface; using a brush for hard-to-get-at surfaces.

appropriate shape) with the coating material. Remember that the article will displace its volume of the liquid. Usually the best results are obtained when the liquid has the viscosity of water. Ordinarily, the articles should be withdrawn rapidly. Hang the coated object to dry and wipe off with a rag before the coating sets.

Remove an old finish by sanding, scraping, or with a specially prepared paint or varnish remover. When using liquid removers, observe the following rules:

1. Read the manufacturer's instructions. Wear rubber gloves. Work in a well ventilated room or out of doors. Ensure that no open flames are in the room.
2. Apply a liberal coating of remover with a brush. Work an area approximately 2 ft. square at a time.
3. Let this stand until the finish is soft. Test it with a putty knife.
4. When the finish has softened, scrape it off with a putty knife (Fig. 32–32a) or use coarse steel wool.
5. To remove finishes from moldings, turnings, or carvings, it may be necessary to use an old toothbrush or a fine wire bristle brush (Fig. 32–32b).
6. Neutralize or wash away the remaining remover with the solvent recommended by the manufacturer. NOTE: do not use water as a neutralizer on veneered surfaces; use a special solvent or turpentine.
7. Allow the surface to dry.

Preparing Wood Surfaces for Finishing

1. Sand the surface thoroughly. Refer to page 501 for sanding operations. Remember that the smoother the surface, the finer the finish it will take.
2. Check the surface carefully for glue spots, cross-grain scratches, or dents. Any of these defects will be magnified with the application of coating materials.
3. Bleach the surfaces if a blond or uniformly stained finish is desired.

Bleaching is normally done with com-

Fig. 32–33. Mixing a two-solution bleach.

Fig. 32–34. Applying bleach with a sponge and rubber gloves.

mercially prepared materials of the two-solution type.

    a. Wear rubber gloves and an apron. Bleaches contain strong chemicals which irritate (burn) the skin and destroy most fabrics.

    b. Read the instructions and mix as recommended. Use a porcelain or glass container (Fig. 32–33).

    c. Apply the bleach with a synthetic-rubber sponge (Fig. 32–34). Allow it to dry on the surface until the desired effect is obtained.

    d. If necessary, neutralize or rinse as recommended.

    e. Allow the surface to dry thoroughly. This takes about 12 to 24 hours.

    f. Since bleaching raises the grain, sand the surfaces smooth.

4. Raise small dents by applying a drop or two of water and letting them dry. Dents or depressions may be raised more quickly by using a damp cloth and hot iron (Fig. 32–35) or a heated soldering copper.

5. If an opaque finish is to be applied, fill all holes, scratches, or dents with water paste or putty. *Important!* De-

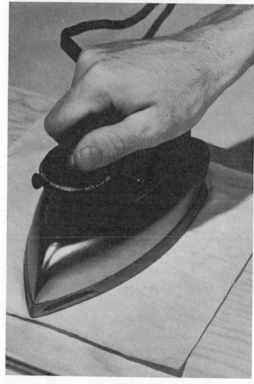

Fig. 32–35. Raising the indentations on a surface with a damp rag and heat.

fects in surfaces to receive transparent coatings should be filled after the staining and sealing operations. This permits matching the surrounding areas. Use shellac sticks of the appropriate color. Apply the sticks

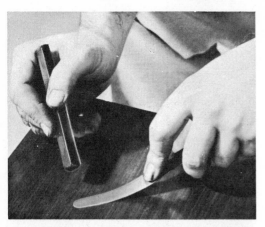

Fig. 32–36. Applying stick shellac with a heated blade.

with a heated flat, flexible blade as shown in Figure 32–36.

6. If necessary, stain the sapwood streaks to match the heartwood. Refer to steps on staining on page 568. Remove all traces of dust. This may be done with a vacuum cleaner or by wiping the surface with a "tack rag." This is a cloth treated to collect dust. Tack rags are available from finishing supplies or they may be made by sprinkling a lint free cloth with a varnish solution that has been diluted with about 25 percent turpentine or mineral spirits. Wring the cloth out until it is almost dry before using it.

Applying a Finish

Staining (Figs. 32–37, 32–38, and 32–39) is one of the most critical steps in finishing. In general, avoid spirit (alcohol solvent) stains. Use an appropriate water, oil, or NGR (non-grain-raising) stain. If water stains are to be used, the surface should be sponged to raise the grain fibers and sanded before the stain is applied. The following tips will be helpful.

Fig. 32–37. Staining a sample of the wood. Here two colors have been mixed by trial and error to get a certain effect.

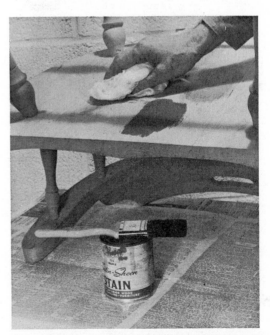

Fig. 32–38. Staining the underside first to get the "feel," the speed of penetration, and amount of wiping necessary.

Fig. 32–39. The excess oil stain must be wiped off.

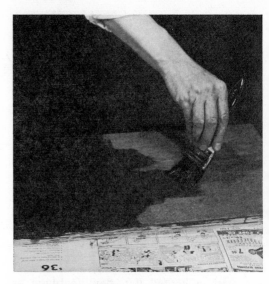

Fig. 32–40. Apply a liberal amount of filler. Brush it with and across the grain.

1. Read the manufacturer's instructions.
2. Stain a piece of scrap and let it dry. Then apply a coat of clear finish to ascertain if shade and color are as desired. Different colored stains of the same type may be mixed to produce the desired effect (Fig. 32–37).
3. Apply the stain to your project with a brush or spray gun. Start in an inside, inconspicuous area (Fig. 32–38).
4. Permit water and NGR stains to soak into the wood. *Do not wipe them off.*
5. Wipe off oil stains that have not penetrated the wood after a few minutes (Fig. 32–39). The sooner the excess stain is removed, the lighter the color. To make the stain darker, allow it to remain longer and apply a second coat.
6. Darkening of end grain may be avoided by first wetting the surface with the solvent used in the stain.
7. If some areas end up too dark,

lighten them slightly by sanding after drying.
8. If a water stain was used, sand the raised grain fibers lightly. Be careful not to cut through to the bare wood.
9. Stains must be covered with a wash coat of shellac or sanding sealer to prevent past wood fillers from further staining the wood.

Filling (Figs. 32–40 and 32–41) with a paste wood filler is usually necessary on open-grain woods. Liquid fillers (shellac) are used on close-grain woods. Paste wood fillers of an appropriate color should be used. White paste wood fillers should be used for bleached or two-toned finishes. White lead should not be used since it tends to discolor or "yellow" slightly as it ages. Here are some suggestions for filling:

1. Paste wood fillers should be in a creamy liquid state, so as to fill the wood pores completely. Apply a liberal coat crossgrain with either a stiff bristle brush (Fig. 32–40) or a coarse rag.

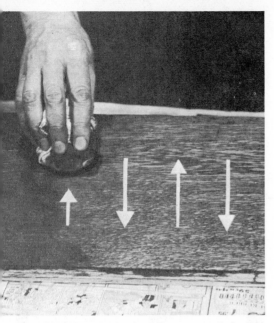

Fig. 32–41. Wipe the filler across the grain to work it into the pores and remove the excess.

2. When the filler starts to lose its glossy appearance, work it into the pores of the wood by wiping across the grain with coarse cloth or burlap (Fig. 32–41). This also removes the excess filler.

3. Keep the wiping rag or pad moist. If a dry one is used, it will tend to remove the filler from the pores.

4. Following the cross-grain wiping, change to long "figure-eight" strokes with the grain. Complete the operation with very light strokes with the grain to remove any streaks.

5. Clean the filler out of corners and recesses with a cloth held over a pointed or wedge-shaped stick.

6. Allow the filler to dry as recommended.

7. Paste wood fillers should be covered with a coat of sealer to "tie down" the stain and filler and to provide good adhesion for the topcoat.

Applying sealers. Use the spray method of application when possible. Sealers may be applied to either the raw wood or over stains and fillers. In general, use shellac as a sealer for varnish topcoats; use sanding sealer or shellac for lacquer topcoats. Shellac and lacquer will not go over oil paint, enamel, or varnish. Lacquer will not go over an oil filler without bleeding. Shellac will protect oil fillers from lacquers. Shellac usually requires overnight drying before sanding. Sanding sealers are usually dry and ready for sanding about 1 hour after their application. Sanding sealers should be used sparingly. Heavy coats will cause lacquer topcoats to craze (crack).

A *popular novelty effect* (Fig. 32–42) that emphasizes the grain may be obtained on open-grain woods by using a filler and a stain of contrasting colors. Briefly, this finish is achieved by: (1) staining, (2) applying a very thin sealer so as not to fill the pores, (3) applying a filler of contrasting color, (4) applying

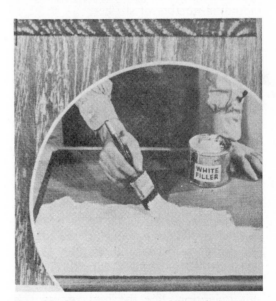

Fig. 32–42. A stain and filler of contrasting colors with a clear sealer between produces this novel two-tone finish on open grain woods. The stained surface must be sealed before the filler is applied.

a sealer, (5) sanding lightly, and (6) applying the topcoats.

Suggestions for topcoating. It should be remembered that an application of two or three thin topcoats (with light sanding between coats of varnish) will produce better results than one heavy application. (Lacquer does not require sanding between coats.) Ordinarily, glossy topcoats are applied. If a semigloss or flat finish is desired, it may be produced by rubbing or by adding a flattening compound to the final coat. The sheen of the final coat may be determined by using commercially prepared semigloss or flat finishes. Spraying is the best method of application, especially for lacquers because of their fast drying properties. Specially prepared brushing lacquers may be applied by brush. The essential requirements for successfully brushing lacquers are: (1) a soft-bristle brush, (2) quick application, and (3) a minimum number of strokes.

Varnish should not be stirred because this will introduce air bubbles into the final finish. In general, the same techniques are employed for brushing both varnish and lacquers. Varnishes should be applied in completely dust free rooms. Varnish requires a much longer drying period. Sometimes the work must dry for 48 hours or more before the next coat is applied. The final coat should dry about one week before rubbing.

Enameling requires the same general preparations to the work surfaces as for varnish or lacquer topcoats. If the enamel (or paint) is to cover knots, they should be sealed (Fig. 32–43) prior to enameling to prevent bleeding. Use shellac for this operation. For the best results (on bare wood), a minimum of three topcoat applications with a light sanding between each coat is recommended. First, prime the surface with a coat of enamel

Fig. 32–43. Knots must be treated to prevent their bleeding through the finish. Here shellac is used as a sealer over a knot for an enamel finish.

undercoat or primer. Apply filler or putty where needed and follow this application with two topcoats. Use masking tape when color separation or protection of adjoining areas is necessary. See Figure 32–44a and 32–44b.

Topcoat rubbing (Fig. 32–45) is generally required to produce the best appearances. Rubbing not only produces a smooth surface, but it also produces a luster or sheen. Before rubbing down the final coat, let it cure and harden for several days. For removing "orange peel" or foreign matter from the finished surfaces (prior to bringing the finish to the degree of gloss desired) use wet-or-dry

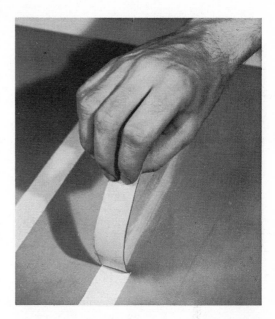

Fig. 32–44. Using masking tape: (a) designs or sharp line color separation is obtained by taping over the area to be protected and then finishing over the tape; (b) the correct way of removing the tape.

abrasive paper and a lubricant. The grit and grade of abrasive paper, to start with, will depend upon the surface condition of the finish. In general, start with 280 or 360 and progress to the 400 or 500 grades as necessary. Use a straight-line reciprocating sander or a hand sanding block as shown in Figure 32–45. Rub until the surface is smooth. Be sure that

Fig. 32–45. The first of a sequence of rubbing operations is performed with wet/dry sandpaper and water.

all the "bright spots" are removed and then clean the surface.

Next, mix pumice stone and water to a paste-like consistency. Rub the surface with this mixture and a felt pad for a *semigloss* effect. For a *high-gloss* finish, use rottenstone and rubbing oil. Apply it with a soft cloth (Fig. 32–46). Commercial rubbing compounds may be used instead of the above. Rub with the grain only. A considerable amount of rubbing is required. Because of the fineness of rottenstone it cuts very slowly and is, therefore, primarily a polishing agent. Finally, clean up the surface with a good grade of furniture cleaner and apply a coat of wax. Polish with a soft cloth or a felt pad.

A high-gloss finish is usually undesirable on modern furniture. The most popular finishes today are semigloss or dull rubbed. When topcoats of this type are used, simply sand the surface lightly and

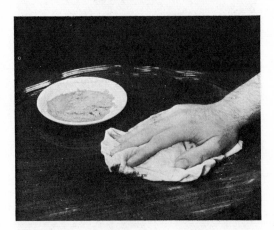

Fig. 32–46. Rubbing powdered rottenstone mixed with rubbing oil to produce a glossy finish.

Fig. 32–47. An enameled surface is rubbed with a fabric impregnated with an abrasive to produce a dull or semigloss surface.

progress to a fine grade of steel wool or a pad of fabric impregnated with abrasive powders (Fig. 32–47). Finish the process with a coat of wax.

Applying penetrating or oil finishes. This type of finish is applied very liberally. Flood the surfaces, applying the coating material with a rag or brush. Allow the liquid to soak into the wood according to the penetration time recommended by the manufacturer. Wipe the surplus off with a dry rag. If necessary, apply a second coat in the same manner. The manufacturer of one type of Danish oil finish recommends sanding with wet or dry abrasive paper before wiping off the excess. In this case, the coating material itself is used as a lubricant. After the surface has dried thoroughly, apply a protective coating of wax as recommended by the supplier.

Applying flock (Fig. 32–48). Flock should be applied only when all other operations have been completed. The surfaces must be prepared as usual. Seal and apply water putty to fill holes and other defects. Apply an undercoat of enamel or rubber-base paint that is the same color as the flock. Allow it to dry thoroughly and then lightly sand the surface.

Apply the binder coat. This can either be a second application of the same undercoating material or a special flock adhesive. While the surfaces are "wet," apply the flock. Use a hand spray gun as shown in Figure 32–48. Spraying is the preferred method of application. The flock is propelled into the wet film to insure a good bond. A special flock spray gun for compressed air equipment (35 lb. of air pressure) can also be used in the school shop. The flock may be sifted

Fig. 32–48. Using a hand operated gun for spraying flock fibers onto a wet binder coat.

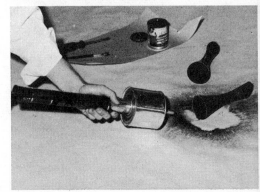

onto the surface by hand, letting the fibers fall onto the wet binder coat. However, this is the least desirable method.

With any method of application, many of the flock fibers are dispersed into the surrounding air. For this reason, flocking should be done in the shop area, not in the finishing room.

Basic Schedules for Wood Finishing

The procedures given below are somewhat of a summary and only suggestive in nature. They are not hard and fast rules. They are intended for lacquer or varnish finishes. They may be modified or varied to suit specific needs. The quality of finish desired, the method of application, the availability and condition of the equipment, the moisture content of the wood, the species of wood, and the project requirements are some of the variable factors which prohibit strict adherence to rigidly prescribed procedures.

The **short schedule.** This is often used for semiporous or nonporous woods and for articles on which a high-quality finish is not required.

1. Apply a wiping stain. Allow the stain to dry. Sand lightly, if necessary.
2. Apply a wash coat of shellac with a spray gun or brush. Allow to dry overnight.
3. Sand with 6/0 finishing paper.
4. Apply the finish coat — varnish,

enamel, or lacquer — and dry for 24 to 48 hours.
5. Sand with 400 wet-or-dry paper and water.
6. Clean and wax the surface.

The **long schedule.** This is suggested for porous woods and it is used for the highest quality of finishes on furniture, etc.

1. Bleach and neutralize the surface and allow to dry.
2. Sand with 5/0 finishing paper.
3. Stain and allow to dry.
4. Apply a wash coat of shellac or sanding sealer as appropriate. Allow to dry.
5. Sand with 7/0 finishing paper.
6. Fill the surfaces and allow to dry.
7. Apply a wash coat of shellac or sanding sealer as appropriate. Let it dry overnight.
8. Sand with 7/0 finishing paper.
9. Tone (if desired) with shading lacquer; dry 15 to 30 minutes.
10. Apply first topcoat and allow to dry 1 to 2 hours for lacquer, 24 hours for varnish.
11. Apply second topcoat and allow to dry as before.
12. Apply third topcoat and allow to dry 1 to 7 days.
13. Rub with 400 wet-or-dry paper and a lubricant. Follow this with pumice, rottenstone, or a rubbing compound for the desired gloss.
14. Clean and wax or polish, then buff with a soft cloth or lamb's wool.

REVIEW QUESTIONS

1. What are the major reasons for finishing wood products?
2. Describe the primary coating materials used until the beginning of the nineteenth century.
3. What features characterize a good brush?
4. What are the five different spraying processes? Describe the principles of each.

Outline the major advantages and disadvantages of each spray method.

5. Compare pressure-feed and suction-feed systems. Which system is more widely utilized for production spraying?
6. Define these spray gun terms: bleeder, nonbleeder, internal mix, external mix, automatic gun, spreader.
7. Describe two kinds of industrial booths.
8. What is the rollercoating process? What type of work is finished by this process?
9. How are rollercoaters used to apply fillers?
10. What is curtain coating? What advantage does this method have over roller-coating?
11. How are dipping operations performed in industry? What are some of the problems or limitations associated with this process?
12. How does flow coating differ from dipping?
13. What other kinds of equipment are used in production plants for finishing?
14. What are the basic ingredients of house paints?
15. What are emulsion paints?
16. What are the advantages and disadvantages of emulsion paints?
17. What are some causes of mechanical failure of exterior paints?
18. How do enamels differ from paints?
19. Name the materials widely used as undercoats for furniture finishes.
20. What are the kinds of wood fillers available? What are their characteristics?
21. What is shellac? What are its common uses and limitations?
22. What is varnish? What are some of the advantages offered by synthetic varnishes?
23. What is lacquer? When was it first developed? What role do lacquers have in furniture finishing?
24. Name some of the new synthetic resin finishes and their principal properties.
25. What is the best clear exterior finish?
26. Describe the characteristics of modern oil and penetrating wood finishes.
27. List the solvents for the major types of finishes available today.
28. Identify other supplies that are associated with coating materials.
29. Which finishing processes are suitable for school shop use?
30. What are the general safety rules that apply to school shop finishing operations?
31. What surface preparation is necessary prior to the application of the various finish coats?
32. What conditions must one observe when applying varnish?
33. What are the steps of procedure involved in cleaning a brush?
34. What classes of operations are performed with air-spray equipment in the school shop?
35. Describe the procedure for preparing the coating material and equipment for spray operations.
36. How are pressures set for suction-feed operation? For pressure-feed operation?
37. Describe the techniques involved in spraying flat surfaces; vertical surfaces.
38. Explain the procedure for spraying inside and outside corners.
39. What are the procedures for cleaning suction-feed and pressure-feed equipment?
40. What maintenance is involved in the care of spray equipment?
41. What governs the use of dipping operations in the school shop?
42. What precautions must be observed in the use of paint and varnish removers?

43. What precautions must be observed when staining end grain?
44. How is filler applied in the school shop?
45. What is meant by the term "orange peel"? How may it be prevented?
46. Why do topcoats usually require rubbing operations? What materials and methods are employed in rubbing topcoats?
47. How are dull, semigloss, or high-gloss finishes obtained?
48. What is flock and how is it applied?

SUGGESTED STUDENT ACTIVITIES

1. Sketch a flow sheet for production finishing.
2. Make a mockup of a curtain-coating machine.
3. Devise a dipping system for finishing small articles such as tool handles.
4. Write to paint manufacturers for literature and prepare a paper on the manufacture of a particular type of coating material.
5. Prepare samples of the various finishes that may be applied in the school shop. Test them for durability.
6. Calculate the cost per square foot for the various coating materials used in the school shop.
7. Visit a store where coating materials are sold. Prepare a report on their facilities for color matching paints and enamels.
8. Examine the furniture in your home and identify the species of wood and type of finish applied.
9. Write a report on the psychological effects of color in the home, industry, and in advertising.
10. Obtain the ingredients for several different kinds of finishes. Prepare samples and test for durability.

Chapter 33 Sharpening and Maintenance

Sharpening includes both the hand- and machine-tool processes that are employed to condition the edges of cutting tools. Sharpening generally involves two basic operations, grinding and honing. *Grinding* is the process by which hardened steel is given shape with an abrasive wheel. *Honing* usually follows the grinding process. It is performed with whetstones and leather straps that "dress" the edge and put it in condition to do the best cutting.

Maintenance is a general term used to describe the numerous jobs involved in the repair and upkeep of equipment and other facilities. Maintenance performed to *keep* a tool or machine working well is known as "preventive maintenance." This is essential so that operator safety and production output can continue uninterrupted. Typical maintenance jobs include the adjustment and alignment of machinery parts; lubrication; cleaning; repairing or replacing dull, worn, and broken parts; and the prevention of rust and other types of wear or depreciation.

The **benefits** gained by conscientious maintenance programs are the same in both industry and the school shop. Some of the benefits may be listed as follows:

1. Sharp tools produce fewer accidents because they function according to design and with better control by the operator.
2. Sharp tools cut cleaner and more accurately, require less power, increase production, and reduce the possibility of permanent damage to electric motors and other parts.
3. Sharp tools reduce operator fatigue and help him maintain a good mental attitude toward his work.
4. Good shop and machine maintenance influences good housekeeping, better workmanship, and the worker's overall pride and appreciation of the tools, machines, and material being used.

The **development** of sharpening processes began when man first used a natural abrasive stone to rub and polish a sharp edge on his crude stone implements. The invention of the wheel, followed by the production and use of metals, led in time to the development of circular abrasive wheels (Fig. 33–1) made of sandstone. These were rotated by a hand crank or a foot treadle. Just as manpower gave way to electrical power, natural abrasives

The Sharpening Tools of Industry

Grinders, grinding wheels, sharpening stones and sticks, coated abrasive products, files, lubricants, special machines,

Fig. 33–1. An early circular grinding wheel made of sandstone.

gave way to artificial abrasives made by the electric furnace processes. Today, tool sharpening processes are more complicated and more important than ever before. Alloys such as high-speed steel and the various carbides require different and better equipment and more precision and accuracy than ever before. As a consequence, tool sharpening has become a specialized business. Carpenters no longer stop to file a saw on the job. Special machines perform this job faster, more economically, and more accurately than can be done by hand.

This unit deals mainly with those sharpening procedures that are most commonly performed in school shops. Saw sharpening is omitted because the authors believe saws should be sharpened by professional saw sharpeners. The nominal cost for this service makes it difficult to justify the time required for this maintenance procedure in the average school shop. However, touch-up filing of circular saws, in order to extend their service life before sending them to a professional, is justifiable. Touch up filing is covered on page 595.

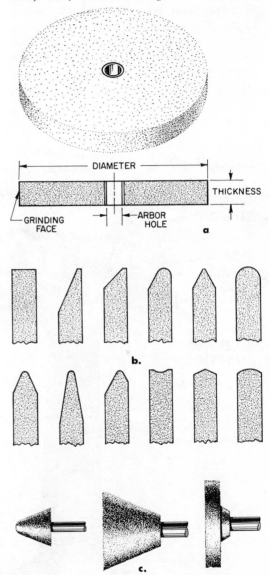

Fig. 33–2. Grinding wheels: (a) straight type, (b) standard grinding wheel faces, and (c) mounted wheels have shafts that fit into collets or chucks.

jigs, gauges, and guides are used in the various tool sharpening processes.

Grinding wheels (Figs. 33–2a, 33–2b, and 33–2c) consist of thousands of uniformly sized *abrasive grains* bonded together in various circular shapes. Each abrasive grain has many sharp cutting edges. The two most widely used abrasives are aluminum oxide and silicon carbide. Generally, they are grouped into coarse, medium, and fine grit sizes. There are five types of bonds: namely, vitrified (clay), silicate, shellac, resinoid, and rubber. Vitrified and silicate bonded wheels are the most widely used for grinding edge tools. Grinding wheels are graded from very hard to very soft. Hard wheels release their abrasive grains slowly; soft wheels release their grains easily and are thus self-sharpening. Grinding wheels also have various degrees of porosity (space between grains) ranging from dense to open. A porous grinding wheel cuts rapidly without excessive heat-

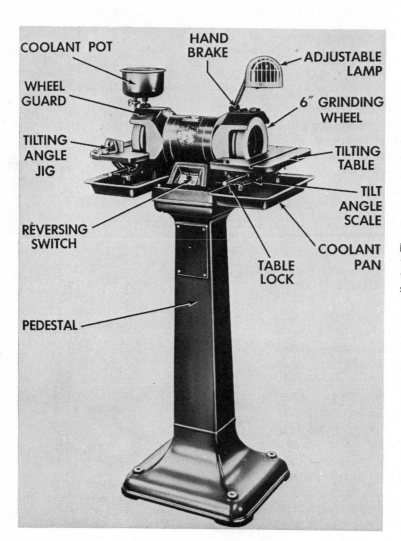

COOLANT POT

HAND BRAKE

ADJUSTABLE LAMP

WHEEL GUARD

6" GRINDING WHEEL

TILTING ANGLE JIG

TILTING TABLE

TILT ANGLE SCALE

REVERSING SWITCH

COOLANT PAN

TABLE LOCK

PEDESTAL

Fig. 33–3. A pedestal tool grinder found in tool rooms and school shops.

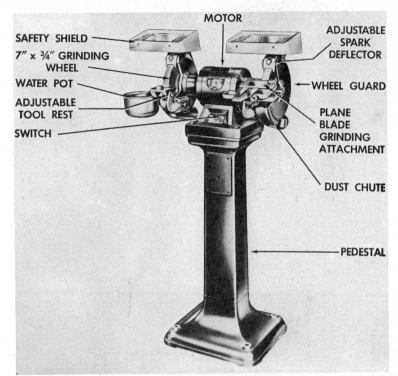

MOTOR

SAFETY SHIELD

7" x ¾" GRINDING WHEEL

WATER POT

ADJUSTABLE TOOL REST

SWITCH

ADJUSTABLE SPARK DEFLECTOR

WHEEL GUARD

PLANE BLADE GRINDING ATTACHMENT

DUST CHUTE

PEDESTAL

Fig. 33–4. A standard 7-inch pedestal grinder suitable for most tool sharpening jobs in the school shop.

ing. Grinding wheels operate safely at the speeds for which they were designed. Each wheel bears a maximum speed designation.

Grinders used for tool sharpening are of various types and sizes. The most widely known types are pedestal and bench grinders shown in Figures 33–3, 33–4, and 33–5. They are widely used for sharpening edge tools such as chisels, twist drills, plane irons, knives, and the cutters of small to medium size machines. These grinders have double arbors that will accommodate two different wheels. *Sizes of grinders* are generally specified according to the diameter of the grinding wheel they carry. Generally, the 6- or 7-in. sizes are the most widely used in the school shop. Motor sizes vary from ⅓ to 1 hp. Speeds are generally 1725 or 3450. The slower speed is preferred

for school shop work. Higher speeds create more heat which draws the temper from the metal and damages the tool. Most grinders are equipped with water

Fig. 35–5. A 7-inch bench grinder.

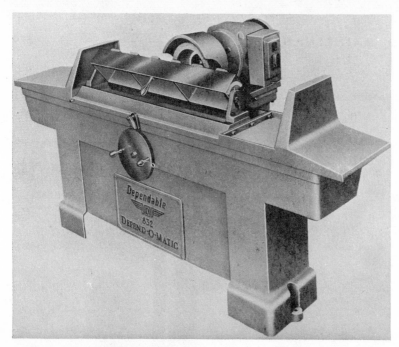

cups in which the tool may be dipped to keep it cool.

Some grinders are equipped with oil-feeding devices. The oil keeps the wheels saturated and helps to prevent the tool from overheating and the wheel from loading with metal particles. Grinders of this type are generally referred to as *oil-stone grinders*. These and other grinders that provide an oil-water coolant are grouped as *wet grinders*. Those without coolants are known as *dry grinders*.

Industrial grinding processes are performed on both wet and dry machines. A few of the many machines used for

Fig. 33–7. This universal tool grinder is set up to sharpen a carbide-tipped saw.

Fig. 33–8. This knife-grinding attachment is used to sharpen planer knives in the cutter-head without removing it from the machine.

grinding tools are illustrated in Figures 33–6, 33–7, 33–8, and 33–9. Often other types of equipment are needed to supplement these grinding machines. Figure 33–10 shows just one of the technical aspects involved in the manufacture of a special cutter for a woodworking industry.

Wheel dressers (Figs. 33–11a and 33–11b) are used to shape and condition the grinding faces of abrasive wheels. By applying a wheel dresser to the revolving wheel, nicks, grooves, and other irregularities on the face of the wheel are worn away. Furthermore, this procedure cleans a loaded wheel and sharpens it by exposing new abrasive grains.

Sharpening stones and sticks (Fig. 33–12) are also commonly called *oilstones* or *slipstones*. These are available

Fig. 33–9. This carbide saw grinder with a diamond wheel can handle face, top, and side dressing of saws. It can also sharpen other kinds of carbide cutters.

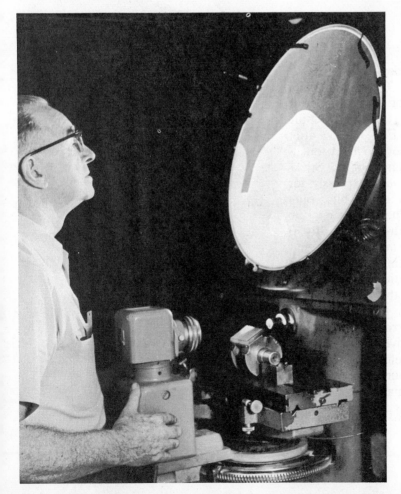

Fig. 33–10. A skilled technician checks the profile of a milled-to-pattern bit with a 50 to 1 optical comparator. This enlarges the profile of the cutter 50 times to permit comparing its shape with that of a very accurately drawn pattern.

used in sharpening edge tools. However, they do have important uses in sharpening scrapers and saw teeth. (Refer to Chapter 19 which discusses some common types of metal cutting files.) Saw sharpening machines utilize either abrasive wheels (Fig. 33–9) or files (Figs. 33–14a and 33–14b).

Fig. 33–11. Wheel dressers: (a) a star type dresser consists of pointed disks loosely mounted on a pin with solid washer-like separaters; (b) a diamond wheel dresser.

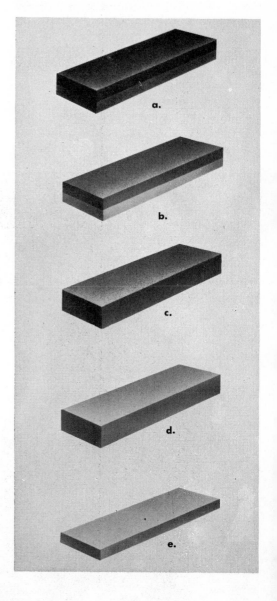

in many sizes and shapes, and in coarse, medium, and fine grits. They are made of either silicon-carbide or aluminum-oxide abrasives. They are used for whetting or honing edge tools (Fig. 33–13) after they are ground and for frequent touching up of edges to prolong tool life. Sticks and stones are often made expressly for certain tools, such as auger bits, plug cutters, and gouges. These tools may be used dry, but a few drops of a 50–50 oil-kerosene mixture makes them cut faster and prevents them from becoming clogged with metal particles.

Coated abrasives, in the past, have had limited applications in tool sharpening. However, with the improvements in machine design and abrasive characteristics, coated abrasives are being utilized more and more for this purpose. Refer to Chapter 28 for information concerning coated abrasives. *Files* are not widely

Safety Precautions for Grinding

1. Only use grinders that have the wheels enclosed in hood-type guards as shown in Figures 33–3, 33–4, and 33–5.
2. Keep the tool rest adjusted to within

Fig. 33–13. Here a technician uses an oilstone to hone a keen edge on a large knife after grinding on a special knife-grinding machine.

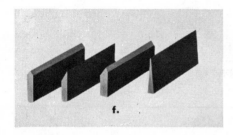

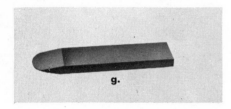

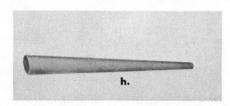

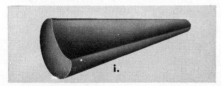

Fig. 33–12. Oilstones and slip sticks: (a, b) combination bench stones having 2 different grits, (c, d) single grit, (e) pocket stone, (f) carving tool slips, (g) skiving or shaving knife stone, (h) round tapered slip, and (i) gouge slip.

⅛ to ¹⁄₁₆ in. from the face of the grinding wheel. Too much clearance may permit the work to jam between the wheel and tool rest. Always make adjustments with the wheel at rest.
3. Always wear goggles and always keep the eye shields in place.
4. *Never* use a machine with cracked or nicked wheels.
5. Stand to one side, away from the line of the wheel when turning on the power. If a wheel is faulty, centrifugal force may cause it to break.
6. Grind on the face of the wheel (Figs. 33–2a and 33–17) unless the wheel is designed for side grinding. Excessive side pressure may break the wheel.
7. Use the entire surface of the wheel face. Move the work back and forth to prevent grooving it. Give the wheel time to warm up before doing heavy grinding. A cold wheel may break as a result of the high heat generated.
8. Avoid bodily contact with the revolving wheel.
9. Ensure that loose clothing does not

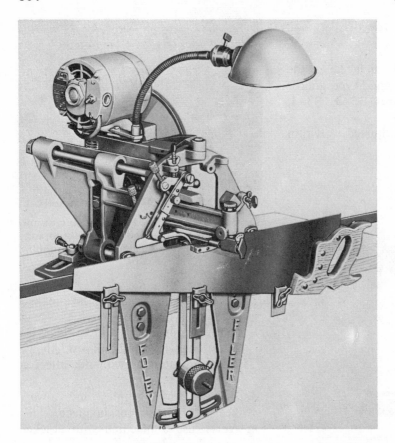

Fig. 33–14a. Automatic saw filing of hand saws.

come into contact with the revolving wheels. *Never* wear gloves or hold the work with a rag. Either may become caught by the wheel and cause bodily injury.

10. Hold the work securely so that it does not slip from your grasp.

11. Do not replace abrasive wheels without supervision.

12. Keep the object being ground cool by dipping it in water frequently.

13. When changing wheels, always place blotter washers between the wheel and the flanges. Always ensure that the grinding-wheel speed does not exceed the manufacturer's recommendations.

Basic Sharpening Procedures

The common tools that require sharpening may be divided into these basic groups: (1) edge tools with straight single bevels such as plane irons, wood chisels, scrapers, and jointer knives; (2) double bevel tools such as knives, hatchets, and skew chisels; (3) curved edge tools such as gouges; (4) auger bits, countersinks, etc.; and (5) special tools such as hollow mortising chisels, router bits, and shaper cutters. Information concerning the recommended cutting angles and other specifications may be found in the particular unit in this chapter dealing with each tool.

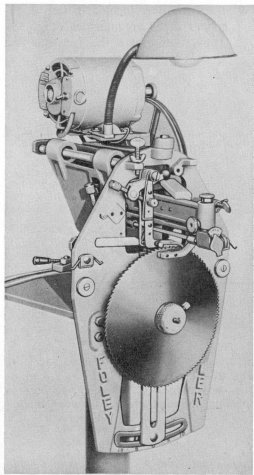

Fig. 33–14b. Automatic filing of circular saws.

Sharpening Single-Bevel Edge Tools

1. Check the cutting edge with a try square to ensure that it is straight and approximately square with the side. If necessary, square the edge by grinding or by moving it back and forth on an oilstone as shown in Figure 33–15. Bear hardest on the side that needs to be taken down most.
2. Grind the edge only when necessary

Fig. 33–15. Squaring the edge of a plane iron.

Fig. 33–16. The face of the blade (a) must be flat to achieve a true cutting edge. Slight depressions (b) or rough spots must be removed as shown in (c) below.

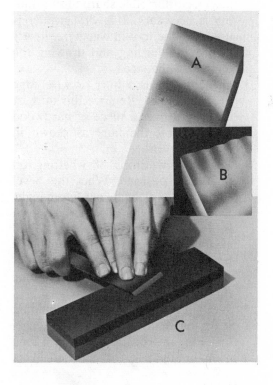

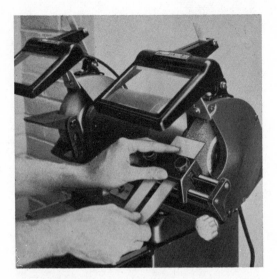

Fig. 33–17. Grinding the plane iron. Here a special blade-grinding attachment simplifies the job.

to restore the bevel or remove nicks (Fig. 33–17). Periodic honing will keep a cutting edge sharp until grinding is necessary. If a dry grinder is used, dip the tool in water *frequently* to prevent burning and drawing the temper of the steel.

3. Grinding forms a burr or wire edge (Fig. 33–18a). Remove this burr by drawing it over a piece of hardwood to break off the burr as shown in Figure 33–18b.

4. Place a few drops of whetting oil on a fine oilstone. Whet the bevel using a long oval or figure-eight movement on the oilstone as shown in Figure 33–19. The heel should clear the stone slightly. Hold the hands and wrists rigid so as to maintain the same angle of blade to stone throughout this operation.

5. Whet the face of the tool by holding it flat on the oilstone with the bevel up (Fig. 33–16c). Move it in a long oval or figure-eight motion. This

thins the burr formed in step 4, removes slight irregularities (Fig. 33–16b), and makes the face flat and true (Fig. 33–16a).

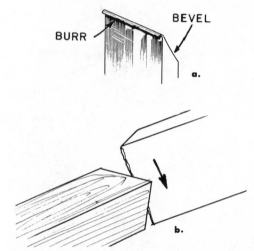

Fig. 33–18. (a) Grinding forms a burr on the chisel edge; (b) removing the burr by drawing the edge over a hardwood block.

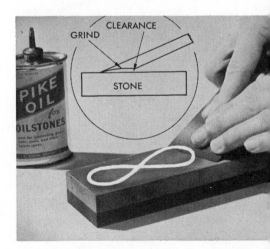

Fig. 33–19. Honing using a "figure 8" movement over the entire stone. Insert shows slight clearance of the heel.

6. Repeat operations 4 and 5 until the cutting edge is razor sharp. Remove the burr formed in whetting as described in step 3.
7. Wipe the surplus oil from the tool and the oilstone. Replace the stone cover.
8. If desired, strop the tool on a piece of leather to produce an even keener edge.

NOTE: This procedure may be applied to all single-bevel edge tools such as the plane iron and chisel (Fig. 33–20).

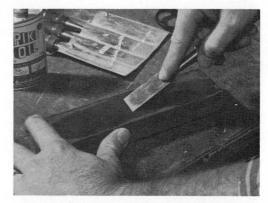

Fig. 33–20. The chisel is honed with the same procedure as the plane iron.

Sharpening Double-Bevel Edge Tools

1. Tools that are nicked or on which the bevel is rounded must first be ground.
2. Hone knives on a fine stone with the blade held in a diagonal position and the back raised slightly (Fig. 33–21). Draw the blade along the surface of the stone, beginning at the heel and ending at the tip.
3. Repeat several times and then hone the other bevel.
4. Continue until the edge is sharp.
5. Strop if desired.

Fig. 33–21. Honing a fine edge on a pocket knife.

NOTE: Hone a hatchet by laying it on a bench with the cutting edge extending over the bench top. Hold the oilstone at the proper angle on the bevel. Push it diagonally the length of the cutting edge. Repeat several times on both bevels.

The **skew chisel** may be ground either freehand on the face of the wheel (Fig. 33–22) or on its side with the aid of a simple fixture clamped to the tool rest (Fig. 33–23a and 33–23b). Each bevel may be ground to the same angle by employing the latter method. The chisel is first held against one of the blocks

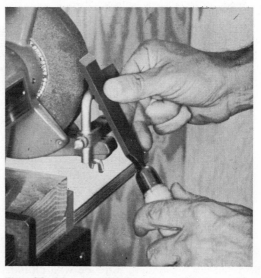

Fig. 33–22. Grinding a skew chisel.

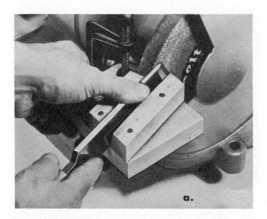

Fig. 33–23. Grinding a skew with the aid of beveled guide blocks.

Fig. 33–24. Honing a skew on a slow speed, power-driven rotary oilstone.

(Fig. 33–23a) and then reversed and held against the other block (Fig. 33–23b). Skew chisels are honed in a manner similar to plane irons. Figure 33–24 shows a powered oilstone which simplifies the honing operation.

Sharpening curved edge tools. Outside bevel gouges are considerably more difficult to sharpen than plane irons and other straightedge tools. This is because the tool must be rotated or guided through an arc while grinding and honing. These tools may be ground by rolling

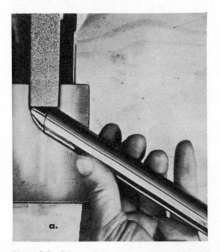
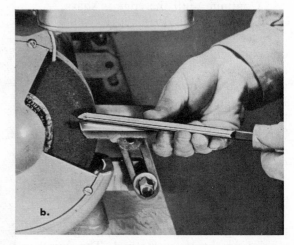

Fig. 33–25. Grinding a gouge with an outside bevel: (a) on the wheel face (b) on the wheel side.

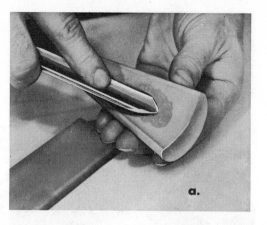
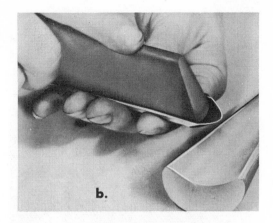

Fig. 33–26. Honing a gouge with a slipstone. (a) the outside, and (b) the inside.

Fig. 33–27. A carving gouge is honed by pushing it forward and moving it from side to side at the same time.

the bevel on the face of the wheel (Fig. 33–25a) or on the side (Fig. 32–25b). To grind inside bevel gouges, use either a cone-shaped mounted wheel (Fig. 33–2c) or a straight wheel dressed to a convex face. Hone the edge of gouges with the appropriate size and shape of slipstone. See Figures 33–26 and 33–27.

Sharpening bits. The following steps apply to most *auger-bit* patterns:

1. Select an auger-bit file or a taper-warding file.

2. File the two cutting lips as shown in Figure 33–28a. File no more than necessary to remove nicks. Note only the top of the lips are filed.

3. File the *inside* of the spurs to a sharp bevel as shown in Figure 33–28b. *Do not file the outside of the spurs* as this will reduce the diameter of the head. Every effort should be made to maintain the original bevel and general form of the bit parts. File the same amount of material from each lip and spur.

4. Hone the filed edges with a slipstone as shown in Figure 33–29.

Countersink bits are generally sharpened with a small file or triangular slipstone. Work only the *face* of the cutting edges until they are sharp (Figs. 33–30a and 33–30b). Avoid removing material from the back of the edge since this may change the angle of the point.

Forstner bits must be sharpened on the inside only so as not to reduce the diameter. The inside bevel of the rim (Fig. 33–31a) must be carefully sharpened using a very small, fine, half-round file with a blunt end or a small slipstone of the appropriate shape. The cutting lips are sharpened in the same manner as

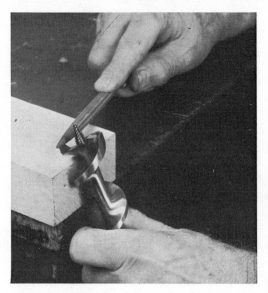

Fig. 33—28. Auger bit sharpening: (a) filing the cutting lips, (b) filing the **inside** of the spurs.

those of an auger bit (Fig. 33–31b).

Plug cutters are sharpened on the outside bevel of the rim (Fig. 33–32a). The work may be done on an abrasive wheel, but care must be taken so as not to burn the edge. The chip lifter is sharpened with a file or slipstone. Slope the edge so that it will be slightly higher toward

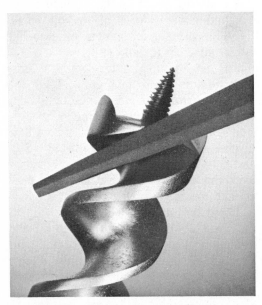

Fig. 33—29. Hone the cutting lips (shown) and the spurs on the inside of the bit only.

FACE

a.

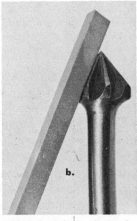

b.

Fig. 33—30. A countersink is honed on the faces (a) of cutters with a small triangular slipstone as shown at (b).

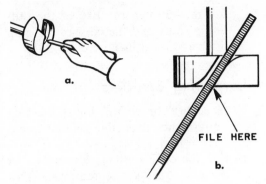

Fig. 33–31. Sharpening Forstner bits: (a) the inside bevel of the rim, (b) the cutters.

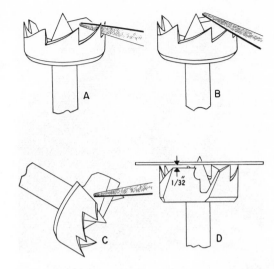

Fig. 33–33. Details for sharpening a multi-spur machine bit.

the inside. The highest point of the chip lifter should be about .005 inches below the rim to ensure smooth cutting. See Figure 33–32b.

Multi-spur machine bits are sharpened with a fine warding file as follows:

1. File the leading edges of the outlining spurs at a 10-deg. angle toward the inside of the spur (Fig. 33–33a).
2. File the trailing edges of the spurs

with a slight angle toward the center tip as shown in Figure 33–33b. All spurs must be the same height.
3. Sharpen the chip lifter cutting edge on the throat side as shown in Figure 33–33c.
4. Assure that there is a clearance of

Fig. 33–32. Sharpening plug and dowel cutters: (a) the rim, (b) the chip lifter.

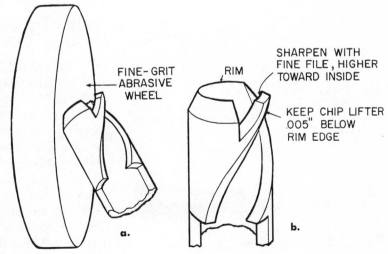

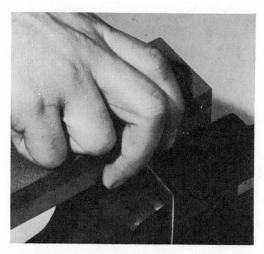

Fig. 33–34. Using a fine oilstone to produce smooth, sharp edges on a scraper blade held in a vise. The oilstone is moved after each stroke to distribute the wear over its surface.

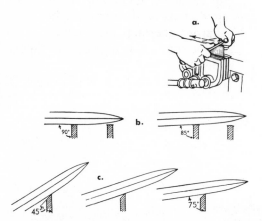

Fig. 33–35. (a) Stroking with a burnisher, (b) producing a burr on a hand scraper, and (c) producing a burr on a beveled cabinet scraper.

Fig. 33–36. A burnisher.

$\frac{1}{32}$ in. between the tips of the outlining spurs and the edge of the chip lifter as shown in Figure 33–33d.

Sharpening Scrapers

The general procedure for sharpening both square and bevel edge cabinet scrapers is as follows:

1. File the edge until it is straight and the old burr(s) is removed. This may be done with a mill file or on an oilstone as shown in Figure 33–16c.
2. Hone the edge and faces (or the bevel and opposite face) on an oilstone (Fig. 33–34). This is a very important step since the edges must be smooth and sharp.
3. Clamp the scraper blade in a vise and burnish the edge(s) (Fig. 33–35). Place a drop or two of oil on the burnisher (Fig. 33–37) and turn the edge(s), using firm strokes to make a small burr along the entire length of the blade. With each successive stroke, tilt the burnisher until the correct angle is obtained. (See Fig. 33–36.) (A screwdriver blade may be used in place of a burnisher.)

Sharpening Hollow Mortising Chisels

To a limited extent, hollow chisels may be sharpened by filing the bevels on the *inside*. Use a small half-round file. Small abrasive sticks may also be used. Specially made, cone shaped, mounted abrasive wheels are also available for this purpose. Milling cutters (Fig. 33–37a) for each size chisel and a special hand operated chisel sharpening machine (Fig. 33–37b) are recommended for hollow chisel sharpening. This equipment ensures that the inside of the chisel will be shaped

Fig. 33–37. (a) The cutter designed for use in sharpening hollow chisels. (b) A hand operated bench machine for sharpening hollow chisels.

so that the bit will fit and function properly.

Sharpening jointer, router, and shaper knives in the shop is done with the aid of fixtures and jigs as shown in Figure 33–38. Knives ground while held in the cutterhead (Fig. 33–38c) must be accurately positioned before each grinding pass. This is best done by clamping a thin flexible steel strip to the infeed table with the tip resting against the face of the knife. The head may be fixed so that it does not rotate by clamping the drive belt to the side of the machine base or by forcing a wooden wedge between the cutterhead and table. All knives must be ground at each setting of the grinding wheel before its position is changed. In this way the weight of the knives can be kept approximately equal and the cutterhead balance maintained. Light cuts must be taken so that the knives are not burned. After two or three such grindings, the knives should be ground and balanced by a professional knife grinder.

Setting jointer knives. Knives that have been removed from the cutterhead must be carefully remounted after grinding.

One method of setting each knife equally is with the aid of a magnet. The knife is placed in the cutterhead slot and held at the required level by the magnet (Fig. 33–39). Then the gib screws are tightened with a wrench. *Caution!* The setting of jointer knives in the school shop should only be done under the supervision of the instructor.

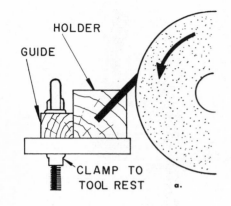

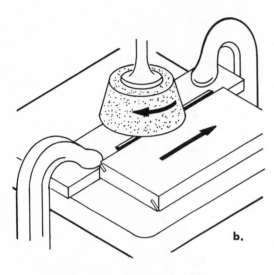

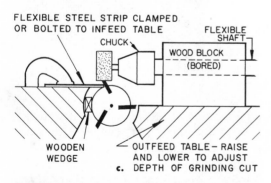

Fig. 33–38. Three methods of grinding jointer knives: (a) on a bench grinder, (b) on a drill press with a mounted wheel, (c) in the cutterhead with a mounted wheel driven by a flexible shaft.

Jointing the knives. Newly sharpened and installed jointer knives must be jointed before they will cut most effectively. Jointing is the process of shaping the cutting edges into a true cutting circle (Fig. 33–40). This is accomplished by lightly touching the edges of the knives with a soft abrasive stone while the cutterhead is revolving at its normal operating speed. To do this, place the stone on the rear table as shown in Figure 33–41a. Gradually lower the table until the stone barely touches the knives. Move the stone the full length of the cutterhead. Then stop the machine and examine the edges to see that all have been touched. This operation may be performed several times between knife grindings. When the jointed edge becomes $\frac{1}{32}$ in. wide the knives must be reground to obtain the necessary back clearance. *Caution:* Knives should be jointed in the school shop only under the supervision of the instructor.

Honing jointer knives. Jointer knives should be honed periodically between jointing operations to keep them sharp. Partially cover an abrasive stone with paper and place it on the front table as shown in Figure 33–41b. Turn the cutterhead (by hand) and adjust the table until the stone rests flat on the bevel. Wedge the head in this position. Hone the knife by stroking it lengthwise with the stone. Repeat this for each knife, using the same number of strokes.

Sharpening router and shaper cutters. Each time shaper cutters are used they should be honed on the flat side of the cutting edge as shown in Figure 33–41c. When necessary, these surfaces may be ground. The beveled edges should not be ground or honed as this may change their length and shape. Bit holders and mounted abrasive wheels are available for sharpening router bits. These work

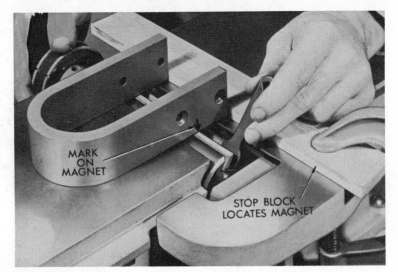

Fig. 33–39. Setting jointer knives with a magnet and a stop block.

MARK ON MAGNET

STOP BLOCK LOCATES MAGNET

satisfactorily when used in accordance with the manufacturer's instructions.

Touch-up filing circular saws. The following procedure may be used three or four times and then the circular saw should be reconditioned by a professional saw sharpener.

1. *Joint* the teeth before removing the blade from the saw by lowering the blade until it is $\frac{1}{64}$ to $\frac{1}{32}$ in. above the table surface. Check the projection by cutting a scrap piece of wood. Start the saw and lightly move an abrasive stone across the blade. (The side of an old grinding wheel is good for this purpose.) This will make the blade perfectly round.

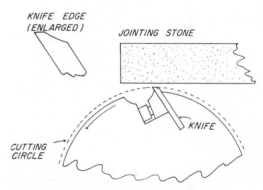

KNIFE EDGE (ENLARGED)

JOINTING STONE

KNIFE

CUTTING CIRCLE

Fig. 33–40. Jointing the knives brings the edges into a perfect cutting circle.

Fig. 33–41. (a) The jointing operation. (b) Honing jointer knives with the oilstone wrapped in paper. (c) Honing the flat side of a shaper cutter on a wet stone.

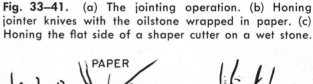

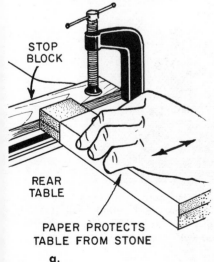

STOP BLOCK

REAR TABLE

PAPER PROTECTS TABLE FROM STONE

a.

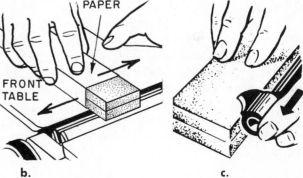

PAPER

FRONT TABLE

b.

c.

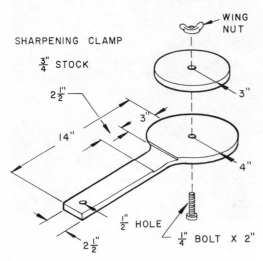

WING NUT

SHARPENING CLAMP

$\frac{3}{4}''$ STOCK

$2\frac{1}{2}''$

3"

3"

14"

4"

$\frac{1}{2}''$ HOLE

$2\frac{1}{2}''$

$\frac{1}{4}''$ BOLT X 2"

Fig. 33–42. This circular saw clamp is useful when touching up the saw teeth.

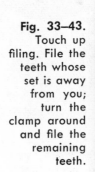

Fig. 33–43. Touch up filing. File the teeth whose set is away from you; turn the clamp around and file the remaining teeth.

2. Remove the blade and clamp it in a holder head held firmly in a vise (Fig. 33–42).

3. Select a single-cut file that best fits the tooth surface to be filed. Hold the file so as to maintain the existing angle.

4. File each tooth slightly, using only enough strokes to remove the flat caused by jointing (Fig. 33–43).

General tool and machine maintenance. Hand tools and the machined surfaces of machinery should be protected against rusting. Rusting pits the surfaces, inhibits the operation of tools and machines, and advertises a lack of appreciation for good equipment. Surfaces should be polished (Figs. 33–44 and 33–45) and protected with paste wax, light oil, or one of the commercial rust inhibitors (Fig. 33–46). The table of jointers, saws, and similar surfaces should be coated with a good paste wax such as that used for polishing automobiles. This prevents rusting due to humidity or perspiration from the operator's hands.

The under parts of machinery that are subject to the accumulation of sawdust and chips should be cleaned out daily. Unless specified otherwise, table saw rack and pinion gears, trunnions, dovetail ways, jack screws, and so on should be

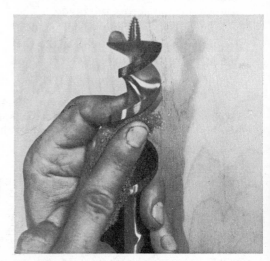

Fig. 33–44. Moisture from hands, wet chips, or the sap from green woods will rust bits, saws and other tools. Here rust is removed from a bit with steel wool.

Fig. 33–45. Using a wire wheel to recondition a square.

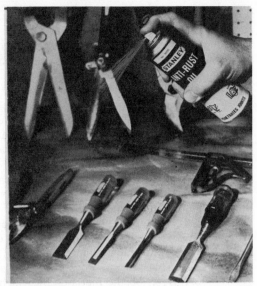

Fig. 33–46. Commercial anti-rust compounds are available in spray cans.

lubricated with a hard wax or graphite. Hard wax or graphite is recommended for these areas because machine oils and grease accumulate sawdust. This eventually becomes a gummy to solid deposit that greatly impairs free movement of these parts.

The **lubrication of machinery** should follow the manufacturer's recommendations as regards the suggested time intervals and the type of lubricant. This is one of the most essential jobs of preventive maintenance. Negligence in this regard eventually leads to unnecessary delays and to expensive replacement of parts. Attention should also be given to bolts, screws, and lock nuts that may work loose because of machine vibration. The correct alignment of belts on drive pulleys minimizes belt wear. Electrical mechanisms, including motors, cords, and plugs, should also be cleaned and checked periodically to ensure against electrical hazards.

REVIEW QUESTIONS

1. What are some of the benefits that result from a good maintenance program?
2. Why are saws, jointer knives, and the like sharpened by specialists rather than the person who uses them?
3. Name the various kinds of tools and materials used for sharpening woodworking tools and cutters.
4. What are the principal types of grinders that are available for tool sharpening?
5. What precautions should one observe when grinding a tool?
6. How are grinding wheels dressed? What sizes and shapes are available?
7. What lubricants are used with slipstones? What functions do they serve?
8. What purposes do files serve in tool sharpening?
9. How are circular saws sharpened in the shop? Describe this procedure.
10. What safety rules must one observe when operating the grinder?

11. Describe the procedure for sharpening and honing plane irons and chisels.
12. How is the "burr" removed from edge tools?
13. How may edge tools be tested for sharpness?
14. What problems are encountered in the sharpening of carving and turning gouges?
15. What factors must one observe when sharpening an auger bit?
16. What steps are involved in sharpening a cabinet scraper?
17. Why are milling cutters best adapted to the sharpening of hollow mortising chisels?
18. In what ways may jointer knives be sharpened in the school shop?
19. How are jointer knives set or adjusted in the cutterhead? How does one "joint" jointer knives?
20. What is the value in honing the jointer knives?
21. What should be included in a check list for general shop maintenance? What is preventive maintenance?
22. What purpose does paste wax serve in maintenance?
23. Describe the methods by which band-saw blades are joined.

SUGGESTED STUDENT ACTIVITIES

1. Sharpen several plane irons, each with different angles. Test each on the same kind of wood and determine the best cutting angle.
2. Devise a method of wet cutting with a standard dry-wheel grinder.
3. Write a report on the method of grinding carbide-tipped tools.
4. List or sketch the ways in which the following machines may be used in tool grinding: (1) the drill press, (2) the table saw, (3) the portable electric router and (4) the lathe.
5. Design and construct a jig for sharpening the correct angle on twist drills for woodworking.

Part III INDUSTRIES

Chapter 34 The Lumbering Industry

The early history of this country shows lumbering to be the first major industry. Lumber was in tremendous demand to meet the needs for housing and other kinds of shelter from the very beginnings of this nation. As the pioneers moved westward from the Atlantic seaboard, land had to be cleared of trees to make room for homes, farms, and roads. Axes and saws were as important as muskets. Most of the trees were burned, but many were used for fuel or lumber. Thus sawmills sprang up all over this country. See Figure 34–1.

These early sawmills got their logs from the nearby forests. As the usable timber disappeared many sawmills were moved to new locations. Others transported logs over great distances. The trees were usually felled and drawn to the banks of rivers by oxen. They were then floated to the mills. Many of the first railroads and steamship lines were extended to these outposts to carry logs or lumber back to the markets.

Because of the early wasteful lumbering practices, the center of the lumbering industry was constantly shifting as shown in Figure 34–1. When men found no new frontiers to explore, they began to think about forest conservation. In 1905

the United States forest service was founded to improve and protect government owned forests.

Currently, there are about 33,000 lumber mills in this country. They vary in size from small ten- or twelve-man mills to large integrated corporations such as the one shown in Figure 34–2. An integrated corporation is one that owns and operates forest lands, transport equipment, mills for lumber and other wood products, and wholesale and retail outlets.

The softwood lumber industry accounts for about 80 percent of total production today. It is concentrated largely in the South and West although some softwood lumber is produced in other regions. Hardwood lumber is produced predominantly in the Eastern half of the country.

Annual production of lumber ranges between 33 and 35 billion board feet today. The value added by manufacture is $1,533 million. The value of shipments is $3,572 million. It is estimated that the lumber produced in this country since its beginning in 1776 would build a walkway 7 ft. wide from the earth to the sun.

Consumption of lumber during the past decade has ranged between 36 and 42 billion board feet annually. The difference between the production and con-

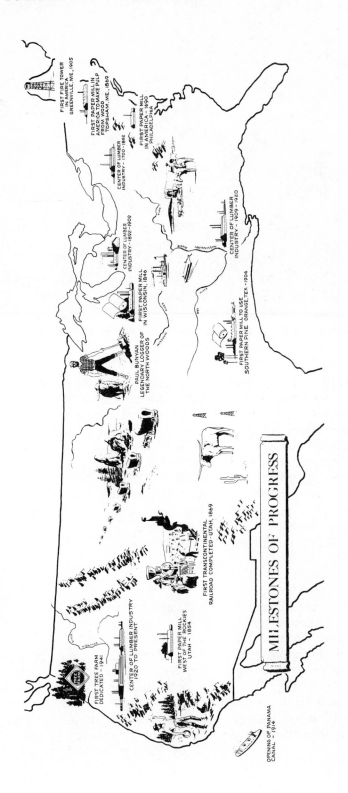

Fig. 34–1. Wood and the forests which supply it have long played an important part in the growth and development of our country.

Fig. 34–2. This integrated company produces lumber, plywood and a variety of wood products.

sumption figures represents the amount imported, principally from Canada. Exports annually fall below one billion board feet, but greater effort to open foreign markets should result in increased shipments. Construction accounts for 70 percent of all lumber consumed and manufacturing the other 30 percent.

In the decade 1952–1962 per capita consumption of lumber declined from 250 to 200 board feet. The drop is largely the result of the growing importance of plywood, particleboard, metals, plastics, and other materials in construction and manufacture. However, expanded research and development and more aggressive marketing are beginning to stimulate the demand for lumber. Estimates place the demand for lumber in 1975 at approximately 50 billion board feet.

Furthermore, there is a trend toward diversification of production and integration with the pulp, paper, and plywood industries.

Employment in the lumbering industry has declined slightly during this decade as a result of intensive competition, the closing of marginal mills, and the increased productivity of the larger, more modern mills. Sawmills and planing mills employed 265,000 persons in 1963. More than 91 percent were production workers. The remainder were clerical, sales, administrative, and other nonproduction employees.

Logging

Logging operations in well-managed forests begin with foresters marking the trees to be harvested as shown in Figure 34–3. Harvesting today is a scientific process. As the forester decides which trees should be removed he also takes steps to provide for a new crop of trees and to prevent soil erosion. This is done by leaving some trees to produce seeds or by various methods of reseeding or

Fig. 34–3. Company forester (right) selects mature redwood tree for cutting and instructs his assistant to mark it with paint gun. Smaller trees are left for additional growth before another round of "selective cutting" is carried out.

Fig. 34–4. A lumberjack fells a tree with a chain saw.

transplanting young trees called seedlings.

In the Pacific coast forests a prelogging operation precedes the main harvest. In this step, all of the small trees are removed for conversion into poles, posts, and pulpwood. If they were permitted to remain during the harvest, they would be damaged or destroyed.

Men with power-driven chain saws cut the trees close to the ground as shown in Figures 34–4 and 34–5. This is called "falling" or "felling." The limbs are removed from the fallen tree and the trunk is *bucked* (cut) into lengths suitable for pulpwood, plywood, or lumber. See Figure 34–6. The log lengths are carefully determined so that the greatest amount of the best grades of wood may result.

After the logs have been bucked, they

Fig. 34–5. Six trees such as this one, if sawed into lumber would build an average size home. Note the men at the base of the tree.

Fig. 34–6. This tree trunk is being cut into lengths suitable for lumber, with a small allowance for trimming. This process is called bucking.

Fig. 34–7. A contract logger uses a tractor and winch and log cart to move logs to the trucking area which may be ½ to 3 miles away.

are skidded to the landing, an open place in the forest. Where the terrain permits, tractors with various log skidding devices are used as shown in Figure 34–7. In unusually rough terrain one tall tree is selected as a spar pole. This tree is topped (see Figure 34–8), guyed with cables, and then used to support other cables that drag or lift the logs into the landing.

A tree harvester, developed to increase wood pulp harvesting productivity, is shown in Figures 34–9 and 34–10. The harvester delimbs branches up to 3 in. in diameter and tops 60-ft. trees. It then cuts through a maximum trunk diameter of 26 in. and bunches the logs at the rate

Fig. 34–8. This highlimber works his way down the trunk to the ground. Next the spar tree will be rigged with cables and pulley for logging operations.

of eight cords per hour. The vertical mast mounts two shears and a delimbing device, all hydraulically controlled.

When the harvesting operation is completed, all of the tree limbs and refuse are collected. The limbs and other usable wood are converted into chips for sale to pulp and paper mills. The refuse is disposed of so that it will not interfere with new tree growth.

Before tractors, trucks, and other equipment can be moved into the forest it is usually necessary to build roads as shown in Figure 34–11. The forester and the logger plan and map the route the road will follow. When the harvest is completed the road is planted with grasses and game foods to prevent erosion and provide food for forest animals. In government-owned forests these roads are sometimes improved and used by vacationers and sportsmen after the harvesting is completed.

Logs are loaded onto trucks or railroad cars and transported to the mills or they are floated down rivers and

Fig. 34–9. This crawler-propelled tree harvester cuts, delimbs, and bunches tree trunks for pulpwood. The operator guides the machine to the tree. The delimber moves up the tree and tops the tree when the diameter measures about 3 inches.

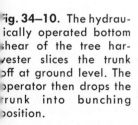

Fig. 34–10. The hydraulically operated bottom shear of the tree harvester slices the trunk off at ground level. The operator then drops the trunk into bunching position.

Fig. 34—11. Building a logging road.

streams. Trucks (see Fig. 34–12) haul the majority of logs. The practice of floating logs to mills is rapidly disappearing in this country. In other parts of the world where transportation is not so well developed, river driving and log rafts still constitute the principal means of moving logs to sawmills or shipping ports (see Fig. 34–13).

Sawmilling

Ideally, a sawmill will be located near the forest which supplies the logs and

Fig. 34—12. Loading logs in the Douglas fir region of Washington state with a heel boom loader. These trucks can carry a 60-ton load.

close to the markets which will use its products. When distances become too great, portable circular or gang mills may be set up in the forest. Thus only rough lumber is transported great distances. Most permanent mills usually get their logs from within a 100-mi. radius. Locations on rivers, lakes, or other bodies of water are desirable so that the logs may be stored in the water until ready

Fig. 34—13. Logs are transported to sawmills by trucks, railroad cars, or ships. Some are still floated down rivers or bound together and towed as shown here. In some cases these log rafts are even taken to sea and towed to mills along the coast.

for sawing. Water protects the logs from end checking, fire, insect damage, and decay. Furthermore, the heavy logs are handled more easily in the water than when stacked in great piles on land. Some hardwood logs sink, however, and must be stacked on land.

Boom or **pondmen** select and guide the logs to the bottom of the *bull chain* (see

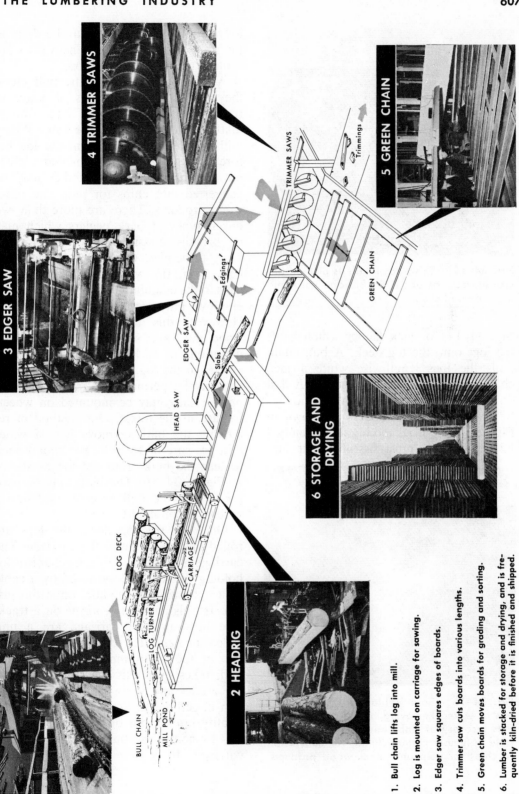

Fig. 34–14.   Lumber manufacture at a typical sawmill.

1. Bull chain lifts log into mill.

2. Log is mounted on carriage for sawing.

3. Edger saw squares edges of boards.

4. Trimmer saw cuts boards into various lengths.

5. Green chain moves boards for grading and sorting.

6. Lumber is stacked for storage and drying, and is frequently kiln-dried before it is finished and shipped.

Fig. 34-15. This tractor with its pick-up device moves logs about the storage yard and onto the bull chain.

Fig. 34-14) or jack ladder which hauls the logs onto the log deck. A bull chain pulls the logs lengthwise while a jack chain moves the logs sideways. Mills that do not have water facilities move the logs by crane or tractor loaders as shown in Figure 34-15. Logs too big to be handled inside the mill must first be split into

Fig. 34-16. Bark is blasted from logs by jets of water. Removing bark from logs permits recovery of slabs and edgings not suitable in lumber manufacturing for conversion to chips for pulp and other wood products.

halves or quarters. This may be done in the millpond or on land. Chain saws are usually used for this purpose.

As the logs move up the bull chain they are sprayed with jets of water to remove sand, rocks, and other foreign matter that might dull the saws. Many mills remove the bark from the log before sawing so that the slabs and edgings not suitable for use as lumber may be converted into chips for pulp and other wood products. There are more than two dozen types of bark peelers which may be broadly classified according to two basic principles. One type separates the bark from the wood by destroying the cells in the cambium layer. The other type employs knives to cut away the bark However, this method removes some wood and leaves some bark depending on variations in bark thickness and irregularities in the log. Mechanical bark peelers may be permanently installed at the mill or they may be mounted on wheels for use in the forest. One method of removing the bark employs jets of water at a pressure of 1500 lb. per square inch to tear the bark from the log as shown in Figure 34-16. The bark may be used for fuel at the mill or converted into a variety of products.

Once on the log deck, the logs are rolled one at a time to the carriage. The carriage is a frame with a mechanism for holding the log. It is powered by a cable or a hydraulic, pneumatic, on steam piston. It rolls past the *headsaw* on a track The headsaw and carriage are a unit called the *headrig*. Here the *head sawyer*, one of the most important men in the mill, takes over. His knowledge of lumber grades and trade requirements guide him in getting the largest amount of high quality lumber out of each log. He does this by controling the movements of the carriage. It is here that the logs are

Fig. 34–17. Forty saws are contained in this gang saw. Cants are fed into the machines and emerge as boards ready for the next operation.

slabbed and cut into *cants* and *flitches*. Cants are huge slices of a log, cut on two or more sides, that are intended for further manufacture into lumber or veneer. Flitches are huge semicircular slabs with bark on one side.

Small mills usually use a circular headsaw. Where large-diameter logs are cut a second circular saw called a top saw is placed above and in the plane of the first saw. Large mills use a band saw as a headsaw. Band saws, being thinner than circular saws, waste less wood as sawdust. The carriage supports the log while it is moved into the saw.

When a cut is completed, the sawyer moves the carriage rapidly back to its starting position, repositions the log, and starts another cut. Modern log carriages are provided with automatic dogging and setting equipment controlled by the sawyer. These remotely controlled devices eliminate the need for men riding the carriage. Some band saws have teeth cut on both edges of the blade to permit cutting on both movements of the carriage, but this is the exception.

The cants and flitches move from the headsaw on a conveyor. In some mills they are moved to a band resaw or a gang saw (see Fig. 34–17) and cut into lumber of standard thicknesses. In other mills, cants pass through a *bull edger* where they are cut into sizes for further manufacture. Edgers have as many as seven movable circular saws on one arbor.

Some mills cut the entire log into rough lumber of standard thicknesses at the headsaw. Then the boards pass through edger saws where they are cut to standard widths.

After the boards have been cut to width and thickness, they are cut to standard lengths at the *trimmer saws*. Defects are also removed at this time. The trimmer man observes each board and raises or lowers the appropriate saws to produce the highest grades possible.

Standard lengths for rough hardwood lumber range from 4 to 16 ft. by 1-ft. increments. Standard thicknesses are as follows: $\frac{3}{8}$ to $\frac{3}{4}$ in. by $\frac{1}{8}$-in. increments; $\frac{3}{4}$ to $1\frac{1}{2}$ in. by $\frac{1}{4}$-in. increments; and

1½ to 6 in. by ½-in. increments. Minimum standard width is 3 in. Hardwood standards are designed primarily for the furniture industry.

American standard lengths for rough softwood yard lumber are multiples of 1 ft. but the practice is to produce in multiples of 2 ft. Thickness dimensions are similar to those for hardwood except that a 1¾-in. thickness is standard and the maximum thickness is less than 5 in. Standard rough widths range upward from 2 in. Structural lumber is cut 2 in. or more thick and 5 or more inches wide. Softwood standard sizes are designed primarily for the construction industry.

The rough lumber moves from the trimmer saws onto the green chain. The green chain is a conveyor on which the still sap-wet boards slowly move into a long sorting shed. Here, highly skilled men grade each board according to its utility value. Finally, the lumber is carefully stacked according to size and grade and dried. See Figure 34–14.

Lumber Grading

Table 34–1 gives a summary of the standard *hardwood grades* as adopted by the National Hardwood Lumber Association. The official rules should be consulted for a full description of grades. In these rules the grade of a piece of hardwood is determined by the proportion of the piece that can be cut into a certain number of smaller pieces of a minimum size with one clear side. The amount of usable material is the chief characteristic of this grading system.

The top grade of hardwood boards is "Firsts" and the next grade is "Seconds." They are nearly always combined into one grade referred to as "FAS." Pieces of FAS lumber must have nominal dimensions of 6 in. or more in width and

8 to 16 ft. in length. Thirty percent of the pieces may be 8 to 11 ft. long, half of which may be 8 and 9 ft. long. At least 60 percent of the pieces must be 12 to 16 ft. long. Firsts must yield at least 91⅔ percent of each piece as clear-face cuttings. One to 3 cuttings in Firsts must produce clear pieces at least 4 in. by 5 ft. or 3 in. by 7 ft. in size. Grades of "Select" and below permit shorter pieces, smaller cuttings, and a smaller percentage of clear-face cuttings. Sound Wormy lumber has the same requirements as No. 1 Common, except that worm holes, a few sound knots, and other imperfections are permitted.

Hardwood flooring is graded under the rules of either the Maple or the National Oak Flooring Manufacturers' Association. Maple-flooring grading rules also apply to beech and birch. Each species covered by these rules has three grades designated as First, Second, and Third grade. Combinations of grades, such as Second and Better, are sometimes made. Four special grades, selected for uniformity of color, are also made. First grade flooring must be practically free of imperfections. Variations in natural color are allowed. Second grade admits tight, sound knots and slight imperfections, but it must lay without waste. The Third grade must give a serviceable floor.

Oak flooring grading rules mainly cover quartersawed and plainsawed oak flooring, but pecan, maple, birch, and beech are included. Quartersawed flooring has three grades: Clear, Sap Clear, and Select. Plainsawed has four grades: Clear, Select, No. 1 Common, and No. 2 Common.

The Hardwood Dimension Manufacturers Association has developed rules for grading *hardwood dimension stock* used by furniture and cabinet manufacturers. They apply primarily to kiln-dried rough

TABLE 34–1 STANDARD HARDWOOD GRADES[1]

Grade and lengths allowed (feet)	Widths allowed	Surface measure of pieces	Amount of each piece that must work into clear-face cuttings	Maximum cuttings allowed	Minimum size of cuttings required
	Inches	Square feet	Percent	Number	
Firsts:[2] 8 to 16 (will admit 30 percent of 8- to 11-foot, ½ of which may be 8- and 9-foot).	6+	4 to 9	91⅔	1	4 inches by 5 feet, or 3 inches by 7 feet.
		10 to 14	91⅔	2	
		15+	91⅔	3	
Seconds:[2] 8 to 16 (will admit 30 percent of 8- to 11-foot, ½ of which may be 8- and 9-foot).	6+	4 and 5	83⅓	1	Do.
		6 and 7	83⅓	1	
		6 and 7	91⅔	2	
		8 to 11	83⅓	2	
		8 to 11	91⅔	3	
		12 to 15	83⅓	3	
		12 to 15	91⅔	4	
		16+	83⅓	4	
Selects: 6 to 16 (will admit 30 percent of 6- to 11-foot, ⅙ of which may be 6- and 7-foot).	4+	2 and 3	91⅔	1	Do.
		4+	(3)		
No. 1 Common: 4 to 16 (will admit 10 percent of 4- to 7-foot, ½ of which may be 4- and 5-foot). Sound Wormy:	3+	1	100	0	4 inches by 2 feet, or 3 inches by 7 feet.
		2	75	1	
		3 and 4	66⅔	1	
		3 and 4	75	2	
		5 to 7	66⅔	2	
		5 to 7	75	3	
		8 to 10	66⅔	3	
		11 to 13	66⅔	4	
		14+	66⅔	5	
No. 2 Common: 4 to 16 (will admit 30 percent of 4- to 7-foot, ⅓ of which may be 4- and 5-foot).	3+	1	66⅔	1	3 inches by 2 feet.
		2 and 3	50	1	
		2 and 3	66⅔	2	
		4 and 5	50	2	
		4 and 5	66⅔	3	
		6 and 7	50	3	
		6 and 7	66⅔	4	
		8 and 9	50	4	
		10 and 11	50	5	
		12 and 13	50	6	
		14+	50	7	
No. 3A Common: 4 to 16 (will admit 50 percent of 4- to 7-foot, ½ of which may be 4- and 5-foot).	3+	1+	[4]33⅓	(1)	Do.
No. 3B Common: 4 to 16 (will admit 50 percent of 4- to 7-foot, ½ of which may be 4- and 5-foot).	3+	1+	[6]25	(5)	1½ inches by 2 feet.

[1] Inspection to be made on the poorer side of the piece, except in Selects.
[2] Firsts and Seconds are combined as 1 grade (FAS). The percentage of Facts required in the combined grade varies from 20 to 40 percent, depending on the species.
[3] Same as Seconds.
[4] This grade also admits pieces that grade not below No. 2 Common on the good face and have the reverse face sound.
[5] Not specified.
[6] The cuttings must be sound, clear face not required.

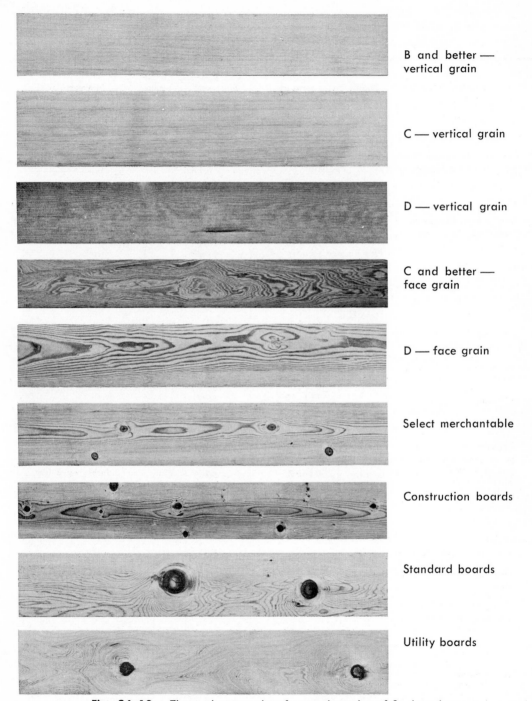

B and better —
vertical grain

C — vertical grain

D — vertical grain

C and better —
face grain

D — face grain

Select merchantable

Construction boards

Standard boards

Utility boards

Fig. 34–18. These photographs of several grades of fir show how they differ in the features that are considered by the lumber graders. Fir is graded into at least 20 different classes or groups for various uses.

lumber and cover three classes of material — glued, solid flat, and solid square dimension stock. Each class may be finished, rough, or semifinished. Dimension flat stock has five grades — Clear two Faces, Clear One Face, Paint, Core, and Sound. Solid squares have three grades — Clear, Select, and Sound.

Softwood lumber is graded under the rules of at least seven different associations. Each softwood has different rules, but in some cases they are graded under different association rules. Softwood grades are, however, based on a set of simplified rules known as the American Lumber Standards. Softwoods are divided into several grades or classes according to quality. See Table 34–2 and Figure 34–18. The grade of a particular piece of lumber is based on the number, character, and location of features that may lower its utility value. Some of the more common features are knots, pitch pockets, shake (a separation along the grain and between the annual rings), check (a lengthwise separation across the annual rings), and stain. The best grades have few, if any, of these features. The other grades contain numerous knots, etc., and constitute the bulk of lumber produced. These features are not correctly classed as defects since most are a natural condition of the tree. All of the grades give satisfaction when wisely chosen for a particular use.

Yard lumber is subdivided into three groups — Finish, Common Boards, and Common Dimension. It is marketed on the basis that it will be used in the form in which it is sold.

Finish Grades A and B are usually sold together as "B and Better." Grade A is practically clear and B allows a few small knots, checks, and stains. They are used for interior work, trim, and flooring where natural finishes will be applied.

Grades C and D contain knots, but they are easily covered with paint. Knots in grade C may be up to 1 in. in diameter; in grade D they may be larger and slightly soft, rough or loose.

Common boards are suitable for general usage and for construction purposes. They are usually of nominal 1-in. thickness surfaced to $^{25}\!/_{32}$. The differences in the grades are due to the character rather than the frequency of such features as knots and pitch pockets.

Common dimension lumber is graded principally on the requirements of framing for buildings, stiffness being of most importance. Common building practice rather than design determines the sizes of members used.

Structural lumber is graded for strength and is intended for use where working stresses are specified. At one time, lumber for this purpose was graded on appearance only. The character of the wood was not so important as it is today because lumber was cheap and obtainable in sizes larger than necessary for economical design. The demand for assured strength values in lumber led to the development of stress grading. Most building codes today give working stresses for wood.

Stress Grading classifies each piece of lumber according to its minimum strength values. A laboratory value for the basic stress of the clear wood of a species is determined. This *basic stress* is a reduction from the average value obtained in strength tests. It provides a safety factor. However, it does not provide for the reduction in strength due to knots, cross grain, or other strength reducing features. An allowance must be estimated for these features. The strength remaining after this allowance has been made is known as the *strength ratio* of the piece of lumber. The basic stress, when multiplied by the

TABLE 34–2   GENERAL CLASSIFICATION SOFTWOOD LUMBER

Softwood lumber is divided into three main classes — yard lumber, structural lumber (often referred to under the general term "timber"), and factory and shop lumber. The following classification of softwood lumber gives the grade names in general use by lumber manufacturers' associations for the various classes of lumber.

			Grades
SOFTWOOD LUMBER (This classification applies to lumber; sizes given are nominal.)	**Yard Lumber** (lumber less than 5 inches thick, intended for general building purposes; grading based on use of the entire piece).	Finish (4 inches and under thick and 16 inches and under wide).	A. B. C. D.
		Common boards (less than 2 inches thick and 1 or more inches wide).	No. 1 No. 2 No. 3 No. 4 No. 5
		Common dimension (2 inches and under 5 inches thick and 2 or more inches wide). — Planks (2 inches and under 4 inches thick and 8 or more inches wide).	No. 1 No. 2 No. 3
		Scantling (2 inches and under 5 inches thick and less than 8 inches wide).	No. 1 No. 2 No. 3
		Heavy joists (4 inches thick and 8 or more inches wide).	No. 1 No. 2 No. 3
	Structural lumber (lumber 5 or more inches thick and wide, except joists and planks; grading based on strength and on use of entire piece).	Joists and planks (2 to 4 inches thick and 4 or more inches wide). Beams and stringers (5 or more inches thick and 8 or more inches wide). Posts and timbers (5 by 5 inches and larger).	
	Factory and shop lumber (grading based on area of piece suitable for cuttings of certain size and quality).	Factory plank graded for door, sash, and other cuttings 1¼ or more inches thick and 5 or more inches wide. Shop lumber graded for general cut-up purposes.	Association grading rules should be referred to for standard grades and sizes.

strength ratio (expressed as a percentage), becomes the *working stress* for structural design with that piece of lumber.

At least two mechanical systems of stress grading have been developed. See Figures 34–19 and 34–20. Both systems apply a flatwise deflection to each piece of lumber as it moves through the mechanism. The force required to produce the deflection is measured and interpreted by the machines as a particular working stress — the modulus of elasticity. A piece of Douglas fir with a stress rating

Fig. 34–19. This machine provides a continuous, non-destructive stress rating of dimension lumber. Maximum capacity is 1⅝" x 12" with 8 feet the shortest length. There is no limit on the longest length. A roll at the outfeed end stamps the stress rating on each piece.

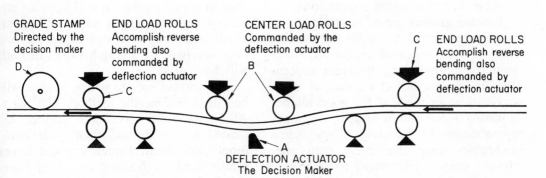

GRADE STAMP
Directed by the decision maker
D

END LOAD ROLLS
Accomplish reverse bending also commanded by deflection actuator
C

CENTER LOAD ROLLS
Commanded by the deflection actuator
B

C

END LOAD ROLLS
Accomplish reverse bending also commanded by deflection actuator

A
DEFLECTION ACTUATOR
The Decision Maker

Fig. 34–20. How dimension lumber is stress rated. The piece enters at C. The center load rolls (B) apply the load which causes the lumber to deflect. The deflection actuator (A) permits a maximum deflection of 0.420 inches between the two inner supporting rolls which are 48 inches apart. If the deflection exceeds this amount the piece is rejected.

of 2050f would indicate a top rating for a dense, select structural member for use in light framing.

The stress applied to the lumber in these mechanical systems is below the proportional limit, but sufficient to give a valid measure of stiffness. Visual grading by conventional methods is also required since the machines do not accurately stress the first and last 16 in. of a piece.

Mechanical grading is still in the developmental stages. Its advantages over visual grading rest in the higher and more accurate stress ratings that result.

Factory and shop lumber is divided into two classes — factory plank and shop lumber. Each has a different set of grading rules which classify it according to the percentage of area, size, and quality of cuttings. It is graded and marketed on the assumption that it will be cut up.

The National Lumber Manufacturers Association is now in the process of implementing a standardization program for softwood lumber grading. It will provide: (1) uniform grade names for the species used in residential and light frame construction; (2) simplified span tables for the new grades; and (3) a guide specification for wood frame construction.

Lumber graders are highly trained and experienced men who apply the grading rules to each piece of lumber. Lumber graders usually serve a two-year apprenticeship. Authorities claim that as much as one-third or more of the good lumber is wasted or lowered in value by improper manufacture or handling. These same authorities insist that every man, mechanic, sawyer, edgerman, trimmerman, resawyer, foreman, etc., should be an expert grader. In this way each person is able to evaluate and cut the highest grades of lumber from each log. Even

pondmen should know enough about grading that they can select logs that will produce the grades necessary for an order.

Lumber Drying

Lumber cut from a log may contain from 30 to 300 percent water. Some of this is free water and some is absorbed in the capillaries of the walls of the wood fibers and ray cells. Changes in the amount of absorbed water are responsible for shrinkage and expansion of wood. The detrimental effects of excess moisture in wood are minimized by seasoning or drying. Seasoning refers to removing the moisture from green wood, and in some cases to the relief of stresses, to improve its serviceability.

Lumber is air-dried and/or kiln-dried to increase its durability, minimize shrinking and checking, increase strength and stiffness, prevent staining, decrease weight, and to increase nail and paint holding capacities. Good air-drying or good kiln-drying have the same effect upon the ultimate strength of wood. Because properly kiln-dried lumber has a 2 to 6 percent lower moisture content than air-dried lumber, it will have a temporary higher strength value. When an equilibrium moisture content point has been reached, the strength values of both will be equal.

The various uses to which lumber will be put determine the methods of drying. All upper-grade softwood lumber intended for finish and flooring is commonly kiln-dried. Dimension and lower grades used for framing are usually air dried. In some cases these items are shipped without drying beyond that which occurs during shipment.

Hardwoods are usually air-seasoned for

several months and then kiln-dried or shipped to a manufacturer who kiln-dries them as needed.

Air-drying is accomplished by carefully stacking the lumber outdoors or in an unheated shed for at least 2 to 6 months. Walnut, oak, and hickory require 3 or more years to air-dry completely. The lumber is open piled on stickers (wood strips) so air can circulate freely. See Figure 34–21. It is protected from sun and rain with a tight roof. Lumber is sometimes sprayed or dipped in an antiseptic solution before stacking to prevent fungus infections.

The moisture content of air-dried lumber will range from 6 percent in arid regions to 24 percent in humid regions. For the country as a whole, the minimum moisture content of air-dried lumber is 12 to 15 percent with the average being somewhat higher.

Dry lumber can be piled solid in the open for relatively short periods, but it should be protected from rain with a suitable cover. Flooring, interior trim, and cabinet work should be stored in a closed, heated shed during cold or humid weather.

Kiln-drying is accomplished by first stacking the lumber on kiln cars as shown in Figure 34–22. Stickers separate the individual boards which are spaced to permit air circulation. The loaded kiln car is then rolled into the kiln. The kiln doors are closed and the lumber is subjected to carefully controlled moisture and heat. In from 3 to 4 days to as long as 3 weeks, the kiln dries the lumber to a moisture content of 6 to 12 percent.

Kilns are classified as either progressive or compartment kilns. Progressive kilns are several hundred feet long and are loaded at one end and unloaded at the other. Kilns are either automatically or

Fig. 34–21. These stacks of lumber represent a fraction of the harvest that this nation's forests yield annually.

Fig. 34–22. Here a loaded kiln car is being rolled into a dry kiln, a large room in which the temperature and humidity may be carefully controlled.

Fig. 34–23. An automatically controlled, steam heated kiln requires good judgment of the operator to produce the best quality of stress-free lumber.

manually controlled. They are either steam heated or of the direct- or indirect-furnace type. Provision is made for the circulation of the air in the kiln. In all cases, kiln operators supervise and adjust the drying conditions. See Figure 34–23. Operators must exercise good judgment since no two kiln loads are exactly alike. They select kiln schedules, prepare and test samples, and in general attempt to produce the maximum quantity of stress-free lumber at the lowest cost. See Figure 34–24.

Unless the kiln is operated in accordance with the best practice, as much as 20 to 25 percent of the lumber may be rendered unfit for its intended use. Too

high a temperature may cause case hardening or honeycomb. *Case hardening* occurs when the outside of a piece of lumber becomes dry and hard and sets in an expanded condition. Later, when the inside dries and shrinks, it opens up or *honeycombs*. If the inside of the lumber does not honeycomb, it becomes stressed. The case-hardened surface of the piece dulls planer knives and when sawn, the wood distorts.

Other troubles caused by improper kiln-drying are collapse, twisting, and warping. Collapse (hollows in the surface of a board) results when very wet wood is dried at too high a temperature. Twisting and warping result from improper piling of the lumber on the kiln car.

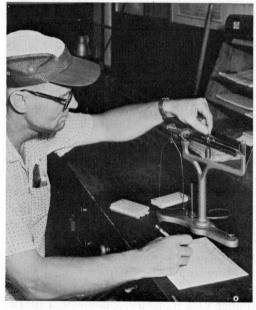

Fig. 34–24. Quality control poses unusual problems in hardwood flooring production; the basic material is subject to unpredictable vagaries in density, hardness, moisture content, grain characteristics, and color. A kiln operator checks the weight of flooring samples for moisture content.

There are two basic schedules for the operation of dry kilns. The *moisture content schedule* requires changing the kiln conditions based on average moisture content of the controlling kiln samples. The *time schedule* requires changing the kiln conditions at predetermined periods of time. Neither schedule is entirely satisfactory. Both may require equalizing and conditioning treatments as dictated by the final use of the lumber.

In general, the drying process for hardwoods begins with a 1 to 24-hour or more warm-up. When the kiln and lumber have reached a temperature of 110 to 120 deg., steam is introduced into the kiln to maintain a high humidity. The steam keeps the outside of the lumber moist while the internal moisture is being removed. As the schedule progresses the relative humidity, regulated by the steam, is gradually reduced and the temperature is increased. At the final stage, the kiln temperature will be about 175 to 180 deg. F. When required, equalizing and conditioning treatments are applied to relieve case hardening. This may require 4 to 48 hours and temperatures to 200 deg. The entire process takes about 3 weeks.

Electric moisture meters are used to ascertain the moisture content of wood. The laboratory method of ascertaining the moisture content of wood was briefly described in Chapter II. This method is most accurate, but it results in the destruction of the sample and takes several hours. Electric moisture meters are instant reading, and they do not destroy the material beyond making two small holes in it. See Figure 34–25.

Electric moisture meters were developed after it was learned that the electrical resistance of wood generally depends on its moisture content. They are most reliably used on wood with a high moisture content. The *resistance-type meters* are most popular. They are basically ohmmeters capable of measuring very high resistances. For example, Douglas fir at room temperature and 7 percent moisture has a resistance of 22,400 megohms; at 25 percent moisture it is .46 megohms. Unlike metals, the electrical resistance of wood decreases as the temperature increases. This effect is very small and may not be true when the moisture content is below 8 percent.

Two other principal types of electric moisture meters have been developed. The *radio-frequency power loss type* measures the electrical conductivity of the moist wood and indicates this value as moisture content. The *capacitance type* indicates the relationship that exists be-

Fig. 34–25. Inspectors depend on accurate moisture meters to make sure moisture content of incoming lumber is not excessive before boards enter kilns.

Fig. 34–26. This planer planes the rough board on four sides reducing it to commercial size at the rate of 200 feet per minute. A rough 2 x 4 will measure 1⅝" x 3⅝" after planing.

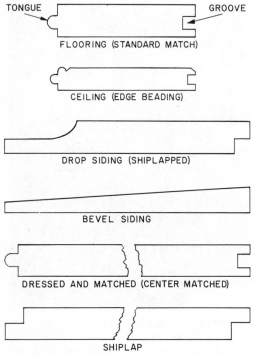

TONGUE   GROOVE

FLOORING (STANDARD MATCH)

CEILING (EDGE BEADING)

DROP SIDING (SHIPLAPPED)

BEVEL SIDING

DRESSED AND MATCHED (CENTER MATCHED)

SHIPLAP

Fig. 34–27. Types of worked lumber.

tween the moisture content of the wood and its dielectric (nonconducting) constant. This type is not marketed in the United States.

The Planing Mill

When an order is received for a quantity of lumber, the proper grade and kind is selected from the air-dried stack. If necessary, it is kiln-dried to the specified moisture content and then machined to the proper dimensions in a planing mill or shipped rough as required.

Most large mills contain a planing section. Small mills send their rough lumber to special planing mills. Manufacturers who use large quantities of lumber usually purchase it in the rough, air-dried condition. They kiln-dry and plane the lumber as it is needed for their particular use.

In the planing mill the rough, dried boards are planed to standard sizes on machines that cut to width and thickness in one pass. See Figure 34–26. Planing generally reduces the thickness of rough boards $\frac{3}{16}$ to $\frac{1}{4}$ in. and the width by $\frac{3}{8}$ to $\frac{1}{2}$ in.

Lumber may be classified into 3 groups by the extent to which it is processed. *Rough lumber* is that which has been sawed on the four longitudinal surfaces. *Dressed (surfaced) lumber* has been planed for smoothness and uniformity of size. It may be surfaced on one side (S1S), 2 sides (S2S), one edge (S1E), two edges (S2E), or a combination of sides and edges (S1S1E), (S1S2E), (S2S1E), or (S4S). *Worked lumber* has been dressed and also matched, shiplapped, or patterned or machined by running through a matcher, molder, or sticker. See Figure 34–27.

Matching means that a tongue and a groove have been cut on the opposite

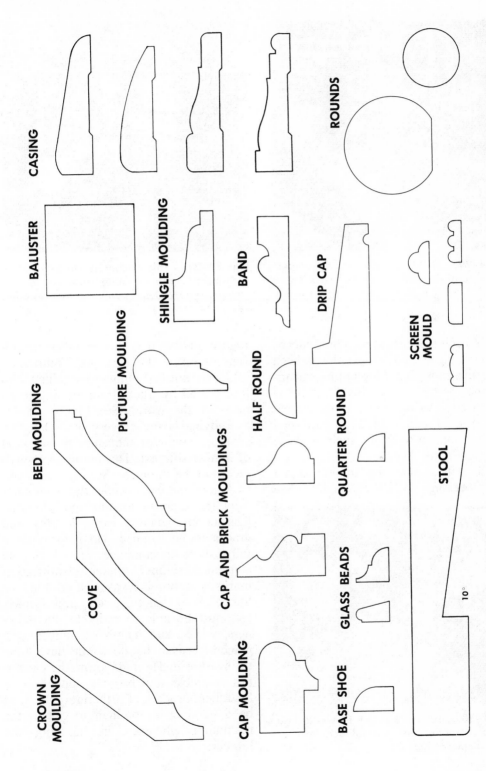

Fig. 34–28. These are just a few of the many shapes and sizes of moldings produced. Architects select molding from the manufacturer's catalog to fit their design needs. Most manufacturers will make cutters to produce special moldings when specified.

Fig. 34–29. Highly skilled graders inspect each piece of finished lumber before it leaves the mill. Lumber is sorted according to grade and size.

Fig. 34–31. This lumber is stacked in the distribution yard awaiting shipment to customers. The overhead crane reduces materials handling costs.

edges of each piece. End matching means that the tongue and groove have been cut on the ends also. Shiplapping means that the pieces have been rabbeted on each edge to provide a close lapped joint. See Figure 34–27. Patterned lumber is shaped to forms such as those shown in Figure 34–28.

Most mills grade the lumber again after processing to insure quality. See

Fig. 34–30. Before flooring is wired into bundles it undergoes careful scrutiny for milling imperfections.

Figure 34–29. It is then bundled to prevent excessive damage. See Figure 34–30. The finished lumber is tallied and transported by truck, train, or ship to all parts of the world. See Figure 34–31.

Tallying is the process of making an accurate count of the amount and kind of lumber shipped. This is the company's record of the shipment. See Figure 34–32.

A good *tallyman* studies the order carefully to ascertain loading and shipping instructions, quantity, sizes, lengths, and grades to be shipped. He records on a tally sheet a complete record of the consignee, shipper, grader, identification marks, car number, as well as kind of lumber, size, length, grade, and species. He must be able to estimate the thickness, width, and length of lumber at a glance because he does not have time to measure it. He must know the capacities of trucks and box cars and how to load them properly. Furthermore, he must be a good crew foreman to obtain the maximum efficiency in handling the lumber.

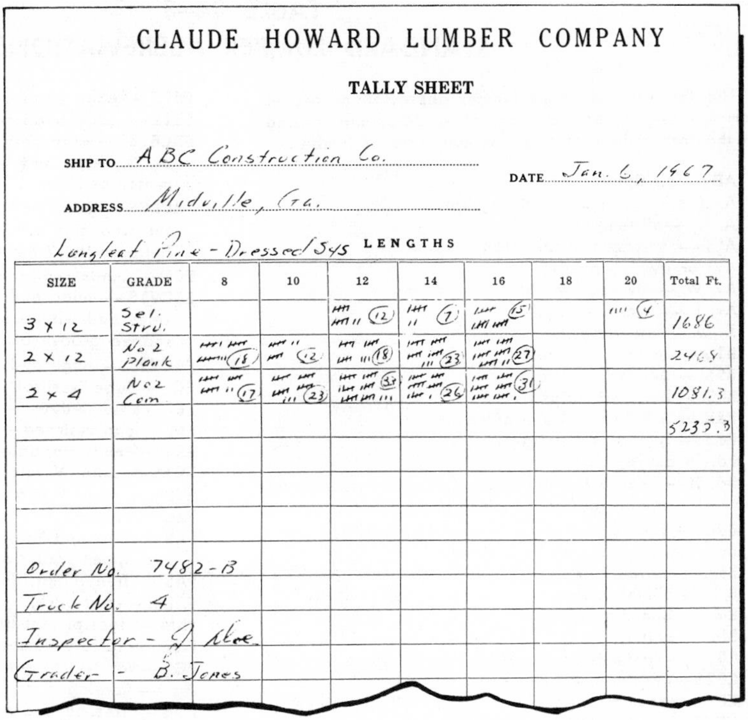

Fig. 34–32. A sample tally sheet.

CLAUDE HOWARD LUMBER COMPANY

TALLY SHEET

SHIP TO: *ABC Construction Co.* DATE: *Jan. 6, 1967*

ADDRESS: *Midville, Ga.*

Longleaf Pine – Dressed/S4S LENGTHS

SIZE	GRADE	8	10	12	14	16	18	20	Total Ft.
3 x 12	Sel. Stru.			(12)	(7)	(5)		(4)	1686
2 x 12	No 2 Plank	(18)	(2)	(18)	(33)	(27)			2468
2 x 4	No 2 Com	(17)	(23)	(34)	(26)	(34)			1081.3
									5235.3

Order No. 7482-B

Truck No. 4

Inspector - J. Doe

Grader - B. Jones

Buying Lumber

The board foot is the standard unit for most items of lumber. A board foot is 1 sq. ft. in area and 1 in. thick in its nominal dimensions. Nominal dimensions are those of the rough sawn, green wood before it was dried or planed. Lumber is bought and sold by the board foot on the basis of nominal dimensions.

A board 1 in. by 12 in. by 10 ft. long contains 10 board feet. The formula for calculating board feet is:

$$\text{Board feet} = \frac{\text{Thickness in inches} \times \text{width in inches} \times \text{length in feet}}{12}$$

Dividing the width in inches by 12 (the number of inches in one foot) converts it into feet.

A rough, dried board may measure 5¾ in. wide. It was 6 in. wide when cut while green. Its width is considered to be 6 in., the nearest full inch, and it is sold that way. Lengths of boards are measured to the nearest even foot. Thus a board 10 ft. 5 in. long is sold as 10 feet; a board 10 ft. 7 in. long is sold as 11 ft. Board foot measure is also calculated to the nearest whole foot.

Lumber with a thickness of less than 1 in. is considered to be 1 in. thick unless otherwise specified. Thus a board ½ in. by 12 in. by 10 ft. would also be considered to contain 10 board feet. This is an exception to the definition of a board foot. Lumber over 1 in. thick is figured as 1¼, 1½, 2, etc., as appropriate.

Lumber thickness is usually specified as a certain number of fourths. One inch thick lumber is sized as 4/4; 2 in. as 8/4; 1½ as 6/4.

TABLE 34–3
STANDARD LUMBER ABBREVIATIONS

The following standard lumber abbreviations are in common use in contracts and other documents arising in the transactions of purchase and sale of lumber.

AD — air-dried.
A. d. f. — after deducting freight.
A. l. — all lengths.
ALS — American lumber standards.
Av. or avg. — average
Av. w. — average width.
Av. l. — average length.
A. w. — all widths.
B1S — beaded one side.
B2S — Beaded two sides.
BBS — box bark strips.
B&B or B & Btr. — B and better.
B&S — beams and stringers.
Bd. — board
Bd. ft. — board-foot (or board-feet); that is, an area of 1 square foot by 1 inch thick.
Bdl. — bundle.
Bdl. bk. s. — bundle bark strips.
Bev. — bevel.
B/L — bill of lading.
Bm. - — board measure.
Btr. — better.
CB1S — center bead one side.
CB2S — center bead two sides.
CF — cost and freight.
CG2E — center groove two edges.
CIF — cost, insurance, and freight.
CIFE — cost, insurance, freight, and exchange.
Clg. — ceiling.
Clr. — clear.
CM — center matched; that is, the tongued-and-grooved joints are worked along the center of the edges of the piece.
Com. — common.
CS — calking seam.
Csg. — casing.
Ctg. — crating.
Cu. ft. — cubic foot or feet.
CV1S — center V one side.
CV2S — center V two sides.
D.B. Clg. — double-beaded ceiling (E&CB1S).
DB. Part — double-beaded partition (E&CB2S).
DET — Double end trimmed.
D&CM — dressed (1 or 2 sides) and center matched.
D&H — dressed and headed; that is, dressed 1 or 2 sides and worked to tongued-and-grooved joints on both the edge and the ends.
B&M — dressed and matched; that is, dressed 1 or 2 sides and tongued and grooved on the edges. The match may be center or standard.
D&SM —dressed (1 or 2 sides) and standard matched.
D2S&CM — dressed two sides and center matched.
D2S&M — dressed two sides and (center or standard) matched.
D2S&SM — dressed two sides and standard matched.
Dim. — dimension.
Dkg. — decking.
D/S or D/Sdg. — drop siding.
E — edge.

EB1S — edge bead one side.
EB2S — edge bead two sides.
E&CB1S — edge and center bead 1 side; surfaced 1 or 2 sides and with a longitudinal edge and center bead on a surfaced face.
E&CB2S — edge and center bead 2 sides; all 4 sides surfaced and with a longitudinal edge and center bead on the 2 faces.
ECM — ends center matched.
E&CV1S — edge and center V 1 side; surface 1 or 2 sides and with a longitudinal edge and center V-shaped groove on a surfaced face.
E&CV2S — edge and center V two sides.
EG — edge (vertical) grain.
EE — eased edges.
EM — end matched — either center or standard.
ESM — ends standard matched.
EV1S — edge V one side.
EV2S — edge V two sides.
Fac. — factory.
FAS — First and Seconds — a combined grade of the two upper grades of hardwoods.
FAS — free alongside (named vessel).
F. bk. — flat back.
FBM — foot or feet board measure.
Fcty. — factory (lumber).
FG — flat (slash) grain.
Flg. — flooring.
FOB — free on board (named point).
FOHC — free of heart center or centers.
F. o. k. — free of knots.
Frm. — framing.
Frt. — freight.
Ft. — foot or feet. Also one accent (').
Feet b. m. — feet board measure.
Feet s. m. — feet surface measure.
GM — grade marked.
G/R or G/Rfg. — grooved roofing.
HB — hollow back.
Hdl. — handle (stock).
Hdwd. — Hardwood.
H&M — hit and miss.
H or M — hit or miss
Hrt. — Heart.
Hrt. CC — heart cubical content.
Hrt. FA — heart facial area.
Hrt. G — heart girth.
Hrtwd. — heartwood.
1s&2s. — Ones and Twos — a combined grade of the hardwood grades of Firsts and Seconds.
In. — inch or inches. Also two accent marks (").
J&P — joists and planks.
KD — kiln-dried.
K. d. — knocked down.
Lbr. — lumber.
LCL — less than carload.
LFT or LIN. ft. — linear foot (or feet); that is 12 inches.
Lgr.— longer.
Lgth. — length.
Lin. — Linear
Lng. — lining.
LR. — log run.

Credit: Handbook 72, U. S. Department of Agriculture

STANDARD LUMBER ABBREVIATIONS (Continued)

Lr. MCO — log run, mill culls out.
Lth. — lath.
M — thousand.
MBM — thousand (feet) board measure.
MC — moisture content.
MCO — mill culls out.
Merch. — merchantable.
M. I. — mixed lengths.
Mldg. — molding.
MR — mill run.
M. s. M. — thousand (feet) surface measure.
M. w. — mixed widths.
No. — number.
N1E — nosed one edge.
N2E — nosed two edges.
Og. — Ogee.
Ord. — order.
P. — planed.
Par. — paragraph.
Part. — partition.
Pat. — pattern.
Pc. — piece.
Pcs. — Pieces.
PE — plain end.
Pky. — pecky.
Pln. — plain, as plainsawed.
PO — purchase order.
P&T — post and timbers.
Qtd. — quartered — when referring to hardwoods.
Rdm. — random.
Reg. — regular.
Res. — resawed.
Rfg. — roofing.
Rfrs. — roofers.
Rgh. — rough.
Rip. — ripped.
R/L — random lengths.
Rnd. — round.
R. Sdg.— rustic siding.
R/W — random widths.
R/W&L — random widths and lengths.
S&E — surfaced 1 side and 1 edge.
S1E — surfaced one edge.
S2E — surfaced two edges.
S1S — surfaced one side.
S2S — surfaced two sides.
S1S1E — surfaced 1 side and 1 edge.
S2S1E — surfaced 2 sides and 1 edge.
S1S2E — surfaced 1 side and 2 edges.
S4S — surfaced four sides.

S4S&CS — surfaced four sides with a calking seam on each edge.
S&M — surfaced and matched; that is, surfaced 1 or 2 sides and tongued and grooved on the edges. The match may be centered or standard.
S2S&SM — surfaced two sides and standard matched.
S2S&CM — surfaced two sides and center matched.
S2S&M — surfaced two sides and center or standard matched.
S2S&S/L — surfaced two sides and shiplapped.
Sap. —sapwood.
SB — Standard bead.
Sd. — seasoned.
Sdg. — Siding.
Sel. — select.
SE Sdg. — square-edge siding.
SE&S — square edge and sound.
S. f. — surface foot; that is, an area of 1 square foot.
Sftwd. — softwood.
Sh. D. — shipping dry.
Ship. — shiplap.
S. m. — surface measure.
SM — standard matched.
Smkd. — smoked (dried).
Smk. stnd. — smoke stained.
S. n. d. — sap no defect.
Snd. — sound.
Sq. — square.
Sqrs. — squares.
Std. — standard.
Stnd. — stained.
Stk. —stock.
SW — sound wormy.
T&G — tongued and grooved.
TB&S — top, bottom, and sides.
Tbrs. — timbers.
Thickness — 4/4, 5/4, 6/4, 8/4, etc. = 1 inch, 1¼ inches, 1½ inches, 2 inches, etc.
V1S — V 1 side; that is, a longitudinal V-shaped groove on 1 face of a piece of lumber.
V2S — V on 2 sides; that is, a longitudinal V-shaped groove on 2 faces of a piece of lumber.
VG — vertical grain.
W. a. l. — wider, all lengths.
Wth. — width.
Wdr. — wider.
Wt. — weight.

Credit: Handbook 72, U. S. Department of Agriculture

An order for lumber should state the following: quantity, size, grade, kind of wood, kind of product (flooring, boards, siding), dry condition, and surface condition. If necessary, the association whose grading rules apply should be named. The abbreviations commonly used in lumber specifications are shown in Table 34–3.

A typical order might appear as follows:

500 bd. ft. 8/4 sugar pine finish lumber, B & B, RWL, AD, Rgh. @ $480.00/M

200 bd. ft. 4/4 birch boards, No. 1

Common, RWL, KD to 12%, S2S to ¾ @ $520.00/M

The sugar pine specifications call for 500 board feet at a nominal thickness of 2 in. (If all the pieces were laid flat on the floor, they would cover 250 sq. ft.) It is to be graded as B and Better and is to be of Random Widths and Lengths as that grade permits. It is to be Air Dried and Rough sawn. The price is quoted at $480.00 per 1000 (M) board feet.

The birch specifications call for a nominal thickness of 1 in. (It will cover 200 sq. ft. of floor when laid out.) The grade is Number 1 Common and the pieces will have Random Widths and Lengths as the grade permits. The birch is to be kiln-dried to 12-percent moisture content. It is to be surfaced on 2 sides to a thickness of ¾ in. The cost is quoted as $520.00 for 1000 (M) board feet — a cost of 52¢ per board foot, or $52.00 per 100 ft.

Softwood yard boards are usually sold dressed on 4 sides and in specified widths and lengths. Thus you might order 10 pieces of 1 in. by 8 in. by 10 ft., No. 1 Common Fir. The material will be delivered dressed to $^{25}/_{32}$ in. thick by 7½ in. wide and 10 ft. long.

Molding and pattern items of small or odd cross section are usually sold by the *lineal* foot. For example, an order might call for 50 lineal feet of Fir ¾ in. quarter round. Some lumber dealers may convert their board foot prices of lumber to a lineal foot basis to simplify cost calculations for their customers.

Sound wood from the lowest grade lumber is equal in quality to that of the top grade. Since grading basically identifies the utility value of wood, the lowest grade that will produce the desired sizes of parts should be chosen. For example, if a product calls for pieces 2 in. wide and 8 to 10 in. long, the greatest econ-omy may result from using the lowest grades of lumber even though considerable waste will result.

If you have any questions regarding specific species, or products, write to the appropriate association listed in the Appendix on p. 741.

Forest-Conservation Practices

In spite of the huge and often wasteful removal of trees during our brief history, forests continue to yield regular crops of saw timber and pulp. More than one half of our present wood supply comes from forest lands that were first harvested by the early settlers. This has been made possible by careful management and protection of our forests.

Trees are an agricultural crop like corn and cotton. Seedlings may be grown in nurseries and transplanted or the seeds may be sown in the area to be reforested. See Figures 34–33, 34–34, and 34–35. Even when left to themselves, trees will scatter their seeds and, in time, replace themselves. See Figures 34–36 and 34–37. But, with proper protection and management, trees grow much faster and produce a cash income like any other crop.

Tree farms are recognized by the American Tree Farm System. This organization is sponsored by the wood-using industries. Tree farms, in addition to assuring the farmer an income, provide other benefits. Trees planted on watersheds help to hold back rainfall and melted snow to prevent soil erosion and permit the water to seep into the earth. This insures a good water supply for cities and farms.

Tree farms also protect forest animals. The streams that flow through well-tended forests are good habitats for fish. This all adds up to good recreation and sporting areas for the public.

Industrial, private, state, and Federal foresters serve as advisors and consultants to farmers and others interested in growing and managing tree crops. Approximately 20,000 persons are employed as foresters or specialists in this country. The Federal Government employs about 7500 and industry another 7000. The minimum educational requirement to become a forester is a bachelor's degree with a major in forestry. Employment opportunities are expected to remain favorable.

Foresters manage, protect, and develop our forests — our greatest natural resource. They estimate the amount and value of timber in a forest area, plan and supervise the harvesting of trees (see Figs. 34–37 and 34–38), purchase and sell trees and timber, and carry out reforestation and improvement activities (Silviculture). Foresters also protect forests from insects, disease, and fire. Some foresters are responsible for wildlife pro-

Fig. 34–33. These seedling pines will be ready for harvest about the time this young boy reaches college. Proceeds from well managed woodlots are making substantial contributions to farm incomes in many sections of the nation.

tection, soil conservation, and watershed control as well as the management of camps, parks, and grazing land.

Fig. 34–34. With a tractor, and the tree planter it tows, two men can set up to ten times as many seedlings in a day as they can by hand method. Replanting assures plenty of wood for the future.

Fig. 34–35. Forest industries use aerial seeding to speed up the job of getting harvested areas back into new timber crops or to give nature a hand in greening up old burns.

Fig. 34–36. Young western pine are springing up all around stumps of the original stand. Larger trees on left are from 12 to 14 years old. Small trees, center foreground, are approximately 2 years old while trees on right of large stand are from 6 to 7 years of age.

Fig. 34–37. In the Douglas fir region shown here, established harvest practice is to cut all trees in designated blocks or patches. Clearcuts will reseed naturally from surrounding timber.

Forest Enemies

Fire, disease, and insects are the enemies of forests today. Fires destroy millions of dollars' worth of timber each year, but insects and diseases destroy about four times as much because they do most of their damage in large overmature trees.

Fire breaks out in some part of our forests every 5 minutes. Man, either deliberately or through carelessness, causes most fires. Lightning is responsible for some. Fires not only kill standing trees, but they also kill seedlings and seeds buried in the soil. By destroying the water holding ability of the land, erosion sets in and soon results in a vast wasteland.

Industry and government have done much to reduce the waste resulting from these enemies. For example, millions of dollars are spent annually on fire prevention, fire detection, and fire fighting.

The goal of fire fighting is to extinguish the fire while it is still small. The plan involves the use of fire spotters. When they detect a wisp of smoke, they report its bearing from their fire tower. A dispatcher plots two bearings on his map of the region to locate the point of the fire as shown in Figure 34–39. He then orders fire fighters to the scene.

The fire fighters may be trained government fire fighters or a nearby industry crew of loggers. Their objective is to cut out all combustible material at or near the head of the fire. When completed, they start a backfire. This smaller fire burns its way toward the main fire. When the flames meet, the fire dies for lack of fuel.

Sometimes water trucks with powerful pumps, bulldozers, plows, and other equipment are used to contain a fire. However, they can be used only where there are adequate roads or fire trails. In

In the life of every forest tree there comes a time when it is best it be removed for man's use. This moment is not the same for all trees. The time differs according to species, region, climate and soil, as well as to the use for which the wood is intended. When a tree is harvested, you can read its life story in rings on the stump. One ring is added for each year of growth.

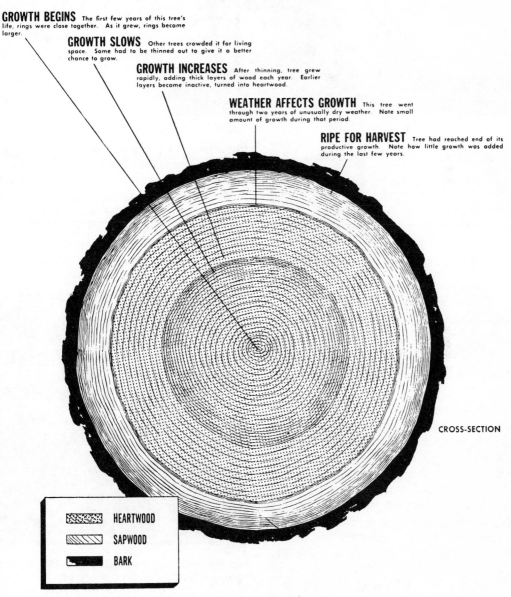

GROWTH BEGINS The first few years of this tree's life, rings were close together. As it grew, rings became larger.

GROWTH SLOWS Other trees crowded it for living space. Some had to be thinned out to give it a better chance to grow.

GROWTH INCREASES After thinning, tree grew rapidly, adding thick layers of wood each year. Earlier layers became inactive, turned into heartwood.

WEATHER AFFECTS GROWTH This tree went through two years of unusually dry weather. Note small amount of growth during that period.

RIPE FOR HARVEST Tree had reached end of its productive growth. Note how little growth was added during the last few years.

CROSS-SECTION

HEARTWOOD
SAPWOOD
BARK

Fig. 34–38. The life of a tree.

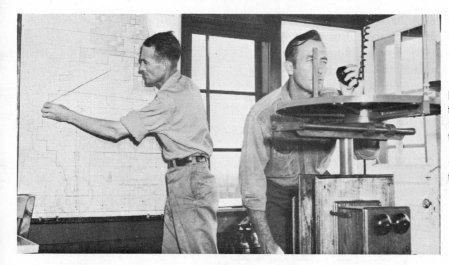

Fig. 34–39. By plotting the bearings of the fire from two observation points, the dispatcher is able to send firefighters directly to the scene of the fire.

tinue to be a problem until all the over-mature, disease-susceptible, trees are removed. Some success has been achieved in developing disease resistant strains of the various species for replanting. Aircraft are being used with some success to spray forests for insect and disease control as shown in Figure 34–40.

remote areas, airplanes may drop fire quenching chemicals to retard or put out the fire. Smoke jumpers may parachute to earth to fight these fires also.

Recently, rotating television cameras have been installed in fire towers. This makes it possible for the dispatcher at headquarters to watch several television screens and know immediately when a fire starts in the area covered by his equipment.

Tree diseases and insects are also being combated. Diseased trees will con-

Fig. 34–40. At tree-top level this plane sprays insecticide over a forest in battle against spruce budworm. These insects threaten vast areas of timber.

DISCUSSION QUESTIONS

1. Why were the pioneers unconcerned about conservation of land and trees?
2. What are the research, development, and marketing practices that are stimulating the demand for lumber?
3. What is the meaning and importance of "diversification" when applied to a manufacturing industry? What is an integrated company?
4. In what way is modern tree harvesting a scientific process?
5. Identify the different machines used in modern logging operations. In your opinion, what changes in mechanical functioning will take place in the next 50 years?
6. How many different occupations are involved in getting a tree cut into lumber and delivered to your school shop? How many are production jobs and how many are nonproduction jobs? What are the earnings of the people in these different occupations?
7. In what ways do hydraulically and pneumatically controlled carriages differ in their mechanical and operational characteristics from the cable controlled carriages?
8. How would you go about determining the amount of force required to shear off a 2-in. diameter tree trunk as does the tree harvester?
9. What are the requirements of a good bark peeler?
10. What different equipment and processes are involved in converting a log into finished dimension lumber?
11. What competencies and knowledge must the following have: lumber grader; mill foreman; talleyman; pondman; accountant; mill owner; timber cruiser; maintenance man; mill electrician?
12. Distinguish the essential differences between the grading rules for hardwoods and softwoods. Why do these differences exist? Where can you get additional information about the various species of lumber?
13. What is the procedure for kiln-drying a load of lumber? What is meant by case hardening, honeycombing, relative humidity, megohm?
14. What is the weight of a 1 in. by 12 in. by 10-ft. piece of Douglas Fir at a moisture content of 12 percent? (One cubic foot of water weighs 62.43 pounds per cubic foot.)
15. Are the total board-feet values shown on the tally sheet in Figure 32 correct?
16. What would be the cost of 3 pieces of lumber 5/4 by 9 in. by 10 ft. if it is priced at $300.00 per M?
17. In what ways do we benefit from good forestry and conservation practices? What efforts are being expended to insure our future timber supply?
18. What are the entrance requirements for the position of forester? What do they do? What are their earnings? What are their working conditions? Where can one obtain the necessary training?
19. What are the chemicals that are used in fighting forest fires?

Chapter 35 The Veneer, Plywood, and Laminating Industries

Veneer is a uniformly thin sheet of wood produced by peeling, sawing, or slicing logs, bolts, or flitches. Veneers are produced in thicknesses ranging from $\frac{1}{110}$ to $\frac{3}{8}$ in. and may be used as a single ply or as a combination of plies bonded together to form plywood. Single ply veneers are used for containers such as baskets, boxes, drums, hampers, and crates. Veneers of rare woods and those with special grain patterns are applied to less beautiful woods and other materials to improve their beauty, strength, and utility. Some of the most common uses of veneer are shown in Figure 35–1.

The art of veneering was developed long before that of plywood making. It is at least 3000 years old. Egyptian furniture removed from sealed tombs suggests that the first veneer manufactured by man was used as an overlay or inlay — for ornamental purposes. An ancient pictorial mural found by archaeologists in Egypt was made as early as 1500 B.C. This mural pictures veneer being cut by means of a tool similar to our present-day hatchet. In all probability it was a laborious process of splitting, scraping, and abrading. Animal glues were probably used as adhesives. After the veneers were spread with glue, they were positioned and weighted with sandbags.

Both the Greeks and Romans used highly figured veneers to decorate their furniture. Julius Caesar is reported to have held a veneered table in highest esteem. During the Middle Ages little creative work was accomplished in this field. But, after the Rennaissance, the art of veneering reappeared during the seventeenth and eighteenth centuries in western Europe when such craftsmen as Duncan Phyfe, Hepplewhite, Chippendale, Sheraton, and the Adams brothers produced their creations.

Hand methods of producing veneer, including ripping thin sheets from a block with a hand saw, were practiced until the early 1800's. At this time, a power-driven veneer saw was developed for this purpose. Shortly thereafter, a machine for slicing veneer was patented. While not too successful, it did demonstrate the feasibility of cutting veneer with a knife.

A patent on a veneer-cutting lathe was issued to John Dresser in 1840, but it was about 1875 before a truly successful lathe was developed. These machines figured in the efforts of manufacturers to mechanize their shops in order to mass-produce furniture. The earlier skill, artistry, and pride in producing a high quality hand crafted item gave way to the urgency of speed and quantity. A variety of veneers and overlays were produced and applied over poorly fabricated articles. This practice overlays was produced and applied over furniture. Buyers began to associate veneers with inferior substitutes for articles made of solid wood. Dictionaries still define veneer as "a valuable or beautiful material for overlaying an inferior one, . . . superficial. . . ." Many uninformed people still hold this opinion of veneered furniture.

The piano industry of the 1830's was probably the first industry to use plywood. Soon it was being used in sewing cabinets, desk tops, organs, chairs, and other items of furniture.

A 3 ft. by 6 ft., stock plywood panel was first produced in the early part of this century. The intention was that this stock panel could be cut into smaller sizes as desired. The idea of plywood serving as a structural building panel was originated in Portland, Oregon, in 1905.

Animal and vegetable glues were all that were available until the mid 1920's. About that time synthetic adhesives were developed. Urea formaldehyde was introduced in the mid 1930's. Today it is the most important glue used in the manufacture of interior plywood. Phenolic-resin glues bond the layers of veneer used for exterior plywood.

Veneering and plywood manufacturing as practiced today need no defense, but instead an intelligent understanding of the purposes and advantages of such construction. Wood technologists, engineers, chemists, designers, and manufacturers have pooled their knowledge and skills

Fig. 35–1. This modern home has factory finished hardwood plywood walls on which are mounted stereo cabinets of teak plywood. The round table has a book-matched veneer top. The door is made of hardwood plywood and has a hollow core.

to produce a superior product that is finding new uses daily.

The Veneer Industry

The veneer industry produces at least 80 different species of veneer from both foreign and domestic woods. Douglas fir constitutes the highest percentage of the veneer produced in the United States. Developments in the production of yellow-pine veneer indicate that it may soon play an important role in the softwood-plywood industry.

Manufacturers usually specialize in producing either softwood or hardwood veneers. The hardwood-veneer manufacturers are further distinguished as producers of face veneers, commercial veneers, or veneers for containers. The most common hardwood veneers are: cherry, redgum, blackgum, tupelo, yellow poplar, oak, birch, maple, mahogany, and walnut.

About fifty face veneer manufacturers are scattered over the eastern half of the United States. They chiefly produce sliced, sawed or rotary stay-log cut fancy face veneers from select logs, burls, crotches, and stumps. The flitches of veneer are sold primarily to manufacturers of furniture, pianos, and decorative interior panels. Sizable inventories are built up because the purchase of specific flitches with certain figure patterns is the practice.

Commercial-veneer manufacturers produce rotary-cut veneers for crossbands, cores, and backs of plywood panels. Veneers are generally produced to specific sizes on order. Most commercial veneers are sold to other manufacturers who make their own plywood. In some instances the veneer plant is a part of a large mill that manufactures its own plywood.

The container-veneer manufacturer produces a wide variety of cheap sliced and rotary-cut veneers for use in crates, cases, hampers, baskets, cheese boxes, drums, hoops, and the like. Plants are usually located near adequate sources of cheap timber and suitable markets for their products.

Softwood veneer is principally a western United States product. Such veneers are made from Douglas fir, Sitka spruce, western hemlock, balsam fir, western larch, ponderosa pine, sugar pine, western white pine, and redwood. The majority are rotary-cut, but some sliced veneers are produced.

Most of the softwood veneer is incorporated into softwood plywood. However, some of it finds use as cores and crossbands for panels faced with hard-

woods. Much Philippine lauan veneer is applied over softwood.

Veneer Manufacturing

Veneers are cut on lathes, slicers, and saws. They are commonly referred to as "rotary," "sliced," or "sawed" veneers according to the method of cutting.

Rotary cutting and slicing of hardwood logs generally yields less than half of the log volume in veneer. Large softwood logs may yield more than ½ their volume in veneer. This compares favorably with the proportion of a log produced as high grade lumber. Sawing produces less than ½ of a flitch as veneer.

The manner in which the veneer is cut determines the visual effect, or figure, obtained. Two logs of the same species, but with their veneers cut differently, will have entirely different visual characteristics even though their colors may be similar. See Figure 35–2. The grain pattern and figure of the veneer face are of utmost importance to the designer and architect, since the whole character of a completed installation may be determined by the choice of veneer used.

The figure in veneers is usually described by its characteristics. Veneer men might say that the figure in the wood "has a great deal of crossfire" or "has a straight or broken stripe," or is "highly figured." "Figure" refers to the highlights or crossfire running at right angles to the grain direction. The grain character and direction is described by using the word "pattern." Some of the common veneer figures and terms are illustrated in Figure 35–3.

Logging operations provide the logs necessary for veneer manufacturing just as they do for lumber manufacturing. Integrated companies harvest trees and transport them to the mill where they

TYPES OF VENEER CUTS

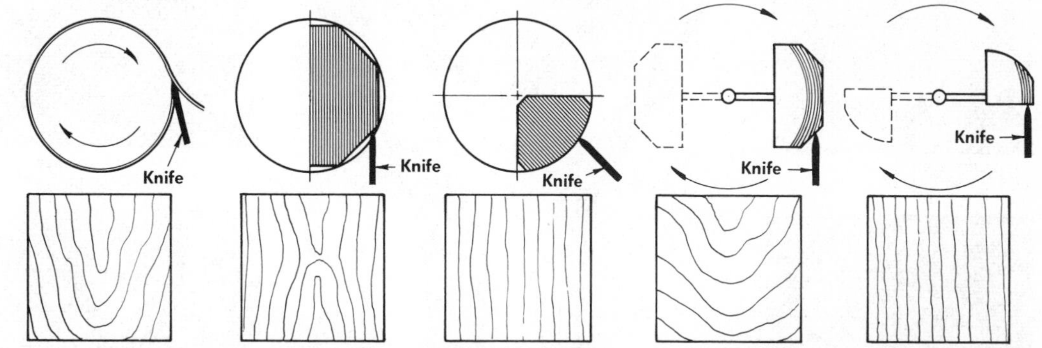

A. ROTARY

The log is mounted centrally in the lathe and turned against a razor sharp blade, like unwinding a roll of paper. Since this cut follows the log's annular growth rings, a bold variegated grain marking is produced. Rotary cut veneer is exceptionally wide.

B. FLAT SLICING

The half log, or flitch, is mounted with the heart side flat against the guide plate of the slicer and the slicing is done parallel to a line through the center of the log. This produces a variegated figure.

C. QUARTER SLICING

The quarter log or flitch is mounted on the guide plate so that the growth rings of the log strike the knife at approximately right angles, producing a series of stripes, straight in some woods, varied in others.

D. HALF-ROUND SLICING

A variation of rotary cutting in which segments or flitches of the log are mounted off center in the lathe. This results in a cut slightly across the annular growth rings, and visually shows modified characteristics of both rotary and plain sliced veneers.

E. RIFT-CUT

Rift cut veneer is produced in the various species of oak. Oak has modullary ray cells which radiate from the center of the log like the curved spokes of a wheel. The rift or comb grain effect is obtained by cutting perpendicularly to these medullary rays either on the lathe or slicer.

Fig. 35–2. In veneer manufacture, five principal methods of cutting veneers are used.

are sorted to make lumber or veneer. Small companies that specialize in veneer usually buy only those logs suitable for veneer production.

Veneer logs are usually cut to the same lengths as sawmill logs. In some cases, special lengths are cut to allow a certain trim allowance on the finished product. Douglas fir is frequently cut to 34-foot lengths, for this permits cutting four 8½-foot bolts or peeler blocks. See Figure 35–4. Bolts are usually kept in water to prevent their drying out because dry wood cannot be properly knife cut.

Bolts to be cut into rotary or sliced veneer are usually heated for 1 to 2 days in large tanks of water or in steam vaults to soften them. See Figure 35–5. The harder woods, such as oak, are heated at 160 to 200 deg. F; gum is heated at 130

to 150 deg. F; and yellow poplar at 90 to 120 deg. F. The softer woods can be cut at room temperatures. Highly figured woods may be heated for as long as one week.

Bolts for rotary cutting can be debarked before or after heating. Heating facilitates removal of the bark. Figure 35–6 shows the bark being removed prior to its being mounted in a lathe. Wood to be sliced is usually first cut into flitches. Logs to be sawed into veneer may be dry and they need not be heated.

Rotary-cut veneer constitutes more than 90 percent of the veneer produced today. See Figure 35–7. The lathes in which the bolts are literally unwound, are all made on the same general plan. They consist of a heavy framework that supports two adjustable spindles. On the

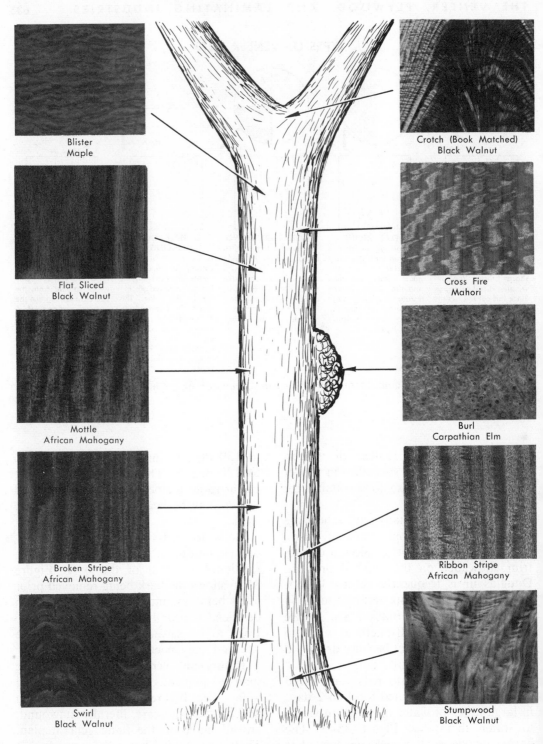

Blister
Maple

Flat Sliced
Black Walnut

Mottle
African Mahogany

Broken Stripe
African Mahogany

Swirl
Black Walnut

Crotch (Book Matched)
Black Walnut

Cross Fire
Mahori

Burl
Carpathian Elm

Ribbon Stripe
African Mahogany

Stumpwood
Black Walnut

Fig. 35–3. The type of figure pattern in a veneer is dependent upon (1) the species of wood, (2) the portion of the tree from which the wood is cut and (3) the method of cutting.

Fig. 35-4. Bark-free logs ready for processing in a plywood plant. First the bark was removed, then they were placed in the log storage pond and sorted. Those destined for the veneer plant were taken to the block-cutting station and cut into peeler blocks. Next they will go to huge steaming vaults for conditioning.

Fig. 35-5. Steam vats "plasticize" debarked logs before peeling to produce better veneer.

end of each spindle is a "chuck" that functions somewhat like the spur center on a wood turning lathe in the school shop. A bolt is hoisted into the lathe and the spindles move the chucks into its ends. As the bolt turns, the lathe carriage with its knife and pressure bar is pressed against the log. The knife removes a continuous sheet of veneer. Figure 35–8 shows some of the details of the lathe carriage. An automatic feed mechanism moves the carriage into the bolt.

As the veneer comes from the lathe it is either wound on a reel or delivered onto a table or conveyor to be carried to the clipper and drier.

Fig. 35–6. A cutter-head type veneer bolt peeler is shown here removing the bark from a heated bolt. The bolt will next be hoisted into the veneer lathe to produce rotary-cut veneer.

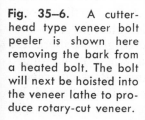

Fig. 35–7. This plywood lathe operator is "unrolling" a log like a roll of paper. Mastering the extensive machinery requires long training and good judgment on the part of the craftsman.

The quality of the veneer that is cut is determined by the quality and condition of the logs, the condition of the lathe, and the skill of the operator. Modern lathes automatically adjust the knife angle as the diameter of the bolt decreases. Unless all factors are carefully controlled, veneer that is uniform in thickness, smooth, and free of excessive checking cannot be produced. Because the veneer is essentially the circumference of a circle, the "lathe checks" on the knife side of the veneer open up when it is flattened out. See Figure 35–9. The thicker the veneer being cut the greater the degree of checking. Veneers $\frac{1}{32}$ in. thick have checks that are barely discernable. On $\frac{1}{8}$-in. veneers, they are clearly visible. In laminating or making plywood the checked or "loose side" is placed inside so as to leave the "tight side" exposed. A scribing or chalking device on some lathes marks the tight side to facilitate its identification.

Rotary-cut veneer, having been removed tangentially from the log, is usually flat-grained. If the log is irregular

in shape, a considerable amount of figure may result. Softwood veneers are usually cut in thicknesses of $\frac{1}{10}$, $\frac{1}{8}$, or $\frac{3}{16}$ in. Hardwoods are commonly cut in thicknesses of $\frac{1}{12}$, $\frac{1}{10}$, $\frac{1}{8}$, $\frac{3}{16}$, and $\frac{1}{4}$ in. for use as cores. Hardwood face veneers are usually cut to thicknesses of $\frac{1}{20}$, $\frac{1}{24}$, and $\frac{1}{28}$ in.

Most lathes operate at 50 to 60 rpm. The veneer emerges from the lathe at 200 to 400 fpm for hardwood logs; up to 1000 fpm for large softwood logs.

Stay-log cutting is a modification of rotary cutting by which fancy face veneers may be produced. (See Figs. 35–21 and 35–10.) The stay-log is a flanged metal carrier that is mounted between the chucks of the lathe. A flitch, burl, crotch, or stump is bolted to it in such a way that the desired grain pattern and figure is produced when it is rotated against the lathe knife. Back-cut veneer, while brittle, is beautifully figured because of the almost continuously radial cut made in producing it.

Cone-cut veneers are fancy figured veneers used on the tops of circular tables.

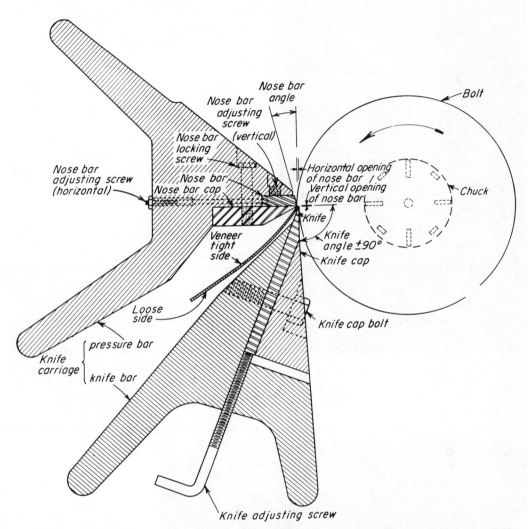

Fig. 35–8. Diagram of a lathe carriage. The nose bar presses against the log and compresses the wood just ahead of the knife to prevent excessive checking. As the peeler block turns, the knife removes a thin, continuous sheet of veneer. Spur knives (not shown), mounted on each end of the pressure bar, cut the veneer to width.

They are cut from the bolt in a manner similar to sharpening a pencil. The lathe knife is set at an angle with the axis of the chucking spindles, and removes the veneer in a spiral. Only small amounts of veneer are produced in this manner.

It is quite brittle since the wood fibers have been cut "short grained."

Sliced veneers are produced on vertical slicers in this country. (See Figs. 35–11 and 35–12.) The previously heated flitch or log moves downward against a

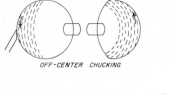

OFF-CENTER CHUCKING

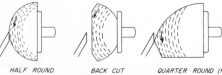

HALF ROUND   BACK CUT   QUARTER ROUND (RIFT)

Fig. 35—10. Stay log cutting. This method of rotary cutting produces veneers with highly figured faces. The dash lines indicate the paths of successive cuts.

Fig. 35—9. The veneer cutting operation on a lathe. The "lathe checks" on the lower surface result from the sharp bending of the veneer as it is cut from the bolt.

stationary knife and pressure bar to cut the veneer. The knife automatically backs away as the flitch moves up to its starting position. It then advances the thickness of the next cut. In a few designs, the knife is powered and the flitch moves only to regulate the thickness of cut. Most slicers operate at speeds between 35 and 100 strokes per minute. Smaller slicers, used to produce box shooks and battery separators, operate at speeds up to 240 strokes per minute. European veneer factories most frequently use horizontal slic-

Fig. 35—11. A vertical veneer slicer. The half-log is "dogged" to a bedplate which slides on angled ways behind it giving a shearing action.

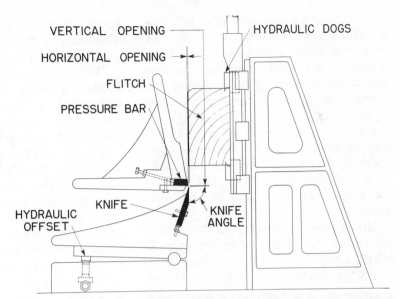

Fig. 35–12. This diagram illustrates the relationship of the various parts of the vertical veneer slicer.

VERTICAL OPENING —
HORIZONTAL OPENING —
FLITCH
PRESSURE BAR
HYDRAULIC DOGS
KNIFE
HYDRAULIC OFFSET
KNIFE ANGLE

ers that operate at slower speeds than those in this country.

Veneer slicers may be used to produce veneers of all types, but they are primarily used for the production of fancy figured face veneers. Usual lengths of veneer range from 12 to 16 ft. It is, for the most part, produced in narrow strips, $\frac{1}{32}$ to $\frac{1}{16}$ in. thick, although $\frac{1}{110}$ in., or less, is possible. Oak is sometimes sliced $\frac{1}{8}$ in. thick.

The logs to be sliced can be halved lengthwise on a saw. Then a skilled operator decides how the halves are to be reduced in order that the best figure may be obtained. If quartered veneers are desired, the half log is reduced to 6 or 8 flitches so that the slices may be removed at right angles to the growth rings. If flat-grain veneer is desired, the half log section is mounted in the slicer. This produces some flat-grained veneer and some quarter-grained.

Just as with rotary-cut veneer, sliced veneer has a tight and loose side. When possible, the loose side is glued down. When veneers are book-matched, how-

ever, this is not possible. See Figure 35–24.

As the veneer slices leave the machine they are turned over by hand and each successive slice is kept in the same relative position it had in the solid flitch. The bundle of veneer, also called a flitch, is usually sold as a unit for the manufacture of matched veneer panels.

Sawed veneers differ from those cut with a knife in that both sides are of equal quality and appearance. This reduces the problems involved in matching face veneers. Sawed veneers are cut $\frac{1}{24}$ to $\frac{1}{4}$ in. thick. They are used chiefly for high-grade furniture and finish veneers.

Sawed veneer is produced on a machine that functions in a manner similar to the circular headrig used in lumber manufacturing. The log or flitch is dogged in a carriage and driven against the saw. The saw blade is made up of segments that are attached to the circumference of a mounting disk. The disk is thicker in the center than at the edges to increase the strength and rigidity of the thin blade. The saw kerf is usually $\frac{1}{20}$ in. Much sawed veneer is cut $\frac{1}{20}$ in. thick and since a portion of the flitch is dogged, it is easily seen that less than half of the wood may be converted into veneer. For this reason less than 5 percent of all veneer is produced by sawing.

Cants, logs, flitches, crotches, and burls may be sawed. The cut veneer is automatically drawn away from the saw blade by a stationary bevel block and piled in the same position it had in the solid wood.

Green clipping veneer. As the rotary-cut ribbon of veneer leaves the lathe it is either rolled up on a reel, stacked in layers, or distributed among the several

Fig. 35–13. This triple storage deck installation has a clipper on each level where defects are removed and veneer is clipped to standard widths.

layers of a conveyorized storage deck. The veneer is then clipped to rough green size, cleared of defects, and dried.

Where floor space is at a premium in hardwood plants, the green veneer is usually rolled on to a reel as it leaves the lathe. The loaded reel is then moved to the clipper and unwound for clipping.

The oldest method of handling rotary-cut veneer requires much labor. It involves carrying the veneer ribbon from the lathe to a conveyor table, breaking the veneer when the end of the table is reached, and carrying the next sheet of veneer over the first, and so on. When a stack has been made, it is moved to the clipper where the entire stack is clipped to widths at once. This is done without regard for defects. This method is least efficient because it wastes a great deal of veneer and drier time.

The storage-deck method is used by the larger hardwood and softwood veneer manufacturers to facilitate single-sheet clipping. Figure 35–13 illustrates such an installation. As the veneer emerges from the lathe, a *tipple* is raised or lowered to guide a single sheet onto an empty storage deck conveyor. A clipper is positioned on each deck. After clipping, the veneer is conveyed to the drier. On some installations, a second tipple unloads each deck onto a conveyor leading to a single clipper.

Rotary-veneer cutting is an intermittent operation. The lathe runs while a bolt is being cut, but it must stop while a new bolt is being chucked. The clipping operation is relatively continuous, but somewhat slower than veneer cutting. Consequently, the storage-deck method of conveying the veneer may be seen as the most efficient since it permits the lathe and the clipper to operate at their optimum speeds with a minimum of labor involved in handling the veneer.

Fig. 35–14. As long strips of veneer come from the lathe to his machine, the clipper operator scans each part and activates the knife from the panel in front of him to remove defects and cuts standard widths.

Fig. 35–15. In this clipping operation the inspector marks defective areas with electrolytic fluid which actuates clipper knives seconds later removing defects.

Veneer clippers are of the *shear* or *anvil type*. The shear clipper utilizes a large knife that moves past a clipper bar with a shearing action. On the anvil clipper the knife strikes a hardwood anvil. The clipper knives are activated electrically, pneumatically, or hydraulically. An operator may control the knife with a switch as shown in Figure 35–14. It may also be set to automatically cut at a certain interval. The clipper in Figure 35–15 employs a different principle of activation.

Veneer drying. Most veneers are very wet and unsuited for gluing. Furthermore, they are susceptible to mold, stain, and fungi when wet. Therefore, it is necessary that the veneer be dried as quickly as possible. This is usually done at the veneer-cutting plant. However, at some West Coast mills, the veneer is dried at the plywood plant. Furthermore, the container industry frequently shapes the wet veneer while it is most pliable and dries it after the product is fabricated.

Veneers are dried by several methods. The eventual use of the veneer and the facilities available to the manufacturer

Fig. 35–16. Before becoming plywood paneling, veneer takes a slow ride through this three-tier chain belt drier. Then it will pass under an electronic moisture sentry to make certain drying has been complete.

determine the method that is used.

Air drying is generally used for the cheaper grades of rotary and sliced veneers that are converted into crates, egg cases, baskets, and the like in the container industry. The sheets are stacked in tiers, separated by stickers, or on end in finger racks to permit the free circulation of air.

Loft drying is performed by hanging

the wet veneer sheets from clips or edge stacking them in finger racks in a well ventilated room. Sheets ½₀ in. thick dry to a moisture content of 12 to 15 percent in 1 or 2 days in this manner.

Kiln drying of veneer in conventional progressive-type or compartment-type lumber kilns is also practiced. Sheets are either stickered or racked, singly or in bulks of 10 sheets, and dried to 6 percent moisture content in about 48 hours.

Mechanical drying in chain-belt conveyor dryers is most common, but hot-plate driers are also used. The conveyor drying chamber is usually a sheet-metal structure and may be 50 to 300 ft. long. See Figure 35–16. It is provided with heating (steam, gas, or oil) equipment and a power-driven chain belt to move the veneer. Drying time at 210 deg. F. or above usually takes 45 minutes or less. These driers are subject to the same limitations as lumber kilns.

Hot plate dryers employ a battery of heated platens to press the veneer flat and

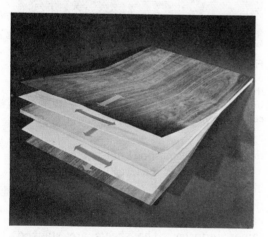

Fig. 35–17. This assembly for a sheet of lumber core plywood shows the core, cross-bands, and face and back veneers. Note that the grain direction is alternated in each layer.

dry it. The platens are intermittently opened and closed to permit the moisture to escape. They are used most commonly to reduce veneer in the air-dry condition to a low-moisture content suitable for gluing.

Plywood

Plywood is an engineered panel of wood. It is made up of an odd number of layers with the grain of each layer placed crosswise to that of the adjacent layer and bonded together with either waterproof or water-resistant adhesives. See Figure 35–17 and 35–18. This method of assembling the veneer components is known as crossbanded construction. The crossbanding of plywoods distinguishes it from laminated wood in which the grain of all layers is parallel. See Figure 35–19. Such construction gives plywood improved mechanical and physical properties over equal sizes of solid wood. Most important of the advantages of plywood over solid wood are its dimensional stability, strength, and wood characteristics. Tensile and compressive strengths of plywood are less than that of equal sizes of solid wood, however.

Plywood is made to a variety of specifications today as shown in Figure 35–18. By applying the veneer to various cores several different plywood constructions are possible. Most plywood is made with a *veneer core*. Strips of lumber are bonded together to make a core in what is called *lumber* (or solid) *core* plywood. It is usually made in thicknesses of ⅝ in. and above and is predominantly five-ply. *Specialty* cores are also used. Particleboard cores are made of wood chips bonded together to form a sheet. The veneer is bonded to this core. Other materials such as metal sheets, hard-

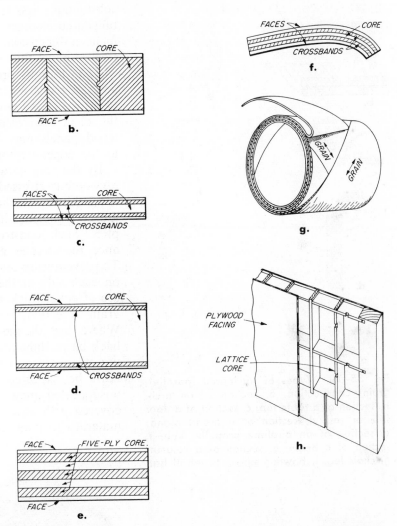

Fig. 35–18. Several types of plywood and crossbanded construction applications are shown here: a, c, and e, sections of all veneer plywood; b, three-ply lumber core plywood. d, five-ply lumber core plywood; f, five-ply veneer, bent work; g, five-ply veneer, spirally wrapped; h, a section of a hollow-core door.

board, kraft paper, plastic foam, and coils of wood are also used as cores to achieve certain properties. See Figure 35–20.

The three-ply panel is the simplest plywood construction. See Figure 35–18a. The *center ply* is sometimes referred to as a *core;* although "core" more correctly is used to refer to a laminated lumber or particle-board core. The outer plies are called *faces* or *backs* depending upon their grade. The plies between the center ply and the face and back of plywood with more than three plies are called *crossbands.*

Unlike solid wood, which shrinks and swells unequally in its three dimensions, plywood length and width dimensions

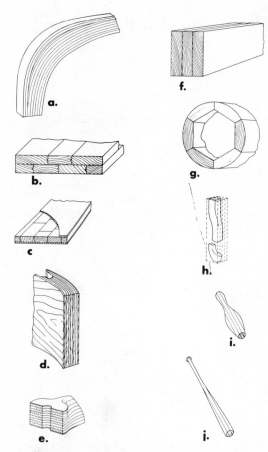

Fig. 35–19. Types of laminated (parallel-grain) construction: a, section of an arch; b, section of a table top; c, section of a door stile or rail; d, section of a grand piano; e, section of an airplane propeller hub; f, section of a beam; g, section of a column; h, chair leg; i, bowling pin; j, baseball bat.

change about equally with changes in moisture content. These dimensional changes are greater than the normal longitudinal changes of solid wood, but substantially less than normal radial and tangential changes. There is no improvement in dimensional stability in the direction of panel thickness.

The strength properties of the wood are also redistributed in the crossbanding operation. See Figure 35–21. Because of the change in cleavage properties, plywood panels may be nailed quite close to the edges without splitting.

By the very nature of its construction, plywood is stressed at the glue line. It is for this reason that plywood flat panels are constructed with an odd number of plies. Such construction serves to balance the stresses as nearly as possible. To prevent warp and twist, matching plies on each side of the center ply, or core, are of equal thickness, moisture content, grain direction, and species of wood. Where use dictates that the face and back be of different species, some measure of imbalance (warping and twisting) must be expected. Furthermore, large, unsupported areas of plywood should be covered with equal amounts of finishing materials to maintain the stress balance.

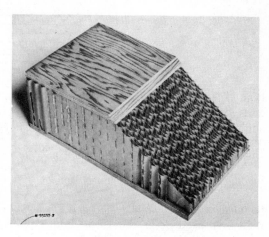

Fig. 35–20. A cutaway section of sandwich construction with plywood facings and a paper honeycomb core. The assembly has high strength and stiffness in proportion to its weight.

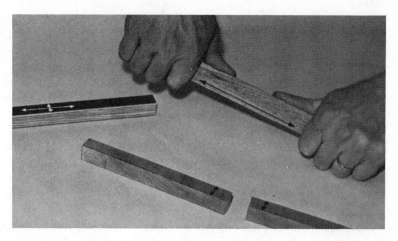

Fig. 35–21. Study the grain direction of the samples of solid wood. The lower piece of wood is easily broken in the direction of the arrows. Plywood (at left) is made so the grain runs in two directions.

An important advantage of plywood over solid wood is that it permits distributing the most desirable wood characteristics where they are most needed. Rare and expensive woods may be used as face veneers only while the less expensive woods make up the bulk of the panel. When a single species is used in a panel, the face may be of the best quality clear veneer while the more defective wood is used in the center and crossbands.

For construction purposes, plywood has several advantages over solid wood. By virtue of its size, a panel may be installed with a minimum of labor. Thin panels with large areas may be fabricated

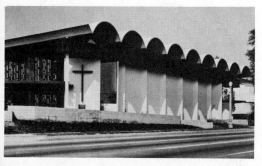

Fig. 35–22. One type of the many special shaped plywood panels forms the roof of this building. The installation of this roof system only took 7 hours.

into curved and irregular surfaces that are not feasible with solid wood. See Figure 35–22. The radius of the curve to which plywood may be bent is dependent upon its thickness and the type of adhesive. Waterproof glue-bonded panels may be soaked or steamed to improve their bending characteristics. In general, dry ¼ in. hardwood plywood may be bent to a radius of approximately 24 in. without support on the tensioned side. Different species have different bend radii.

Plywood Manufacture

Softwood and hardwood plywood manufacturers employ varying practices. Even within either division varying practices exist. However, the practice is sufficiently common throughout the industry that a general understanding of plywood manufacturing may be developed. The basic operations are: (1) preparing veneer stock; (2) gluing; (3) pressing; and (4) finishing. (See Figure 35–23.)

Preparing veneer stock differs as the uses of the finished panel differ. Low-priced container plywood requires little work before gluing. Cabinet-quality plywood, however, often requires as many man-hours in preparing the veneers for gluing as for all the other operations combined. Basically, this operation consists of converting the sheets of veneer into plies that meet the specifications of grade, figure, pattern, and size. It involves grading and matching veneers, redrying, dry clipping, jointing, taping or splicing, inspecting and repairing, and sizing.

Grading and matching is most important in the preparation of face veneers. If a 1-piece face is required, then whole sheets must be selected. If multiple-piece faces are permitted, the veneer must be clipped and matched to give the specified appearance.

Panels may be specified with faces selected for color, figure, or a pattern. In such cases, selecting, clipping, and matching requires a considerable amount of care, skill, and experience. This is particularly true when burl, crotch, or butt veneers are used. Figure 35–24

shows some of the common patterns made by veneer matching. Even though matching may not be necessary, all face veneers must be graded. As in lumber grading, size, kind, and number of "defects" determine the grade. Face veneers are graded into three groups: A — clear, B — sound, and C — utility and Back.

Redrying of the veneer is usually necessary before it may be glued. Ideally, the moisture content of the finished panel will be near the average expected in service. In most parts of the United States, this is about 8 percent for interior panels. In arid regions, it averages about 6 percent; in humid coastal regions, about 11 percent. Exterior panels average about 12 percent moisture content with 9 percent the average in arid regions.

The different glues and curing methods affect the moisture content of the plywood. Therefore, redrying the veneer to a moisture content below that desired in the finished products is necessary. This is

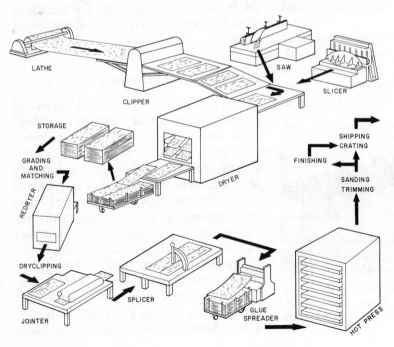

Fig. 35–23. The various steps in the manufacture of plywood.

VENEER MATCHING – BASIC MATCHING EFFECTS

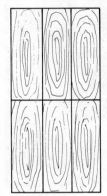

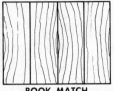

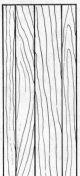

RANDOM MATCH

Veneers are joined with the intention of creating a casual unmatched effect. Veneers from several logs may be used in the manufacture of a set of panels.

BOOK MATCH

All types of veneers are used. In book matching, every other sheet is turned over just as are the leaves of a book. Thus, the back of one veneer meets the front of the adjacent veneer, producing a matching joint design.

SLIP MATCH

In slip matching, veneer sheets are joined side by side and convey a sense of repeating the flitch figure. All types of veneer may be used, but this type of matching is most common in quarter-sliced veneers.

VERTICAL BUTT AND HORIZONTAL BOOKLEAF MATCH

Where the height of a flitch does not permit its fabrication into the desired height of panel, it may be matched vertically as well as horizontally.

SPECIAL MATCHING EFFECTS

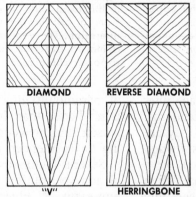

DIAMOND   **REVERSE DIAMOND**

"V"   **HERRINGBONE**

FOUR-WAY CENTER AND BUTT

This type of match is ordinarily applied to Butt, Crotch or Stump veneers, since it is the most effective way of revealing the beauty of their configurations. Occasionally flat cut veneers are matched in this manner where panel length requirements exceed the length of available veneers.

Fig. 35–24. Veneers are cut and matched in various ways to produce patterns of great beauty. No two pieces of veneer are identical in figure.

usually performed in progressive platen (plate) driers.

Dry-clipping reduces the veneer to size and squares it for assembly into plies. Sheets may be clipped singly or in groups called books. A book or jointer clipper clamps the stack of veneer firmly and cuts the edges square, ready for splicing or taping without jointing. The main disadvantage of book clipping is that it is a slow process.

Jointing the veneer edges produces a square, straight edge so that two edges may be taped or spliced together with an inconspicuous joint line. Traveling head jointers and fixed head jointers are used for this purpose. See Figure 35–25 and 35–26. Both jointers automatically apply glue to the veneer edges.

Taping and splicing holds the matched panels together. This is accomplished with gummed tape or by gluing the edges together. Figure 35–27 shows two pieces of veneer being jointed together with tape. Another type of machine, a tapeless slicer, joints the glued edges and an electrically heated strip cures the glue. The advantage of this machine lies in the fact that there is no tape to be sanded off the veneer or to fill the glue joint.

Fig. 35–25. The multiple knife traveling cutterhead on this jointer planes the edges of carefully selected veneer. A glue spreader roll follows the cutterhead. From here, veneer heads for tapeless splicing operation before panel assembly.

Fig. 35–26. Edges of core veneer are planed in this fixed head jointer and glue is applied from a roll in the table prior to splicing operation. The veneer, in a vertical position, is moved over the cutterhead by means of a power chain feed.

Inspecting and repairing the face plies insures their meeting the grade standards. When defects are small enough, they are cut out and patched. Defects in softwood veneers are cut out and patched on a machine designed for this purpose. High priced cabinet veneers are carefully patched by skilled workmen.

Lumber cores for thick plywood panels are made from kiln-dried dimension stock. The lumber is dressed and major defects are removed. Strips between 1 and 4 in. wide are then glued together to produce the core. The cores may be glued with cold setting or heat setting glues and clamped in a glue reel or clamp carrier. Some glues are cured by placing the core on a hot plate while others utilize a high-frequency alternating current.

Adhesives with various properties are used in the manufacture of plywood. Other things being equal, relative cost is usually a most important consideration. However, the performance of a glue is

of paramount importance since a panel is no better than its glue. It is for this reason that plywood is classified according to its intended use.

Several factors associated with the use of adhesive during manufacture are also important. A glue must be compatible with extenders, if used. It must mix easily, have an extended working life, permit a long assembly time, tolerate moisture, cure in a reasonable time, etc. *Extenders* are low cost materials added to the glue to make it cover more area. They usually reduce the quality of the glue mix, but not sufficiently to reduce the quality of the glue joint. *Fillers,* such as walnut or pecan shell flour, are added to synthetic-resin adhesives to reduce the flow properties and prevent bleed-through and starved joints.

The adhesives used are either proteins of plant or animal origin or synthetic resins. The most commonly used adhesives are casein glue, soybean glue, blood glue, or synthetic resins of either the

Fig. 35–27. Paper tape joins veneer pieces destined for panel backs. Taper machine pulls veneer together and applies thin tape strip which will be sanded off back of finished panel after pressing.

thermosetting or thermoplastic types. Pheno-formaldehyde and urea-formaldehyde resins are the two important classes of thermosetting resin adhesives.

Adhesive mixing is commonly performed in large dough-type mixers. The various ingredients are carefully weighed or volume measured into the mixer. The quantity of glue prepared depends on its working and storage life.

Glue spreading is usually performed in a machine such as the one which is shown in Figure 35–28. Two power-driven, grooved rolls apply the adhesive to both sides of the veneer in an even film. Roll pressures up to 1 ton flatten

Fig. 35–28. Dark colored panels are sheets of veneer which have been covered with a film of glue by this glue spreader. They will form the crossbands in a plywood "sandwich" to be bonded in huge presses.

Fig. 35–29. Walnut for gunstocks is shown being clamped in this clamping press while the bond sets up. Plastic sheets separate the units.

out the irregularities in the veneer on some of the newer models. Speeds range from 10 to 100 fpm on the older models to as high as 588 fpm on the newer ones. A pump delivers the glue to the spreader through overhead pipes. Doctor rollers regulate the amount of glue applied by the spreader rolls. The amount of glue spread is commonly described by the number of pounds per thousand feet of glue line. The hardwood plywood industry uses the single glue line as a basis; the softwood plywood industry uses the double glue line. Best practice dictates that the minimum quantity of glue be applied to a joint.

Pressing the plywood "sandwich" insures alignment and intimate contact of the wood and glue. It is performed in different types of presses. The plywood may be cold-pressed or hot-pressed. Pressure may be applied by means of hand-

Fig. 35–31. The world's largest plywood press is four stories high. Plywood rolls continuously and automatically from the 60-opening hot press. The new type of panels have a tough, smooth built-in resin surface (overlay plywood) on both sides, yet sell in the same price range as ordinary fir plywood.

Fig. 35–30. This multi-opening press depicts hand loading of plywood veneer assemblies from an elevator lift.

tightened clamps or in hydraulic presses.

Most plywood is produced in hydraulic presses as shown in Figure 35–30. Most presses are manually loaded and unloaded; however, some are completely automatic such as the one shown in Figure 35–31. Pressures of 150 to 250 psi are applied to the panels. Temperatures of the platens in hot presses range from 210 to 350 deg. F. Platens are heated with steam, hot water, or hot oil. Curing times vary with the thickness of the panels from 2 to 30 minutes. Cold presses remain closed for 8 to 24 hours to permit the glue to set up.

Fig. 35–32. Sheathing grade plywood is shown being inspected and stacked after leaving the trim saws. No further processing is necessary.

The faces of the plywood are protected during pressing with *caul boards*. These are waxed sheets of plywood or sheets of aluminum. As many as 2 to 5 assemblies may be separated by caul boards and placed in one opening in the press.

Synthetic glues, because of their dielectric (nonconducting) nature, may be cured with high-frequency current. Several installations of hot presses designed to cure plywood glue by this means have been made. However, the high costs for equipment and amounts of electrical energy consumed have discouraged widespread use.

Sizing and **sanding** the panels complete the production of most plywood. After the panels have completed curing, they are conveyed through trim saws that cut them to width and length. (See Figure 35–32.)

Plywood to be sanded is passed through endless belt or drum sanders. (See Figure 35–33.) Here the tapes are sanded off and both faces are sanded smooth and to equal thickness. Some panels are sprayed with a thin glue sizing that dries quickly. This raises and fixes the loose wood fibers and permits their removal in a second and final sanding operation.

Panels that need repair are identified in final inspection and grading. Checks, splits, and pitch pockets are removed and sound pieces of veneer added. If V grooves or other special cuts are required, the panel is sent through a machine that performs this work. Some details must be completed by hand as shown in Figures 35–34 and 35–35.

Finally, the panels are prepared for shipment as shown in Figure 35–36. Some grades of plywood are stacked and secured to pallets for shipment.

Fig. 35–33. Eight-drum sander gives 4 x 8 panels first sanding on face and back. Then a glue sizing is applied to raise and hold the grain for a final sanding operation.

Prefinished veneers and plywood panels are becoming increasingly popular. Prefinished veneers, with a cloth backing, find use as wall coverings. They are applied in much the same manner as wallpaper. Flexible wood tapes in several species are also available for covering the edges of plywood panels. (See Figs. 35–37 and 35–38.)

Plywood panels are automatically prefinished as shown in Figures 35–39 to 35–44. The initial cost of these panels is higher than unfinished panels, but the quality of the finish and the savings in

Fig. 35–34. In manufacturing Colonial "V-Plank" panels cross-grooving between V-grooves is cut as shown. After cross-grooves have been cut, panels are ready for veneer drilling and pegging.

Fig. 35–36. Final step in a plywood manufacturing plant is the packaging of big sheets of finished plywood for shipment.

Fig. 35–35. Actual wood plugs of contrasting veneer are glued into specially drilled holes in face veneer.

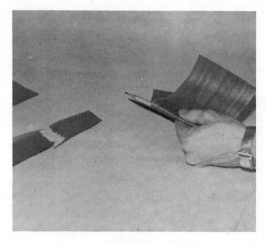

Fig. 35–37. Prefinished veneers (on right) are very flexible compared to standard veneers which break if bent as sharply.

on-the-site finishing costs make them competitive.

Fig. 35—38. Wood trim is primarily used for covering edges of plywood, but can be used for decorative purposes as well.

Fig. 35—39. This straight line production machine turns out three completely finished, dried, and waxed panels a minute. Panels with rotary cut veneers are grooved and edged on either of two portable grooving machines which can be positioned at the head of the line to achieve either single or double grooved panels.

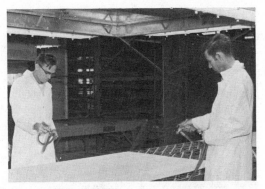

Fig. 35—40. Some panels require sap staining as an initial treatment. This is the same process manufacturers of fine furniture put their woods through, when they are blending sapwood into the regular tone of the heartwood.

Fig. 35—41. Drum-type brushes clean up stain and sealer coat as panels pass underneath on the conveyor line.

Classification of Plywood

Softwood plywood is made in two basic types: *interior* and *exterior*. The type and frequently the grade is stamped on the edge and back of the panel. The interior type, which comprises two thirds of all plywood produced, is mostly hot-pressed and is made with protein glues having a soybean-blood base. It is designed to withstand temporary wetting

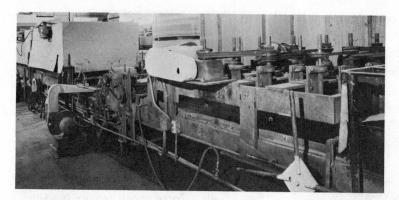

Fig. 35–42. Rotary brushes, removed for cleaning, force the finish into the wood and distribute it evenly. The brushes rotate on the spindles shown above the conveyor belt. From here panels go to cooling chamber (left) where wax is hardened before being given final sheen.

Fig. 35–43. Slow ride through convection oven dries lacquer. Panels leave oven in fives and are destacked by automatic elevator at right.

Fig. 35–44. At end of the line, panels are inspected and packaged six to a carton for shipment to distributors throughout the country.

during construction and to serve permanently in interior service.

Exterior plywood, comprising the other third of production, is made only with a hot-pressed phenolic-resin adhesive which is permanent and insoluble under any exposure condition, including boiling. It is designed for permanent exterior positions.

Each softwood type is manufactured in several appearance grades to fit a wide variety of uses as shown in Tables 35–1, 35–2, and 35–3. *Grade* designation is based primarily on the quality of the veneer used on the face and back. There are five grades of veneer, ranging from N (the best) through A, B, C, and D (the lowest). Most veneer may be repaired to raise its quality. Repairs consist of various sizes and shapes of patches, plugs, and long, narrow shims which fill voids in the veneer sheet or replace knots and pitch pockets.

Softwood plywood grades are indicated by two letters such as "A–D." This refers

TABLE 35-1
INTERIOR TYPE GRADES — MINIMUM QUALITY OF VENEERS

Grade	Face	Back	Inner Plies	Additional Limitations[1]
N-N, Int. (Natural Finish Two Sides)[2]	N	N	C[3]	Sanded 2 sides.
N-A, Int. (Natural Finish)	N	A	C[3]	Sanded 2 sides.
N-D, Int. (Natural Finish One Side)[4]	N	D	D	Sanded 2 sides.
A-A, Int.	A	A	D	Sanded 2 sides.
A-B, Int.	A	B	D	Sanded 2 sides.
A-D, Int.	A	D	D	Sanded 2 sides.
B-B, Int. (Concrete Form, Int.)	B	B	C (All Inner Plies)	Edge-sealed and, unless otherwise specified, mill-oiled. Sanded 2 sides.
B-B, Int.	B	B	D	Sanded 2 sides.
B-D, Int.	B	D	D	Sanded 2 sides.
Int. Underlayment	C (Plugged)[5]	D	C[6] and D	Sanded 2 sides or touch-sanded[7].
C-D (Plugged)[5], Int.	C (Plugged)[5]	D	D	Unsanded or touch-sanded[7].
C-D, Int. (Sheathing, Int.) with Exterior Glue[8]	C	D	D	Unsanded grade.
C-D, Int. (Sheathing, Int.)	C	D	D	Unsanded grade.

TABLE 35-2
EXTERIOR TYPE GRADES — MINIMUM QUALITY OF VENEERS

Grade	Face	Back	Inner Plies	Additional Limitations[2]
Marine, Ext.[8]				. . . .
A-A, Ext.	A	A	C	Sanded 2 sides.
A-B, Ext.	A	B	C	Sanded 2 sides.
A-C, Ext.	A	C	C	Sanded 2 sides.
B-B, Ext. (Concrete Form, Ext.)	B	B	C	Edge-sealed and, unless other wise specified, mill-oiled. Sanded 2 sides.
B-C, Ext.	B	C	C	Sanded 2 sides.
C-C, Ext. (Plugged)[5]	C (Plugged)[5]	C	C	Sanded 2 sides or touch-sanded[7].
C-C, Ext. (Sheating, Ext.)	C	C	C	Unsanded grade.

TABLE 35-3
OVERLAID PLYWOOD — MINIMUM QUALITY OF VENEER

Grade	Face[9]	Back[9]	Inner Plies
A-A, Ext. — High Density Overlay	A	A	B
B-B, Ext. — High Density Overlay	B	B	B
B-B, Ext. — High Density Concrete Form Overlay	B	B	B
B-B, Ext. — Medium Density Overlay	B	B	C[10]

Credit: U. S. Dept. of Commerce CS 122–60.

[1] See also grade and type descriptions.
[2] A "two sides Natural Finish" item, intended primarily for cabinet work, generally only in ¾ in. thickness. Available only from certain mills.
[3] All inner plies shall consist of C veneer with crossbands jointed.
[4] A "one side Natural Finish" item, intended primarily for paneling and wainscoting, generally only in ¼ inch thickness. Available only from certain mills.
[5] See glossary for definition.
[6] Veneer immediately adjacent to face shall be C or better.
[7] Available touch-sanded when so specified (see glossary for definition).
[8] Special Construction details apply.
[9] For overlaid plywood the grade designation for face or back refers to the . . . . laid plywood is surfaced on two sides unless otherwise specified. When only one . . . . .C or better.
[10] Medium Density Overlay also available with B grade inner plies.

to a panel with an A face and a D back. The inner plies for any interior grade are also D or better; for exterior grades inner plies are C or better. Exterior plywood does not permit veneer faces below C grade.

The U. S. Department of Commerce Commercial Standard CS122-60 classifies softwood veneers as follows:

Softwood Veneer Classification

Veneer Classification. — All veneers used in the different plywood grades shall be one of the following (grade N being the best of the five classifications):

Grade N veneer (Intended for natural finish).
General.
Shall be — smoothly cut 100 percent heartwood, free from knots, knotholes, pitch pockets, open splits, other open defects, and stain.
— of not more than 2 pieces.
— well matched for color and grain and well joined with joint parallel to edges, when of more than one piece.
Permits — suitable plastic fillers to fill:
  a. Small cracks or checks not more than $\frac{1}{32}$ inch wide.
  b. Small splits or openings up to $\frac{1}{16}$ in. wide if not exceeding 2 inches in length.
  c. Small chipped areas or openings not more than $\frac{1}{8}$ in. wide by $\frac{1}{4}$ in. long.
Growth Characteristics.
Permits — pitch streaks averaging not more than $\frac{3}{8}$ in. in width and blending with color of wood.
Repairs.
Shall be — neatly made and parallel to grain.
— limited to a total of six in number in any foot by 8-ft. face, with proportionate limits for other sizes.
— well matched for color and grain.
Permits — patches limited to three "router" patches not exceeding $\frac{3}{4}$ in. in width and $3\frac{1}{2}$ in. in length.
— no overlapping.
— shims not exceeding 12 in. in length.
Grade A veneer (Suitable for painting.)

General.
Shall be — firm, smoothly cut and free from knots, pitch pockets, open splits and other open defects.
— well joined when of more than one piece.
Permits — suitable plastic fillers to fill:
  a. Small cracks or checks not more than $\frac{1}{32}$ in. wide.
  b. Small splits or openings up to $\frac{1}{16}$ in. wide if not exceeding 2 in. in length.
  c. Small chipped areas or openings not more than $\frac{1}{8}$ in. wide by $\frac{1}{4}$ in. long.
Growth Characteristics.
Permits — pitch streaks averaging not more than $\frac{3}{8}$ in. in width, blending with color of wood.
— sapwood.
— discolorations.
Repairs.
Shall be — neatly made and parallel to grain, limited to a total of 18 in number, excluding shims, in any 4 ft. by 8-ft. face; proportionate limits on other sizes.
Permits — patches:
  a. Which are symmetrical and of "boat," "router" and "sled" type only, including die-cut patches if edges are cut clean and sharp.
  b. Not exceeding $2\frac{1}{4}$ in. in width singly.
  c. Multiple, consisting of not more than 2 patches, neither of which may exceed 7 in. in length if either is wider than 1 in.
— shims, except as multiple repairs.

Grade B veneer.
General.
Shall be — solid and free from open defects except as noted.
Permits — slightly rough but not torn grain.
— minor sanding and patching defects, including sander skips not exceeding 5 percent of panel area.
— suitable plastic fillers to fill:
  a. Small splits or openings up to $\frac{1}{16}$ in. wide if not exceeding 2 in. in length.
  b. Small chipped areas or openings not more than $\frac{1}{8}$ in. wide by $\frac{1}{4}$ in. long.
Growth Characteristics.
Permits — knots up to 1 in. if both sound and tight.
— pitch streaks averaging not more than 1 in. in width.
— discolorations.

Open Defects.

Permits — splits not wider than $\frac{1}{32}$ in.

- vertical holes not exceeding $\frac{1}{16}$ in. in diameter (caused by ambrosia beetles) if not exceeding an average of 1 per square foot in number.
- horizontal or surface tunnels limited to $\frac{1}{16}$ in. across, 1 in. in length, and to 12 in number in a 4 ft. by 8-ft. panel, or proportionately in panels of other dimensions.

Repairs.

Shall be — neatly made.

Permits — patches ("boat," "router," and "sled") not exceeding 3 in. in width individually where occurring in multiple repairs or 4 in. in width where occurring singly.

- plugs (circular, "dog bone," and leaf shaped) not exceeding 3 in. in width individually where occurring in multiple repairs or 4 in. in width where occurring singly.
- shims.
- synthetic plugs which present solid level, hard surface not exceeding above dimensions.

Grade C veneer.

General.

Permits — sanding defects that will not impair the strength or serviceability of the panel.

- C grade backs to be narrow on one edge or short on one end only, but by not more than $\frac{1}{8}$ in. for $\frac{1}{2}$ panel length or width.

Growth Characteristics.

Permits — knots, if tight and not more than $1\frac{1}{2}$ in. in least dimension.

Open Defects.

Permits — knotholes not larger than 1 in. across grain.

- open pitch pockets not wider than 1 in.
- splits not wider than $\frac{3}{16}$ in. that taper to a point.
- worm and borer holes not more than $\frac{5}{8}$ in. wide and $1\frac{1}{2}$ in. long.

Repairs.

Shall be — neatly made.

Permits — patches (boat, including die cut) not exceeding 3 in. in width individually where occurring in multiple repairs or 4 in. in width where occurring singly.

- plugs (circular, "dog bone," and leaf shaped) not exceeding 3 in. in width individually where occurring in multiple repairs or 4 in. in width where occurring singly.
- synthetic plugs which present solid, level, hard surface not exceeding above dimensions.

Grade D veneer. (May be used only in Interior type panels.)

General.

Permits — except as otherwise specified, any number of plugs, patches, shims, worm or borer holes, sanding defects, and other characteristics, provided they do not seriously impair the strength or serviceability of the panel.

- D grade backs to be narrow on one edge or short on one end only, but by not more than $\frac{1}{8}$ in. for $\frac{1}{2}$ panel length or width.

Open Defects.

Permits — knotholes not exceeding $2\frac{1}{2}$ in. in maximum dimension.

- pitch pockets not exceeding 2 in. wide by 4 in. long or of equivalent area if of lesser width.
- splits

$\frac{1}{2}$ in. by $\frac{1}{4}$ panel length.

$\frac{1}{4}$ in. by $\frac{1}{2}$ panel length.

$\frac{3}{16}$ in. by full panel length.

Require to taper to a point.

Shall not exceed $\frac{1}{2}$ in. width at widest point.

White Pocket (see glossary).

In inner plies only —

Any area 24 in. wide across the grain and 12 in. long, in which light or heavy white pocket occurs, shall not contain more than 3 of the following characteristics, in any combination:

a. 6 in. width of heavy white pocket.

b. 12 in. width of light white pocket.

c. One knot or knothole, $1\frac{1}{2}$ in. to $2\frac{1}{2}$ in., or 2 knots or knotholes, 1 in. to $1\frac{1}{2}$ in.; knots and knotholes less than 1 in. shall not be considered. Size of any knot or knothole shall be measured in greatest dimension. Any repair in white pocket area shall be treated for grading purposes as a knothole.

On backs —

white pocket in any area larger than the size of the largest knothole, pitch pocket, or split, specifically admitted in this paragraph, shall not be permitted.

Overlays. — Overlaid plywood in Western softwood plywood to which has been added resin-impregnated fiber faces on one or both sides. It is made in 2 standard types, "High Density" and "Medium Density," with the type referring to the surfacing materials as hereinafter defined. In addition, there may be other surfacing materials having special characteristics which do not fit the exact description of High Density or Medium Density. These must meet the test requirements . . . and shall be identified as "special." The resin-impregnated faces are permanently fused to the base panel under heat and pressure. Although designed for either exterior or interior service, all overlaid plywood is made in the Exterior type. This refers to the adhesive bond between plies, between the overlay surface and the base panel, and to the durability of the surface itself.

High Density Type. — The surfacing on the finished product shall be hard, smooth, and of such character that further finishing by paint or varnish is not required. It shall consist of a cellulose-fiber sheet or sheets, in which not less than 40 percent by weight of the laminate shall be a thermosetting resin of the phenol or melamine type. The resin-impregnated material shall be not less than 0.009 in. thick and shall weigh not less than 60 lb. per 1000 sq. ft. of single face before pressing, including both resin and fiber. The resin impregnation shall be sufficient to attach the surfacing material to the plywood. This bond shall be equal in performance to the glue lines between the sheets of veneer which make up the plywood. The overlay face usually comes in natural translucent color, but certain other colors are available or may be used by manufacturers for identification.

Medium Density Type. — The resin-impregnated facing on the finished product shall present a smooth, uniform surface suitable for high-quality paint finishes. It shall consist of a cellulose-fiber sheet in which not less than 20 percent by weight of the laminate shall be a thermosetting resin of the phenol or melamine type. The resin-impregnated material shall be not less than 0.012 in. thick and shall weigh not less than 65 lb. per 1000 sq. ft. of single face before

pressing, including both resin and fiber. An integral phenolic resin glue line shall be applied to one surface of the facing material to bond it to the plywood. This bond shall be equal in performance to the glue lines between the sheets of veneer which make up the plywood. The overlay face shall be a solid color. Some evidence of the underlying grain may appear, but, compared to the nature of the "High Density" surface, there shall be no consistent show-through.

U. S. DEPT. OF COMMERCE CS 122-60

Softwood plywood is commonly made in the sizes shown in Tables 35–4, 35–5, and 35–6, but other lengths including 4, 14, and 16 ft. are available from certain mills. Some companies make panels in lengths "limited only by handling and shipping restrictions." This is accomplished by joining two panels with a scarfed joint as shown in Figure 35–45. The scarfed joint is made by beveling an edge of each panel and then bonding the joint with a waterproof adhesive. Scarfed joints generally have a slope of 1 to 8. They are stronger than the panels themselves.

Plywood is available in many textures and designs for both interior and exterior

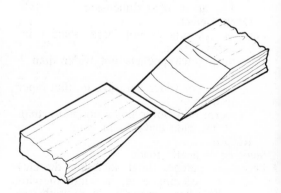

Fig. 35–45. Joining two panels by use of a scarfed joint.

TABLE 35–4   STANDARD STOCK WESTERN SOFTWOOD PLYWOOD SIZES[1] — INTERIOR TYPE

Grade	Width (in.)[2]	Length (in.)[2]	Thickness (in.)[3][4][5]				
N-N, Int.	48	96	¼	....	....	....	¾
N-A, Int.	48	96	¼	....	....	....	¾
N-D, Int.	48	96	¼	....	....	....	....
		72	¼	....	....	....	¾
A-A, Int.	36	96	¼	⅜	½	....	¾
		72	¼	⅜	½	⅝	¾
		84	¼	⅜	½	⅝	¾
	48	96	¼	⅜	½	⅝	¾
A-A, Int.	60[6]	108	¼	⅜	....	....	¾
		120	¼	⅜	½	⅝	¾
		144	¼	....	....	....	¾
A-B, Int.	36	96	¼	⅜	½	⅝	¾
		72	¼	⅜	½	⅝	¾
		84	¼	⅜	½	⅝	¾
	48	96	¼	⅜	½	⅝	¾
A-B, Int.	60[6]	108	¼	....	....	....	¾
		120	¼	⅜	½	⅝	¾
		144	¼	....	....	....	¾
		60	....	....	....	....	¾
		72	....	....	....	....	¾
A-D, Int.	30	84	¼	....	....	....	¾
		96	¼	....	....	....	¾
		120	....	....	....	....	¾
		60	....	....	....	....	¾
		72	¼	⅜	½	⅝	¾
A-D, Int.	36	84	¼	⅜	½	⅝	¾
		96	¼	⅜	½	⅝	¾
		120	¼	....	....	....	¾
		60	¼	⅜	½	⅝	¾
		72	¼	⅜	½	⅝	¾
	48	84	¼	⅜	½	⅝	¾
A-D, Int.	60[6]	96	¼	⅜	½	⅝	¾
		108	¼	⅜	½	⅝	¾
		120	¼	⅜	½	⅝	¾
		144	¼	⅜	½	⅝	¾
B-B (Concrete Form, Int.)	48	96	....	....	....	⅝	¾
	60[6]						
		60	¼	⅜	½	⅝	¾
		72	¼	⅜	½	⅝	¾
	48	84	¼	⅜	½	⅝	¾
B-B, Int.	60[6]	96	¼	⅜	½	⅝	¾
		108	¼	⅜	½	⅝	¾
		120	¼	⅜	½	⅝	¾
		144	¼	⅜	½	⅝	¾
B-D, Int.	48	84	¼	⅜	½	⅝	¾
	60[6]	96					

[1] Sizes most commonly available from distributors.

[2] A tolerance of 1/32 (0.0312) in. over or under the specified width and/or length shall be allowed, but all panels shall be square within ⅛ (0.125) in. All panels shall be sawn so that a straight line drawn from one corner to the adjacent corner shall fall within 1/16 in. of panel edge.

[3] A tolerance of 1/64 (0.0156) in. over or under the specified thickness shall be allowed on sanded panels, and a tolerance of 1/32 (0.0312) in. on unsanded panels.
See stction 11 for definition of touch-sanding.

[4] Minimum number of plies required for standard construction:
  3 plies for ¼-, 5/16-, and ⅜-in.
  5 plies for ½-, ⅝-, and ¾-in.
  7 plies for ⅞- to 1-3/16-in.

[5] Sanded two sides, except Underlayment, C-D (Plugged), C-D Sheathing-Exterior Glue, and C-D Sheathing.

[6] Available from a considerable number of mills, but not all.

NOTE: Any panel furnished in dimensions ordered conforming in all other respects to the various requirements of this standard shall be considered as conforming to this standard. However, panels manufactured to other than standard nominal thicknesses shall be clearly identified on each panel as to the manufactured thickness.

TABLE 35–4 (Cont.)

Grade	Width (in.)[2]	Length (in.)[2]	Thickness (in.)[3 4 5]				
Int. Underlayment	48	96	¼	⅜	½	⅝	¾
	60[6]		¼	⅜	½	⅝	¾
C-D (Plugged) Int.	48	96	¼	⅜	½	⅝	¾
	60[6]						
C-D, Int. (Sheathing, Int.) with	48	96	5/16	⅜	½	⅝	¾
Exterior Glue (See Section 7,	60[6]	120	5/16			⅝	
Special Constructions)						⅝	
C-D, Int. (Sheathing, Int.)	48	96	5/16	⅜	½	⅝	
	60[6]	120	5/16				¾

TABLE 35–5 STANDARD STOCK WESTERN SOFTWOOD PLYWOOD SIZES[1] — EXTERIOR TYPE

Grade	Width[2] (in.)	Length[2] (in.)	Thickness (in.)[3 4 5]						
A-A, Ext.	48 60[6]	60	¼	⅜	½	⅝	¾	....	....
		84	¼	⅜	½	⅝	¾	....	....
		96	¼	⅜	½	⅝	¾	⅞	1
		108	¼	⅜	½	⅝	¾	....	....
		120	¼	⅜	½	⅝	¾	....	....
		144	¼	⅜	½	⅝	¾	....	....
A-B, Ext.	48 60[6]	84	¼	⅜	....	....	¾	....	....
		96	¼	⅜	½	⅝	¾	....	1
		120	¼	⅜	½	⅝	¾	....	....
		144	¼	⅜	½	....	¾	....	....
A-C, Ext.	36	96	¼	⅜	½	⅝	¾	....	....
A-C, Ext.	48 60[6]	72	¼	⅜	½	⅝	¾	....	....
		84	¼	⅜	½	⅝	¾	....	....
		96	¼	⅜	½	⅝	¾	....	1
		108	¼	⅜	½	⅝	¾	....	....
		120	¼	⅜	½	⅝	¾	....	....
		144	¼	⅜	½	⅝	¾	....	....
B-B (Concrete Form) Ext.	48 60[6]	96	....	....	....	⅝	¾	....	....
B-C, Ext.	48 60[6]	96	¼	⅜	½	⅝	¾	....	....
C-C (Plugged) Ext.	48 60[6]	96	¼	⅜	½	⅝	¾	....	....
C-C (Sheathing) Ext.	48 60[6]	96	¼	⅜	½	⅝	¾	....	....

[1] Sizes most commonly available from distributors.

[2] A tolerance of 1/32 (0.0312) in. over or under the specified width and/or length shall be allowed, but all panels shall be square within ⅛ (0.125) in. All panels shall be sawn so that a straight line drawn from one corner to the adjacent corner shall fall within 1/16 in. of panel edge.

[3] A tolerance of 1/64 (0.0156) in. over or under the specified thickness shall be allowed on sanded panels, and a tolerance of 1/32 (0.0312) in. on unsanded panels. See Glossary 11 for definition of touch-sanding.

[4] Minimum number of plies required for standard construction:
- 3 plies for ¼-, 5/16-, and ⅜-in.
- 5 plies for ½-, ⅝-, and ¾-in.
- 7 plies for ⅞- to 1-3/16 in.

[5] Sanded 2 sides except C-C Plugged and C-C- Sheathing.

[6] Available from a considerable number of mills, but not all.

NOTE: Any panel furnished in dimensions ordered conforming in all other respects to the various requirements of the standard shall be considered as conforming to this standard. However, panels manufactured to other than standard nominal thicknesses shall be clearly identified on each panel as to the manufactured thickness.

TABLE 35-6   STANDARD STOCK WESTERN SOFTWOOD PLYWOOD SIZES[1] — OVERLAID PLYWOOD

Grade	Width[2] (in.)	Length[2] (in.)	Thickness[3] (in.)
A-A High Density, Ext.	48	96	$\frac{5}{16}$ (3-ply)[4] $\frac{3}{8}$ (3-ply) $\frac{1}{2}$ (5-ply) $\frac{9}{16}$ (5-ply) $\frac{5}{8}$ (5-ply) $\frac{3}{4}$ (5-ply) $\frac{7}{8}$ (7-ply) 1 (7-ply) $1\frac{1}{8}$ (7-ply)
B-B High Density, Ext.	48	96	Same as for grade A-A, above.
B-B High Density, Ext. (Concrete Form)	48	96	$\frac{1}{2}$ (5-ply) $\frac{9}{16}$ (5-ply) $\frac{5}{8}$ (5-ply) $\frac{3}{4}$ (5-ply)
B-B Medium Density, Ext.	48	96	Same as for grade A-A, above.

[1] Sizes most commonly available from distributors.

[2] A tolerance of 1/32 (0.0312) inch over or under the specified width and/or length shall be allowed, but all overlaid panels shall be square within $\frac{1}{8}$ (0.125) inch. All panels shall be sawn so that a straight line drawn from one corner to the adjacent corner shall fall within 1/16 inch of panel edge.

[3] A tolerance of 1/32 (0.0312) inch over or under the specified thickness shall be allowed on overlaid panels.

[4] Number of plies refers to veneers. Resin-impregnated surfaces are not included.

NOTE: Any panel furnished in dimensions ordered conforming in all other respects to the various requirements of this Standard shall be considered as conforming to this Standard. However, panels manufactured to other than standard nominal thicknesses shall be clearly identified on each panel as to the manufactured thicknesses.

TABLE 35-7   TYPES OF HARDWOOD PLYWOOD

Limiting factors	Technical	Type I	Type II	Type III
Bond	Fully waterproof	Fully waterproof	Water-resistant	Moisture resistant
Species or density of veneer	Specify	Specify	Specify	Specify
Grade of faces or face and back	do	do	do	do
Grade of inner plies	2 under 1 3 under 2	2 or 3	2 or 3[1]	2 or 3[1]
Grade of lumber core	None	Specify	Specify	Specify
Grade of Softwood Veneer Core	None	Specify	Specify	Specify
Particle Board Core	None	Specify	Specify	Specify
Edge joints	No tape	No tape	Tape	Tape
Maximum veneer thickness, in inches:				
High density	$\frac{1}{12}$	$\frac{1}{8}$	Not specified	Not specified
Medium density	$\frac{1}{16}$	$\frac{3}{16}$	do	do
Low density	$\frac{1}{8}$	$\frac{1}{4}$	do	do
Percentage of wood in face direction	40 to 60	Not specified	do	do
Sanding	Specify	Specify	Specify	Specify
Tests	(a) Dry shear (b) Cyclic boil	(a) Dry shear (b) Cyclic boil	Cold soak (15 cycles)	Cold soak (2 cycles)

[1] Grade 2 or 3, where 1/16-in. or thicker faces are used, will permit Grade 4 or better inner plies.

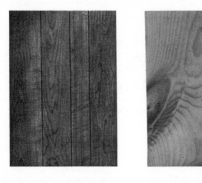

Fig. 35–46. Some of the interesting surfaces that are available in plywood sheets.

purposes as shown in Figures 35–46 and 35–47. Plywood siding is also exterior-type.

Hardwood plywood made in this country is of four *types* as shown in Table 35–7. They are described as follows:

1. *Technical* — fully waterproof bond. Its construction is designed to provide approximately equal tension and compression strength in both length and width. The bond withstands full water and weather exposure, is unaffected by micro-organisms, and withstands dry shear and cyclic-boil tests with a specified minimum strength.
2. *Type I* (*Exterior*) — fully waterproof bond. This bond withstands full weather exposure, is unaffected

by microorganisms, and has same test strength as Technical type.
3. *Type II* (*Interior*) — water resistant bond. This bond retains practically all of its strength when occasionally thoroughly wetted and dried.
4. *Type III* (*Interior*) — moisture resistant bond. This bond retains practically all of its strength when occasionally subjected to moisture.

Hardwood veneers may also be classified by their density. A wood with a specific gravity of 0.56 and above is of *high density;* one of 0.41 through 0.55 is *medium density;* and one of 0.40 and below is *low density.*

Grade designations of the quality of face, back, and inner plies of hardwood plywood as specified by the U. S. Department of Commerce, Commercial Standard CS35-61 are as follows:

Fig. 35–47. This lap siding for horizontal application is one of a wide line of architecturally-styled plywood sidings. Prefinished siding is also available.

Hardwood Plywood Grades

Premium grade (1). — The face shall be of the species of hardwood specified and each face shall be made of tight and smoothly cut veneers. When the face consists of more than one piece, the joints shall be tight and approximately parallel to the vertical edge and matched as outlined in Table 35–8. The inherent natural characteristics and the types of matching which will be permitted for each species and the defects which will not be permitted, are listed in Table 35–8. Veneers not covered in Table 35–8 can contain a few small burls, occasional pin knots, slight color streaks or spots, and inconspicuous small patches. Unusual characteristics of a given species will be permitted. Knots (other than pin knots), wormholes, splits, shake, doze, and other forms of decay shall not be permitted.

Good grade (1) — (for natural finish). — The face shall be made of tight, smoothly cut veneer containing the natural character markings inherent in the species. When the face consists of more than one piece, the joints shall be tight and approximately parallel to the vertical edge. The piece need not be matched for color or grain, but sharp contrasts (see below) will not be permitted. A few small burls, occasional pin knots, slight color streaks or spots, and inconspicuous small patches shall be permitted. Knots (other than pin knots), wormholes, splits, shake, doze, and other forms of decay shall not be permitted. The inherent natural characteristics which will be permitted for each species, and the defects which will not be permitted are listed in Table 35–9.

Sharp contrasts. — For purposes of this standard, this term means that veneer of lighter than average color should not be joined at the edges with veneer of darker than average color, and that two adjacent pieces of veneer should not be widely dissimilar in grain, figure, and natural character markings.

Sound grade (2) — (for smooth paint surfaces). — The face shall be free from open defects to provide a sound, smooth surface. The veneer is not matched for grain or color. It may contain mineral streaks, stain, discoloration, patches, sapwood, sound tight knots up to ¾ in. in average diameter, and sound smooth burls up to 1 in. in average diameter. Rough-cut veneer, brashness, splits, shake, doze, or other forms of decay are not permitted. A summary of the inherent natural characteristics which will be permitted, and the defects which will not be permitted are listed in Table 35–10.

Utility grade (3). — This grade shall permit discoloration, stain, mineral streaks, patches, tight knots, tight burls, knotholes up to ¾ in. in diameter, wormholes, splits or open joints not exceeding $\frac{3}{16}$ in. and not extending half the length of the panel, cross breaks, not greater in length than that of the permissible knotholes, and small areas of rough grain. A summary of the inherent natural characteristics which will be permitted, and the defects which will not be permitted are listed in Table 35–10.

Backing grade (4). — The species of veneer may be at the option of the manufacturer. Knotholes not greater than 2 in. in maximum diameter and no group of knotholes in any 12-in. square exceeding 4 in. in diameter shall be permitted. Splits 1 in. wide at the widest point may be ¼ panel length; those not more than ½ in. wide at widest point may be ½ panel length; those not more than ¼ in. wide may be full panel length. Mineral streaks, stain and discoloration, shims, plugs, patches, filler, knots, burls, wormholes, borer holes, and other characteristics are permitted, provided they do not seriously impair the strength or serviceability of the panel for the use for which they were manufactured. A summary of the inherent natural characteristics which will be permitted and the defects which will not be permitted are listed in Table 35–10.

Specialty grade (SP). — This grade includes plywood that does not conform to any of the above grades, such as architectural plywood, matched-grain panels for special uses, and special veneer selections. The grade description and characteristics shall be agreed upon by buyer and seller.

Standard sizes and **thicknesses** of finished hardwood plywood are as follows:

Widths: 16, 24, 32, 36, and 48 in., ± $\frac{1}{32}$-in. tolerance.

Lengths: 48, 60, 72, 84, 96, and 120 in., ± $\frac{1}{32}$-in. tolerance.

TABLE 35–8 SUMMARY OF CHARACTERISTICS AND DEFECTS PERMITTED IN GRADE 1 (PREMIUM) VENEER

Characteristics and defects	Rotary cut ash, basswood, elm, sycamore	Rotary cut birch					Plain sliced cherry	Rotary cut gum, tupelo, bay and magnolia			Quarter sliced gum	Quarter sliced limba	Plain sliced mahogany
		Natural	Selected for white	Selected for red	Uniform light	Uniform dark		Natural	Selected for white	Selected for red			
Sapwood	Yes	Yes	Yes	No	Yes	No	Yes	Yes	Yes	No	Yes	No	No
Heartwood	Yes	Yes	No	Yes	No	Yes	Yes	Yes	No	Yes	Yes	Yes	Yes
Color streaks or spots	Yes	Yes	Slight	Yes	Slight	Yes	Yes	Yes	Slight	Yes	Yes	Slight	Slight
Color variation	Yes	Slight	Slight	Slight	Slight	Slight	Slight	Slight	Slight	Slight	Slight	Slight	Slight
Mineral streaks	Slight	Yes	Slight	Yes	Slight	Slight	Yes	Yes	Yes	Yes	Few	Slight	Slight
Small burls	Yes	Yes	Few	Few	Few	Few	Yes	Small	Small	Small	Yes	Few	Few
Occasional pin knots	Small	Small	Yes	Small	Yes	Few	Small	No	No	No	Small	Yes	Yes
Inconspicuous patches	No	No	Small	No	No	Yes	No	No	No	No	No	Small	Small
Knots (other than pin knots)	No	No	No	No	No	No	No	No	No	No	No	No	No
Worm holes	No	No	No	No	No	No	No	No	No	No	No	No	No
Open splits or joints	No	No	No	No	No	No	No	No	No	No	No	No	No
Shake or doze	No	No	No	No	No	No	No	No	No	No	No	No	No
Rough cut	No	No	No	No	No	No	No	No	No	No	No	No	No
Gum spots	....	....	....	....	....	....	Small	....	....	....	....	....	....
Cross bars[4]	....	....	....	....	....	....	....	....	....	....	....	....	....
Type of matching	Book¹ or Slipped²	Book¹	Book¹	Book¹	Book¹ or slipped²	Book¹ or slipped²	Book¹	(3)	(3)	(3)	Book¹ or slipped²	Book¹	Book¹

¹ Book matched. Matched for color and grain at joints.
² Slip matched. Must be matched in sequence with tight side out.
³ Matched at the joints for color with tight side out.
⁴ Sharp contrast will not be permitted.

TABLE 35–8 (Continued)

	Quarter sliced mahogany	Rotary cut maple, sliced maple		Red oak and white oak			Walnut		Lauan (Philippine mahogany)		Rotary cut cativo
		Natural	Selected for white	Rotary cut	Half round plain sliced	Rift sliced	Half round plain sliced	Quarter sliced	Rotary cut	Quarter sliced	
Sapwood	No	Yes	Yes	Yes	No	No	No	No	No	No	No
Heartwood	Yes	Yes	No	Yes	Yes	Yes	Yes	Yes	Yes	Yes	Yes
Color streaks or spots	Slight	Yes	Slight	Slight	Slight	Slight	Slight	Slight	Slight	Slight	Slight
Color variation	Slight	Slight	Slight	Slight	Slight	Slight	Slight	Slight	Slight	Slight	Slight
Mineral streaks	Slight	Slight	Slight	Slight	Slight	Slight	Slight	Slight	Slight	Slight	Slight
Small burls	Few	Yes	Few	Yes	Yes	Few	Yes	Yes	Yes	Few	Yes
Occasional pin knots	Yes	Yes	Yes	Yes	Yes	Yes	Yes	Yes	Yes	Yes	Yes
Inconspicuous patches	Small	Small	Small	Small	Small	Small	Small	Small	Small	Small	Small
Knots (other than pin knots)	No	No	No	No	No	No	No	No	No	No	No
Worm holes	No	No	No	No	No	No	No	No	No	No	No
Open splits or joints	No	No	No	No	No	No	No	No	No	No	No
Shake or doze	No	No	No	No	No	No	No	No	No	No	No
Rough cut	No	No	No	No	No	No	No	No	No	No	No
Gum spots	.....	.....	.....	.....	.....	.....	.....	.....	.....	.....	.....
Cross bars[4]	Few	.....	.....	.....	.....	.....	.....	Few	.....	Few	.....
Type of matching	Book[1]	Book[1]	Book[1] or slipped[2]	(3)	Book[1] or slipped[2]	Book[1] or slipped[2]	Book[1]	Book[1] or slipped[2]	(3)	Book[1]	(3)

[1] Book matched. Matched for color and grain at joints.
[2] Slip matched. Must be matched in sequence with tight side out.
[3] Matched at the joints for color with tight side out.
[4] Sharp contrast will not be permitted.

TABLE 35–9   SUMMARY OF CHARACTERISTICS AND DEFECTS PERMITTED IN GRADE 1 (GOOD) VENEER

					SPECIES						
Defects	Bass-wood, syca-more, ash, and elm (rotary cut)	Birch (rotary cut)	Cativo	Cherry	Gum, tupelo, magnolia, bay, and poplar (rotary cut) Unselected for color	Selected for Color	Gum, red (quarter sliced)	Lauan Philippine mahogany	Limba	Mahogany (rotary cut)	Mahogany (plain sliced or flat cut)
Knots, other than pin knots	No	No	No	No	No	No	No	No	No	No	No
Occasional pin knots	Yes	Yes	Yes	Yes	Yes	Yes	Yes	Yes	Yes	Yes	Yes
Small burls	Yes	Yes	Yes	Yes	Yes	Yes	Yes	Yes	Yes	Yes	Yes
Doze	No	No	No	No	No	No	No	No	No	No	No
Mineral streaks	Slight	Slight	Slight	Slight	Slight	Slight	Slight	Slight	Slight	Slight	Slight
Discolorations	do	do	do	do	do	do	do	do	do	do	do
Wormholes	No	No	No	No	No	No	No	No	No	No	No
Splits or open joints	No	No	No	No	No	No	No	No	No	No	No
Cross breaks	No	No	No	No	No	No	No	No	No	No	No
Patches (small)	Yes	Yes	Yes	Yes	Yes	Yes	Yes	Yes	Yes	Yes	Yes
Sapwood	Yes	Yes	Yes	Yes	Yes	Yes	Yes	Yes	No	No	No
Shake	No	No	No	No	No	No	No	No	No	No	No

Defects	Mahogany (quarter sliced)	Maple (rotary cut)	Oak, red and white (rotary cut)	Oak, red and white (half round and plain sliced or flat cut)	Oak, white (quarter sliced or sawn and comb-grain sliced or sawn)	Walnut (rotary cut)	Walnut (half round and plain sliced or flat cut)	Walnut (quarter sliced)
Knots, other than pin knots	No	No	No	No	No	No	No	No
Occasional pin knots	Yes	Yes	Yes	Yes	Yes	Yes	Yes	Yes
Small burls	Yes	Yes	Yes	Yes	Yes	Yes	Yes	Yes
Doze	No	No	No	No	No	No	No	No
Mineral streaks	Slight	Slight	Slight	Slight	Slight	Slight	Slight	Slight
Discolorations	do	do	do	do	do	do	do	do
Cross bars	....	....	....	....	....	....	....	Few, small
Wormholes	No	No	No	No	No	No	No	No
Splits or open joints	No	No	No	No	No	No	No	No
Cross breaks	No	No	No	No	No	No	No	No
Patches (small)	Yes	Yes	Yes	Yes	Yes	Yes	Yes	Yes
Broken flake	....	....	....	....	No	....	....	....
Sapwood	No	Yes	Yes	No	No	Yes	No	No
Shake	No	No	No	No	No	No	No	No

Thicknesses: $\frac{1}{8}$, $\frac{3}{16}$, $\frac{1}{4}$, $\frac{5}{16}$, $\frac{3}{8}$, $\frac{1}{2}$, $\frac{5}{8}$, $\frac{3}{4}$, $\frac{13}{16}$, $\frac{7}{8}$, and 1 in.

Tolerances: Unsanded panels $\pm$ $\frac{1}{32}$ in.

Sanded panels + 0, — $\frac{1}{32}$ in.

Panels are manufactured square within $\frac{1}{16}$ in., measured on the short dimension.

Buying Plywood

Softwood plywood is ordered by denoting the species; the number of plies, width, length, grade, type, and finished thickness; and whether sanded or unsanded. Width refers to the distance across the grain of the face plies; length refers to the distance along the grain. Width is always specified first.

If the requirement is for plywood to be used on the interior of a structure with one side nailed against a wall and the other exposed to view and painted, it would be ordered as follows:

25 pieces, Douglas fir plywood, 3 ply, 48 in. by 96 in. interior type, A-D grade, sanded two sides to $\frac{1}{4}$ in. thickness.

Plywood is sanded for most uses ex-

TABLE 35–10
SUMMARY OF CHARACTERISTICS
AND DEFECTS PERMITTED IN
GRADES 2, 3, AND 4 VENEERS

Defects	Grade 2 Sound[1]	Grade 3 Utility[1]	Grade 4 Backing[1]
Sound tight knots	Max. diam. ¾ in.	Yes	Yes
Sound tight burls	Max. diam. 1 in.	Yes	Yes
Mineral streaks	Yes	Yes	Yes
Discolorations	Yes	Yes	Yes
Knotholes	No	Max. diam. ¾ in.	Max. diam. 2 in. Sum of diam. 4 in. in any 12-in. square
Wormholes	Filled or patched	Yes	Yes
Splits or open joints	do	Yes; ³⁄₁₆ in. for one-half-length of panel	1 in. for one-fourth length of panel; ½ in. for one-half length of panel; ¼ in. for full length of panel
Cross breaks	No	Max. ¾ in. in length	Yes
Patches	Yes	Yes	Yes
Sapwood	Yes	Yes	Yes
Gum spots	Yes	Yes	Yes
Bark pockets	No	Yes	Yes
Brashness, Shake, doze, and decay	No	No	No
Stain	Yes	Yes	Yes
Rough cut	No	Small area	Yes
Laps	No	No	No

[1] Defects permitted in Grade 1 shall be allowed in this grade. (See table 8 and 9.)

cept sheathing. Where sanded surfaces are not necessary unsanded panels are specified.

Buying hardwood plywood involves specifying the following: number of pieces, type of plywood, number of plies, thickness, width across the grain, length with the grain, species or density of face ply, density of inner plies in Technical type and Type I only, grade of face, grade of back, grade of lumber core if required, whether sanded or unsanded, and use to which plywood will be put.

When *lumber core plywood* is specified, it may be obtained with a *banded* core of any species, width, and combination of sides and edges. Specifications of banded cores are abbreviated as follows:

B1E   Banded one end.
B2E   Banded two ends.
B1S   Banded one side.
B2S   Banded two sides.
B2E1S   Banded two ends and one side.
B2S1E   Banded two sides and one end.
B4   Banded two sides and two ends.

Plywood Production

Over 900 companies are involved in the production of plywood. At least 150, mostly in the West, are classified as softwood plywood manufacturers. Hardwood veneer is manufactured primarily in the eastern half of the United States. Approximately 70,000 people are employed in plywood manufacturing industries. About 88 percent are production employees. The value added in manufacture is almost one half billion dollars annually. The value of the product shipped is over one and one quarter billion dollars annually.

Softwood plywood production is approximately 11 billion sq. ft. of ⅜ in. basis annually. Residential construction accounts for about 40 percent of softwood plywood consumption. The average home uses about 2500 sq. ft. as sheathing, subflooring, and floor underlayment. Nonresidential construction plus maintenance and improvements on all types of properties, constitute another major market which may equal the usage in residential build-

Fig. 35–48. Southern pine plywood, product of a new industry for the Southern states, will be used interchangeably with long-familiar Douglas fir plywood. Stenciled sheathing panels on this research house are pine, while unmarked panels are fir.

ing. Approximately 95 percent of the plywood used in construction is Douglas fir plywood. The other 23 western softwoods account for the remainder. Southern yellow pine is beginning to offer promise as a major softwood plywood.

The softwood plywood industry's growth rate has resulted in large part from its aggressive marketing programs and intensive research. Efforts are continually being made to improve the product, production processes, uses, and methods of application. (See Fig. 35–48.) Exports of about eighteen million square feet in 1963 were about twice the amount of imports. Canada is the chief source of imported softwood plywood. The industry's export promotion drive is expected to increase exports in the future.

Hardwood plywood production averages less than one billion square feet annually. Consumption of hardwood plywood runs about two billion square feet annually.

Hardwood plywood usage more than doubled during the last decade, but United States production remained almost static. In the early 1950's, imported hardwood plywood was about 7 percent of the U. S. market. Today, imports from Japan and other low wage countries constitute about 60 percent of annual consumption.

Special Plywoods and Laminates

Plywood and veneer laminates are produced in a variety of forms for specialized applications.

Compreg is a relatively new material made by saturating green veneers with a synthetic resin, usually phenol-formaldehyde resinoid, and then bonding them at temperatures of 300 deg. F and pressures of 1000 to 1200 psi. The veneer is saturated either by soaking or pressure tank treatment. The veneer plies are usually assembled with the grain parallel. The wood is compressed as much as one third to one half its original dimension.

The material is dimensionally stable and fairly resistant to decay, termites, and marine borers. It has high resistance to electricity, moisture, acids, and fire. It is ten to twenty times as hard as normal wood but more brittle. It works best with tools used for machining brass or plastics. It turns well on a metalworking lathe and sands and polishes well. It has found use in furniture tops, specialty flooring, airplane propellers, knife handles, dies, jigs, small tools, silent gears, and the like. It is sold under various trade names.

Compreg may be molded by precompressing the dry resin treated veneer, cutting it to fit a mold, and then reheating. The method is known as expansion molding. Treated veneer, $\frac{1}{10}$ in. thick, is heated at 200 to 240 deg. F. At this temperature, the wood is plasticized, but it does not cure. Single sheets of the heated veneer are then compressed between cold platens for about 15 seconds. The compressed veneer is next cut to fit and fill a metal mold. When the mold is locked and heated, the veneer plies expand and bond, filling the mold contour. Pressures up to 750 psi are exerted by the expanding wood.

Impreg is made of veneers that have been treated with phenol-resins, dried, and then bonded in the manner of regular plywood. The grain is usually parallel in all plies. It has good dimensional stability and resistance to decay, fungi, insects, moisture, and weather. Strength properties are not materially altered. It finds extensive use for die blocks, die models, and pattern stock. The automobile industry is a leading consumer of impreg pattern stock. See Figure 35–49. It is sold under various trade names.

Staypak is a compressed product, tougher than compreg, but containing no resin. It is made by modifying the compression conditions to cause the lignin (intercellular substance) to flow sufficiently to eliminate the internal stresses. It is not as resistant as compreg to water, decay, and insects. It is as useful as compreg where high water resistance is not necessary.

Wood Laminating

Wooden arches (Fig. 35–51, Chapter VIII), sporting equipment, furniture, ship keels and frames, auto bodies, nose fairings, and dozens of other products (Figs. 35–53 to 35–59) are produced in the wood-laminating industry.

Laminated wood arches were first made in Germany during the first decade of

Fig. 35–49. Skilled die model makers are shown at work on an Impreg laminated wood model for the rear end of a Chevrolet. These models are used as patterns for making the metal dies that will be used to stamp out the metal parts.

Fig. 35–50. Spruce veneer is laid up alternately vertically and horizontally and bonded together to form the nose fairing for a Polaris missile. The wood chars as the missile enters the atmosphere, but it does not burn.

Fig. 35–51. Various articles produced on the Schreiber shell forming presses.

Fig. 35–52. This Marcos 1800 Grand Touring car sports a laminated wood body built over a wooden frame. The body and frame weigh only 200 pounds. The car has won several European racing championships.

Fig. 35–53. This 165-foot minesweeper hull shows the use of laminated members for the keel, ribs, and frames.

this century. The widespread use of wood for construction in America led to its early acceptance. Research during World Wars I and II helped to perfect the process for a variety of purposes. The U. S. Navy sponsored much research to develop laminated structural members for mine sweepers. Wooden hulls were a necessary protection against magnetic mines.

Technically, laminated wood is that in which layers of veneers or boards are glued together with the grain running in the same direction. In practice, however, some "laminated" wood is made up of layers at right angles to one another as in the case of plywood.

Essentially, laminating consists of bonding pieces of wood together to "make big ones out of little ones." The process is used to produce members of unusual shape or to combine woods with different properties so that advantage may be taken of the best in each.

Wood lamination provides a substitute for scarce lumber of large size and high quality. When thoroughly dried, lumber may be laminated into members that will not check, shrink, or warp. They will have a better appearance and strength than similar-sized solid lumber. Research has shown that uniform moisture content at the time of gluing, and at a level comparable to that expected in service, is of major importance to the quality of laminated wood.

Laminated wood for interior use where moisture content ranges between 5 and 15 percent may be glued with casein glue. Where moisture contents range as high as 30 percent as in exterior use, resorcinal resin glues develop stronger bonds than any of the other glues. In any case, the glue used must permit a sufficient assembly time that it does not cure (harden) before the work is clamped. Some resor-

Fig. 35–54. This air operated shell forming press produces a wrap-around shell of 360 degrees, in any shape, within two minutes.

cinal glues provide the best bond when heated to 300 or 400 deg. F. Laminated members used in exterior locations should be pressure treated to prevent decay.

Curved laminations are formed and bonded in dies under pressure. (See Figure 35–55.) The wood to be lami-

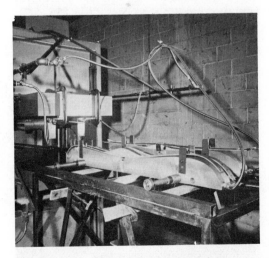

Fig. 35–55. This hydraulic hot plate press is used to laminate wood and fiber glass for archery bows.

Fig. 35–56. Custom laminating involves the problem of clamping the lay-up in a form.

Fig. 35–58. Hollow-core laminated doors are stacked and clamped while the glue cures.

nated is coated with glue, stacked in the die, and then subjected to pressures of 100 to 200 lb. per square inch while the glue cures. Some laminating presses have integral heating units that facilitate the curing of the glue. High-frequency dielectric heating is used where thin veneers are laminated into relatively small assemblies. Custom laminating of one or just a few pieces often requires more hours in the preparation of forms than in the actual laminating process (Fig. 35–56).

Doors and counter and table tops are laminated in a relatively simple process (Figs. 35–57 to 35–59). Slow curing

Fig. 35–57. Plastic laminates are pressed onto a counter top in this rotary press.

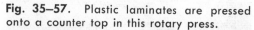

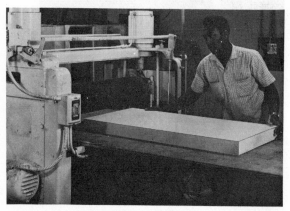

glues are applied to the frames of doors and to the plywood with which they are covered. These are then stacked and clamped until the glue cures. Plastic laminates and table tops are coated with contact cement and pressed together in rotary presses (Fig. 35–57).

Fig. 35–59. Glue is applied to the core in this roller coating machine. The laminated door faces are then positioned and the assembly is stacked to await pressing.

DISCUSSION QUESTIONS

1. What is veneer? How does it differ from plywood?
2. What are some common uses of veneer?
3. How do the methods of preparing veneers differ?
4. Why does heat soften wood? In what ways may wood be heated? What is the effect of heat and moisture on the strength of wood?
5. What are "lathe checks"? Why are they formed?
6. What are the problems involved in producing yellow pine veneer? Yellow pine plywood?
7. How do the strengths of equal size pieces of plywood and solid wood compare as moisture content and temperature vary?
8. How do the costs of covering an 8 by 82-ft. wall with ⅜-in. plywood compare with using 1 in. by 6-in. dressed sheathing? Use local material and labor costs. Establish a time rate for each operation by observing and clocking some local carpenters.
9. What are the different types and grades of hardwood plywoods? Of softwood plywoods? Why are hardwood and softwood plywood graded differently?
10. In what patterns are hardwood veneers matched?
11. What processes are involved in the production of plywood?
12. What details must be specified when ordering plywood?
13. What are the advantages of laminated wood over solid wood? How does the strength of each compare?
14. How would you design and make the necessary forms to produce 1000 one-piece laminated chair seats and backs?
15. Describe a test that would help one to decide which of several glues was best for a laminated arch.

Chapter 36 The Wood-Composition-Board Industry

High quality lumber and plywood are prized for their figure, grain, color, and unique mechanical properties. Their production, however, results in considerable wood residue or waste. For many years, as much or even more wood was burned and wasted as was used. As the need to conserve our wood supply became evident, efforts were made to find uses for all of the tree. These efforts resulted in the development of wood products in which grain, color, figure, and texture are relatively unimportant. The industries that make these products either use wood as a chemical raw material (such as the pulp and paper industry) or they reduce it to small pieces or particles and then reassemble them.

The wood-composition-board industry mechanically reduces wood to small components and then reassembles it into special forms. The products may be classified into two groups: *fiberboards* and *particle boards*. Fiberboards are produced from mechanical pulps. Particle boards are manufactured from chips, flakes, or slivers. Fiberboards are further classified as *insulation board* and *hardboard* depending upon their density.

Table 36–1 compares the industries that manufacture composition board and the products produced.

Fiberboards

Insulation board is a felted wood or cane fiberboard with a specific gravity of 0.4 or below. "Felted" refers to the matting and pressing together of the basic wood fibers. Insulation board is produced in a preformed, rigid form. Insulation board gives strength and thermal and/or sound insulation to a structure. Its good insulating qualities are primarily the result of minute air cells that are formed between the fibers during manufacture. Most boards are factory finished in a variety of surface types.

Insulation board finds use as decorative interior finish, structural building and insulating board, a base for other finishes, padding in containers, roof decks, ceiling panels, wall sheathing, and sound deadening board. (See Figs. 36–1 and 36–2).

Insulation board is easy to saw, nail, staple, glue, and paint. All products designed for interior finish uses have a flame-resistant surface.

Fig. 36–1. Ceiling tiles may be cemented, clipped, stapled, nailed, or interlocked in place. Acoustical tiles absorb up to 70 percent of excess noise.

Fig. 36–2. This insulating roof deck provides the roof deck itself, the finished inside ceiling, and effective insulation. The units are nailed to the ceiling beams and either a built-up or asphalt shingle roof system is applied over them.

Manufacture of Insulation Board

Insulation board was first produced in May, 1914, in International Falls, Minnesota. It was the result of the efforts of Carl G. Muench to find a use for "screenings" — bits of wood pulp too coarse for papermaking. Muench had been a production expert in a factory making flax-straw insulation for ice boxes. He recognized the potentialities of dry, matted wood fibers as an insulator and set about adapting the paper-making process to this purpose. Within ten weeks he had developed a machine and produced the first sheets of insulation board. See Figure 36–3.

Demand for the product far exceeded the supply. Within two years, a new plant

Fig. 36–3. This is a diagram of the first insulation board producing machine. Wood fibers carried in water flowed onto the lower wire mesh belt conveyor. The second wire mesh conveyor pressed and matted the fibers and squeezed out most of the water. Rollers compressed the mat further. The sheets were then dried in an oven.

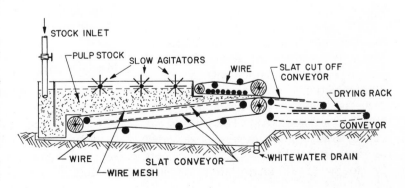

STOCK INLET

PULP STOCK SLOW AGITATORS WIRE SLAT CUT OFF CONVEYOR

DRYING RACK

CONVEYOR

WIRE
WIRE MESH
SLAT CONVEYOR
WHITEWATER DRAIN

Fig. 36–4. Hardboard is available in plain, textured, printed wood grain, and perforated (remanufactured) patterns.

was built with a daily capacity of 60,000 sq. ft. In 1919, Muench and several associates moved to New Orleans. There they created the Celotex Corporation and began to make insulation board from bagasse — the residue left from the manufacture of cane sugar. This first plant had a daily capacity of 200,000 sq. ft. Today this same plant produces three million square feet daily.

The basic process for producing insulation board, as it was developed by Muench, is still used today, but with several additional refinements. Wood or other materials containing cellulose fibers, such as bagasse, are mechanically reduced to a coarse pulp. The pulp is carried by water onto a moving wire screen where it is matted, pressed to thickness, cut to size, and finally dried in long

ovens. The fibers are bonded together with natural lignin, synthetic resins, or added binders.

Most insulation building boards are made 4 by 8 ft., but 9-, 10-, and 12-ft. lengths are also made. Other products are made as narrow as 12 in.

Production plants are located where the raw materials are most readily available. Most are in the eastern half of the United States.

Hardboard

Hardboard is a manufactured wood panel without knots or grain. It consists of matted and hot-pressed wood fibers held together by lignin, the natural cohesive substance found in all wood. The product is strong and hard and has a specific gravity of 0.8 or above. It is basically a building material, but hundreds of uses have been found for this versatile material. It is made in a variety of patterns and surface finishes as shown in Figure 36–5.

Hardboard was discovered by accident. William H. Mason was working on a process for extracting turpentine and other oils from green wood. As he traveled from mill to mill, he was appalled by the great quantities of wood that were burned for want of a better use for it. He reasoned that there must be a useful product that could be made from wood residue — possibly an insulation board.

Mason began experimenting with the explosion process for making wood fibers in March, 1924. He installed a small steam gun (steel cylinder) in a shed next to a lumber mill in Mississippi. He loaded it with wood chips, sealed it, and heated it with a blowtorch. When the pressure had built up, he suddenly released the plug. A terrific explosion resulted, but the wood chips were changed into valuable wood fibers.

Mason tested his idea for producing insulation board in a pilot plant. His success brought him financial support. Soon a factory for full scale production was designed and construction begun in Laurel, Miss. However, a lucky accident was to change the construction plans.

Mason was working to refine his process for making insulation board in a paper mill in Wisconsin. He had placed some of the wet wood fiber mat in a screw press with the intention of squeezing out the water and then drying the board in an oven. The press had one steam heated platen. He had turned off the steam and gone to lunch, but when he returned, he found that the valve had sprung a leak. The press was still hot. The wood fiber mat had turned into a hot, dense, dry board that looked like the leather soles of his shoes. And so, the first hardboard was made. It was later called Masonite.

Foreseeing the commercial possibilities of his new product, Mason and his backers redesigned the Mississippi mill and in 1926 produced about six million square feet of hardboard. In 1929 the Masonite Corporation was organized.

The Hardboard Industry

As shown in Table 36–1, eighteen plants produce hardboard in this country. In 1964 production was 2675 million square feet of $\frac{1}{8}$-in. basis. Consumption was 3195 million square feet. Imports, which are increasing annually, account for more than one half billion square feet. Foreign producers are able to ship by ocean freight at lower cost than domestic producers can ship to the same markets by rail. Also, the value of imported hardboard has declined 33 percent since 1956. Imports now amount to 18 percent of domestic production. Exports

TABLE 36–1 TYPES OF COMPOSITION BOARD COMPARED

Type of Board	No. Plants	Annual Production Billion Sq. Ft.	Basis	Process	Specific Gravity	Wood Form	Binder Added	Board Thickness
Insulation	24	3.0	½″	Wet Wet	0.1–0.4	Fiber	None or Adhesive	½–3″
Hardboard	18	2.6	⅛″	Semidry Dry	0.8–1.3	Fiber	None or Adhesive	1/10–2″
Particle board	61	0.5	¾″	Dry	0.4–0.8	Chips	Adhesive	⅛–4″

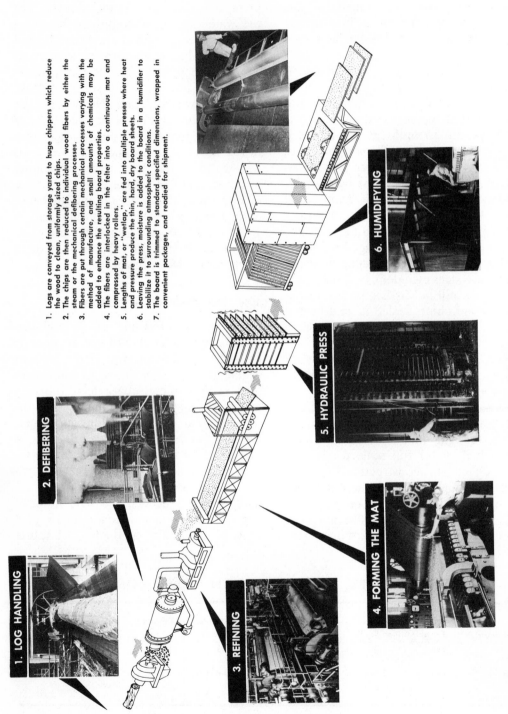

1. Logs are conveyed from storage yards to huge chippers which reduce the wood to clean, uniformly sized chips.
2. The chips are then reduced to individual wood fibers by either the steam or the mechanical defibering processes.
3. Fibers are put through certain mechanical processes varying with the method of manufacture, and small amounts of chemicals may be added to enhance the resulting board properties.
4. The fibers are interlocked in the felter into a continuous mat and compressed by heavy rollers.
5. Lengths of mat, or "wetlap," are fed into multiple presses where heat and pressure produce the thin, hard, dry board sheets.
6. Leaving the press, moisture is added to the board in a humidifier to stabilize it to surrounding atmospheric conditions.
7. The board is trimmed to standard specified dimensions, wrapped in convenient packages, and readied for shipment.

1. LOG HANDLING

2. DEFIBERING

3. REFINING

4. FORMING THE MAT

5. HYDRAULIC PRESS

6. HUMIDIFYING

Fig. 36–5.   The basic steps in the manufacture of hardboard are shown above.

were less than 20 million square feet in 1964. The value of shipments in the U. S. was about $150 million in 1964.

Production of hardboard is expected to increase annually. The construction industry accounts for more than 50 percent of the hardboard consumed each year. Exterior house siding in a variety of patterns has become popular. Other uses include fencing, paneling, floor underlayment, animal feeders, and utility structures.

The furniture and cabinet manufacturing industry uses about 20 to 25 percent of the annual hardboard production. It is used with a variety of surface finishes in exposed and hidden parts of mirrors, drawers, upholstered pieces, store and office fixtures, television sets, radios, bars and counters, and card and game tables.

Automobile station wagons use hardboard as a ceiling liner. Other uses are in toys, sporting goods, electrical equipment, and railway cars. Per capita consumption was 13 sq. ft. in 1964.

Hardboard Manufacturing

Hardboard production (see Fig. 36–5) begins in the forest with the felling of trees. After cutting, the trees are sawed into convenient lengths, stripped of their bark, hauled to the mill, and stacked to air dry. While hardboard was originally developed by using wood residue, demand for the product necessitates cutting trees to supplement the supply of raw materials.

When the logs are dry, they are conveyed into the "breakdown mill." Here they are *chipped* into pieces about the size of a thumb nail. The chipper contains a large revolving disk fitted with several sharp knives. As the log moves endwise into the knives it is cut into chips of the proper size. The chips are then *screened* and those too large are sent back to be chipped again. The screened chips then move to a storage building to await the defibering process.

The chips are reduced to fibers by one of two *defibering* processes — either the explosion process developed by Mason, or the machine process.

The *explosion process* takes place in thick-steel high-pressure cylinders called "guns." Each gun is loaded with about 260 lb. of chips and then sealed. Steam pressure of 400 psi is introduced into the gun. After 15 seconds, the pressure is raised to 1000 psi and held for 1 to 1½ minutes. At the end of the steaming cycle an hydraulic valve is quickly opened and the pressure suddenly released. The chips explode into a mass of wood fibers.

The explosion operation performs two functions. First, the high pressure steam, moisture, and heat hydrolyze (decompose by addition of water) and break down the lignocellulose bond. Secondly, the sudden release of pressure tears the chips apart to produce the characteristic brown, fluffy wood fiber.

The *machine defibering process* is continuous in contrast to the batch-type explosion process. It is performed in machines known as defibrators and refiners. The chips are screw fed from a hopper into a preheater. Here they are heated in steam at a pressure of 125 to 175 psi, to partially hydrolyze the lignin. The hot chips are then screw fed into the space between two grinding disks. (Defibrators and refiners differ in the shape, number, and motion of the grinding disks.) As the chips are forced over the grinding surfaces they are converted into fiber.

After the defibering process the mass of fiber bundles is reduced to individual fibers in a refiner. They are then washed and screened to remove the components of the wood that will not be used.

Next, the fibers are *matted* in one of two ways distinguished by the amount of moisture present. They are termed the wet process or the dry (air-suspension) process.

In the *wet process,* a water suspension of fibers is flowed onto a moving wire screen in a Fourdrinier machine. The water is squeezed through the screen by heavy rolls and the fibers are "felted" or matted together in a continuous strip. The mat is called "wetlap." (The Fourdrinier machine was developed in 1803 for making paper.)

Some wet-process boards are made in a batch-forming process. A measured quantity of water and fiber is introduced into a form the size of the finished board known as a "deckle box." The bottom of the deckle box is a wire screen through which the water is suctioned off to form the mat. Additional water is removed by compressing the mat or running it through a continuous drier. This drying operation is sometimes applied to the Fourdrinier-made wetlap. It is called the *semidry process.*

In the *dry process,* the fibers are first dried. The mat is formed by an air-felting operation in which the dry fibers are carried onto the moving screen of a cylinder board machine by air instead of water.

After the wetlap or mat has been formed it is cut into convenient lengths and a tipple guides it to a shelf in a stationary rack. When the rack is filled (20 sheets), it is unloaded into a portable rack that transfers the load into the hot press.

Hot pressing converts the mat or wetlap into hardboard in approximately 10 minutes. Temperatures up to 410 deg. and pressures up to 750 psi cause the lignin and wood fibers to bond together in a hard, dense sheet. Wetlap is squeezed between a screen and a polished, chromium-plated steel plate. As the water turns to steam the screen permits it to escape. The screen impression may be seen on the back of many types of hardboard. Dry and semidry process boards produce much less steam and may be pressed without the use of screens. Such boards have two smooth surfaces. Some dry process boards have a small quantity of synthetic-resin adhesive added to serve as a binder.

The pressed sheets of hardboard are so dry that a small amount of moisture must be added to prevent any tendency to warp. The boards are placed in a *humidification* chamber until they soak up enough moisture to approximate the conditions they will meet in actual use.

After humidification, the boards are *inspected* and *tested* to insure that they meet quality standards. They are then *trimmed* to correct size, stacked on pallets, and stored for shipment. Panels are delivered to building supply dealers in heavy paper-wrapped bundles.

Classification of Hardboard

Hardboard is classified as *standard, tempered,* and *service.* Tempered hardboards are also called treated boards. *Tempered hardboard* is made by first soaking the panels in drying oils such as tung oil, tall oil, soybean oil, or linseed oil. The impregnated boards are then baked for several hours in an oven at 300 deg. F. to "polymerize" or harden the absorbed oil. Carefully tempered hardboard is stronger, smoother, harder, and more water resistant than the untreated product. It has a specific gravity of 1.0 to 1.20.

Standard and service hardboards are ordinarily untreated, although both may be treated or special additives included

Fig. 36–6. A technician observes the quality of the hardboard following application of a prime coat by a roller.

Fig. 36–7a. The shield on this neutron counter is made of molded wood fibers.

during manufacture to give them improved characteristics. Standard hardboard is produced in greatest quantity. Standard hardboard is substantially the same as when it comes from the humidification chamber. It has high strength and water resistance and a specific gravity of 0.96 to 1.20. Service-type hardboard has less strength and water resistance than standard hardboard. Its specific gravity is in the range of 0.80 to 0.96. It is usually used for interior purposes where minimum weight is desired.

Table 36–2 compares the characteristics of the basic hardboards.

The *remanufacture of hardboard* is an important part of the industry. Panels are scored, punched, grooved, tiled, perforated, painted, and decorated in a variety of ways as shown in Figure 36–4. Figure 36–6 shows a panel being roller coated with paint. Some surface textures are produced (embossed) at the time of pressing.

The processes for making hardboard have been applied to the manufacture of furniture parts and other products from wood fibers. (See Figs. 36–7a, 36–7b, and 36–7c.) The wood fibers are heated

Fig. 36–7b. These salad bowls and servers are made of compressed wood fibers and an unfilled melamine-urea resin.

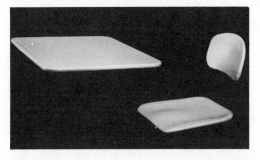

Fig. 36–7c. Finely ground hardwood fibers and pigments are compression molded with heat and pressure into one strong, homogeneous piece to make desk tops, chair seats and backs.

TABLE 36–2 DETAIL REQUIREMENTS OF BASIC HARDBOARDS

Classification	Surface	Nominal thickness designations	Thickness limits (minimum-maximum average per panel)	Modulus of rupture (minimum average per panel)	Tensile strength (minimum average per panel)		Water resistance	
					Parallel to surface	Perpendicular to surface	Water absorption (maximum per panel)	Thickness swelling (maximum per panel)
		Inch	Inch	P.s.i.	P.s.i.	P.s.i.	Percent	Percent
Standard	S1S	$\frac{1}{12}$	0.070–0.090				43	30
		$\frac{1}{10}$	.090– .110				25	22
		$\frac{1}{8}$	.115– .155				20	16
		$\frac{3}{16}$	.170– .205	5,000	2,500	100	18	14
		$\frac{1}{4}$	.225– .265				16	12
		$\frac{5}{16}$	.290– .335				14	10
	S2S	$\frac{1}{10}$	.090– .110				30	25
		$\frac{1}{8}$	.115– .155				25	18
		$\frac{3}{16}$	.170– .205	5,000	2,500	100	25	18
		$\frac{1}{4}$	.225– .265				18	14
		$\frac{5}{16}$	.290– .335				15	12
		$\frac{3}{8}$	.350– .400				12	10
Tempered	S1S	$\frac{1}{8}$	.115– .155				15	11
		$\frac{3}{16}$	.170– .205	7,000	3,500	150	12	10
		$\frac{1}{4}$	.225– .265				10	8
		$\frac{5}{16}$	.290– .335				8	8
	S2S	$\frac{1}{8}$	.115– .155				15	15
		$\frac{3}{16}$	.170– .205	7,000	3,500	150	15	12
		$\frac{1}{4}$	.225– .265				12	12
Service	S1S	$\frac{1}{8}$	.115– .155				30	25
		$\frac{3}{16}$	.170– .205	3,000	1,500	50	25	15
		$\frac{1}{4}$	.225– .265				25	15
		$\frac{3}{8}$	.350– .400				25	15
	S2S	$\frac{1}{8}$	.115– .155				30	25
		$\frac{3}{16}$	.170– .205	3,000	1,500	50	27	25
		$\frac{7}{32}$	.205– .250				27	25
		$\frac{1}{4}$	.225– .265				27	25

Credit: U. S. Dept. of Commerce CS 2 1–63.

and compressed into a mold the shape of a leg, arm, back, etc. As early as 1949, a New Jersey company was producing molded products from ground wood and thermosetting resins. One company calls their material "cultured wood." A very dense (85 to 89 lb. per cubic foot) hardboard product, in thicknesses up to 2 in., is also manufactured for use in press forming or stretch forming dies for metals. Because these dies are lighter in weight than if made from metal, they are easier to handle.

Particle Board

Wood particles are manufactured into products of two general types: flat wood particle boards and molded wood particle products, *Flat wood particle board* (see Fig. 36–8) is a relatively dense, engineered panel made by combining wood flakes, chips, and slivers with resins and hot pressing them into shape. The panels are known as chipboard, coreboard, chipcore, flakeboard, synthetic lumber, and composition board. They can be made from any species of wood and from almost any type of wood waste. *Molded wood particle* products are generally produced from wood flour or sawdust-type particles.

The use of wood waste for the manufacture of particle board on a semicommercial basis originated in Europe in the late 1930's. The idea for this product was fathered by the diminishing forests and the need to conserve wood.

Particle board was first manufactured in this country about 1948. Today about 61 plants compose the industry. See Table 36–1. Most are located in the South but the greatest production capacity exists in the West. Total annual production capacity is estimated at 770 million square feet of ¾-in. basis. Present production is about 70 percent of capacity. The value of shipments was estimated at $51 million in 1964. Value added by manufacture is approximately 50 percent of the value of the shipments. Imports have been very small, but are expected to increase.

Flat particle board has won acceptance in the furniture, plastic laminating, and home-construction industries. It finds wide use as core stock for laminated panels, table and counter tops, shelving,

Fig. 36–8. Particle board is one of the products resulting from efforts to conserve wood.

cabinets (See Figure 36–8), wall panels, siding, sheathing, floor and ceiling tile, doors, billboards, and toys. As shown in Figure 36–9, particle board can be worked by every wood machining process. It can be machined to take any conventional hardware. Some common molded wood particle products are chair backs and seats, toilet seats, gun stocks, spools, carton separators, paper-roll plugs, serving trays, and bowls.

Manufacture of Particle Board

Particle board is made either by *flat-platen pressure* or by *extrusion pressure*. Each method produces a board with different properties. Flat-platen manufac-

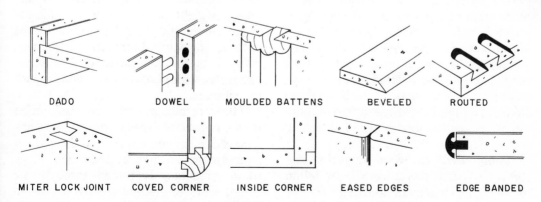

DADO   DOWEL   MOULDED BATTENS   BEVELED   ROUTED

MITER LOCK JOINT   COVED CORNER   INSIDE CORNER   EASED EDGES   EDGE BANDED

Fig. 36–9. Particle board can be worked by every wood machining process.

ture applies the pressure perpendicular to the surface of the board. This consolidation of the mixture of resin and wood particles is made in single or multi-platen hot presses. A variation of the flat-platen press produces particle board in a continuous strip. Flat-platen manufacture accounts for about 85 percent of all particle board production in the United States.

The remaining 15 percent of particle-board production utilizes the extrusion-press process. Here, the resin-particle mixture is consolidated by pressure applied parallel to the plane of the sheet (toothpaste is extruded from the tube when you squeeze it). This process produces particle board in a continuous sheet by forcing the mixture through a long die. The die is essentially two long platens, with side stops, spaced the desired sheet thickness apart. The platens are heated and the resin cures as the board passes through the die. Extruded board is made in horizontal and vertical presses.

There are many variations of the two basic particle board manufacturing processes. Most of the variations are associated with original engineering developments. There are more variations of the flat-platen process than of the extrusion process. This is due to the fact that extruded boards are manufactured exclusively from hammermilled particles. Flat-platen boards may utilize a wider variety of particles because they may be formed in layers with higher quality faces than cores. Some utilize combinations of hammermilled sliver-shaped particles and flakes, combinations of two different quality flakes, or combinations of fine and course hammermilled particles.

Hammermills are wood-fracturing machines. The particles are made by blunt, free-swinging hammers attached to a cylinder. The hammers extend from the cylinder by centrifugal force during operation. As they strike the wood, chips are broken off rather than cut as on the chipping (knife-cutting) machines. These machines are also called wood hogs, chip shredders, and rechippers.

Knife-cutting machines are known as *chippers* or *knife hogs*. These machines employ disk, cylinder or V-shaped cutter heads in which several knives are mounted. As the wood in the form of rounds, slabs, edgings, veneer clippings, furniture plant trimmings, branches, brush, etc., is fed into the rotating knives, it is cut into chips or flakes. Chips are normally $\frac{3}{4}$ to $1\frac{1}{4}$ in. long. They are usually further processed by grinding to a size approximately $\frac{3}{32}$ by $\frac{3}{32}$ by $\frac{1}{2}$ in. long. Flakes are cut to an average size of 1 by 1 by .015 in. and then further split into widths of 0.200 in. Bark is generally considered undesirable in particle board although some products permit up to 1 percent bark content.

After hammermilling or chipping, the particles are screened. Pieces too large are returned for further reduction in size. Finer sawdust-type particles constitute 20 to 25 percent of the yield. Some of the fines are used as surface layers in certain types of flat-platen boards, but most of it is burned. Fines are undesirable because of their high absorptiveness and added weight without added strength. Furthermore, they tend to settle to the bottom side while horizontally produced board is being manufactured. The different surface properties of the board lends to warpage.

The screened particles are next dried in one of several types of driers. A drum-type drier is common. Air, heated to temperatures as high as 1800 deg. F. in some instances, is forced through the drum. Fins on the inside of the drum keep the particles tumbling while their moisture content is reduced to 6 to 10 percent. Moisture above 10 percent may cause blowouts or blisters in the board. Moisture content below 5 percent may reduce the flow of the adhesive resin by excessive penetration and result in a weak bond of the particles.

Urea-formaldehyde is the most commonly used adhesive resin. The amount mixed with the particles is dependent upon the requirements that the particle board must meet. Usually 5 to 12 percent resin solids, based on the weight of the particles, is used. Core stock board usually contains 5 to 8 percent resin solids. Resin content of 9 to 12 percent gives higher density, better surface properties, better water resistance, and more flexural strength. Phenolic binders in the proportions of about 5 to 7 percent solids are used in particle boards intended for use as sheathing and subflooring.

In addition, extenders, catalysts (hardeners), waxes, petrolatums, and emulsions may be added to the wood particles and adhesive during mixing. These materials facilitate manufacture of the board by extending the working life of the binders, the time permitted for assembly, and the curing time.

Mixers are of the *batch* or *continuous* mixing type. Batch mixers are similar to conventional glue mixers. A measured quantity of particles and adhesive is introduced into the chamber and thoroughly mixed.

Continuous mixers provide a continuous flow of the product mix. Particles and adhesive are metered into a chamber and agitated as the mix passes through to the mat-forming operation.

Most flat-pressed particle board is made in multiple-opening hot presses similar to those used in plywood or hardboard manufacture. See Figure 36–10. The resin and particle mix is measured

Fig. 36–10. This huge particle board press turns out 20 panels, 5' x 16', every 15 minutes. The 400-ton giant stands three stories tall.

into a caul tray either by volume or weight. The mat is several inches thick before it is prepressed by rolling or by squeezing in a single opening hydraulic press as shown in Figure 36–11. The pressed mats and their caul plates are fed into a press loader which automatically fills the twenty press openings at one time. Heat and pressure consolidate the board, the pressing cycle being determined by the board thickness and the curing properties of the adhesives. Special sizes of boards are made in the press shown in Figure 36–12.

Layered boards are produced by modifying the mat-forming process to permit the back, center, and face particles to be metered separately into the caul tray.

The standard flat-pressed process is basically a batch process. However, a special continuous process, developed in England, is sometimes employed. Known as the Bartrev process, it permits the production of particle board in a continuous strip. In this process the mat is

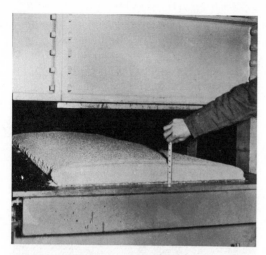

Fig. 36–11. This is a downward acting press. In the photograph, the top platen face projects below the edge of the restraining yoke surrounding the top platen. During prepressing cycle, this restraining yoke bears against the bottom platen or caul sheet forming a frame around the independently moving top platen, which then consolidates the mat by pressure to a thickness of less than 2 inches.

Fig. 36–12. Each platen on this hot plate board press weighs over 18 tons. The total platen pressure of 3,500 tons is exerted through 40 hydraulic rams, pressing to positive stops.

laid on a stainless-steel endless belt caul. The mat passes through a high-frequency preheating unit and then into a pressing unit. A second stainless-steel belt is located above the mat in the pressing unit. Here, a moving chain of electrically heated platens applies pressure through the steel belt. The properties of the finished board are similar to those of the conventional flat-pressed board.

Extrusion presses are fed from the mixing hopper by a reciprocating ram. The ram forces the particle and adhesive mixture into the die where it is cured into an endless sheet under the influence of heat and pressure. This process also permits the production of *fluted boards* 1 to 4 in. thick. Holes throughout the board's length decrease its weight. Metal rods in the die opening form the holes. The rods are heated to aid in curing the adhesive.

Pressures of 150 to 200 psi are used in compressing particle board; temperatures range from 250 to 350 deg. F. Lower temperatures retard production and higher temperatures char the wood particles.

The boards are cut to length by means of a moving saw in the continuous process. Multi-platen press boards are trimmed to length and width on a series of trim saws after they have been inspected and conditioned in a cooling oven. See Figure 36–13. Some particle boards are sanded to improve surface qualities. Prefinished panels are also being marketed.

Types of Particle Board

The physical and strength properties of particle board are dependent upon several factors. Some of the more important are: (1) type and size of particle; (2) manufacturing process — flat-platen pressed or extruded; (3) kind and amount of resin; (4) density; (5) quality of manufacture; (6) moisture content during pressing; and (7) post-manufacturing treatment. Because of these and several other variables, it is impossible to present a single set of values for the various properties.

Flat-platen boards have their particles oriented in a plane parallel to the surface of the board. Extruded boards have their particles oriented in planes perpendicular to the surface of the board and across it. This results in differences in bending strengths for the two types of board depending upon the direction in which the tests are made. To overcome some of the weakness in extruded boards, facings are usually applied.

Table 36–3 presents a summary of the property requirements for mat-formed particle board as presented in the U. S.

Fig. 36–13. Three electronic sensitive monitors gauge the thickness of each particle board panel on its way to the cooling "oven." Any minute variation is automatically signaled for immediate adjustment.

TABLE 36–3 PROPERTY REQUIREMENTS

Type (use)	Density (Grade) (min. avg.)	Class	Modulus of Rupture (min. avg.)	Modulus of Elasticity (min. avg.)	Internal Bond (max. avg.)	Linear Expansion (max. avg.)	Screw Holding Face (min. avg.)	Screw Holding Edge (min. avg.)
			psi	psi	psi	percent	lbs	lbs
1	A (High Density, 50 lbs./cu. ft. and over)	1	2,400	350,000	200	0.55	450	—
		2	3,400	350,000	140	0.55	—	—
	B (Medium Density, between 37 and 50 lbs./cu. ft.)	1	1,600	250,000	70	0.35	225	160
		2	2,400	400,000	60	0.30	225	200
	C (Low Density 37 lbs./cu. ft. and under)	1	800	150,000	20	0.30	125	—
		2	1,400	250,000	30	0.30	175	—
2	A (High Density, 50 lbs./cu. ft. and over)	1	2,400	350,000	125	0.55	450	—
		2	3,400	500,000	400	0.55	500	350
	B (Medium Density, Less than 50 lbs./cu. ft.)	1	1,800	250,000	65	0.35	225	160
		2	2,500	450,000	60	0.25	250	200

Type 1 — Mat-formed particleboard (generally made with urea-formaldehyde resin binders) suitable interior applications.
Type 2 — Mat-formed particleboard made with durable and highly moisture and heat resistant binders (generally phenolic resins) suitable for interior and certain exterior applications.

Credit: National Particleboard Assn.

Department of Commerce Commercial Standard — CS 236-61.

Commercial Standard CS 236-61 further specifies that moisture content, aging resistance, and hardness should fall within certain limits. *Moisture content* should conform to one of three requirements: (a) it is consistent with known end use of panel; (b) it is as specified by customer; and (c) it is not in excess of 10 percent. *Aging resistance* is specified as that which is "not less than 50 percent of the minimum average modulus of rupture before aging. . . ." *Hardness* of A and B density panels is specified as a minimum average of 1800 and 500 lb. respectively.

Flat-platen boards are made as thin as ⅛ in. but they have their greatest use in thicknesses above ⅜ in. The maximum practical thickness is 1 in. Greater thick-nesses are made by laminating two or more boards. Extruded boards are almost exclusively ¾ in. or more in thickness. Panels come in 4- and 5-ft. widths with lengths up to 20 ft. The standard panel is 4 by 8 ft.

The Future of the Composition Board Industry

As has been shown, this industry group had its origin shortly before World War I. Its greatest development occurred after World War II. It represents one of the most rapidly expanding segments of the wood-products industries. Developments come with rapidity. Research is revealing knowledge that will permit improvements in fiber and particle production, adhesives, manufacturing technique, and uses for the products.

DISCUSSION QUESTIONS

1. What is the distinction between fiberboard and particle board?
2. Why does insulation board reduce heat loss and absorb sound?
3. How does the steam gun reduce wood chips to fibers?
4. What are the physical properties of the various composition boards?
5. What are the advantages and disadvantages of batch manufacturing processes over continuous processes?
6. Define: wet lap; mat; tipple; deckle; Fourdrinier machine; hydrolyze.
7. How does tempered hardboard differ from standard hardboard?
8. If an industry is producing at 70 percent of capacity, what steps might be taken to utilize full productive capacity?
9. How can a plant produce at more than 100 percent of capacity?
10. What is the extrusion process? What materials may be extruded? What are some extruded products?
11. Why is sawdust an undesirable ingredient in composition boards except in certain instances?

Chapter 37 The Construction Industry

The *Construction Industry* includes more than just house construction. The U. S. Department of Commerce, Business and Defense Services Administration classifies all construction as private or public. *Private construction* consists of residences, farm construction, public utilities, and nonresidential buildings for industrial, commercial, religious, educational, social, and other uses. *Public construction* consists of all building done by local, state, and federal governments. It includes residences, nonresidential buildings, military facilities, highways, sewer and water systems, conservation developments, and the like.

Expenditures for new construction in 1966 were estimated at $73.8 billion. Private construction cost $50.6 billion and public construction $23.1 billion. This was a continuation of a long term increase in construction. However, the rate of increase in construction expenditures is expected to decline in the next few years. This prediction is based on such factors as: the stabilization of family formation rates, a lag in the establishment of new residential areas and the supporting complex of commercial establishments, and minor anticipated construction cost increases.

Residential construction in 1966 was estimated at 1,250,000 units; 1,205,000 were private nonfarm units valued at $24.6 billion. More than one out of three new housing starts were of the multi-family type (two or more families). This trend toward more families living closer together in urban areas is expected to continue.

Residential construction is the largest sector of the construction industry. It uses about ⅓ of all the lumber produced. The average house requires about 10,500 board feet of lumber. This consists of 7400 board feet of framing lumber, 2200 board feet of sheathing lumber, 325 board feet of siding lumber, and 575 board feet of hardwood flooring and trim. Plywood, hardboard, and insulating board used in housing amounts to about 1½ billion square feet annually.

Today, most houses are built by businessmen builders; one third are built by about 1000 builders who put up more than 100 houses each. Five out of six houses are built for sale to an unknown buyer. Consequently, architects, builders, financing agencies, dealers, and realtors all have prior choice over the buyer on what will be accepted or rejected.

The construction industry provides *employment* for 4.4 million architects, engineers (architectural, civil, electrical,

TABLE 37–1
EMPLOYMENT IN SKILLED BUILDING TRADES
Thousands of workers in construction, early 1965[1]

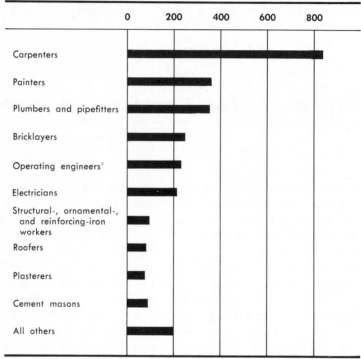

[1] Estimated.
[2] Construction machinery operators.

mechanical), interior designers, landscape architects, technicians (draftsmen, surveyors), building trades craftsmen, contractors, supervisors, and a host of related occupations.

Building-trades craftsmen constitute the nation's largest group of skilled workers. Over one fourth, 2.5 million are in this group of occupations. As shown in Table 37–1, there were over 800,000 carpenters (about one third of all building craftsmen) employed in 1965. Employment is expected to expand in most building trades over the next ten to fifteen years despite advances in technology.

Certain disadvantages are associated with employment in the building trades. Changes in general business conditions

result in sharp employment fluctuations. Furthermore, building is somewhat limited in certain parts of the country during seasons of bad weather.

The best way to enter the building trades is through apprenticeship. Part of the skills may be acquired by attending vocational schools or by taking correspondence courses. Many workers have acquired their skills by working many years as laborers and helpers, observing and being taught by experienced craftsmen. Building-trades craftsmen with business ability have good opportunities to establish their own businesses, such as contracting, furniture upholstery and repair, and cabinetmaking.

Development of the Construction Industry

The time at which man first consciously sought more than temporary shelter from the elements can only be surmised. We know that Stone Age man lived in natural caves. In time, some primitive cave dwellers learned to enlarge their quarters by piling rocks on both sides of the entrance and covering the open top with logs or skins. These were the parent forms of masonry dwellings.

In tropical regions, prehistoric man learned to build huts. Sticks were placed in a circle bound together with vines, and covered with thatch or leaves to form a cone-shaped roof. These were the parent forms of all frame type dwellings.

Most of the early dwellings were one-room affairs. With the development of a more complex civilization, the need arose for structures for the production of goods, education, religion, trade and commerce, transportation, and public functions. Some of the earliest accommodations of this kind existed in the Neolithic Age. Several huts were combined within an enclosure to provide separate rooms.

During the Bronze Age, rectangular houses with two or more rooms were built in Central and Northern Europe. Some of these were of the hut type, built on piles over lakes. Others were built of logs, overlapping at the corners, much like log-cabin construction. In Southern Europe, houses were sometimes built of clay blocks. In some cases, the clay blocks were burned to make them harder and more durable. Some of the houses had courtyards to enclose a garden or a stable.

Lumber was used in construction several centuries before the time of Christ. The Bible (3 Kgs 6:15), in describing Solomon's temple to the Lord states: "And he built the walls of the house on the inside with boards of cedar, from the floor of the house to the top of the walls, and to the roofs . . . and he covered the floor of the house with planks of fir."

Ancient Grecian law and custom prescribed relationships between contractors and the government. The principles established are evident in the contractual arrangements which prevail today. Contractors were required to work continuously, to hire sufficient numbers of qualified workmen, and to guarantee the quality of the work. There were penalties for delays, payments were made in installments, and a percentage of the contract price was retained until the project was completed.

Construction companies were formed during the days of Imperial Rome. While their Greek predecessors worked independently, the Roman contractors formed large companies to undertake the huge construction jobs. They realized that the complexity and risks involved could be minimized and better controlled under a single management. Contracts for whole projects were awarded under a bidding system similar to that which exists today. After the fall of Rome, the construction industry seems to have generally faded from view. During the medieval period, construction of a durable nature was carried on mainly by the Church.

Between the third and seventh centuries, the Syrians built houses in which the roofs, walls, doors, railings, and screens were of stone. The highest qualities of craftsmanship were exemplified in such construction.

Huts with low walls of masonry or earth-banked sod persisted in Europe into the nineteenth century. They were mainly inhabited by serfs. Pioneers lived in houses of this type on the western plains of the United States.

Country houses with stone walls and

slate roofs appeared in France by the thirteenth century. Hand-hewed timbers and boards were commonly used for house construction in Germany, Switzerland, and Scandinavia. During the thirteenth to fifteenth century houses grew in size and number of rooms in order to provide for more privacy.

Contractors reappeared in medieval England. They seem to have risen from the ranks of free masons. Later, the training of masons was specialized to develop two types of masons: one skilled in actual stone work and the other in the planning and designing of buildings. The former apparently was the forerunner of the modern contractor; the latter, of the modern architect and structural engineer.

After the Industrial Revolution in this country, the size of houses decreased as urban development took place. However, the number of rooms in a house increased in order that privacy might be preserved.

Prefabricated Houses

Man has traditionally built his houses stick by stick or stone by stone. Each structure involved the contractor in planning, cutting, fitting, and fastening hundreds of pieces together. Each building required much time and effort of many skilled workers. It is not surprising that in time some men began to experiment with ways to build houses more efficiently.

The art of manufacturing (prefabricating) a structure had its beginnings centuries before the Christian era when the inhabitants of the Middle East burned clay bricks and transported them many miles to build their houses. More than two million limestone blocks were cut to shape at quarries and hauled to the site to build the Great Pyramids in Egypt. Hannibal is recorded as having carried prefabricated huts with him when he crossed the

Alps to war on the Romans.

The first known "prefabricated" house to be erected in this country was made in England about 1623. It was a two-story frame building. It was constructed for the Dorchester Company, which founded the Massachusetts Bay Colony. The "Great House," as it was called, was erected at Gloucester on Cape Ann in what is now the state of Massachusetts. It was constructed of precut oak timbers which, when fitted together, formed the frame of the house. While records do not indicate it, the exterior siding was apparently made of hand-hewn shakes or shingles. The house was dismantled, moved, and erected on a new site several times. It was dismantled for the last time in 1680.

In 1727, two houses, "all cut to be erected," were shipped to the West Indies from New Orleans. Thus, in this country, England, and in Europe prefabrication of houses had an early start. The motivation seems to have been that of providing immediate shelter for colonists arriving in new lands.

While wood has been the mainstay of the manufactured-homes industry, it is only recently that great strides have been made in the use of metal for exteriors. As early as 1801, an English firm constructed factory buildings of cast iron. In 1830 an all-metal prefabricated house was erected in Staffordshire, England, for the use of a lockkeeper on one of the canals. The walls were made of flanged, cast-iron panels and were bolted together. The interior walls were lathed and plastered. When torn down in 1925, the building was still in excellent condition.

Prefabrication in the United States received an impetus from the California Gold Rush in 1848. Prospectors and adventurers flocked to the strike area by the thousands. Some trekked overland

and others sailed around Cape Horn from the East Coast. The influx was so great that the limited amount of housing was available only at extremely high rates.

Lumbermen on the East Coast, in England, Germany, Belgium, and France began producing houses made of wooden panels in an effort to satisfy the housing demand. Even New Zealand and China began exporting prefabricated houses to California. A prefabricated house that sold for $400 in New York commanded as much as $5,000 in the gold rush area. By 1850, over 5000 prefabricated houses had been shipped from the New York area alone. One English company shipped houses that were complete in every detail, even to paper on the walls, carpets on the floors, water closets, and furniture.

This manufacturer's dream ended in 1850 when enterprising lumbermen and carpenters began to develop California's sources of lumber. Within a short time, the area was flooded with cheap, readily available housing; the costly prefabricated house disappeared from the market.

During the Civil War, the prefabricated house made a strong comeback in and around the training camps of the Union troops. Except for tents, prefabricated, panelized wooden camp buildings offered the cheapest, quickest, and easiest way of quartering the men.

Up to this time, prefabricated houses had been made with nonloadbearing walls. Walls were fastened to a frame that carried the weight of the building. In 1882, a German firm began producing the first loadbearing prefabricated walls. Production was confined to small buildings and cabins which were exported all over the world.

In 1892, a young woodworker in Boston named Ernest F. Hodgson, began producing wooden panelized buildings. At first he confined his production to beach houses, chicken coops, dog houses, hunter's cabins, and children's playhouses. When the "horseless carriage" became commonplace, he began to manufacture "auto stables." In addition to creating a need for garages, the automobile created a demand for vacation cottages. Hodgson met this need, and in a short time was producing year-round houses.

Hodgson's construction called for a 1 by 2-in. wall stud, 12 in. on center. A fiber lining was used as sheathing and was covered with a special waterproof paper. Floor joists were 1 by 6 in. and roof rafters 1 by 2 in. or 1 by 3 in., all 12 in. on centers. All panels were fastened together with a wedge-key bolt — a bolt with a slot in the end. When a triangular key was driven into the slot, it pulled the sections together. No sawing or cutting was required at the site. Wall panels were screwed to the floor panels; special lock-washer nuts joined interior wall panel partitions.

Hodgson used only quality materials in his manufactured houses. He once refused to accept an entire carload of West Coast lumber when he found one knot in a board. His packaged house was quite complete and required virtually no carpentry skill in assembly. The roof used clapboards rather than shingles. By the standards of the day it was not a cheap house in its initial cost, but quick assembly with unskilled labor more than offset this. The company, known as Hodgson Houses, Inc., is still operating. Located in Dover, Massachusetts, it is the oldest house manufacturer in the country.

The turn of the century saw many new companies enter the manufactured-house industry. It was at this time that the "precut" or "mail-order" house appeared as a Sears Roebuck catalog item. These houses were marketed under the brand name of "Honor Bilt Homes." They included such things as prefabricated medicine chests, cupboards, china closets, colonnades, ironing boards, breakfast alcoves, door and window frames, and doors mortised for locks. In 1928, Sears advertised over 100 standardized house designs. The company claimed that one of its houses could be erected and ready for occupancy in 352 hours, compared with an erection time of 583½ hours for a comparable conventionally built house.

During the early 1900's, precast hollow-core concrete panels were designed for use in the floors, walls, and roofs of houses. Several hundred such houses were erected in a New York City suburb between 1910 and 1918. The individual units were hauled to the site in trucks and positioned with derricks. The system was found to be suitable for large scale projects, but did not lend itself to the construction of individual houses.

In 1908, Thomas Alva Edison proposed to pour an entire two- or three-story house of concrete, even to poured-in-place bathtubs. Cast-iron forms were to be used, but they proved to be too costly. Wooden forms also proved to be impractical and Edison abandoned the project. He did build a two-story prefabricated frame house to demonstrate some of his ideas. It was transported to Ft. Meyers, Florida, where it stands today.

Much prefabricated steel construction was developed in Great Britain in the period 1920 to 1930. Houses were constructed of sheet steel, expanded metal sprayed with concrete, rolled steel frames, and precast concrete units. None of these proved too successful, however, and the country reverted, for the most part, to conventional construction. Germany and France evolved several steel houses with a variety of surface materials. In the United States, builders were enjoying a

boom, and the industry did not concern itself with house manufacturing. What little progress was made was achieved by small manufacturers and individuals.

In the early '30's, the picture changed. Interest in the field began developing, brought on largely by the depression. There was an urgent need for new industries, and broader investment markets had to be developed. More and more manufacturers of houses appeared. A four room and bath model sold for $4,000; a two-story model with more rooms, an extra bath, a sun deck, and garage sold for $12,000.

When the United States started mobilizing for war in 1940, the manufactured house industry received its greatest boost — one that later turned out to be one of its worst black eyes. The industry outdid itself in providing shelter for thousands of temporary war workers. But the building standards, lowered to provide for rapid erection of housing units, created a public image of the "prefab" that was based on what they had seen during the war.

Since 1946, the house manufacturing industry has grown steadily. During the period 1935 to 1940, the industry produced about 1 percent of the housing in America. In 1940, there were about 30 manufacturers active in the industry. Today, there are about 750 manufacturers in the United States and about 50 in Canada. Production capacities range from 5 to 10 houses per day to as many as 70 per day in the highly automated plants. In 1963, the industry produced 198,316 houses, 20 percent of the single-family housing units built that year. See Table 37–2. Predictions are that by 1975 the house manufacturing industry will account for at least 50 percent of single-family housing construction.

Manufactured houses are now a part

of our way of life. They no longer look like inverted boxes. They are styled and priced to suit anyone. Prices range from $8,000 to $200,000. Styles such as Ranch, Cape Cod, Colonial, Georgian, and contemporary are available. Structurally, they are better than conventionally built houses because they are manufactured of quality materials under optimum factory conditions.

The **manufactured house** is one whose components have been built in a factory and trucked to the site in preassembled parts and sections. The house package usually consists of exterior and interior walls with windows and doors installed, roof and floor systems, exterior siding, cabinets, appliances, heating, and plumbing. The degree of factory fabrication varies with the manufacturer, but the trend is toward the more complete house package. Several manufacturers are producing completely finished sectionalized homes. These homes are transported to the building site in sections, fastened together, and are ready for occupancy in just one working day. Only concrete and masonry need be purchased at the site.

Some of the nation's top architects and engineers are employed to design manufactured houses. Style and flexibility to meet individual needs is the rule. Some manufacturers offer as many as 100 different house models and several designs for apartment houses up to three stories high. Room sizes and arrangement vary within wide limits. In some "prefab" plants it is literally true that no two identical houses ever come off the assembly line. A wide variety of exterior finishes, window and door styles, and other features are available. See Figure 37–1.

Manufactured houses begin in the company's research and development department. Here, architects and engineers de-

TABLE 37–2
YEARLY PROGRESS OF
HOME MANUFACTURING

Year	Manufactured House Shipments	Single Family Housing Starts	Percentage Manufactured Homes
1946	37,200	590,000	6.31
1947	37,400	742,000	5.04
1948	30,000	766,600	3.91
1949	35,000	794,300	4.41
1950	55,000	1,154,100	4.78
1951	50,000	900,100	5.56
1952	57,000	952,500	5.98
1953	55,000	937,800	5.89
1954	77,000	1,000,000	7.70
1955	93,000	1,189,000	7.88
1956	94,790	990,000	10.00
1957	93,546	872,700	11.00
1958	110,080	977,300	11.26
1959	132,054	1,100,000	12.00
1960	126,867	965,600	13.13
1961	156,004	941,300	16.57
1962	186,152	965,000	19.29
1963	198,316	977,300	20.29
1964	212,506	948,600	22.40
1965	232,829	965,500	24.11

Credit: Home Manufacturers Assn.

sign the houses to meet regional building codes and FHA minimum property standards as well as the stringent demands of mass production in the factory (Figs. 37–2 to 37–9). Models and prototypes are constructed, tested, and studied.

Next, the house designs and working drawings are subjected to a cost analysis. Target dates are then set up for the release to builders, another for the initial factory production, and yet another for the completion of renderings and literature for sales representatives.

After pricing has been completed, the house is ready for production. Top quality materials are purchased in carload lots. Working drawings are interpreted and "code sheets" made up for the hundreds of component parts.

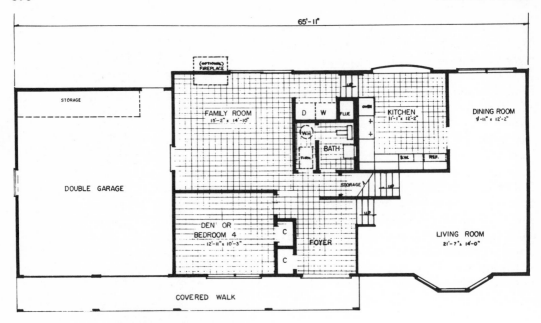

FIRST FLOOR   FLOOR AREA 1867 SQ.FT.

SECOND FLOOR

Fig. 37—2. At the beginning of the wall assembly line, the pre-cut components are placed in fixtures and nailed together. One operator can nail plates and studs for 2,500 feet of wall per 8-hour shift.

Fig. 37—1. One of the many designs available in manufactured homes.

These code sheets tell how each part is to be manufactured to the correct size.

Specialized precision machines cut and shape all parts of the house to exact size. Some of these machines make as many as twenty-three different kinds of cuts on certain structural members. They can cut a carload of lumber in one hour.

The precision cut parts are delivered to the assembly line as needed. Here, the workers assemble the pieces in a huge fixture that assures their proper location.

Fig. 37–1. Continued.

Fig. 37–3. Multi-nailers drive from 12 to 29 nails to fix wall board or sheathing in place. One machine can handle walls for 15 houses in an 8-hour shift.

Then they glue, cement, and nail the parts in position. As the wall sections move along the assembly line, insulation, windows, doors, and interior and exterior wall coverings are added. See Figures 37–2 to 37–8.

Production of the house is so scheduled that all parts arrive at the loading ramp in reverse order to the way in which they will be erected on the building site. No more than three trucks are

required to transport an average-size house. Smaller houses can be loaded on one truck.

The trucks are scheduled to arrive at the building site at the beginning of a working day. The wall sections are first removed from the truck and secured in place. Then the trusses and roof panels are positioned and fastened. By the end of an eight-hour day, a crew of seven men can erect an average single-family

Fig. 37–4. A glue spreader applies glue to the sheathing and prefinished aluminum siding is then pressed in place at a rate of 1 foot per second.

Fig. 37–5. The house units are loaded into vans in the reverse order to which they will be erected. From one to three vans are necessary to transport a house.

house. Within four to six weeks, the siding, wiring, painting, and other finish work can be completed. See Figures 37–9 to 37–10.

Shell houses should not be confused with prefabricated houses. As the term "shell" implies, these houses have completely finished exteriors, but the interiors look like an unfinished attic. They are mass produced to building code stan-

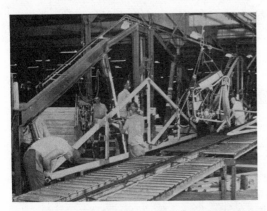

Fig. 37–6. Roof trusses are assembled in fixtures that insure accuracy.

Fig. 37–7. These men route out window and door openings through the siding and sheathing in just five seconds.

Fig. 37–8. Window units are fastened in place as the wall sections move along the assembly line.

dards, much like the prefabricated house. The builder puts up the foundation, floors, walls, and roof, and paints the outside. The owner then completes the plumbing, wiring, heating, and interior finishing at his leisure.

Approximately 100,000 shell houses are sold annually. They are sold in one of the following ways: (1) as a basic shell; (2) as a shell plus the necessary materials to finish the interior; and (3) as a completely finished house. Prices range from $2,000 to $5,000 for a full-size two- or three-bedroom shell. A typical three-bedroom house sells for approximately $3,200 in the shell form, $4,400 for the shell plus materials, and $5,800 completely finished. By doing his own work, the owner can save about $1,400 or 25 percent.

The many prefinished materials and kits on the market make it possible for almost anyone with initiative and a few tool skills to complete a shell house interior. For those who recognize their limitations in this respect, professional help may usually be purchased.

Fig. 37–9. The roof trusses are lifted into place and then the roof sections are fastened down. By the end of an 8-hour day, the house is weathered-in.

House Trailers

The history of the house-trailer industry has been brief, but its growth has been rapid. "Trailer coaches" were first produced in the 1930's. They were used mainly as migratory living quarters. After World War II, the housing shortage forced thousands of families to turn to

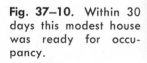

Fig. 37–10. Within 30 days this modest house was ready for occupancy.

them. They found them to be practical, low cost, and, of course, mobile. To meet the demand, house-trailer manufacturers sprang up all over the United States.

Approximately 400 factories with about 29,000 employees produce house trailers. In 1964, some 250,000 units were sold for about $778 million. It is predicted that production will increase roughly 15 percent annually for the remainder of this decade.

House trailers are classified as mobile homes or travel trailers. Travel trailers constitute about 40 percent of production.

Mobile homes (Figs. 37–11, 37–12, and 37–13) are defined as movable or portable dwellings built on a chassis, connected to utilities, and designed without a permanent foundation *for year-round living.* All of today's mobile homes come fully equipped with major appliances, sanitary facilities, and furniture plus draperies, lamps, and carpeting. The home is centrally heated by gas, oil, or electricity. Large mobile homes are towed to their sites by trucks.

A typical *floor plan* of a mobile home is shown in Figure 37–12. These units sell for $3,000 to $12,000 with the average being $5,600. It is estimated. that over 4 million people live in 1.5 million mobile homes today. One in eight new single family dwellings sold is a mobile home.

Construction of the typical mobile home is shown in Figure 37–13. In 1963, mobile home construction utilized the following wood products:

Fig. 37–11a. This is the kitchen-dining area of a mobile home.

Fig. 37–11b. The living room of a mobile home. This model is known as an "expansible." The section of the room on the left is carried inside the living room while the mobile home is being transported. When parked on the lot, it is fastened to the end of the living room to increase its space.

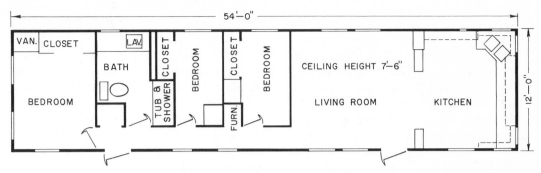

Fig. 37–12. A typical mobile home floor plan. Mobile homes are made in 8-, 10-, and 12-foot widths and in expansibles and double widths (up to 20 feet wide). Lengths range from 30 feet to over 65 feet. Approximately three-fourths of the mobile homes produced are 10 feet wide.

Lumber	226,350,000 board feet
Plywood	276,000,000 sq. ft. of $\frac{3}{8}''$ basis
Fiberboard	135,300,000 sq. ft. of $\frac{1}{2}''$ basis
Hardboard	15,750,000 sq. ft. of $\frac{1}{8}''$ basis
Particle board	900,000 sq. ft. of $\frac{1}{2}''$ basis

Production techniques typical of the prefabricated house industry characterize the manufacture of mobile homes.

Travel trailers are defined as vehicular, portable structures built on a chassis, designed to be used as a *temporary* dwelling for travel, recreational, and vacation uses. Body widths do not exceed 8 ft., lengths do not exceed 29 ft., and total weight does not exceed 4500 lb. They

Fig. 37–13. This exploded view of a mobile home shows its construction. All structural members above the chassis are wood; floor sheathing is plywood and walls are covered with pre-finished plywood. Exterior wall surfaces are aluminum and the roof is enameled galvanized steel.

are towed by the owner with a standard automobile.

There are over 400,000 travel trailers in use today; one-third by persons employed in skilled occupations and one fifth by persons in professional occupations. They are equipped with plumbing, heating, and electrical systems, appliances, and furniture for families of four to six persons.

Construction details of travel trailers are similar to those of mobile homes, the main difference being in size.

Architects

Architecture had its origin when man first modified his cave or made a crude hut. When man first scratched the shape of his intended shelter in the sand, he initiated the concept of planning and designing structures.

Today, architects and architectural and civil engineers utilize the accumulated knowledge of centuries to design houses, schools, churches, factories, highways, bridges, and other structures. Like other designers, they must follow the basic rule of design — form follows function. They must keep abreast of the technological changes and advancements in materials and engineering design. They must also understand the science and engineering of architecture and be able to arrange and balance space in order to produce structures that are beautiful, sound, and functional.

Architects must have a license to practice architecture. All states require this by law. The purpose of these laws is to ensure that work which may affect life, health, or property is performed by qualified architects. Each state establishes its requirements for admission to the licensing examination. These generally include graduation from an accredited profes-

sional school (5 years) plus three years of practical experience in an architect's office. Most states accept 10 to 12 years of practical experience for admission to the licensing examination as a substitute for the formal training.

Architectural and Civil engineers must also have a license to practice. Either 4 to 5 years of college or practical experience are required for admission to the examination.

Residential Design

Architects have used a variety of methods to design a structure. Generally they attempt to organize rooms so as to get the maximum amount of space for the minimum cost.

Various economies of design have been incorporated into prefabricated or custom built homes. For example, in 1962 the National Lumber Manufacturers Association introduced a new house-construction system known as the *Unicom method*. The Unicom method of construction is intended to permit faster planning and erection of a house. Consumers benefit by obtaining a well-designed, soundly built house at less cost (Figs. 37–14 to 37–16).

The name "Unicom" was derived from the words "uniform components." The method uses modular (part or room) co-ordination and dimensional standards to provide a uniform basis for the manufacture of components. The method is said to be applicable to on-site or shop fabrication and is based on standard lumber sizes. Furthermore, design flexibility, limited only by the architect's imagination, is claimed for the method.

Custom Residential Building

Approximately 80 percent of the houses erected in the mid-sixties were

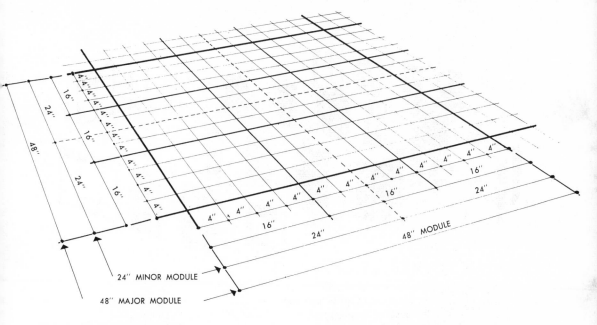

THE MODULAR PLAN

Fig. 37–14. A complete system of modular coordination involves all three dimensions — length, width and height. The modular length and modular width dimensions form the base and are the two most important dimensions in combination. The modular planning grid, a horizontal plane divided into equal spaces in length and width is divided into equal spaces of 4, 16, 24 and 48 inches. Increments of 24 and 48 inches are used for the overall exterior dimensions of the house. Floor, ceiling, and roof constructions are coordinated with these modules for optimum inventory control.

custom built. However, practically all of these houses used some prefabricated components such as doors, windows, jambs, staircases, fireplaces, cabinets, roof trusses, and the like. Even large public and private nonresidential structures used manufactured components such as trusses, laminated arches, windows, and doors.

The emphasis today is on the reduction of on-site labor costs. In 1950, the average house was fastened together with 65,000 nails. It is estimated that one-quarter million hand motions still go into the nailing of the average house. With on-site labor costing 10 cents a minute, the builders' desire to use components is understandable. The cost of a particular item is not important, but its in-place, finished, ready-to-use cost is important.

Large-scale contractors are building houses in 10 to 15 working days, not including the slab or foundation. The goal is 5 to 8 days. They are able to do this by integrating all phases of house construction. Some few builders own saw mills; door, window, truss, stair, and cabinet plants; heavy construction equipment; and several other facilities that permit them to control building time and costs.

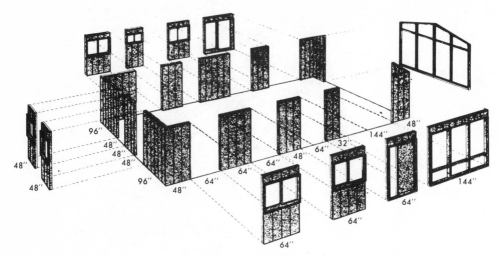

A series of blank wall areas and open areas form the walls of the house. The proportion of blank walls and "holes" is an important factor in the design of house exteriors and interiors. The materials used on the blank areas and the window and door design in the "holes" completes the exterior and interior wall composition. The illustration graphically shows the need for modular coordination in these components.

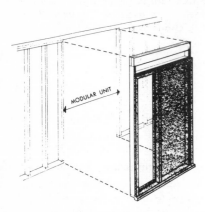

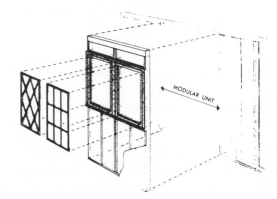

The 64-inch modular door and side-light panel is integrally designed to become a part of the 16-inch modular system for wall, door and window components. The pre-assembled unit with built-in header fits the 64-inch wall opening.

Two standard 32-inch casement window units are shown mullioned to become a 64-inch window unit to fit a 64-inch wall opening. The structural jambs of the window panel combine with adjacent blank wall studs to provide required double framing at openings.

Fig. 37–15. Exterior wall elements are separated at natural 16-inch module division points. This precise location of wall openings eliminates the extra wall framing common in non-modular planned houses.

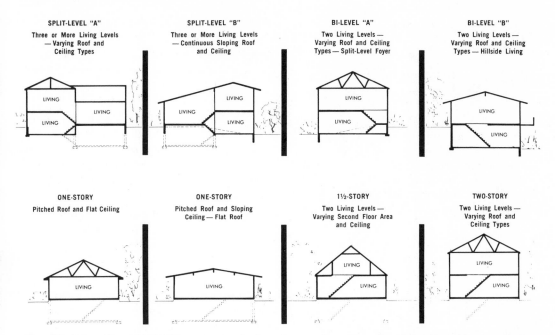

Fig. 37–16. The UNICOM method of planning and construction is adaptable to all type houses. The architectural renderings show some typical designs that have been developed.

Before the 5- to 8-day building schedule can be attained, certain technological developments must take place. Some of these are new interior wall finishing materials, new long-lasting paints, partially assembled lightweight plumbing lines, wiring assemblies, economical surface wiring, and completely prefinished wall components related to the development of modular construction.

About 80 percent of the houses built today are in the modified ranch style. In general, the dining room is disappearing and the kitchen is becoming larger. Over $\frac{4}{5}$ of the houses have either a concrete slab or a crawl-space type of foundation. This trend toward houses without basements seems to be continuing Another trend is toward larger and better houses. It is estimated that 60 percent of the population increase to 1970 will be in families that can afford to pay at least $23,500 for a good house.

Even government lending agencies are encouraging the purchase of more expensive houses.

House Construction

Planning is a most important part of house building. The prospective buyer hires a registered architect to do this. The architect studies the building site, its contours, soil, services, and zoning restrictions. This information, and the buyer's wishes, are then designed into the house.

When the house plans are completed, several contractors are invited to "bid" on the contract for construction. The contractors analyze the plans to determine the labor, materials, and profit that will be required. Experience and published estimating tables help them arrive at the price they submit as their "bid" to do the work. The buyer and his architect select

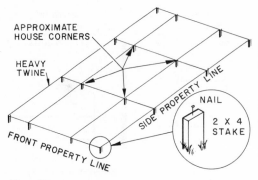

Fig. 37–17. The house location is established on the site.

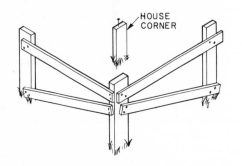

Fig. 37–18. Batter boards are erected just far enough from the house corners so that they will not interfere with excavating the foundation.

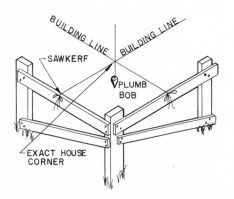

Fig. 37–19. The exact exterior foundation dimensions are located from the batter boards. The building lines aid in laying out the footings which are usually 16" to 18" wide.

the best bid and, with the aid of a lawyer, a formal construction contract is drawn up and awarded to the contractor.

The contractor's job is to hire the necessary workers, purchase all materials, and see that they are installed according to the plans. He is responsible for paying his workers wages, insurance, social security payments, and other worker's benefits. He must have a good credit rating with building-supply dealers who sell him the necessary materials.

The architect inspects the building as it progresses. As a part of his fee, he ensures that the quality of materials and construction methods meet those written into his plans and specifications.

Building begins when the contractor *stakes out* the approximate house location on the site as shown in Figure 37–17. He does this with a builder's transit (or level) and chains (steel measuring tapes). Next, he sets batter boards about 4 ft. away from the house corner stakes (Fig. 37–18). The batter-board stakes are driven deeply into the ground so they will not move. The horizontal members are nailed in place so as to be perfectly level. The exact height is not important, but all batter-board horizontal members must be at the same elevation. This is accomplished with the transit-level.

With the batter boards in position, the contractor then determines the exact location of the house. With the transit-level and steel measuring tapes he lays out each building line and marks its location on the batter boards with a saw kerf. When heavy twine is strung between the batter boards, the exact outline of the house is determined (Fig. 37–19). As a final check on the accuracy of the layout, the contractor measures the diagonals and the corner angles.

Foundation construction begins with staking out and excavating the ground

Fig. 37–20. Typical foundation construction: (a) for houses with wood floors, and (b) for houses with concrete slab floors. Most concrete slab floors are covered with tile or carpeting although prefinished wood tile is becoming popular.

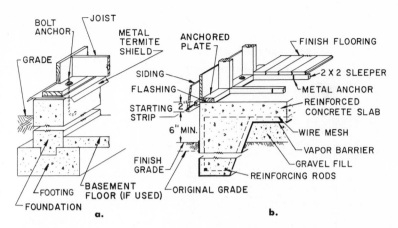

for the building *footings*. Footings, made of poured concrete, carry the weight of the house. They are placed below the frost line and on soil of sufficient bearing capacity to insure the stability of the house. The foundation walls are constructed on top of the footing. They are made of poured concrete, blocks, or brick. Figure 31–20 shows the details of two typical foundation constructions.

Floor framing (Fig. 37–21) carries the above-foundation weight of the building. Houses without basements in which wood floor framing is used must have a minimum crawl space of 24 in. In areas infested by termites, termite shields and pressure-treated lumber are used.

Wall framing (Figs. 37–22a, 37–22b, and 37–22c) is of either platform or balloon construction. For single-story houses, platform construction is the rule. For one and one half or two-story houses either the platform or balloon construction may be employed. The studs run from the sill to the plate in balloon construction. Since lumber has practically no dimensional change lengthwise, houses built with this system experience fewer

Fig. 37–21. Typical floor framing. The diagonal sub-flooring provides lateral bracing. Sheathing grade plywood is frequently used for this purpose.

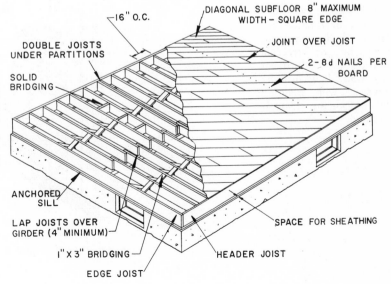

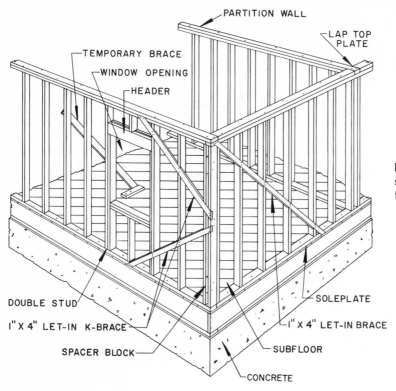

PARTITION WALL

LAP TOP PLATE

TEMPORARY BRACE

WINDOW OPENING

HEADER

DOUBLE STUD

1" X 4" LET-IN K-BRACE

SPACER BLOCK

SOLEPLATE

1" X 4" LET-IN BRACE

SUBFLOOR

CONCRETE

Fig. 37–22a. Single story platform construction.

Fig. 37–22b. Two-story balloon construction. Exterior wall sheathing may be of gypsum board, fiber board, or plywood. It is usually covered with building felt before the siding is applied.

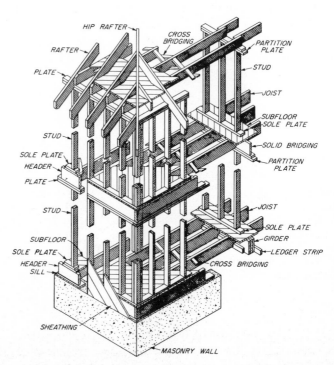

HIP RAFTER

CROSS BRIDGING

PARTITION PLATE

RAFTER

STUD

PLATE

JOIST

STUD

SUBFLOOR

SOLE PLATE

SOLE PLATE

SOLID BRIDGING

HEADER

PARTITION PLATE

PLATE

STUD

JOIST

SUBFLOOR

SOLE PLATE

SOLE PLATE

GIRDER

HEADER

LEDGER STRIP

SILL

CROSS BRIDGING

SHEATHING

MASONRY WALL

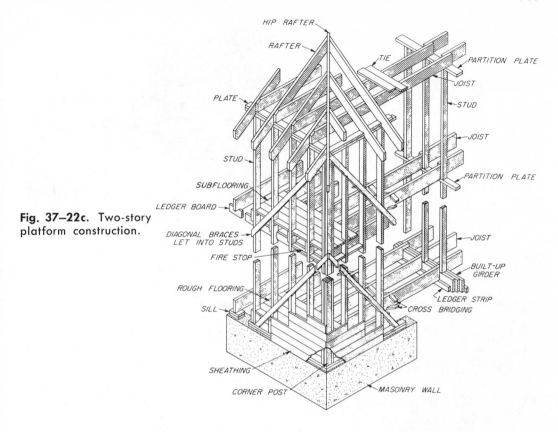

Fig. 37–22c. Two-story platform construction.

HIP RAFTER

RAFTER

TIE

PARTITION PLATE

JOIST

PLATE

STUD

JOIST

STUD

SUBFLOORING

LEDGER BOARD

PARTITION PLATE

DIAGONAL BRACES LET INTO STUDS

FIRE STOP

JOIST

ROUGH FLOORING

BUILT-UP GIRDER

SILL

LEDGER STRIP

CROSS BRIDGING

SHEATHING

CORNER POST

MASONRY WALL

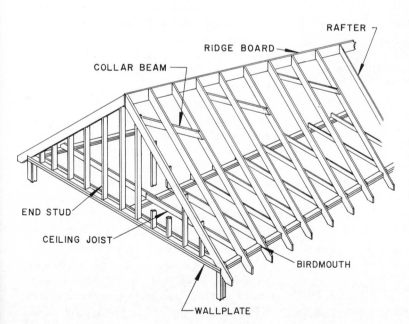

RAFTER

RIDGE BOARD

COLLAR BEAM

Fig. 37–23. Typical gable roof construction. Roof sheathing is usually 1 x 6 boards or sheathing grade plywood.

END STUD

CEILING JOIST

BIRDMOUTH

WALLPLATE

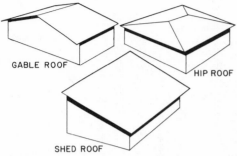

Fig. 37–24. The common shapes of roofs. The hip roof is most complicated to construct since many of the rafters (jack) must be cut with a compound miter at one end.

Fig. 37–26. This business establishment utilizes timber and plank construction.

Fig. 37–25. The structural members are covered with sheathing, building paper, and siding or roofing, as appropriate. Asphalt shingles are frequently used.

expansion and contraction problems than those using platform construction.

The sills, studs, plates, and headers are usually assembled on the subfloor of the house. They are then raised into position, temporarily braced, and nailed in place.

Roof framing (Figs. 37–23 and 37–24) completes the structural work on a

house. Roof shapes are most frequently of gable, hip, or shed design as shown in Figure 37–24.

Sheathing (Fig. 37–25) is applied to all structural framing. It strengthens and insulates the house. Sheathing may be 1 by 6 lumber, sheathing grade plywood, gypsum board, or a composition board. After being nailed in place, it is usually covered with building paper to help insulate the house. Window and door units are then installed and the house is said to be "weathered in." Siding and roofing are nailed to the sheathing. If brick veneer is used, it is laid-up with about a 1 in. air space between it and the sheathing.

Interior work involves installation of the plumbing, wiring, heating, and air conditioning systems. Wall and ceiling insulation is then installed and the interior wall covering — plaster, paneling, or gypsum board — is applied.

Men called *finish carpenters* install the prefinished plywood wall paneling, trim, flooring, and cabinets. Their work involves a great deal of measuring, precision cutting, and fitting. Many houses use wood or asphalt tile or carpeting in lieu of tongue and groove wood flooring.

Painting is the final step in the work

on the house. Painting a house frequently requires as many man hours as were spent by the carpenters in erecting it.

Nonresidential construction (Fig. 37–27) includes all buildings which are designed for educational, religious, social, business, governmental, and other purposes. It is usually construction of great size.

Large buildings are commonly thought to consist of steel, aluminum, masonry, and other ceramic materials. However, wood plays an important role in practically every structure.

Forms (Fig. 37–47) for concrete are usually made of lumber and plywood. Carpenters do all of the preparation and erection of the forms. The wood is usually lightly coated with oil to prevent the concrete from adhering to it.

Timbers (Fig. 37–48) and **posts** are used in the construction of trestles and large, mill-type buildings (Fig. 37–49). Some types of construction permit the

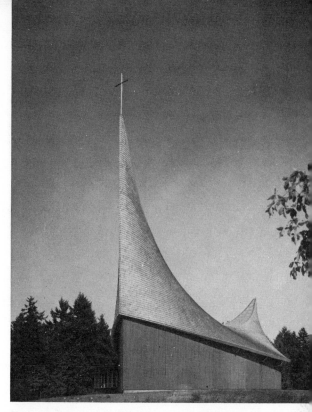

Fig. 37–27. This church provides an interesting example of design and construction in wood.

Fig. 37–28. Plywood forms hold the concrete in position while it hardens.

Fig. 37–29. Timbers have been used as structural members for centuries.

Fig. 37–31. A charred timber supports two steel beams that became plastic and collapsed in the heat of the fire.

Fig. 37–30. This hanger is made of timbers and planks.

use of green timbers. Heavy timber construction is fire resistant because of the slow rate of burning of wood in massive form. The wood chars as it burns and serves as an insulator to protect the interior of a timber (Fig. 37–31). The design and construction of such structures is a specialized area of the construction industry.

Glued structural members are of two types — *glued-laminated* and *wood-plywood*. *Glued-laminated construction* (Fig. 37–32) consists of two or more layers of wood glued together with the grain of

Fig. 37–32. Laminated wood finds many uses.

Fig. 37–33. Giant presses and clamps are used to hold laminated parts while the glue sets.

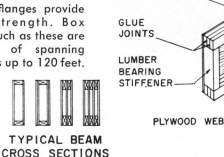

Fig. 37-34. The vertical plywood webs provide shear resistance. The lumber flanges provide axial strength. Box beams such as these are capable of spanning distances up to 120 feet.

SCARF JOINT IN PLYWOOD WEB

SCARF JOINT IN LUMBER FLANGE

BUTT JOINT BETWEEN PLYWOOD WEBS

LUMBER FLANGE

GLUE JOINTS

LUMBER BEARING STIFFENER

PLYWOOD WEB

PLYWOOD WEB

PLYWOOD SPLICE PLATE

LUMBER STIFFENER

GLUE JOINT

LUMBER FLANGE

LUMBER STIFFENER

NAILING AS REQUIRED FOR GLUING

TYPICAL BEAM
CROSS SECTIONS

TYPICAL BOX BEAM

all layers approximately parallel. This type of construction originated in Europe in 1907. The development of moisture-resistant synthetic resin glues led to increased use of glued-laminated construction. Public acceptance of this construction has resulted in its becoming an important segment of the wood industry.

Laminated members remain relatively constant in dimensions under normal dry-use conditions. They may be produced in a thoroughly dry condition in a relatively short time. Furthermore, laminating permits nearly complete utilization of short and narrow lumber. However, the costs of preparing laminated members usually raises their final cost above that of solid timbers. Furthermore, specialized equipment is needed to clamp laminated members while the glue sets (Fig. 37-33).

Wood-plywood beams (Figs. 37-53 and 37-34), girders, and panels in vari-

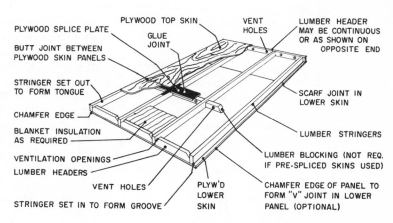

Fig. 37-35. Stressed skin panels are structural coverings for floors, walls, or roofs. The plywood skins are bonded to each side of the stringers to form a series of "I" beams.

PLYWOOD SPLICE PLATE

BUTT JOINT BETWEEN PLYWOOD SKIN PANELS

STRINGER SET OUT TO FORM TONGUE

CHAMFER EDGE

BLANKET INSULATION AS REQUIRED

VENTILATION OPENINGS

LUMBER HEADERS

VENT HOLES

STRINGER SET IN TO FORM GROOVE

PLYWOOD TOP SKIN

GLUE JOINT

VENT HOLES

LUMBER HEADER MAY BE CONTINUOUS OR AS SHOWN ON OPPOSITE END

SCARF JOINT IN LOWER SKIN

LUMBER STRINGERS

LUMBER BLOCKING (NOT REQ. IF PRE-SPLICED SKINS USED)

CHAMFER EDGE OF PANEL TO FORM "V" JOINT IN LOWER PANEL (OPTIONAL)

PLYW'D LOWER SKIN

TYPICAL STRESSED SKIN PANEL

Fig. 37–36. This delta structure uses several types of box beams and stressed skin panels in its assembly.

ous cross sections are designed to carry the same loads as solid members. The result is a considerable saving in wood and weight. Fabrication costs, however, are higher.

Wood-plywood stressed skin panels (Fig. 37–35) are essentially box beams laid flat. The panel consists of longitudinal stringers to which top and bottom plywood skin is bonded so that the entire assembly acts as a unit (Fig. 37–36).

DISCUSSION QUESTIONS

1. What are the divisions of the construction industry?
2. Identify the different occupations that make up the construction industry. Select one occupation and describe how one prepares for, enters, and progresses in it.
3. How were trees prepared for use in houses and other buildings in Colonial times?
4. In what ways are manufactured houses superior to custom-built houses? Inferior?
5. How does the concept of mass-produced housing fit the image of twentieth century life in the United States? In Africa or South America?
6. What suggestions can you make for improvements in the manufacture of houses? House trailers?
7. Distinguish between a prefabricated house and a shell house.
8. What is the difference between a house and a home?
9. What are the advantages of designing a house using the "Unicom" method?
10. From the standpoint of a contractor, what is involved in submitting a "bid" on a house to be constructed?
11. What do architect's plans and specifications include?
12. Why must a contractor make a profit?
13. Should an architect's fee decrease as the cost of the project he designs increases?
14. What new uses for laminated construction can you suggest?
15. Identify the structural members of a house.
16. What is the outlook for the construction industry? For wood in construction?

SUGGESTED STUDENT ACTIVITIES

1. Prepare a display of occupational information dealing with the construction industry.
2. Prepare a diorama(s) showing the evolution of housing. Use accurately scaled models. Place them in a setting that illustrates the level of civilization at the time.
3. Prepare a display of construction tools, either ancient or modern.
4. Prepare a display showing the evolution of a tool used in construction.
5. Sketch the front and side elevations of houses of the following styles: Cape Cod, Ranch, Colonial, Georgian. Select other styles and make similar sketches.
6. Construct a model house in one of the popular styles.
7. Design a model city and construct a diorama to display it.
8. Design and construct a model of a travel trailer for a hunter. A fisherman. A camper.
9. Obtain a set of plans and specifications from an architect. Prepare a bill of material for the job. Estimate the cost of construction.
10. With a builder's level or transit, stake out the foundation of a house. Check the layout of your school baseball diamond with a transit.
11. At an appropriate scale, design and construct models of the various details of a typical house.
12. At an appropriate scale, design and construct a public building. Use laminated structural members and component parts where feasible.
13. Design and construct a house of the future. A house trailer of the future.

Chapter 38   Chemically Derived Products From Wood

In Chapter II, we learned that the primary constituents of wood are hemicellulose, cellulose, and lignin. Hemicellulose is a carbohydrate (a compound of carbon, hydrogen, and oxygen which includes the sugars and starches). It can be separated from the more resistant cellulose by hydrolization (chemical decomposition with acid and water). Lignin is the highly complex aromatic polymer (two or more compounds consisting of the same elements, but with different molecular weights) residue that remains after the hemicellulose and cellulose have been isolated. While hardwoods and softwoods differ slightly in composition, the most important difference, chemically, is in the sugars that make up the hemicellulose fraction.

Organic chemists have long been interested in the chemical utilization of wood. The history of their efforts shows some notable successes as well as many failures. Most of the failures can be attributed to limited knowledge of the complex chemical nature of wood and to an overemphasis on producing a single chemical product. Research is providing the knowledge to eliminate both of these causes. The latter is being remedied by making chemical plants a component part of an integrated forest products complex.

In this chapter, we will concern ourselves primarily with some of the most important products that are chemically derived from wood. It is not possible to go deeply into the chemistry of wood in this book. The subject is too vast to be included here. However, this survey of the field will prepare anyone who wishes to go on to a deeper study of the chemical structure of wood and the cellulose molecule. Furthermore, with this background, it will not be difficult to understand how so many carbon, hydrogen, and oxygen compounds can be derived from wood by breaking down the molecule with heat or by hydrolyzing it with dilute acids.

Wood Distillation With Heat

When wood is heated to the ignition temperature in the presence of oxygen, it burns spontaneously. Heat, carbon dioxide, water, and a mineral ash are produced. If, however, the wood is heated in the *absence* of oxygen, it does not burn. Both the lignin and the cellulose breakdown into chemicals such as carbon monoxide gas, acetic acid, wood alcohol, tar, charcoal, and other less important materials. The process is called *destructive distillation*.

To produce the different products, three distinct processes are used: (1) destructive hardwood distillation; (2) destructive distillation of resinous woods; and (3) steam distillation and solvent extraction of resinous woods. The latter process removes soluble extracts such as tannin, dyes, and volatile oils, including turpentine. In this process, the wood remains unchanged until it is subjected to the second process. The first process has the greatest commercial importance. Generally, only beech, birch, and maple are economically profitable, but any dense hardwood may be used. The second process produces pine oils, tars, and charcoal. A cord of fat pine produces about 12 gallons of refined turpentine, $1\frac{1}{2}$ gallons of pine oil, 50 gallons of tar, and 800–900 pounds of charcoal.

Destructive distillation can be demonstrated by heating small chips of wood in a glass test tube. Place a vented stopper in the test tube and support it over a gas burner. As the wood heats, a mixture of gases [carbon monoxide (CO), carbon dioxide (CO_2), marsh gas (CH_4), hydrogen (H_2), and ethylene (C_2H_4)] are driven off. They may be ignited at the vent. (The carbon dioxide does not burn.) A dark-colored liquid (pyroligneous acid) will condense on the sides of the test tube. This liquid contains acetic acid (CH_3COOH), acetone (CH_3COCH_3), wood alcohol (CH_3OH), and some tar and oils. In the bottom of the test tube, tar and charcoal (nearly pure carbon) will be formed.

Commercially, this process is performed in closed retorts (vessels). By varying the temperatures, rates of heating, and atmospheres, the proportion and composition of the various substances may be altered. For example, lignin heated in the presence of hydrogen at very high temperature and pressure produces a clear liquid composed of wood alcohol and several complex compounds and a hard, glass-like resinous material. Also, gasoline may be produced from lignin. Temperatures of at least 518 deg. must be applied to the retorts to start the decomposition. From that point, the breakdown continues spontaneously with the internal generation of heat (exothermic action). The time involved is usually 24 to 30 hours.

The main use for *wood alcohol* is in the manufacture of formaldehyde, a disinfectant and fungicide and an ingredient in synthetic resins, plastics, and glues. *Acetic acid* is widely used in the chemical industries and in the manufacture of cellulose acetate films, lacquers, rayon, and in solvents. *Acetone* is used as a solvent for cellulose lacquers and films and in the manufacture of cordite, an explosive. *Wood tar* is used for flotation oils, insulating pitch, and to a limited extent in the manufacture of wood creosote. *Charcoal* is used chiefly as a fuel in blast furnaces and home charcoal grills. It is also used in case-hardening compounds and in black gunpowder. Activated charcoal is used for gas absorption in gas masks.

Hydrolization

When wood cellulose is treated with dilute acids, part of it is hydrolized or converted into sugars. Strong acids will dissolve the cellulose without hydrolizing it. If sawdust is treated with dilute hydrochloric acid, it will yield from 60 to 66 percent of the weight of the dry wood in glucose, mannose, and pentose sugars.

Fig. 38–1. The products of pulp and paper mills range from the finest kinds of writing and book papers to newsprint, waxed papers, soft tissues, durable and sturdy container board and cartons of every description.

This is one way in which sugar is made from wood.

The glucose and mannose (hexoses) may be fermented biologically with yeast to yield ethyl alcohol [$CH_3CH_2(OH)$]. When coniferous woods are treated with 0.2 to 1.0 percent strength sulphuric acid and fermented, they produce 63.5 gallons of ethyl alcohol per ton of dry chips. Ethyl alcohol is used as industrial alcohol. It is also produced by yeast fermentation of the waste sulphite liquor of pulp mills. Hardwood wastes have been used to produce wood-sugar molasses for livestock feed by this process.

Chemical Pulp by Hydrolization

Chemical pulping is a process by which the wood fibers are separated from each other with a minimum mechanical damage. The object is to remove the soluble cementing elements, lignin and hemicellulose, and leave a fibrous mass (pulp) consisting essentially of pure cellulose. Commercial chemical pulp is made by either the *acid sulfite process* or the alkaline methods known as the *soda process* and the *sulfate process*.

Pulp may be made from most vegetable or plant growth. Some plants, however, yield a pulp with a higher pure cellulose (alpha cellulose, such as that in cotton fibers) content. Trees fall in the preferred category. They are relatively abundant and easily processed. Both hardwoods and softwoods are used. The softwoods are of greatest importance. The most important conifers are southern yellow pines (over 50 percent of U. S. pulpwood) spruces, western and eastern hemlocks, jack pine, and several balsam firs. The most important hardwoods are the cottonwoods, aspen, beech, birch, maple, red and black gum, and yellow poplar. About 60 percent of the nation's pulping capacity is in the South; the North has 25 percent and the West Coast 15 percent.

Trees to be converted into pulp are harvested, cut into 5- to 8-ft. lengths, and then transported to the mills. Here they are stacked in high piles to await processing. The mills are located near sources of fresh water because vast quantities of water are needed in commercial pulp manufacture.

Debarking. The bark is removed from the logs by tumbling in a huge barking drum (Fig. 38–2). This is a slightly inclined, slowly rotating cylinder about 10 to 12 ft. in diameter and 30 to 68 ft. long. The logs are conveyed into the high end of the drum. As it rotates, the logs tumble against one another while streams of water play on them. Clean logs gradually work their way to the other end and are discharged onto another conveyor.

Chipping. The clean logs enter the chipper at a 45-deg. angle to be reduced to chips ½ to 1 in. long and $\frac{1}{16}$ to $\frac{1}{8}$ in. thick (Fig. 38–3). The chipper contains a large rotating disk fitted with several heavy knives. Chippers will reduce 5 to 30 cords of wood to chips in an hour. The chips are then screened to separate the wood dust and large material. The dust is blown to the boiler for fuel. The large slivers are run through rechippers where they are crushed or cut into smaller sizes. Small, uniform chips are necessary so that the chemicals may act upon them. The chips are then conveyed to a silo or storage bin to await

Fig. 38–2. Only bark-free logs may be used for pulp making. The drum barker shown above is one of several kinds.

Fig. 38–3. The wood chipper reduces logs up to 16" in diameter to thumbnail size chips.

Fig. 38–4. The chips are conveyed to a storage silo. A new "Vac-Sink" process separates bark from chips by waterlogging wood chips in a vacuum tank. The fibrous wood sinks; the bark floats and is skimmed off.

conversion into pulp (Fig. 38–4).

Sulphite pulp. An American chemist first cooked wood in sulfur dioxide in 1866 and 1867. Because of inferior equipment, the process never became commercially successful. A Swedish chemist introduced the first commercially successful process in 1874. In 1887 the sulphite process was reintroduced in the United States.

The principal woods used in this process are spruces, hemlocks, and balsam fir. Resinous woods and hardwoods produce an inferior pulp. Southern pine under 25 years of age has little or no resinous heartwood and may be successfully pulped by this method.

The active reagents in the sulphite process are sulfurous acid (H_2SO_3) and calcium bisulfite [$Ca(HSO_3)_2$] although sodium and magnesium bisulfites are also

Fig. 38–5. This flow diagram illustrates a typical calcium base sulfite pulping process. The chemical conversion, digesting, and washing portions of the cycle are included.

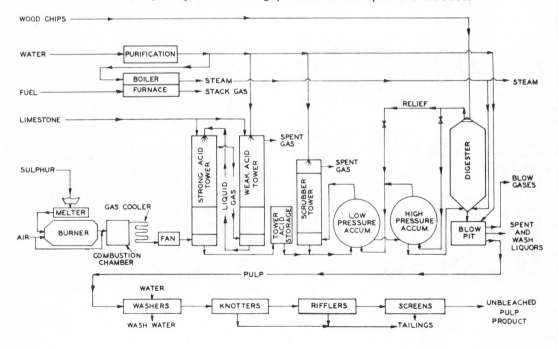

used. This *cooking liquor* is produced at the mill (Fig. 38–5). Sulfur, or pyrites, (FeS₂), is burned to produce sulfur dioxide gas (SO₂). Limestone (CaCO₃) and water (or milk of lime) is used to dissolve the sulfur dioxide and form the sulfurous acid. This is accomplished in 100 ft. tall tanks about 10 ft. in diameter. The cooking acid (liquor) is stored in tanks until needed for use.

Cooking. Wood chips, equivalent to 20 to 75 cords of wood, are loaded into the top of a *digester* (Figs. 38–6 and 38–7). This is a large steel pressure cooker, 10 to 17 ft. in diameter and 40 to 70 ft. tall. The digester is closed, the cooking liquor is pumped in, and the temperature gradually raised until the pressure is 75 to 90 lb. per square inch. Approximately 2000 gallons of cooking liquor are required for each ton of pulp produced.

The procedure for cooking varies considerably from mill to mill. On an average, 7 to 10 hours are required to complete a cook. Temperatures may range as high as 270 deg. F. In some mills, steam is introduced directly into the digester. This dilutes the liquor and necessitates the use of stronger solutions. For this

Fig. 38–6. Digesters such as these are kept in operation 24 hours a day, 7 days a week. Most plants shut down for maintenance only once or twice a year.

reason, sulfite digesters are lined with an acid-resistant material.

When the cooking is completed, the blow-off valve is opened and the digester contents, under about 50-lb. pressure, are emptied into the blow pit. The blow pit is a large acid resisting tank. The cooking liquor, with its dissolved lignin

Fig. 38–7. The digester acts as a pressure cooker. This is a generalized chart of the cooking process.

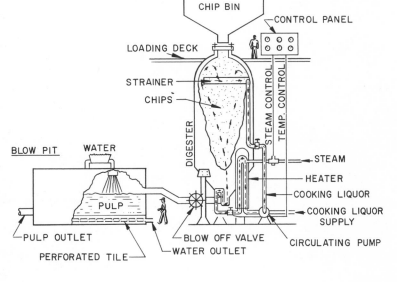

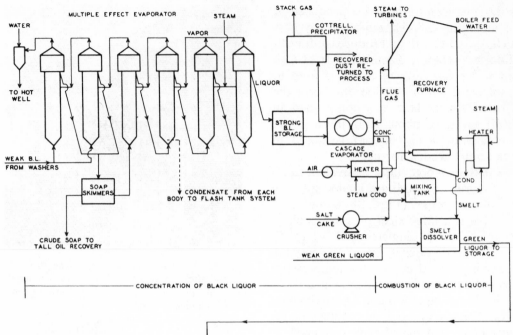

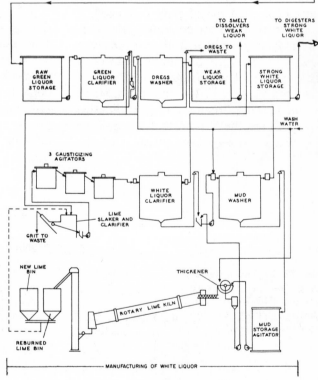

Fig. 38—8. This flow diagram illustrates a typical system for the recovery and manufacture of cooking liquor for the sulphate pulping process.

and noncellulosic wood components, drains through the bottom of the blow pit and is piped to a nearby plant. Here the by-products are recovered. The pulp is washed for several hours until all traces of liquor are removed. It is then pumped to a storage tank. The pulp is now a clean, light-colored fibrous mass.

Huge quantities of waste water are to-day being purified before they are dumped into streams and rivers. The wood substances removed in the purification process contain many valuable constituents. In the past, most pulp mills dumped the spent liquor and its dissolved materials without regard to the pollution of rivers. Certain microorganisms on the organic matter decreased the oxygen content of the water and increased its carbon dioxide content. The result was the destruction of aquatic life. Most pulp mills today dump only pure waste water and are thereby helping to eliminate the problem of water pollution.

The sulphite process produces about 50 percent of the weight of the drywood as pulp. An average of 1.8 cords of rough wood are needed to make 1 ton of pulp. Unbleached pulp is used with ground-wood pulp in the making of newsprint and other inexpensive papers. Bleached pulp is used in higher grades of paper. When purified with an alkali, the pulp is used in the manufacture of rayon and other cellulose products.

Sulphate pulp. There are two principal alkaline processes used in the manufacture of pulp: (1) the *soda process* developed in England in 1853, and (2) the *sulphate process,* developed in Germany in 1879. Both processes use caustic soda (NaOH) as the active pulping agent. About 85 percent of the soda is reclaimed in both processes. The loss is made up by adding soda ash (Na_2CO_3) in the soda process and salt cake (Na_2SO_4) in the

sulphate process. The sulphate process differs from the soda process in that sodium sulfide (Na_2S) results from the addition of the sodium sulphate (salt cake). See Figure 38–12.

Cooking. Any kind of wood, but usually resinous woods, can be pulped by the sulphate process. Three cycles may be identified in the cooking process: (1) the liquor penetration period; (2) the full-pressure period; and (3) the gassing-down period. In the first stage, the chips are subjected to the liquor and about 70 lb. of steam pressure for about 30 minutes. All air and noncondensable gases are exhausted from the digester. Turpentine is distilled from the exhaust steam. The cooking liquor dissolves the lignin *between* the wood fibers.

During the second stage, the pressure is raised quickly to 100 lb. per square inch and the temperature is increased to 340 deg. F. or more. In this stage, the intercellular lignin is dissolved.

Gassing down begins 2½ to 6 hours after the start of the cook. The pressure is reduced to about 60 lb. The digester is then blown into a blow pit or a blow tank.

A blow tank is a large steel shell which is elevated above the digester. The sudden release of pressure as the stock enters the blow tank causes the chips to disintegrate into a fibrous state. The released steam is passed through a separator to remove the turpentine and then used to heat the pulp-washing water.

Washing. Thorough washing is essential in the sulphate process. It determines the purity of the pulp and the completeness of chemical recovery. Washing is carried on in wash pans, diffusers, or vacuum washers. *Wash pans* are false bottom tanks in which the water flows over the pulp and out the bottom. *Diffusers* are large steel tanks with false

Fig. 38–9. The fibers are washed by water sprays as they revolve on the drum of this washer.

bottoms. The pulp is washed with hot water and agitated under pressure. The washed stock is then soaked in a storage chest to remove the last of the soda. The *vacuum washer* is a large screen-covered cylinder rotating in a vat of pulp (Fig. 38–9). A vacuum is applied to the inside of the cylinder. The pulp clings to the screen and is washed by a shower of hot water. The pulp is then washed into a storage chest. The filtrate from the washers is treated for the recovery of chemicals.

Sulphate pulp is usually a brownish color as a result of being intentionally undercooked to produce a strong fiber. The lignin that remains gives it the color. This pulp is used for "Kraft" (German word for strength) papers which are used for bags, wrapping paper, paperboard, boxes, and the like. Bleached sulfate pulp is used for newsprint, rayon, and other cellulose products. Pulp yields are about 45 to 48 percent of the dry weight of wood.

Semichemical pulp is produced by sulfite-cooking wood chips for a short time, and then breaking them into pulp mechanically in such devices as rod mills and disk fiberizers, and other devices. If the cooking is carefully controlled, pulp yields of 60 to 80 percent of the dry weight of wood are obtained. The pulp varies from a light brown color to a dirty white. Its principal use is in the manufacture of corrugated paperboard.

Mechanical pulp (groundwood pulp) is made by grinding bark-clean logs (principally spruce and balsam) into a fibrous state. The logs are pressed laterally against a huge grinding wheel by means of an hydraulic piston. As the wheel turns, the wood fibers are ground off, screened, and washed into a storage tank to be thickened. Pulp yields are about 90 percent of the dry weight of wood. Much of the pulp is used in the production of inexpensive papers. Because of the lignin content, the paper deteriorates and yellows quickly. Mechanical pulp is added to chemical pulp to make newsprint, towels, cheap box paper, wallpaper, wall board and other items which do not require strength.

Treatment of Pulp

Mechanical and chemical pulps must undergo a series of treatments before they are ready for use. *Screening* is the first treatment. Coarse screening removes dirt, foreign material, knots, and other uncooked pieces of wood. Fine screening separates the fibers according to size. This is accomplished by a series of screens ranging from coarse to fine.

Riffling, the second treatment, is performed in a long level trough containing pockets of rough felt fabric at the bottom. Sand, pieces of mineral, particles of digester lining, and other fine impurities settle in the pockets. The diluted pulp, being lighter in weight, flows to a pump at the end of the riffler.

Fine Screening is the third treatment. The different grades of paper require fibers of different lengths and diameters. Fine screening separates the fibers into several grades. This is accomplished by controlling the size of the openings in the screen, the pressure used in passing the fibers through the screen, and the ratio of water and pulp in the stock.

Thickening is the fourth treatment. After fine screening, the stock is from 0.25 to 0.6 percent solid. Thickening increases the solids to 3 to 6 percent. The process is also called slushing, deckering, dewatering, or concentrating. A decker is used to thicken the stock. It consists of a cylinder covered with a fine-mesh wire screen revolving in a vat of fine screenings. The pulp collects on the wire mesh. The "white water" that runs through the screen is used again in thinning the stock for screening.

Bleaching, the fifth treatment, removes small amounts of lignin and other non-cellulosic substances that still remain to discolor the pulp. Bleaching whitens and purifies by chemically dissociating them from the cellulose. Chlorine, as a gas or in a compound, is the most important agent. Bleaching is performed in single-stage, two-stage, or multiple-stage operations. The choice depends upon the process by which the pulp was produced, the degree of whiteness desired, and economy of materials and fiber strength. Two-stage treated sulphate pulp must be neutralized (usually with caustic soda) and washed to remove the residual lignin and color. It is then bleached and washed a second time.

Lapping. If the pulp is not used immediately at the mill, the water is extracted and the pulp made into sheets or bundles. This final treatment is called *lapping*. It is performed on a *wet press*. This machine is similar to a decker. A cylinder picks up the pulp, transfers it to a felt belt, and then passes it through a series of squeeze rollers. A smooth roll collects the pulp from the belt. As the pulp thickness builds up on this roll, it is cut off as rectangular sheets. The sheets are folded to a size of about 18 by 24 in. called *laps*. They contain about 55 to 70 percent water by weight. Additional water may be removed (to 40 percent) by pressing the laps in a hydraulic press. When pulp with less water is required, it is processed in a cylinder or Four-drinier-type machine. These machines are used in paper making and are described in that section.

Some mills are exclusively pulp (chemical cellulose) producers. They ship their product to other plants to be made into paper and hundreds of products such as rayon and acetate textiles, sporting ammunition, military explosives, photographic film, cigarette filters, football helmets, detergents, cellophane, cosmetics, ice cream, tire cord, lacquers, luggage, plastics, and toys.

Paper Manufacture

Most paper mills produce pulp and immediately convert it into paper (Fig. 38–10). The first operation performed on the pulp is called *beating* or *refining*. It is a mechanical treatment in which the fibers, suspended in water, are separated, cut, split, and crushed. After beating, the stock has a slimy feel and is a compact and uniform mass of pulp. It may be spread into sheets in which the beaten fibers cling to one another strongly when allowed to dry. This is the result of two kinds of action: (1) mechanical — the cut and deformed fibers interlock; and

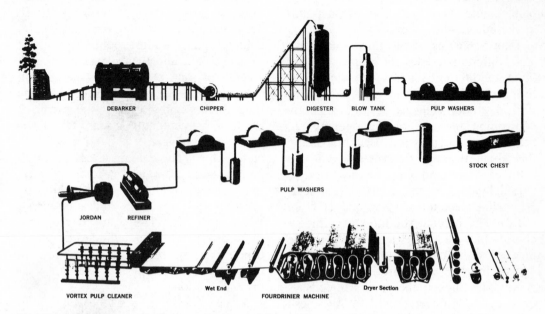

DEBARKER   CHIPPER   DIGESTER   BLOW TANK   PULP WASHERS

STOCK CHEST

PULP WASHERS

JORDAN   REFINER

VORTEX PULP CLEANER   Wet End   FOURDRINIER MACHINE   Dryer Section

Fig. 38–10. This flow diagram illustrates the sequence of operations employed in some papermaking mills. A refiner is used here instead of a beater. The refiner contains adjustable rotating disks that cut and fray the fibers so they will mat and interlace well.

Fig. 38–11. In the beater the fibers are cut, split, separated, and crushed. Lap stock, fillers, and sizes may be added at this stage.

(2) chemical — the molecules of water and the fiber surfaces which they contact form a chemical bond with adhesive properties.

The **beater** (Fig. 38–11). Beating is done in one of several kinds of beaters. The most common is a Hollander, or one of its modifications. It consists of a large open tub, 15 to 25 ft. long (or more), 6 to 11 ft. wide, and 3 to 5 ft. deep. It is built of wood, concrete, or metal. The tub is divided with a partition known as a *mid-feather*. It extends to within 2 or 3 ft. of each end. Thus, the pulp may flow continuously around the tub. A roll is mounted between the mid-feather and wall on one side of the tub. This roll, and a bedplate beneath it, are fitted with metal bars. The bedplate is an integral part of a backfall (dam) (Fig. 38–12). The pulp fibers are separated and deformed when they pass between the roll and bedplate as the roll revolves. The pulp is thrown over the backfall to form a head (higher elevation) and causes the mass to travel around the tub and back to the roll again. The pulp is beaten for several hours.

Fillers and **sizing** are added to the beater stock at this stage of manufacture. They regulate the absorbent qualities and transparency of the finished paper. Fillers are minerals such as clay (kaolin), talc, agolite, and certain compounds containing calcium sulfate, titanium dioxide, and zinc sulfide. Filler particles occupy the spaces between fibers and make the paper smooth and opaque. *Sizes* are water-repellent materials that coat the fibers and make the paper less absorbent to ink and moisture. The most common sizes are rosin and wax. Rosin is cooked with soda ash (Na_2CO_3) to produce a thick fluid called *rosin soap*. The rosin soap is diluted and introduced into the beater along with a quantity of alum. Paraffin (wax) is emulsified in water to make a wax size. Instead of internal sizing, as above, some papers are surface sized after leaving the wet end of the paper making machine. Such sizes are thermosetting resins, gelatine glues, and starches. Surface sizing increases the bursting strength of paper. Synthetic resins give paper *wet strength*. These papers retain a high percentage of their dry strength when wet.

Coloring. The natural color of bleached pulp is yellowish. Blue is added to neutralize the yellow and make the paper white. Paper of most any color may be made by adding the appropriate dye or pigment to the pulp in the beater or by applying it directly as a coating to the surface.

Pigments are usually mineral colors which are insoluble in water. They are deposited on the surface of the fibers and

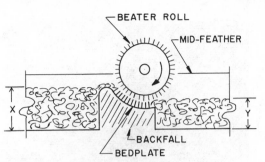

Fig. 38–12. This diagram illustrates how the beater builds up a head as it deforms the cellulose fibers.

held in place by mechanical means such as sizing. Aniline dyes are the dyes most frequently used to color paper. Dyes penetrate the fiber walls. They are classed as direct dyes, basic dyes, and acid dyes. The results obtained by coloring are affected by factors such as the type of pulp to be colored, the degree of beating, amount of sizing and filling, and the water characteristics. Consequently, color matching is a most exacting operation, requiring considerable understanding and ingenuity on the part of color technicians.

Refining. After the pulp has been beaten and treated it passes to a refining

Fig. 38–13. The fibers are rubbed and cut to the required degree in Jordans.

Fig. 38–14. The wet end of a Fourdrinier papermaking machine.

machine called a *Jordan* (Fig. 37–13). The cone-shaped shell is lined with bars or "knives" on its interior surface. A cone-shaped plug revolves inside the shell. It also is fitted with bars. The pulp is fed into the Jordan in a very dilute suspension for its final treatment before reaching the paper machine. The Jordan rubs, cuts, and separates the fibers so that they will make a uniform sheet of paper. The bars may be adjusted to turn out a longer or shorter fiber with rougher or smoother edges, depending on the kind of paper to be made.

The Fourdrinier Paper Machine

The Fourdrinier papermaking machine may be divided into four parts for purposes of description: (1) the Fourdrinier, or wet end, (2) the press section, (3) the drier section, and (4) the calender section.

The *Fourdrinier* (Fig. 38–14) end receives the pulp stock consisting of about 1 percent fiber and 99 percent water. It

flows into a storage chest or head box and onto an endless wire screen. This wire screen has as many as 6000 tiny holes per square inch. As the screen moves lengthwise, it also vibrates from side to side. The water drains through the screen and the fibers become interlaced. This wet sheet of pulp is called a *web*. Near the end of the Fourdrinier, a suction box in which a vacuum is created, draws off more of the water from the web. If a watermark is to be made on the paper, it is applied at this time with a *dandy roll*. This is a wire-mesh-covered roll on which the design (usually a trademark) is worked in fine wire or to which brass letters are mounted. As the roll runs on the surface of the web, the raised design makes the wet pulp thinner at its point of contact. The design shows clearly when the finished paper is held to the light.

The *press section* receives the web on a belt of wool felt which carries it through several pairs of heavy rollers. As the web enters the press rolls, it contains about 90 percent water; as it leaves, it contains 60 to 70 percent water. Thus, the press rolls remove as much water as possible without injuring the wet sheet.

The *drier section* (Fig. 38–15) reduces the water content of the web to 7 to 10 percent based on the dry weight. The wet paper is passed over 48-in. diameter, steam-heated, cast-iron rolls called *driers*. Different papers dry at different rates. For cigarette papers, a series of rolls only 20 ft. long is necessary; for heavy wrapping paper, up to 350 ft. is required. The paper is strong enough to support its own weight in the driers. It travels at speeds as high as 30 mph.

The *calender section* (Fig. 38–15) of the papermaking machine consists of *calenders, slitters,* and *winders.* Calenders are heavy, very smooth rolls. As the paper

Fig. 38–15. The drier, calender and winder (from right to left) sections of a Fourdrinier machine.

passes between them, the weight and friction imparts a smooth finish to it. As the paper comes from the calenders, it is wound on a reel. When one reel is full, the sheet is torn and led to a second reel — all without stopping the machine. The full reel of paper is then rewound on winders. If the full width of paper is not necessary, slitters slice it into the desired widths as it is being rewound.

A newsprint papermaking machine produces a 300 in. wide sheet at the rate of about 2000 lineal feet or about 50,000 sq. ft. of paper per minute. Tissue paper machines produce a 70 in. wide sheet at a rate of 100 ft. per minute or about 2 tons of paper every 24 hours.

The Cylinder Paper Machine

The cylinder paper machine (Fig. 38–16) is another standard paper machine. It is especially suited to the manufacture of tissue paper, paperboard, and bristols. This machine consists of one or more mesh covered cylinders, partially immersed in vats of diluted paper stock. As the cylinders revolve, a thin film of pulp

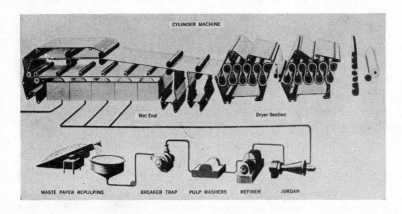

Fig. 38–16. The cylinder paper machine is used to make paper and paberboard from waste paper.

forms on the wire mesh. An endless felt belt passes over the top of the cylinders. The felt, being smoother than the mesh, picks off the wet stock.

If the felt is passed over more than one cylinder, it will pick up a layer of wet stock from each. The first and last layers are called liners. They may be composed of better-grade, colored-paper stock, while the center layer may be made of a poorer grade of stock. The paper or board is then passed through pressure rolls, drying cylinders, and calenders similar to those of the Fourdrinier machine.

Use of Wastepaper

Wastepaper ranks second to wood as a source of fiber for pulp and paper making. Annual consumption is about ten million tons or about one third of the total domestic wood-fiber demand. Wastepaper is widely used because of its ready availability, low cost, economical conversion to pulp, and relatively high quality.

Wastepaper is classified into about 40 grades. However, for purposes of pulp production, it can be separated into three groups: (1) mixed wastepapers; (2) book and magazine papers; and (3) clean trimmings and cuttings. Almost two thirds of the total wastepaper tonnage falls into the first group. It finds use in the container industry for the manufacture of solid-fiber and corrugated boxes. It also finds use in wallboard, newsprint, bags, roofing, and wrapping paper. The wastepaper is deinked with sodium carbonate and sodium hydroxide. For better grades of paper, it is also washed and bleached.

Wastepaper is primarily converted into pulp by a combination of chemical and mechanical processes. Breaker-beater machines reduce either shredded or baled paper to minute pieces. Cooking in caustic soda or soda-ash solutions reduces the mass to pulp.

History of the Paper Industry

Primitive man drew pictures on the walls of caves. The ancient Egyptians chiseled their picture stories in stone. The industrious Babylonians kept records on heavy clay tablets and in time developed the first true alphabet. The Egyptians made a writing material by building up layers of strips taken from the papyrus plant. (The modern word "paper" comes from the name of this plant.) They also invented the brush and quill pen to write on this new medium. The Persians invented parchment when they learned to split the skins of goats, sheep, and calves, soak them in a lime solution, and then scrape and dry them.

A young Chinese scholar named Ts'ai Lun invented the first real paper in A.D. 105. He pounded the inner bark of the mulberry tree into a pulp and added water. When the mixture was spread out and dried, it formed a matted fiber sheet on which messages could be written. Ts'ai Lun's paper-making secret remained in Central Asia until about A.D. 700. It reached Europe about A.D. 1100. By this time, rags were being used for pulp, but paper was still a handmade product.

In 1799, a Frenchman, Nicholas Louis Robert, patented a hand-cranked machine for making paper in a sheet 15 to 20 yards long. By 1803, two Englishmen, Henry and Sealy Fourdrinier had improved the machine so that it would produce a continuous sheet.

Linen and cotton rags were used throughout this period, but their scarcity led to a search for a cheaper and more abundant material. Jute, straw, hemp, and other plants, and asbestos were used. Paper was so scarce that only the most important messages were recorded. Each piece of paper was saved and, if possible, reused many times before it was discarded.

In the early part of the eighteenth century, a Frenchman named Rene de Reaumur, came up with the idea of making paper from wood. He watched a wasp take wood fibers from a dry post, mix them with body secretions, and form the paper-like material used to build a nest. The soundness of this observation was proven in 1844. A German named Kellar ground wood into pulp, added water, and formed the fibers into paper. The chemical process for making wood pulp was patented in 1853 by two Englishmen, Hugh Burgess and Charles Watt.

Today, paper manufacture is one of our major industries. It is comprised of three distinct divisions: (1) paper mills; (2) paperboard mills; and (3) building paper and board mills. Several hundred specific grades of paper and board are produced by these industries. The major categories are printing papers, including newsprint; fine papers; coarse papers; sanitary and tissue papers; special industrial papers; container boards; wet machine boards; and construction paper and boards.

In 1963, 469 companies with 817 establishments produced paper and board in all but 8 states. Production exceeds 40 million tons annually. Georgia leads the nation with an output of 2.7 million tons, followed by Wisconsin with 2.5 million tons. Washington, Michigan, Florida, and Louisiana each produce over 2.0 million tons annually. New York, Maine, Pennsylvania, and Ohio each produce between 1.7 and 1.9 million tons. These 10 states account for approximately one half of the nation's total output.

The paper and board industry has remained competitive in both domestic and foreign markets. The industry has spent large and growing amounts on research, development, and marketing. The success of the industry's modernization program is evidenced in the fact that 258,300 employees produced 26.6 million tons of paper and board in 1953; and in 1963 283,000 employees produced 39.2 million tons (103 and 139 tons per employee respectively for these years).

Consumption of paper and paperboard continues to follow a long time upward trend. Per capita consumption in the United States has risen from 345 pounds in 1947 to an estimated 499 pounds in 1965. Exports rose from 383,000 to 1,149,000 tons between 1953 and 1963. This indicates successful competition for a share of the growing world demand for this industry's products. United States production represents about 40 percent of the world output.

The value of paper and paperboard shipments was $7.4 billion in 1965. This was a 7 percent increase over the 1964 level of $6.9 billion. Net profits after taxes have ranged from 6.4 percent in 1953 to a low of 4.0 percent in 1961.

Cellulose-Derived Products

Cellulose is used for an almost unlimited number of different products and the field is constantly increasing. In fact, the field is so great that we can do little more than mention some of the more important products. A few of the more common items made from highly purified cellulose are rayon and acetate filaments and fabrics, transparent films, photographic films, artificial sponges, sausage casings, lacquers, plastics, and explosives. Wood pulp and the seed hairs of cotton (cotton linters) are the principal sources

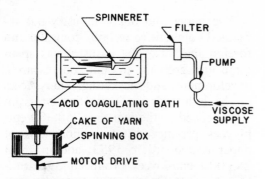

Fig. 38–17. Spinning process produces rayon filaments.

of cellulose for these products.

Rayon, first produced in 1892, is a cellulose filament or yarn. It was initially marketed as "artificial silk." The term "rayon" was adopted by the trade in 1924. Rayon may be made by at least four different processes. Two of these processes, the *viscose* and the *acetate,* are the most important in this country.

The *viscose process* of making rayon includes, as the first step in manufacture, the steeping, pressing, and shredding of sheets of cellulose (lap stock). In *steeping,* the hemicellulose and other impurities are removed in a 17.5 to 18 percent caustic solution. The cellulose swells and absorbs sodium hydroxide to form an alkali cellulose. The operation requires about one hour at a temperature of 18 to 20 deg. C. After steeping, the cellulose is squeezed to remove most of the liquid and then *shredded.* The shredded cellulose particles are called *crumbs.*

The crumbs are placed in large cans and aged for about 48 hours in temperature-controlled rooms. During aging, both physical and chemical changes take place. The aged cellulose is then treated with carbon disulfide (CS_2) which converts it into an alkali-soluble cellulose derivative known as *cellulose xanthate.* The operation is performed in a rotating steel drum called a *churn.* The cellulose changes

from white to orange. The carbon disulfide is drained off and caustic soda is added to the cellulose xanthate in a *mixer.* The cellulose xanthate dissolves and produces an orange-colored viscose solution called *viscose.* The viscose is filtered and allowed to ripen. It is then ready for *spinning.*

Spinning (Fig. 38–17) is the process by which rayon filaments are produced. The viscose is forced through holes 0.002 to 0.005 inch in diameter in a platinum spinneret (a device like a shower head). The spinneret is immersed in an acid-coagulating bath containing warm water, sulfuric acid, sodium and zinc sulfates, and glucose or magnesium sulfate. The bath neutralizes the caustic soda, breaks down the cellulose xanthate, and causes the regeneration of solid cellulose in the form of filaments.

The filaments pass around a wheel and then to a spinning box known as a *centrifugal pot.* Here a group of filaments are rotated at 6,000 to 10,000 rpm and twisted into a thread. The speed of the wheel determines the diameter of the filament by causing the filaments to draw out prior to coagulation. Some filaments are wound on bobbins to be twisted later. The yarn as it comes from the spinning machine is washed, treated with an alkaline sulfide solution, and then dried.

When the yarn leaves the spinning machine, it is a dull yellow. When treated with a hypochlorite solution, the rayon returns to a bright color. Yarns intended for cloth are bleached after they are woven. Colored rayons are made by adding a dye to the viscose solution. Several lusters may be imparted to the yarns by incorporating an insoluble pigment into the rayon filament.

Cellulose acetate is a cellulose derivative (an ester of cellulose) rather than a regenerated cellulose. It has a distinct chemical nature with physical and chemical properties different from the original cellulose.

The *cellulose acetate process* of manufacture begins with a mild bleaching of the sheets of cellulose. The pulp is then treated with acetic acid. Then it is transferred to batch reactors and mixed with acetic anhydride, glacial acetic acid, and a suitable catalyst. Here the cellulose is mixed until its fibrous structure disappears. At this stage it is called *primary cellulose acetate*. The batch is next dropped into a vat containing acetic acid and 5 to 10 percent water. The mixture is held in the vat for 10 to 20 hours to permit the primary acetate to hydrolyze into *secondary acetate*.

The secondary acetate is injected into a tank of cold water where it precipitates from the solution in the form of flakes. The tank is then emptied into a settling tank. The clear liquor is siphoned off and piped to the recovery plant. The precipitated acetate is washed and then dried.

The dry acetate flakes are finally dissolved in acetone, filtered, and forced through spinnerets. The spinnerets eject the filaments into the top of a vertical cabinet through which warm air circulates. The air, at a temperature above the boiling point of acetone, evaporates the acetone causing the acetate to coagulate. The filaments are wound on bobbins, spools, or tubes.

Uses of Cellulose Derivatives. Rayon and acetate *fibers* are used extensively in textiles. They may be used alone or with other fibers in woven and knitted fabrics, hosiery, and yarns. Industrial uses include tire cord (Tirex); conveyer and V belts; abrasive, polishing and sanding wheels; safety belts; and reinforcements for paper and plastics. Special forms of cellulose acetate are used for raincoats and type-writer ribbons. Others find use in the electrical industries because of their low conductivity, dimensional stability, and flexibility.

Transparent cellulose *films* are produced by several processes. *Cellophane* is the most important. It is made by the viscose process and accounts for 95 percent of the total output. The viscose is forced through a long slit instead of a spinneret. The sheets are regenerated in an acid bath, bleached, washed, softened in a glycol bath, and finally dried and rolled. Since cellophane is permeable to moisture, some grades are treated with a thin film of cellulose nitrate lacquer to make them water resistant. Sausage casings are extruded through annular slots into a coagulating bath.

Cellulose acetate films are extruded through a thin slot onto a polished metal drum which rotates in a drying chamber. The film is peeled off the drum, passed between hot rolls, and reeled. These films are more water resistant than cellophane; have good electrical resistance; do not become brittle in sunlight; are self-sealing under heat and pressure; but are permeable to gases. Most acetate film is used for food wrappers, photographic films, and sound recording tapes.

Cellulose *sponges* are made by mixing vegetable hairs and crystals of salt in a viscose solution. The batch is poured into molds and heated. The salt crystals dissolve, leaving holes. The sheet of sponge is then washed, dried, and cut to size.

Lacquer is made by mixing *cellulose nitrate* with plasticizers (agents to impart softness and flexibility), resins, and organic solvents. (Cellulose nitrate is made by treating cotton linters and shredded wood pulp with nitric and sulfuric acids in the presence of water.) Newer lacquer formulations contain mixed cellulose esters and ethyl cellulose. They produce lacquer films with greater resistance to light and heat, greater water resistance, and lower inflammability. They are more expensive than nitrocellulose lacquers. Because of their extreme toughness, ethyl cellulose lacquers are expected to attain major importance.

Cellulose derivatives also find use in peel and hot melt coatings, fabric and paper coatings, and in water base paints.

Plastics

Within recent years a bewildering array of synthetic resins and plastics have been introduced to the market. These man-made materials are found in almost every manufactured product. Their presence is so commonplace that we take them for granted. At one time they were viewed as substitutes for natural materials. But, today we know them for properties that make them superior to other materials.

Plastics are chemical compounds or formulations of organic and, sometimes, inorganic materials that may be molded, cast, extruded, or pressed. Heat and pressure are usually associated with their manufacture into objects of finite form. Man-made plastics are classed as thermosetting or thermoplastic.

Thermosetting plastics form a hard, infusible substance that *cannot* be remelted or remolded after they have *polymerized* under heat and pressure. Polymerization is the chemical union of two or more molecules of the same kind into another compound having the same elements in the same proportions, but a higher molecular weight and different physical properties. All thermosetting plastics are not heat-resistant. While they do not soften, some char and even decompose in only moderately high levels of heat.

Thermoplastics are composed of binders that polymerize completely, but when exposed to heat, they soften. Some thermoplastics have excellent heat-resistant properties and give good service when exposed to temperatures about 200 deg. F.

Ingredients of plastics include binders, fillers, plasticizers, solvents, lubricants, and coloring materials.

Binders are the principal, and in some cases the only, constituent in a plastic. Most plastics get their name from that of the binder used. Thus, a cellulose acetate plastic is made with a cellulose acetate binder. The principal binders are synthetic resins, derivatives of cellulose, casein, and soybean proteins, and to a small extent lignin. The synthetic resins of major importance are the phenols, melamines, urea formaldehydes, acrylics, indenes, styrenes, and vinyls. The most important cellulosic binders are cellulose nitrate, cellulose acetate, cellulose acetate-butyrate, and ethyl cellulose. Highly purified wood pulp or cotton linters are used to prepare the cellulose binders.

Fillers are used to increase the bulk of the plastic binders and to impart many desirable physical and chemical properties to the finished article. They may be of organic or inorganic origin. A good filler is inexpensive and has good strength properties, a low affinity for moisture, low specific gravity, good resin and dye whetting properties, and low abrasiveness. Other desirable properties for some products are: high dielectric strength, heat resistance, machinability, nonflammability, chemical inertness, particle size, color, and odor. Wood flour, walnut and pecan shell flour, alpha cellulose, paper, asbestos, mica, graphite, diatomaceous silica, and glass fibers are among the most commonly used fillers.

Wood flour is the most widely used filler. It is made by grinding or pulverizing white pine, basswood, cottonwood, balsam fir, spruce, oak, maple, birch, or redgum. Particle sizes do not usually exceed 60 mesh screenings. Nut shell flours are made by cleaning, deoiling, and grinding the shells of walnuts or pecans.

Plasticizers are organic materials with low melting points. They are added to plastic formulations to improve their molding properties and to make the finished product more flexible. Camphor, methyl, and ethyl phthalates are most generally used with cellulose plastics.

Solvents include several alcohols and acetone. Cellulose nitrate is dissolved in acetone and added to a wood flour filler to make "plasticwood."

Lubricants are added to plastic mixes to increase their flow during molding and to prevent the article from sticking in the mold. Waxes, stearic acid, and metallic stearate salts are used most frequently.

Coloring materials include dyes, lakes, or pigments. They are added to plastic mixes to improve their appearance.

Lignin plastics. Several lignin-plastic materials have been developed beyond the pilot-plant stage. Although they are suited for several industrial applications, they offer no special economic or physical advantages over other better known materials.

The Forest Products Laboratory has developed a lignin-plastic made from mill-run residues of hardwoods such as maple, redgum, oak, hickory, cottonwood, and several softwoods. The product is named "Hydroxylin." It is made by first hydrolizing sawdust with 1 percent sulfuric acid. Then, aniline, furfural, and barium hydroxide are added as plasticizers. The mixture may be molded under heat and pressure to form a strong and useful kind of plastic. Both laminated sheets and hardboard have been made with hydroxylin. They are not be-

ing manufactured in any commercial quantity.

Benalite is a lignin-plastic hardboard manufactured by the Masonite Corporation. Production involves: (1) the steaming of wood chips under high pressure; (2) their reduction to fibers; and (3) their formation into sheets.

The wood chips are placed in "guns." Live steam is introduced at pressures up to 1200 psi for 30 to 45 seconds. Under this heat and pressure, acetic and formic acids are formed from the wood substance. These acids cause the rapid hydrolysis of the hemicellulose. When the gun is quickly opened, the hydrolyzed chips with their high internal pressures explode into fiber masses and bundles. The hydrolyzed products are then washed out. The residual wood, consisting largely of reactivated lignin and hydrated cellulose, is ready for manufacture into panel form.

The fiber masses are formed into mats and placed in multiplaten presses. Pressures of 50 to 1500 psi or more are exerted depending on the density of panel desired. Platen temperatures are then raised to 175 to 180 deg. C to cause the reactivated lignin to flow around the fibers and cure. Finally, the platens are chilled and the panels removed. Panels are made in thicknesses of .100 to 1 in.; 4 ft. wide and up to 12 ft. long.

Benalite is the first American ligninplastic to be produced commercially. It is used for sheathing, wallboard, simulated tile, and template stock. Many other future uses are anticipated.

Lignin-enriched filler is a hydrolyzed wood molding powder manufactured by the Marathon Paper Mills Company. Hardwood chips are placed in a rotary digester. Neutralized, vanillin free, spent sulfite liquor is then pumped into the digester and the charge cooked for 30 minutes at 250 psi of steam pressure. During this time the hemicellulose is reduced to sugars and the lignin in the liquor is precipitated onto the residual fibers, raising the lignin content by as much as 20 to 35 percent. The mass is then washed and dried. The resultant fibers (powder) are mixed with 33 percent of Vinsol resin, a plasticizing agent, and molded into high strength, water resistant products.

Hydrolyzed redwood plastic is one of the newer members of the lignin-plastic group. It is a redwood powder that requires no additional plasticizing agent for the molding of finished goods. The material is prepared by cooking redwood chips for 8 to 15 seconds in a closed vessel with steam pressures as high as 800 psi. After cooking, the water is evaporated. The products of hydrolysis and the extractives are retained. Tannins and phlobaphenes, among the extractives, possess plastic and resin forming properties under the heat and pressure of the molding operation and thus serve as binding agents. Other binding resins and formaldehyde may be incorporated to improve the molding properties if desired.

Urea-plasticized wood. Wood may be soaked in an aqueous solution of urea, dried, and easily bent when heated to about 215 deg. F. With this knowledge, a plastic material made of urea-impregnated sawdust has been developed. The sawdust is mixed with 25 percent by weight of dry urea and enough water added to make a paste. The mixture is then dried to a moisture content of 2 or 3 percent. Zinc stearate, in a proportion of 1 to 5 percent, is added as a lubricant. The mix may be molded at pressures up to 1500 psi and temperatures of 185 deg. C for 3 to 5 minutes. When the mold temperature has been reduced to 60 deg. C, the product may be removed.

This molded material is gray to black in color, noncorrosive, and as strong and machinable as many other plastics. However, it possesses poor water resistance properties.

Lockwood. Atomic energy is being used by nuclear chemists to transform the most inexpensive woods into a rich, glamorous material for furniture and millwork. The Lockheed-Georgia Company is producing this new commercial wood plastic under the trade name "Lockwood." This super-wood may be fabricated as readily as ordinary wood. It is harder, stronger, more moisture resistant, and richer looking than the natural material. Cost studies show that it may be produced for about $1.00 per board foot. The product is the result of an atomic age transmutation technique.

The wood is first soaked in a liquid plastic such as methyl methacrylate. It is then irradiated by the cobalt 60 source of gamma rays. The transmuted wood retains all of its natural grain and beauty. When turned, planed, or sanded the wood has a satin-smooth finish.

The Future for the Chemical Utilization of Wood

The chemical utilization of wood is in its infancy. The future looks bright, but there is great need for more research on fundamental chemistry and on engineering applications. When the necessary research and development have been completed, we can expect the forest-products industries to benefit in two ways. First, the waste disposal problem will be practically eliminated. Secondly, the costs of growing, harvesting, and transporting the wood to the mill will be carried proportionately by the entire wood fraction, rather than the 50 percent or so of the tree that now ends up in product form.

Because of the extent of the world's wood resource and the fact that this resource is rapidly renewable, it can be predicted with confidence that wood will someday equal petroleum as a source of industrial chemicals.

REVIEW QUESTIONS

1. What are the primary constituents of wood? What use is made of each?
2. Describe destructive distillation. What are some of the products produced by this process?
3. How are woods hydrolyzed? What are the principal products produced by this process?
4. What are the essential differences between the sulfite and sulphate processes for making cellulose?
5. Why do spent pulping liquors constitute a serious water-pollution problem when dumped into streams and rivers?
6. What are the principal steps involved in converting trees into paper?
7. Why are sawdust and shavings unsuitable for making paper? What uses may be made of these wastes other than for fuel?
8. What are the essential differences between the Fourdrinier and the cylinder paper machines?
9. In what ways is the paper industry dependent upon other industries?
10. Describe the production of rayon by the viscose process.
11. What are plastics?
12. In what ways is wood used in plastics?
13. What is the difference between a binder and a plasticizer used in plastics?
14. What different plastics are in use today besides the ones described in this chapter?
15. What occupation in the industries discussed here interests you most? Where can you obtain more information about it?

SUGGESTED STUDENT ACTIVITIES

1. Make charcoal by destructive distillation.
2. Produce a piece of paper by first reducing wood to pulp by a chemical process.
3. Place a tissue paper, such as Kleenex, in a quart of water and allow it to stand for about 30 minutes. Beat the solution with an egg beater until the fibers are thoroughly separated. Dip a piece of fine mesh screen into the solution and collect a layer of fibers on it. Allow the fibers to dry and then press with a hot flat iron. Devise a deckle (tray with a screen bottom) and attempt to make several uniform sheets of paper. (You will probably need to make several gallons of stock solution.)
4. Design and construct a working model of a debarker, chipper, beater, decker, Jordan, or Fourdrinier machine.
5. Examine a piece of paper under a microscope. Observe the interlaced fibers. Observe the torn edge of a scrap of paper. Compare several different kinds of paper.
6. Visit a paper mill. Identify the various occupations involved. Select the one that interests you most and prepare a report describing the entrance requirements, duties, and responsibilities of a person employed therein. Ask your school counselor to help you find current information.

Appendix   Associations Which Give Information on Specific Species of Wood

National Lumber Manufacturers Association
1619 Massachusetts Ave., N.W.
Washington, D. C.

American Walnut Manufacturers Association
666 N. Lake Shore Drive
Chicago 11, Ill.
    (American walnut)

Appalachian Hardwood Manufacturers, Inc.
1015 Mercantile Library Bldg.
414 Walnut Street
Cincinnati 2, Ohio
    (Appalachian ash, basswood, beech, birch, butternut, chestnut, cherry, elm, hickory, maple, yellow poplar, red oak, white oak, and walnut)

California Redwood Association
617 Montgomery Street
San Francisco 11, Calif.
    (Redwood)

Red Cedar Shingle & Handsplit Shake
  Bureau
5510 White Building
Seattle 1, Wash.
    (Certigrade red cedar shingles, certigroove cedar shakes, and certi-split handsplit red cedar shakes)

Southern Cypress Manufacturers Association
P.O. Box 16413, 1640 West Road
Jacksonville 16, Fla.
    (Tidewater red cypress)

Southern Hardwood Lumber Manufacturers
  Association
805 Sterick Building
Memphis 3, Tenn.

Southern Pine Association
National Bank of Commerce Building
P.O. Box 52468
New Orleans 50, La.
    (Longleaf and shortleaf pine)

West Coast Lumbermen's Association
1410 S.W. Morrison Street
Portland 5, Ore.
    (Douglas fir, West Coast hemlock, Sitka spruce, and western red cedar)

Western Pine Association
510 Yeon Building
Portland 4, Ore.
    (Ponderosa pine, Idaho white pine, sugar pine, larch, Douglas fir, white fir, Lodgepole pine, Engelmann spruce, red cedar, and incense cedar)

Fine Hardwoods Association
666 N. Lake Shore Drive, Suite 1730
Chicago 11, Ill.
    (Fine hardwoods)

Hardwood Dimension Manufacturers
  Association
3813 Hillsboro Road
Nashville 12, Tenn.
    (Hardwood dimension stock)

Hardwood Plywood Institute
2310 South Walter Reed Drive
Arlington 6, Va.
    (Hardwood plywood)

Maple Flooring Manufacturers Association
35 E. Wacker Drive
Chicago, Ill.
    (Maple, beech, and birch flooring)

National Oak Flooring Manufacturers
Association
814 Sterick Building
Memphis 3, Tenn.
    (Oak, birch, beech, maple, and pecan
flooring)

Northeastern Lumber Manufacturers
Association, Inc.
271 Madison Avenue
New York 16, N. Y.
    (Northern white pine, Norway pine,
eastern spruce, balsam fir, eastern hemlock, birch, maple, beech, ash, and oak)

Northern Hardwood and Pine Manufacturers
Association
Suite 207, Northern Building
Green Bay, Wis.
    (Hemlock, birch, maple, basswood, elm,
ash, beech, tamarack, and white pine)
    (northern white pine, Norway pine,
eastern spruce, and western white
spruce)

Index